RAINBOOK

RESOURCES FOR APPROPRIATE TECHNOLOGY

Schocken Books • New York

RAINBOOK: Resources for Appropriate Technology

Lane deMoll, Editor
Tom Bender
Steve Johnson
Lee Johnson
Rhoda Epstein
Special thanks to Anne McLaughlin and Lauri deMoll, who held down the fort.

Design and Layout
Tom Bender
Marcia Johnson
Tode Oshin

Typesetting:
Irish Setter (Text)
Archetype (Index)
Harrison Cold Type (Headlines)

Contributors:
Bob Benson, Evan Brown, Nancy Bell Coe, Meg deMoll,
Rich Duncan, Becky Deryckx, Woody Deryckx, Jack Eyerly,
Anita Helle, Peter Johnson-Lenz, Trudy Johnson-Lenz,
Bart Jones, Cathy MacDonald, Craig Mosher, Mark Musick,
Ancil Nance, Diane Schatz, Ken Smith, Sim VanderRyn,
Bob Wallace, and Mary Wells.

The cover drawing is from a poster, "Visions of Ecotopia,"
by Diane Schatz, available for $3 from RAIN Magazine,
2270 N. W. Irving, Portland, Oregon.

Most of the uncredited graphics are from the Dover Pictorial Archives.
Drawings on pages 84 and 93 are by Meg deMoll. Drawings on page
124 are by Diane Schatz.

A NOTE ON CREDITS

It's been very hard to give credit for contributions to many of
these sections because everybody has shared in writing bits
and pieces of different subject areas. So even though Tom,
say, is given credit for the Shelter section, there are entries
in there by most of the rest of us. We decided not to put our
initials with most of these little pieces because it seemed like
it would make it all too cluttered. The exceptions occur where
information conveyed is particularly personal or stands out as
being obviously different.

STEALING BOOKS AND HELPING FRIENDS

If you add up the cost of the resources in this book that would
be useful to you, they would probably amount to a fortune.
We're not trying to be publicity agents for book publishers—
we're trying to help people get access to useful resources. So
before you think about buying something, see how else you
can get hold of it. See if your local library has it (doubtful,
but ASK!). Check local bookstores—and read it there. Check
university libraries—if they won't let you borrow it, you can
almost always read it there. See if a neighbor or friend has a
copy.

Most importantly, almost every local library has an Inter-
Library Loan Department and can borrow almost anything
they don't have that exists for you for just the cost of postage.
They usually need to believe something really exists before
they will try, which is why we've included so much access
information on entries (also so you can order things directly
yourself if you wish). We also know people who have set up
book buying co-ops and then share the books and their costs.
And there are several specialized book lending libraries operating or being set up (Earth Books Lending Library in Sweet
Home, Idaho; Alternative Sources of Energy Lending Library,
etc.—see Communications section—Libraries, and Energy
section).

Also, PLEASE remember—if you're writing to any of the
small research and community groups listed, they're almost
all underfunded and not equipped to handle other people's
problems. At least send a dollar and a self-addressed, stamped
envelope (SASE) with your letter if you want to hear back.

First published by SCHOCKEN BOOKS 1977

Copyright © 1977 RAIN Magazine

Library of Congress Cataloging in Publication Data

Main entry under title:
Rainbook: resources for appropriate technology.

Includes index.
1. Technology—Information services. 2. Human
ecology—Information services. I. Rain.

T10.6.R34   301.31'07   76-49721

Manufactured in the United States of America

WATERSHED

From time to time, travelers pass from one watershed into another as their travels take them into every new territory. At first the way feels normal, then gradually it becomes an uphill struggle to keep things going as they have been. The path becomes more difficult and life may appear more sparse. And finally at some point—which may or may not be sensed before being passed—we become aware that things seem different. Our travel begins again to gain momentum. The way becomes easier. The rivers flow in new directions, and the life of the place may seem to follow different laws and behave in foreign ways. If we are lucky, we may come to some point where the whole terrain is laid out before our eyes and we can grasp how things go together. Or perhaps we have to learn it piece by piece as we travel on. Once we learn the rules of life in this new territory and begin to move in more appropriate ways, the beauty of life in this new place dawns upon us and the old territory and its ways fade into dim memories of strange and now unfamiliar customs.

Our society is passing over a watershed in its history. The terrain of abundant resources and rapid growth is giving way to a territory where living at equilibrium within our resource limits prevails. The dreams of growth and of inexhaustible resources to satisfy our every desire that have fueled our recent history have lost their power. New dreams and new values are urgently needed today to catalyze and guide our transition into an equilibrium society. Without such visions, our future appears to us as an ever poorer backsliding version of our recent past, overcast with an everpresent sense of our failure.

New dreams are possible. The Golden Age of almost every society in history has occurred not when all a culture's energies were focussed on increasing its wealth and power, but rather when the attainable limits of those dreams were reached and people realized that such goals had not left them with the quality, beauty or personal happiness they had envisioned. A careful analysis of the balance sheet can reveal today, as it has in the past, that vast resources of society are being channeled into now unattainable and undesired visions—resources which can be rechanneled toward new ends. Once we realize that greatness is not achievable through great expenditures of resources but requires the development and refinement of our own personal abilities, we discover that our present wealth is more than adequate to achieve an equitable and golden age for the whole world.

The shape of our new potentials is beginning to become visible today—though still in somewhat piecemeal fashion. This book tries to document some of these new potentials and the work that has been done to demonstrate what we can achieve with them. We dedicate it to the possibility of a new and gentle age and to the guides that help make our way possible.

CONTENTS

Oregon Historical Society

APPROPRIATE TECHNOLOGY   1

Appropriate Technology   *—LdeM, TB*   1
Resources   *—LdeM, TB*   3
A.T. Groups   *—LdeM*   5
Think Simple, Think Wise   *—TB*   7
Continuing Access   *—LdeM, TB*   9
Learning from the Past   *—TB*   10

PLACE   11

A Habit at Teatime   *—B. Benson*   13
Weather   *—SJ*   14
In Ecotopia's Big Woods   *—E. Callenbach*   15
Historical Perspectives   *—SJ, LdeM*   18
Pioneering Communities   *—G. Brown*   19
The World from Above   *—SJ*   21
Regional Perspectives   *—TB*   23
Maps   *—SJ, B. Benson*   25
Mental Maps   *—SJ*   27
Resource Inventories   *—SJ*   29
Making the City Observable   *—SJ*   30

ECONOMICS   31

Corporate Power   *—TB*   32
Cost of Energy Slaves   *—TB*   33
What Is Worth Doing?   *—TB*   34
Ethics & Economics   *—TB*   34
Stolen Goods   *—TB*   35
Who's Using Your Money?   *—TB*   37
Unnecessary Activities?   *—TB*   38
Size and Growth   *—TB*   39
Good Priorities?   *—TB*   41
Taxing the Pavement, Not the Earth   *—SJ*   41
Seven Laws of Money   *—M. Phillips*   42
Energy, Employment & Economics   *—TB*   43
Community Economics   *—TB*   45
Community Finance   *—TB*   47
Bootstraps   *—TB/LdeM*   49
Making Work Worth It   *—TB*   51
Research Groups   *—TB*   52

COMMUNITY BUILDING   53

Newsletters   *—SJ, LdeM*   57
Environmental Groups   *—LdeM*   58
Citizen Participation   *—SJ*   59
Red Star Over China   *—LdeM*   61
Rural Roots   *—SJ, C. Mosher*   63
Sharing and Gathering   *—SJ*   65
    Fairs & Festivals   65
    Community Meetings   65
    Crime Prevention   66
    People to People Indexes   67
    Talent Pools & Skills Banks   68
    Learning Exchanges/
      Community Memories   69
Networking   *—SJ*   70

COMMUNICATIONS   73

Information Mantra   *—SJ*   74
Bridges, Fields & Omega Points   *—SJ,*
   P. and T. Johnson-Lenz   75
Problem Solving   *—SJ*   77
Brainstorming   *—A. Helle*   80
The Map Is Not the Territory   *—SJ*   81
Learning   *—LdeM*   83
Directories & Catalogs   *—SJ*   86
Self-Publishing   *—SJ, LdeM*   91
Information Access & Research   *—SJ*   93
Community Research   *—LdeM*   97
Small Scale Computers   *—B. Wallace*   99
Information Centers   *—SJ*   101
Libraries   *—SJ*   103
Information Needs   *—SJ*   106
Information & Referral   *—SJ*   107
Media   *—RE*   108
Broadcasting   *—RE*   111
Public Broadcasting   *—RE*   112
Cable   *—RE*   113
Satellite   *—RE*   114
Mixed Media   *—RE*   115
Mixed Media Centers   *—RE*   117

No Soap, Radio —RE 119
Community Radio Stations —RE 121
Carrier Current Neighborhood Radio —RE 122

TRANSPORTATION 123

Reducing the Need for Travel —TB 124
Adapting Existing Transport —TB 125
Air Ships and Sailing Ships —TB 126
$8 for a Gallon of Gasoline? —TB 126
Bicycles —LdeM 127
Repair —B. Jones 128
Organizations —LdeM 129
Wise Travel —LdeM, TB 131
Taking Pictures and Taking Souls —TB 133
Costs of Tourism —TB 133

SHELTER 135

Simple Building —TB 137
How-To —TB 139
Spirit and Space —TB 140
Rebuilding —TB 141
Local Materials —TB 142
Hands-on Building Courses —TB 143
Research —TB 143
Energy Conserving Landscaping —TB 145
Make Where You Are a Paradise —TB 147

AGRICULTURE 149

Energy and Agriculture —TB, LJ 150
Agriculture and Scale —TB 151
Land —B. Deryckx 153
    Land Reform 153
    Land Trusts 155
New Food Sources —TB 157
Agricultural Tools —TB 158
Agricultural Organizations —LdeM 159
Agricultural Publications —LdeM, SJ 159
Urban Gardening —LdeM 161
Natural Pest Control —B. Deryckx 163
Food Distribution & Marketing
    —M. Musick 167
Homesteading —LdeM, SJ 171
Eating High & Lightly —LdeM 173

HEALTH 177

New Paths —TB 178
Professional Care —LdeM, TB 179
Self Care —LdeM, TB 181
Women and Health —LdeM 183

WASTE RECYCLING 185

Recycling —LdeM, TB 186
Industrial Waste Recycling —TB 188
Recycling Oregon Style —R. Duncan 189
Drying Up the Toilets —TB 191
What's Safe? —TB 192
Taking Pipe —TB 192
Waterless Toilets —TB 193
Land Application of Sewage —TB 195
Water —TB 196

ENERGY 197

Limits to Growth —TB, LJ 198
Nuclear Electric Chainsaws —LJ,
    A. Lovins 199
You Can't Switch Horsepower —TB 201
Energy Overview —LJ 202
Energy Policy —LJ 203
Dirty-Handed A.T. —LJ 203
Information Resources —LJ 205
Newsletters and Magazines —LJ 206
A Faustian Bargain —LJ 207
Utilities —LJ 209
Fossil Fuels —LJ 210
Waste Not, Watt Not —TB 211
In the Bank or Up the Chimney? —TB 212
Living Lightly —TB, LdeM 213
Energy Conservation Policy —TB, LJ 214
Home Insulation —TB, LJ 215
Energy Conservation in Building —LJ 217
Community Conservation —TB 218
Solar —LJ 219
Direct Solar —LJ, TB 221
Solar Greenhouses —LJ 225
Air and Water Solar Systems —LJ 227
There'll Be a Heat Pipe in Your Future
    —LJ 228
Solar Access —LJ 229
Wood Energy —TB 231
Stretch Your Energy and Cover Your
    Bets —TB 232
People Power —TB 233
Bioconversion: Methane Production
    —K. Smith, E. Brown, LJ 235
Bio-Gas Economics —Undercurrents 238
Wind Energy —LJ 239
Wind-Mechanical Power —TB 241

RAINMAKING 243
INDEX 243

APPROPRIATE TECHNOLOGY

The development and demand for "appropriate technologies" today arise from the realization that our resource conditions are changing and that our present ways of doing things are inappropriate for the futures we face. They arise also from a realization that our present technologies serve ends which threaten the fundamental values of our society and new ways of doing things must be developed which support and evoke those values.

Appropriate technology demands that we ask, "Appropriate for what?" "Appropriate for whom?" No technology is value-free. Some technologies are appropriate for conditions of growth, vast resources and small populations. Others are appropriate for conditions of stability, plentiful labor and scarce resources. Some technologies increase the wealth of a few

while impoverishing the many. Others tend to equalize wealth and power. Some technologies degrade and destroy the people using them, while others give opportunity for growth of skills, confidence and abilities. Some technologies consume energy, some provide employment. Some technologies produce goods, others produce good.

The existence of a technology does not require its use any more than the existence of a gun requires us to shoot. It only requires that we examine what happens if we don't use it and others do, and the effects its use would have on our lives.

Appropriate technology reminds us that before we choose our tools and techniques we must choose our dreams and values, for some technologies serve them, while others make them unobtainable.

Appropriate technologies can be simply defined but not so simply created. They are small in scale, conservative of resources, controllable, and wise. They extend and deepen our own capabilities and experiences and unify them with those of others and with our surroundings. This whole book is about such tools—this section is merely an introduction to some of the main ideas and resources.

Our primary concern in this book is technologies appropriate for overdeveloped countries such as the U.S. There are several reasons why we are concerned with that rather than with focusing on other countries that seem to need help more desperately:

* We need to live what we talk if we ever expect other people to take us seriously. You can't sell compost toilets to others if you won't use them yourself.
* We haven't been asked to solve other people's problems.
* We are a large part of poorer countries' problems. If we can get off their backs they have a lot better chance of working things out.
* Rethinking and changing the economics and culture we've spread throughout the world can have as broad an effect coming from our own culture as from any other.
* There's enough to keep us busy here!

Finding viable technologies for overdeveloped countries is in many ways a very different problem from poorer countries and provides a very different challenge. We don't need machines—we've got too many. Our needs aren't obvious (to us)—we're not hungry, and we seem to have everything, yet we're not particularly happy. In any case, the future promises big changes. We're going to have less wealth from fossil fuels, fewer of the rest of the world's resources and more economic, political and military competition from other countries.

As a result, the technology appropriate for changing conditions in the U.S. has several requirements:

* It must improve our quality of life. Any reduction in material well-being must be more than offset by improved well-being in other areas.
* It must eliminate need for continued use of fossil fuels and further extraction of non-renewable materials.
* It must reconnect us with the rewards of meaningful interaction with other people.
* It must deal with the *causes* of economic inequality in this country and between this country and other nations.
* It must convert work into a meaningful and rewarding process.
* It must convert our institutional structures to sustainable forms.
* It must help us realign our actions with our basic values.

Appropriate technology in these conditions is not merely a question of machines and tools, but of the nature of all the conceptual, organizational, political, physical and spiritual tools and techniques which we bring into play by our actions. And it is these "softer" tools that we lack the most—the tools with which to control our machines and actions.

It may seem wrong to categorize dreams and values together with machines and tools as "appropriate technology," but those very different things need desperately to be brought together. Action without vision and vision without action are equally impotent, but together they can perform miracles. And a shift of our concern from quantity to quality, from powerful to skillful tools, and from material and energy resources to human resources imples a shift toward such softer, less visible and more integral tools.

We are taking a broad view of technology here, for what "Appropriate Technology" adds to technology is the question "What is Appropriate?" That question requires that we get into the intricately interconnected web that links everything together—a web where a small change in something seemingly far removed can allow big changes in what you're concerned with. You have to look broadly enough to see whole shifts in patterns in addition to adjustments to what exists. Every step of the baking industry, for instances, may be marvelously efficient, yet when compared to baking at home, the whole process of sending wheat thousands of miles to be milled and baked and then setting up an intricate delivery system appears incredibly expensive and unnecessary. So things such as public interest accountants, community radio stations, maps, or bootstraps economics for communities all have their place in helping our large and intricate society make some major adjustments. Public access and use of many of these tools is a revolution in itself, and the missing element in many otherwise highly useful developments is an accounting skill or a sense of the territory where something can be useful.

New technologies, whether nuclear power or video portapacks, may not achieve their initial potential once their internal and external interaction is more fully understood. Xerox machines may increase the overload of useless information more than they increase availability of good information. Or they may just get us farther into being concerned with information about things rather than the things themselves. So we need to be concerned with the context as well as with the tool itself. Why has big business and big government been so receptive to appropriate technology? Do they not understand its implications, or do they see different potentials? A big equipment manufacturer in the Philippines openly admitted their expectations—small firms would develop the new technologies, work out the bugs, and develop the markets, then they would come in and take over. Is a.t. a "poor people's technology" that can permit us or our government from feeling any responsibility for inequality? Many questions remain, yet what has happened so far is good.

3

Resources

Small Is Beautiful, E. F. Schumacher, 1973, $2.45 from:
    Harper & Row
    10 E. 53rd Street
    New York, NY 10022
"Economics as if People Mattered." If you're only going to read one thing from this whole list, pick this. Clear, concise, important, it's a classic (and a best seller). It deals with the economics appropriate to present resource conditions and contains experienced insights into the need for restructuring our principles, actions and dreams on a more equitable and rewarding basis. Schumacher is founder of the Intermediate Technology Development Group in England and author of "Buddhist Economics" (contained in the book).

Several Schumacher essays, originally published in *Resurgence* ($10/year surface, $15 airmail from Pentre Ifan. Felindre, Crymych, Dyfed, Wales, UK) are also available in back issues of RAIN ($1 each):
    "Conscious Culture of Poverty"—October 1975.
    "On Inflation"—November 1975
    "Think About Land"—December 1975
    "On Land Speculation"—February/March 1976
    "Plant a Tree"—July 1976
    "Technology and Political Change, Part I"—December 1976
    "Technology and Political Change, Part II"—January 1977

"The Other Way," BBC, $35 rental film from:
    Time Life Multimedia
    District Center
    100 Eisenhower Dr.
    Paramus, NJ 07652
The NOVA program on Schumacher and intermediate technology—gives a lot of examples, including a brick works, egg carton plants and a cable-drawn tractor that uses only 1% of the energy used by our normal tractors. It has been shown many times on National Educational Television, making numerous converts.

Radical Technology, Godfrey Boyle and Peter Harper, eds., 1976, $5.95 from:
    Pantheon Books
    201 E. 50th St.
    New York, NY 10022
An impressive collection of essays, reports, access information and counter-culture philosophy that surveys a broadly-viewed range of "technology." Interesting essays on tree farming, textile making, biological chemicals, metal working and paper making. Much of the writing is not particularly penetrating but does pull together in one place an introduction to a.t. from a counterculture perspective. By the editors of *Undercurrents*. Makes accessible much of the information on European developments that is difficult to obtain in the U.S.

Tools for Conviviality, Ivan Illich, 1973, $1.25 from:
    Harper & Row
    10 E. 53rd Street
    New York. NY 10022
This book was important in crystallizing our thoughts about the appropriateness of many of our present institutions (cultural and physical). It is a perceptive and eloquent analysis of the need for new patterns of, among other things, health, education and transportation.

Sharing Smaller Pies, Tom Bender, 1975, $2 from:
    2270 N.W. Irving Street
    Portland, OR 97210
Good discussion of the need for institutional change tied in with energy and economic realities. Begins to lay out new operating principles, including some criteria for appropriate technology.

A Handbook on Appropriate Technology, 1976, $7.50 from:
    Canadian Hunger Foundation
    75 Sparks St.
    Ottawa, Ontario, Canada K1P 5A5
A good working document for people interested in a.t. Compiled in cooperation with the Brace Research Institute. Essays explaining a.t., case studies from many countries, a catalog of tools and equipment, bibliography, and a beginning international listing of groups and individuals involved in a.t. development.

Some British tree products suitable for direct human consumption.

Tree	Part used	When gathered	Preparation
Almond	Nut	Sept/Oct	Cook as meat
Ash	Seeds	From July	Boil twice and pickle
Beech	Nuts	Sept/Oct	Raw/bake and salt
	Leaves	April/May	Young leaves cooked as vegetables
Crab apples	Apples	July to Dec	Make into cider or jelly
Elder	Flowers	Before fully open	Raw/infused boiling water (drink)
	Berries	When ripe	Raw/add to apple pie
Hawthorn	Fruit	Early Autumn	Not raw. Make into preserve
	Leaves	April	Use in baking (see Mabey)
Hazel	Nut	Late Aug/Oct	Chopped on salads/salt and store
Lime	Leaves	Summer	Sandwich filling (raw)
	Flowers	July	On salads
Medlar	Fruit	Mid-Winter	Bake or make into jelly
Mountain Ash	Berries	Oct	Make into jelly
(Medlar)	Not leaves		Poisonous
Oak	Acorn	Oct	Shell, grind, boil until water is dark, change water. Repeat, and rinse for up to 12 hours
Sweet Chestnut	Nuts	Oct/Nov	Roasted or made into stuffing
	Leaves	June/July	Not raw
Walnut	Nut	July	High vit C when raw
	Nut	Oct/Nov	Pickle/make into a marmalade
	Leaves	June/July	Infuse as tea

Radical Technology

Coming Around—Sourcelist on Appropriate Technology, Lane deMoll, 1976, $1 from:
RAIN
2270 N.W. Irving
Portland, OR 97210

Eleven-page annotated a.t. bibliography. A good introduction to what a.t. can mean in a lot of different areas. Does not include how-to publications or alternative energy stuff, but steers you to them.

Spectrum, 1975, $2 from:
Alternative Sources of Energy
Rt. 2, Box 90A
Milaca, MN 56353

Catalog of tools and processes for small-scale use of solar, wind, water & other forms of income energy.

Appropriate Technology Sourcebook, Volunteers in Asia, 1976, $4.00 from:
Box 4543
Stanford, CA 94305

The outstanding sourcebook for practical tools and techniques for village and small community technology. Focuses on books and plans with useful how-to information, and draws on world-wide sources. A fine and useful complement to this book.

Low Cost Technology: An Inquiry into Outstanding Policy Issues, Nicolas Jaquier, 1975, Worldtech Report No. 2
Control Data Technotec, Inc.
8100 34th Ave. So.
Minneapolis, MN 55440

A study based on the 1974 OECD seminar of "low cost" technology practitioners. The full proceedings of the seminar will be out later this year and should be worth reading. The present report gives a general overview of major issues discussed—information mechanisms for low-cost innovations, a.t. and appropriate government policies, the role of universities, building up new industries and identifying new opportunities for innovation. Gives good feeling for the "managerial" and institutional pressures on a.t. that are going to develop as the money starts to flow. An instructive comparison is given between our present costly information services and innovative low-cost access techniques.

First Steps in Village Mechanization, by G. A. Macpherson, 1975, $9.50 from:
Tanzania Publishing House
P.O. Box 2138
Dar Es Salaam, Tanzania

A handbook prepared for cooperative development villages in Tanzania. How to start from nothing except people and the things around them and finish in 4 to 5 years with village workshops producing equipment for agriculture and other rural activities.

A fine, clearly illustrated, step-by-step guide with good design drawings, especially notable for its commonsense advice on things like how a tractor may harm a village and warnings about the effects of free aid money. Of value to overdeveloped countries for its simple and straightforward advice on doing things: don't start with a workshop building—build a bench under a tree; don't build a jig for holding wheelbarrows during construction—dig a hole for the wheel and work on the ground; don't cut the tread off an old tire to make a wagon wheel—stuff planks into the tire and build the wheel inside it!

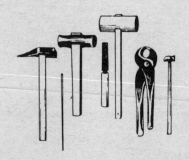

Village Technology Handbook, revised 1970, $9 from:
VITA
3706 Rhode Island Ave.
Mt. Ranier, MD 20822

How-to manual on useful tools and techniques—digging wells, salting fish, building bamboo pens. Oriented to developing countries. Other good how-to publication also available from VITA.

Lectures on Socially Appropriate Technology, Bob Congdon, ed., 1975, $6 seamail from:
Stichting TOOL
Mauritskade 61a
Amsterdam, The Netherlands

A clear, down-to-earth report on what has been accomplished, mostly by the Intermediate Technology Development Group, in many areas: pedal power, intermediate building technology, agriculture tools, chemical technology, education, water technology and industrial liaison. Well documented with good photographs and case studies that should show convincingly that a.t. comprises a vastly broader and more effective range of applications than merely alternative energy hardware.

Environmentally Appropriate Technologies, 3rd edition, by Bruce McCallum, limited numbers of free copies available from:
Information Services
Environment Canada
10th Floor, Fontaine Bldg.
Ottawa, Ontario, Canada K1A OH3

Excellent, 162-page introduction to biotechnology, renewable energy sources, resource and energy conservation in city planning, transportation, industry, agriculture and housing. Covers vital areas often neglected or underemphasized because their potential is not yet fully understood: energy storage; decentralized on-site energy generation, conversion and utilization; wood heating. Excellent suggestions for further reading.

*See Economics section for reviews of the following basic resources:

Size, Efficiency and Community Enterprise, Barry Stein, 1974, $5 from:
Center for Community Economic Development
639 Massachusetts Avenue, Suite 316
Cambridge, MA 02139

Technology and Employment in Industry, A. S. Bhalla, ed., 1974, $14.95 from:
International Labor Office
1750 New York Ave., N.W.
Washington, DC 20009

A.T. Groups

Here are the older and/or more active a.t. groups we know of. For more complete lists of international groups, check with TRANET and look in The Handbook on Appropriate Technology *by the Canadian Hunger Foundation (see previous page). Probably the most comprehensive listing for the U.S. is being prepared by Integrative Design Associates, 1740 N Street, N.W., Washington, DC 20036 (Eugene Eccli, Cecil Cook and Ann Becker). It will contain 700-800 listings coded into 25 categories relating to the group/person's activities. Inquire about availability, as it is not out as of this writing.*

UNITED STATES

The New Alchemy Institute
P.O. Box 432
Woods Hole, MA 02543

One of the best of the small, lean and creative research groups developing highly productive integrated small-scale agricultural systems and related support technologies. Their most recent project is The Ark—a laboratory facility for integrated food and energy production—funded by the provincial government in Prince Edward Island, Canada. See the Winter 1976 *Co-Evolution Quarterly* for a nice account of the opening of The Ark. Each issue of the *Journal of the New Alchemists* is really a book: Vol. 1, $4; Vol. 2, "The Compleat Backyard Fish Farmer," $6; and the new Vol. 3, $6, includes an article by Nancy Jack Todd, "Women and Ecology."

Farallones Institute
15290 Coleman Valley Road
Occidental, CA 95465
The Farallones Rural Center is an appropriate technology research and apprentice learning center located on 80 acres in the hills of Sonoma County in Northern California. 20-30 students a term work with 11-15 staff designing and building solar-heated showers and forms, composting privvies and grey water recycling systems. There is also work in carpentry, gardening, food processing and blacksmithing. The energy is high, the sense of community strong—everyone helps in the kitchen on a rotating basis and trades off on other jobs necessary for a community of 40-plus to operate. It is one of the very best ways we know of to get experience in the practical aspects of alternative energy systems, building and agriculture, as well as cooperative living. Write for information on tuition, dates, etc. Academic credit is available through Antioch West and UC Berkeley.

*Look under Shelter for more "hands-on" building/a.t. learning programs.

Farallones Integral Urban House
1516 Fifth Street
Berkeley, CA 94710
If you're into urban things, Farallones has an equally impressive program in Berkeley. A remodeled Victorian house complete with solar water heater, composting privy, greenhouse, bees, chickens, rabbits and garden all on a tiny city lot. Especially good programs in biological pest control and waste management. Courses with credit available including a Masters in Ecosystem Management. Write for details. This is also a fun place to visit—they're open for tours Saturdays, 1-5 p.m. Open your eyes to new potentials for urban living!

Institute for Local Self-Reliance
1717 18th St., N.W.
Washington, DC 20009
A brick townhouse in the Adams-Morgan neighborhood of D.C. with food gardens on the roof and beans sprouting in the basement. It is full of mellow people putting hard numbers onto good dreams. See reviews in Economics, Recycling and Urban Gardening for details on their programs and publications, and read *Self-Reliance* ($6/year for six issues).

Office of Appropriate Technology
State of California
P.O. Box 1677
Sacramento, CA 95808
Things are moving along at OAT. Current projects underway include designing a traveling energy van, putting together materials on the relationship between jobs and energy, training solar technicians, and the incorporation of a.t. ideas into the Capitol Area Plan (a design for the downtown Sacramento urban renewal area). They're also beginning a project to test the health problems of waterless toilets for urban and rural areas, as well as a study on the use of waste heat from state heating plants and buildings. A series of annotated bibliographies are available on a.t., solid waste management, sun-tempered greenhouses, landscaping for energy conservation, methane and more. Write for a complete publications list.

Intermediate Technology/USA
556 Santa Cruz Ave.
Menlo Park, CA 94025
Organizers of the extensive annual E.F. Schumacher United States tour, their focus is to get awareness of a.t. into government agencies, institutions and corporate business. Their newsletter is $10 a year.

Acorn/Midwest Energy Alternatives Network
Governor's State University
Park Forest South, IL 60466

Bethe Hagens and Jim Laukes are well on their way to spearheading a strong network of people involved in energy and technology alternatives in the Great Lakes region. Their newsletter—getting better by leaps and bounds—costs $6/yr. for individuals and $10 for institutions for six bi-monthly issues. The latest (No. 4) had articles on passive solar orientation and design, federal grants availability, advocacy and environmental impact statements, and lots of access information. I came away with quite a few new hits. If you live in their region or are interested in what other regions are up to, you should definitely be in touch.

National Center for Appropriate Technology (NCAT)
P.O. Box 3838
Butte, MT 59701
It's been a long time a-comin' but NCAT is finally getting off the ground with $3 million federal money from the Community Services Administration (formerly OEO). Their purpose is to get appropriate technologies out to the people in this country who need them by funding a.t. development for low-income communities. Strong national and regional networking components are planned. Because of the present close tie with Community Action Agencies (see Community Building section), the center's primary focus at the moment is weatherization, but they should be expanding beyond that before long. There are some excellent people involved—if they can resist the tendency towards centralized bureaucracy building, NCAT will be an important element in the a.t. movement. Write for a copy of their proposal and for current information about funding guidelines.

Northeast Appropriate Technology Network (NEAT-Net)
c/o Craig Decker
Box 134, Harvard Square
Cambridge, MA 02138
A new and promising network for New England which includes groups such as Northeast Carry, the Maine Audubon Society, Boston Wind, Vermont Alliance, New Alchemy and more. Contact them if you want to know who's doing what in that corner of the U.S.

INTERNATIONAL

Intermediate Technology Development Group (ITDG)
9 King Street
Covent Garden
London WC2E 8HN
England

Small but effective organization founded by E. F. Schumacher to catalyze development and access to appropriate technologies for developing countries. Many useful publications and developed products, including the now-famous metal bending and egg carton machines. ITDG's own structure is an interesting organizational model for effective, low-cost marshalling of human and institutional resources involving brainstorming panels of academics, business people and bureaucrats.

Brace Research Institute
MacDonald College of McGill
University
St. Anne de Bellevue 800
Quebec, Canada H0X 3MI

One of the oldest and most experienced a.t. research centers, blending academic resources with practical development and testing of prototypes. Emphasis is on easily-built and -maintained small-scale technologies for arid countries—water desalination, irrigation, crop dryers, greenhouses, windmills and solar heaters. Many good publications available—in English, French, and some in Spanish and Arabic.

Volunteers in Technical Assistance (VITA)
3706 Rhode Island Avenue
Mt. Rainier, MD 20822

ITDG develops more generalized solutions to problems, VITA responds to the specific and unique problems and situations in developing countries. Its organization is another example of effective low-cost operation. VITA acts as a clearinghouse linking up more than 6000 volunteers in the U.S. to assistance requests from abroad: installing wind energy generating equipment for a Honduran village, advising on development of soap out of local Bangladeshi materials, or finding a commercial use for seaweed along the Indian coast. All by mail. Many years of experience are summed up in their available publications. Write also for their free newsletter.

Minimum Cost Housing Group
School of Architecture
McGill University
Montreal, Quebec, Canada

These are the folks whose *Stop the 5-Gallon Flush* started a whole movement to change our toilet and sewage practices a few years back. Since then they've been building low-cost experimental housing of recycled and waste materials, developing uses of sulfur blocks in building, designing recycling toilets and a host of other interesting projects. Write for publications list.

Department of Rural Development
Agency for International
Development
Department of State
Washington, DC 20523

AID has a checkered history of often being an instrument for American economic colonialism and CIA activities in other countries but appears to be making an honest attempt to support local development of a.t. within developing countries themselves. They've set up a private non-profit corporation outside the government to channel $20 million in funding into a.t. development for other countries. AID's proposal for that center contains listing of active a.t. groups in Latin America, Africa and India which might provide useful contacts for people working in those areas.

TRANET
c/o William Ellis
7410 Vernon Square Drive
Alexandria, VA 22306

This international a.t. networking organization grew out of the a.t. exhibition at Habitat Forum in Vancouver, BC, in June of 1976. The *TRANET Newsletter* (quarterly, $15/year) seems headed for a useful role of keeping people up with the goings-on from Botswana to the Phillioubes.

National Centre for Alternative Technology
Llwyngwern Quarry
Pantperthog
Machynlleth
Powys
Wales

What these good folks have been doing in Great Britain is an important element in developing any new patterns. They've set up a demonstration center for alternative technologies where people can come see, kick, shake, try out and get a feeling for the reality of things like compost toilets, windmills and solar heaters. Very few people can visualize that sort of thing without seeing it, and seeing it puts it into a category of reality right along with the traditional options they're familiar with. This British center has had more than 50,000 visitors this year, Farallones Urban House has 150 visitors every Saturday, and new understandings of what's happening are spreading like wildfire. Inquire about the Center's series of Do-It-Yourself (DIY) plans for windmills, waterpumps, etc.

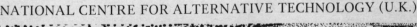

NATIONAL CENTRE FOR ALTERNATIVE TECHNOLOGY (U.K.)

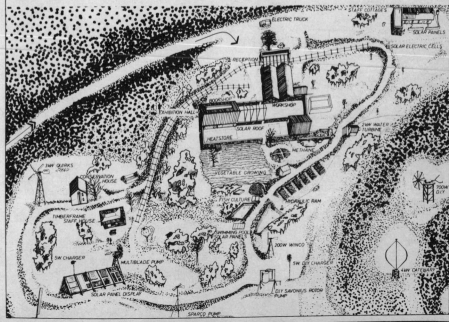

Think Simple, Think

INVISIBLE TECHNOLOGIES

The best technologies are often the invisible ones—where people have figured out how to avoid problems rather than to solve them. Often all that is required is a perceptual change such as seeing grasshoppers as an airborne mobile protein harvesting and conversion unit—a food source—rather than a destructive pest. Or living near where we work rather than building better transportation technologies. Or eating lower on the food chain so you don't have to pay for or grow food for the conversion losses of meat animals. Or planting trees rather than air conditioners.

The second-best technologies are also invisible. They're based on people's skills and relationships rather than machines —the skilled calligrapher drawing a line or carpenter cutting a line rather than needing a jig or machine; good neighbors rather than locks on doors; caring for the ill or elderly at home rather than in a Home; hiking rather than mini-biking; an auto mechanic or piano tuner's ear rather than a tuning machine. But there's always a range of skills and scales and situations where things need to happen, and we're interested in expanding the range of tools for situations that have been neglected, and learning when there are good reasons for choosing one scale rather than another. One size can't fit every situation well, and a technology that tries is likely not to fit *any* well.

Be resourceful, be clever, be wise.

Having to solve problems without money usually results in people getting resourceful and finding creative ways to use what is already there. Money usually makes us lazy—and we end up paying for our laziness and second rate solutions to

New industrial mini-plants such as this egg carton machine developed by ITDG allow efficient production at a small fraction of previous scales.

CHEMICALS FROM BIOLOGICAL SOURCES
Products obtained by dry-distillation of 1 ton of hardwood scrap (ca. 70% maple, 25% birch, 5% ash, elm and oak)

Charcoal	600 lb
Gases:	5,000 cu ft
Carbon dioxide (38%)	
Carbon monoxide (23%)	
Methane (17%)	
Nitrogen (16%)	
Methanol	3 gall
Ethyl acetate	15 gall
Ethyl formate	1.3 gall
Acetone	0.7 gall
Creosote oil	3.3 gall
Sol. tar	22 gall
Pitch	66 lb

Alan J.P. Dalton, 'Chemicals from Biological Resources', *ITDG*

WASHING MACHINES

You're right—the best thing is to wear clothes that require less washing and ironing—sweaters, cotton shirts, dark or strong colored fabrics that don't need "cosmetic" cleaning. But eventually things need cleaning. Traveling in Japan a few years ago we came across two simple washers. The cheapest, costing all of 50¢, was a plastic plunger like a Plumber's Friend. Used with a bucket and warm water left in the Japanese bath, it turned out to be a real effective way to wash cloths in youth hostels. We later found a tin version from 1873 in a Goodwill Store in Portland. You could make one yourself from a normal Plumber's Friend. Same scientific agitator action as in a $300 automatic washer, but without all the machinery attached.

The Japanese also produce a mini-washer and dryer—smaller and cheaper than American versions. The most interesting feature is that they use a very fast spinning drum to extract almost all the water from the clothes, allowing them to dry very rapidly even in Japan's humid summer. A very effective alternative to American clothes dryers that use heat to evaporate the moisture instead of just removing it. The Hoover Company, North Canton, Ohio 44720, imports or makes these for the U.S.—also mini-refrigerators.

Wise

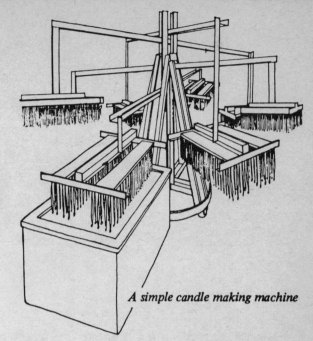

A simple candle making machine

problems. **Appropriate Technology** *repeatedly contains good examples of a.t. equipment and ideas. Here are some of the interesting projects they've covered recently.*

▪ A Nigerian project making medical aids such as arm splints, spinal jackets and cervical collars from broken plastic drain-pipes. The products are made by marking the pipe with a paper template, cutting out with a hacksaw and handstretching the plastic softened over a flame. The resulting equipment works better than previous products, as they can be easily adjusted by a nurse or doctor for a perfect fit for every individual and are waterproof, strong, cheap and reusable.

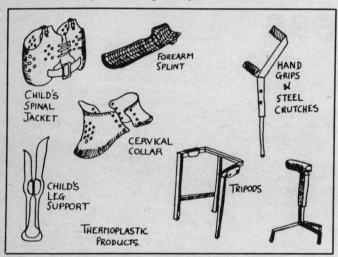

▪ A candle-making merry-go-round that produces 600 candles per hour with a single operator (could be solar heated?).
▪ Nethouse horticulture in Botswana, where it is noted that a high percentage of a plant's water requirement is not for growth but to cool it during respiration. Nethouses shade and cool, reducing water use by 2/3, and keep birds, insects and hail out.

▪ A rice storage bin of non-reinforced cement mortar, costing less than $10 U.S. to build.
▪ An oscillating water-pumping wind mill.

▪ A process for hand-forming chain-link fences, by the same Nigerian group. A simple manual procedure was worked out that avoids the need for capital-intensive machines, resulting in a very competitive and profitable operaton. Four men make six rolls of fencing six feet wide and 25 yards long each week. Each roll sells for £60, paying workers £75 per month and still giving a gross profit of £10-£15 per roll.

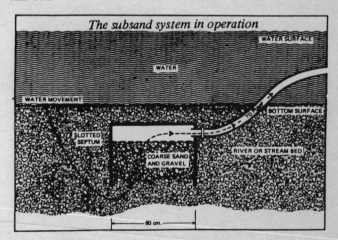

The subsand system in operation

▪ A simple, low maintenance water filter for villages that is buried in the bed of a stream and uses the sand and gravel already there to filter the water. Total capital costs per person served is figured to run 1 to 5% of any other clean supply.

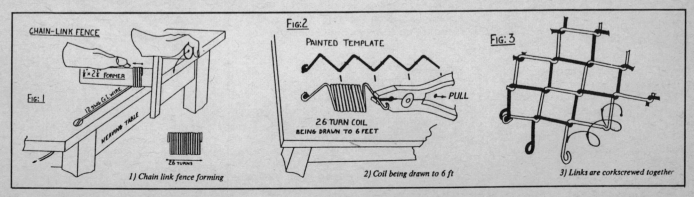

1) Chain link fence forming   2) Coil being drawn to 6 ft   3) Links are corkscrewed together

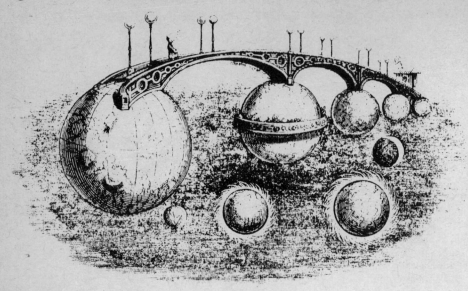

Continuing Access

Appropriate Technology, Quarterly Journal from ITDG in England, $7/yr. ($10.50 airmail) from IT Publications

Excellent technical journal geared mostly towards a.t. for developing countries, though most of the tools and processes can be applied to overdeveloped cultures as well. Everything from hydraulic rams and metal bending machines to sugar milling and other agricultural processes.

RAIN—Journal of Appropriate Technology, $10/yr., 10 issues, from:
    2270 N.W. Irving
    Portland, OR 97210

We're a monthly information access journal and reference network, trying to provide technical support for evaluating and implementing new ideas, ecological and philosophical perceptions for creating more satisfying options, and up-to-date information on current projects, groups, events and publications. Send us useful resources that should be shared with others.

Undercurrents, $6.50/6 issues, from
    11 Shadwell,
    Uley, Dursley, Gloucestershire
    GL11 5BW England
Gives interesting coverage of British events, projects and publications. Much of their past material is summarized in their *Radical Technology*, by Boyle and Harper, 1976, Pantheon Books, $5.95.

Alternative Sources of Energy, $5/year, quarterly, from:
    Route 2, Box 90-A
    Milaca, MN 56353
One of the earliest grassroots networking groups in the alternative energy area, ASE has grown up into a much more sophisticated and useful journal while continuing to contain useful practical information for the small experimenter or homesteader using alternative energy sources. Good information on new products, materials and equipment in the energy field, and lots of that "Old Geezer" technology that makes ERDA go into spasms. Also has a useful lending library on energy books and papers.

Co-Evolution Quarterly
    Box 428
    Sausalito, CA 94965

($8/yr., quarterly). Continuing update by the granddaddy of the access catalogs: appropriate tools, books, philosophy and stories all mixed in with a bit of gossip on the state of the art. A must if you're not already addicted to it.

Metastasis
    P.O. Box 128
    Marblemount, WA 98267
Mail order access for hard-to-get how-to publications. Write for new price list (over 250 excellent publications). In the U.S., many foreign publications can be obtained more easily and rapidly from Metastasis than ordering from their original source.

Conserver Society/Notes, free
    c/o Science Council of Canada
    150 Kent Street, 7th Floor
    Ottawa, Ontario K1P 5P4
Published every two months for people interested in doing something now about Canada's future. It is part of a Science Council project exploring the implications of a Conserver Society in Canada—a society that conserves and nourishes the resources that support its life rather than consuming them. The Dec. 1975 issue contains a good survey of energy accounting developments, an article on the costs of consumption, and access information on developments on the Canadian front.

Conserver Society News
    512 Blvd. Wilfred Lavigne
    Aylmer, Quebec J94 3W3
    Canada
Bi-monthly, $5/yr. for individuals, $15 for institutions. Not to be confused (but why not?—they sound alike) with *Conserver Society Notes* put out by the Science Council of Canada, *CS News* is a grassroots newsletter for Canadians developing a society in harmony with the biosphere. It's edited by Bruce McCallum, author of *Environmentally Appropriate Technology*.

It has inputs from reporters in almost every province and is beginning to provide a good coverage of events, projects and goings on in Canada.

The same group has set up a nonprofit cooperative company, Conserver Society Products, to distribute environmentally appropriate technologies. Initial function is as a buyers' co-op, with emphasis on wood-burning technologies. Contact: Conserver Society Products, P.O. Box 4377, Station E, Ottawa, Ontario, Canada.

*Most of the groups listed on the previous pages have newsletters or journals that contain valuable information on their activities.

Learning from the Past

We don't have to start from scratch to develop ways of doing things that are more humane and more appropriate for our emerging resource conditions. We have the legacy of the work of millions of people throughout history who have explored untold numbers of different ways to do almost everything. They've forgotten more than we'll ever know, but a lot has been written down in these and other sources. Relatively minor changes in the balance of costs of people's work, materials and transportation have caused us to set aside perfectly workable techniques that are still valid. Compared, combined, improved, newly-understood, and openly shared, they can offer a lot. Most of the rest is scaling down, simplifying, borrowing from others, refining and trying.

Science and Civilization in China,
Joseph Needham, 1962, from:
   Cambridge University Press
   32 East 57th
   New York, NY 10022

A vast goldmine of information on ways of thought different from our own and the incredible technologies developed over 4000 years in one of the most productive cultures on our planet. The volumes produced so far include introductory orientations, history of scientific thought, mathematics, sciences of the heavens and the earth, physics, mechanical engineering and building, chemistry and medicine. The volumes are very expensive ($30-$50 each), so get them at the library (or through inter-library loan).

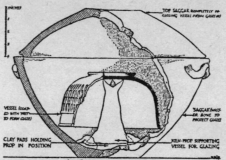

—Applying a lead-glaze to a vessel by firing it upside down on a pronged support inside another vessel (making a muffle-kiln).

History of Technology, 5 vols., Charles Singer, ed., 1954-58, $53 each from:
   Oxford University Press
   200 Madison Ave.
   New York, NY 10016

A massive collection of fascinating information on how things were done in different times and places—Ancient Empires, Mediterranean Civilizations, Middle Ages, Renaissance, and 19th Century. This does for the European culture what Needham does for China. Waterwheels and grain mills built on boats anchored in the middle of streams, how to make lost-wax castings and a wealth of other techniques that turn the impossible into the possible by just being clever.

Traditional Crafts of Persia, Hans Wulff, 1966, $7.95 from:
   MIT Press
   28 Carleton St.
   Cambridge, MA 02142

Records in readable yet technically clear language the wide range of technologies of the traditional Persian culture: metallurgy and metal working, jewelry, lockmaking, woodworking, comb making, building, brickmaking, tiles and glazing, textiles, carpet weaving, irrigation, agricultural methods, windmills and oil milling. A wealth of valuable information.

China at Work, Rudolf P. Hommel, 1937, $3.95 from:
   MIT Press
   28 Carleton Street
   Cambridge, MA 02142

The sometimes strange-seeming tools and ways of working of other cultures can be a mind-opening stimulus to re-thinking our own patterns. Why do the Japanese pull their saws instead of pushing them? Why do some Chinese boats look so strange—with bow and stern twisted to opposite sides? How can such "primitive" tools work so efficiently? How could the Persians make their beautiful geometrically-inlaid boxes so cheaply? *China at Work* surveys the traditional Chinese tools and their uses—tools for making tools, producing food, making clothing, providing shelter and enabling transport. Excellent box bellows, how to mend cast iron, the Chinese origin of the "American" washboard, making roof tiles and caulking boats. The expedition that assembled this material was organized by Henry Mercer, whose tool museum in Doylestown, PA, is one of the most fascinating collections of tools in the world.

Charcoal Stoves

Science and Civilization in Islam,
Seyyed H. Nasr, 1968, $15 from:
   Harvard University Press
   79 Garden Street
   Cambridge, MA 02138

Far less comprehensive than Needham's masterpiece, but contains an extremely thought-provoking introductory section explaining the underlying purposes and practice of Islamic sciences—conceiving of science as a means for spiritual growth and considering an individual who specialized in one aspect of science or life to the detriment of others to be unbalanced and a danger to society and oneself. The basis of Islamic sciences can offer a valuable yardstick with which to evaluate our own.

MENDING OF CAST IRON. Sketch showing how a fragment of a cast iron is held in a hole of a cast iron brazier which is to be mended. The outer shaded surface represents the wall of the brazier in which the hole is found. Pieces of bamboo hold the mending piece in place and the space between mending piece and the edge of the hole is filled out by successive applications, one next to the other, of the liquid iron taken from the crucible. As soon as the mending piece is held fast in the hole by a few applications of the liquid cast iron (which cools as soon as applied) the bamboo strips are removed.

David Pearson

PLACE

A sense of place may seem an odd "technology." Yet knowing the differences between various regions—difference in climate, landforms, geology and soils, vegetation and creatures, how they all go together, and how we fit in with them—is essential to developing ways of living attuned to real problems and potentials. Technologies that can take advantage of local resources rather than overpower them at considerable cost must grow out of this sense of place. And the experience that such knowledge comes from also brings an awareness that living closely with a place and the people and weather and other creatures that inhabit it is more rewarding in itself than the isolated, alienated and uniform patterns required by our present technologies.

Regionalism may seem like an odd fitting piece. How can we float into a sense of place (which is sometimes associated with tradition, provinciality, conservatism) and simultaneously comprehend our relation to a "global village" and the earth? If you stay in one place long enough, you either continue to figure out the place's special qualities or you get bored. It may take some of us longer than others (maybe because of our habit of fixing, finding, figuring out things out of context) but we can if we stand still long enough to hear the idea that each place is murmuring about.

WHAT'S HAPPENING WHERE I LIVE?

*"Where is Truth?" I ask the rain
tapping its questionnaire over the hill.
It comes back hollow, and I ask again,
"Is there a house with an open door
where Truth used to live without an address?"
Rain taps once more, then still.*

*These questions reach to touch my face
every day in this wilderness.*

William Stafford

Rock, Time & Landforms, Jerome Wyckoff, 1966, $8.95.
> Harper & Row
> 10 E. 53rd St.
> New York, NY 10022

The natural forces and processes that create and change our landscapes—presented vividly yet accurately. "To become more aware of landscapes is to gain a wider consciousness of life; it is to share, in a sense, the physical existence of the planet itself." Good perspectives from which to develop an enduring society. Less technical than *Natural Regions*, with vivid photographic illustrations.

Landscapes—Selected Writings of J. B. Jackson, ed. by Ervin H. Zube, 1970, $6.00 from:
> University of Massachusetts Press
> Amherst, MA 01002

J. B. Jackson was editor/publisher of *Landscape Magazine* for 16 years, and his collected essays from that journal and other writings are among the few clear visions of modern America. The night-jeweled cities from the air, the stranger's path through a city, the susuburbia of old Rome and New York—Jackson's essays reveal the places of modern America with unequaled clarity.

Earth Geography Booklet, 12, 13, 14
> Io Publications, $3.50
> 370 Mitchell Rd.
> Cape Elizabeth, Maine 04107

These three issues, Economics, Technology & Celestial Influence; Regions & Locales; and Space, through poems, interviews, essays, photos, journals, circumscribe a sense of place recognizable by both poet and scientist.

". . . in terms of efficient and elegant associations of natural systems, the sort that men are going to have to, and want to, live in the long run (if there's going to be a condition of harmonious growth rather than outrageous growth) requires this kind of knowledge: that people have to learn a sense of region, and what is possible within a region, rather than indefinitely assuming that a kind of promiscuous distribution of goods and long range transportation is always going to be possible . . . since the energy resources apparently won't be there, quite likely won't be there." (Gary Snyder, from interview)

Era of Exploration, Weston Naef, 1975, $9.75 from:
> New York Graphic Society
> 140 Greenwich Avenue
> Greenwich, CT 06830

Our images and perceptions of ourselves and our world usually change more dramatically and rapidly than the physical places themselves. This fascinating chronicle of the rise of landscape photography in the American West, profusely illustrated with the photographs that make up that revolution, provides an absorbing insight into those changes in perception. Photographs made by three fine photographers, within a two-year period, of the same view of Yosemite and other places, from precisely the same spot create an entirely different feeling of the idyllic beauty, power, awesomeness, quietude or harmony of nature. A record of people affecting landscapes, landscapes affecting people, and the images of both evolving into a new sense of our place in our world.

Natural Regions of the U.S. & Canada, by Charles B. Hunt, 1974, $15.95
> W.H. Freeman & Co.
> 600 Market St.
> San Francisco, CA 94104

Our personalities and our cultures are strongly influenced by the geology, climate, landforms, soils, vegetation and resources that are specific to different regions, and a tracing of geomorphic regions reflects closely the boundaries of our regional cultures, dreams and ways of life. *Natural Regions* gives a detailed explanation of the forces forming and transforming our various regions and the characteristics and history of the different regions. Heavily illustrated with maps, charts and drawings.

Geology Illustrated, by John S. Shelton, $14.50 from:
> W. H. Freeman and Company
> 660 Market St.
> San Francisco, CA 94104

What's good about this introduction to geology is the emphasis on carefully selected photos which are worth at least 75 words. It is a textbook, but a good self-learning primer too.

Van Loon's Geography, Hendrick Willem van Loon, Simon and Schuster, 1932, out of print   A truly beautiful and basic book on the geography and history of our planet—one to read aloud in front of the fireplace. The pen and ink illustrations are gems that will blow your mind and tweak your perceptions of how things are. Check in the library or old bookstore and try to find one with a dust jacket—it folds out into a colorful map! We paid $4. Here's what he was saying in 1932: "We are all of us fellow passengers on the same planet and we are all of us equally responsible for the happiness and the well-being of the world in which we happen to live

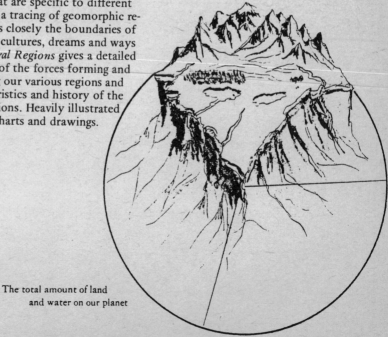

The total amount of land
and water on our planet

A Habit At Teatime

The legendary Bridge of the Gods near Hood River before the big flood. Drawing by Jimmie James.

There are signs, plain to see, in many parts of the Northwest, pointing to a great and catastrophic flood in the not-far-distant past. The rushing waters have worn deep channels down to bedrock in the country southwest from Spokane. These districts are called the Channeled Scablands, and the channels themselves are called Scabland Channels—a rare case of logical, consistent nomenclature.

The Grand Coulee itself is one of these channels, the greatest of all, in fact, and for a few hours the ledge across the Coulee was host to the planet's mightiest waterfall at the place now known as Dry Falls. Other easily-recognized scabland channels are just south from Arlington, at Shutler's Flat, and Sullivan Gulch in Portland itself. The turbulent flood waters boiled and tumbled into all parts of the lowland Northwest, entering the Tualatin Valley, for example, by way of the scabland channels at Tonquin (as well as the gaps at Oswego and south of Gaston).

There is a question of grammar here: ought we to say that this flood "did" this or that, or that it "does"? English provides us with a special tense, the "habitual" or "on-going present:" "I am skiing" is the "momentary present," but "I ski a lot" is the "on-going present" of the same verb. These floods recur at intervals of many thousands of years, so we ought to use the "on-going present" in referring to them. They are not past, they are past-and-future, or "habitual."

Every twenty thousand years or so, it seems, the various cycles of the earth's perihelion, the precession of the equinoxes, and the moon's perigee, not to mention several others still less well known, conspire together, as all cycles must, to bring about an extreme of weather conditions for North America. Most of Canada goes under ice, the Rockies spawn great glaciers which fill the intervales between the ranges. The vast trench which we know as the Kootenay and Flathead Valleys becomes, for a long time, a sea of solid ice, and then, as the climate moderates, an ice-locked lake the size of Lake Erie. For many centuries an ice dam, remnant of the glaciers, keeps the lake a prisoner. Then, as the cycles creep, a certain August afternoon swells to a torrid crescendo, the ice dam breaks, and Lake Kootenay spills out over Idaho, Washington and Oregon.

What heights of civilization the pre-Indian inhabitants of the Columbia may have reached, what towers they may have erected, what circuses watched, we shall never know, for all were swept away (are swept away, will be swept away) between teatime and dusk of that awful day. (Bob Benson)

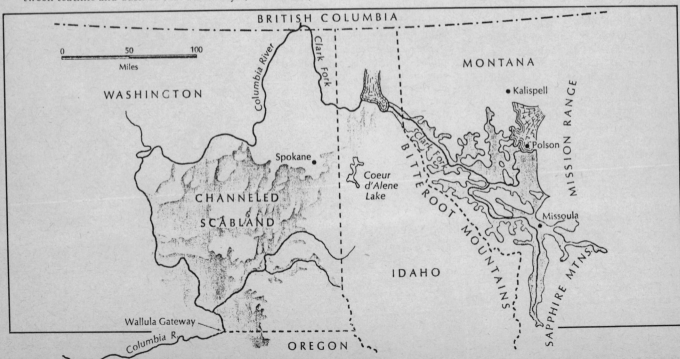

Ancil Nance

For two weeks in Wilton, California, it rained sheets of filmy transparent plastic; in November 1957 a small top-shaped object with hieroglyphics on the outside fell near Scarborough, England. A 5-pound steel ball fell near Tacoma, Washington in August 1951; one clam fell from the sky in Yuma, Arizona, August 20, 1941; some hair descended in Charleston, South Carolina, in October 1952; it rained hot water in Inverness, Scotland, on June 3, 1817; red hot pieces of cast iron fell upon Woodside, California, in the summer of 1954.

It has also rained butter, blood, navy beans, sandalwood, lizards, frogs, frozen bubbles, nails, axes, money and little colored balls.

Weather

We tend to see weather, unlike growing old, as something that we see change day by day, but not in our lifetimes. Weather is seasonal or cyclical and isn't going much of anywhere in general, or forward, or in the long run. It just is, like death and taxes.

Recently there has been much speculation, and due to more concern and new technologies, much evidence to support the thesis that we are going through a climate change. We may be moving toward a small ice age.

"Temperatures are dropping, and a little means a lot. If the mean annual temperature drops one degree centigrade (or 1.8 degrees Fahrenheit) where you live, it's as if you moved 300 miles north, say from Boston to Quebec. In the last 25 years the mean annual temperature of North America seems to have dropped 1.5 degrees c. (that's 2.7 degrees F.)" (*Country Journal*)

But it's coming in with mixed reviews. The last couple of years the coastal areas of Oregon and Washington have had cool and rainy summers, warm and dry falls, mild winters.

Particles in the air from manmade pollution may be cooling the surface of the earth by reflecting solar radiation; on the other hand, thermal waste may be warming it up and either may or may not have a sizeable influence on the general cooling trend.

Volcanic eruptions have had major influences on weather around the world for years, as forest fires, especially in the nineteenth century, influenced weather locally in the Pacific Northwest.

We have also begun to try influencing weather directly with such techniques as cloud seeding. A recent cloud seeding project in eastern Oregon was disputedly responsible for giving parts of eastern Oregon one of its coolest, wettest summers in quite a while.

Standing out in two feet of snow about two years ago while living in the Cascade foothills, I worried about the climate change. Cold. What if it was just cold mostly, and the sun would only warm you like the sides of a cheap wood stove in the morning.

Weather is always changing. One should know and love it like a cantankerous invisible being with a wild imagination. Prepare with it by knowing it like the back of your hand. It is not a detachable, separable part of place or environment. You can't have a rain forest without Rain.

The Weather Machine, How our weather works and why it is changing, **Nigel Calder, Viking Press, 1974, $14.95**
One of the clearest written, well-illustrated overviews of weather I've seen. Something in the formatting/style reminds one of Time/Life books. Lots of pictures, diagrams, charts.

The Elements Rage, **Frank Lane, Chilton Books, 1965, out of print—obtain through interlibrary loan.**
A wonderful and beautifully illustrated collection of eyewitness accounts by people present when Nature flexes her muscles. We live so much of our lives in the interstices of space and time between these normal "cataclysms" that we shake with fear and surprise when they occur. Fascinating—worth digging out at a library.

The Elements Rage

Lightning flashes through the volcanic dust clouds above Surtsey.

Ecotopia, Ernest Callenbach, 1975, $2.75 from:
    Banyan Tree Books
    1517 Francisco St.
    Berkeley, CA 94703

Ecotopia is a singular work, like the wheel it looks obvious. A steady state, spiritual rather than economic conscious society. It's more like a kit than any Utopia I've read—or like a ten-year plan. . . . *Yes, flawed, of course, but even these are nicely angled odd things. It felt like I had felt a new feeling when I read it. I remembered how to ask "What can we make the world into?"*

Somehow looking at the earth from the moon, even second hand, teaches you something about your neighbor. We need big pictures. Ecotopia *is a unique one.*

In Ecotopia's Big Woods

Healdsburg, May 17. Wood is a major factor in the topsy-turvy Ecotopian economy, as the source not only of lumber and paper but also of some of the remarkable plastics that Ecotopian scientists have developed. Ecotopians in the city and country alike take a deep and lasting interest in wood. They love to smell it, feel it, carve it, polish it. Inquiries about why they persist in using such an outdated material (which of course has been entirely obsoleted by aluminum and plastics in the United States) receive heated replies. To ensure a stable long-term supply of wood, the Ecotopians early reforested enormous areas that had been cut over by logging companies before Independence. They also planted trees on many hundreds of thousands of acres that had once been cleared for orchards or fields, but had gone wild or lay unused because of the exodus of people from the country into the cities.

I have now been able to visit one of the forest camps that carry out lumbering and tree-planting, and have observed how far the Ecotopians carry their love of trees. They do no clear-cutting at all, and their forests contain not only mixed ages but also mixed species of trees. They argue that the costs of mature-tree cutting are actually less per board foot than clear-cutting—but that even if they weren't, it would still be desirable

because of less insect damage, less erosion, and more rapid growth of timber. But such arguments are probably only a sophisticated rationale for attitudes that can almost be called tree worship—and I would not be surprised, as I probe further into Ecotopian life, to discover practices that would strengthen this hypothesis. (I have seen fierce-looking totem poles outside dwellings, for instance.)

Certainly the Ecotopian lumber industry has one practice that must seem barbarian to its customers: the unlucky person or group wishing to build a timber structure must first arrange to go out to a forest camp and do "forest service"—a period of labor during which, according to the theory, they are supposed to contribute enough to the growth of new trees to replace the wood they are about to consume. This system must be enormously wasteful in terms of economic inefficiency and disruption, but that seems to disturb the Ecotopians—at least those who live in and run the lumber camps—not a bit.

The actual harvesting of timber is conducted with surprising efficiency, considering the general laxness of Ecotopian work habits. There is much goofing off in the forest camps, but when a crew is at work, they work faster and more cooperatively than any workmen I have ever seen. They cut trees and trim them with a strange, almost religious respect: showing the emotional intensity and care we might use in preparing a ballet.

I was told that in rougher country ox-teams and even horses are used in lumbering, just as they were in Gold Rush times. And in many areas a tethered balloon and cables hoist the cut trees and carry them to nearby logging roads. But in the camp I visited (which may be a showplace) the basic machine is a large electric tractor with four huge rubber tires. These are said to tear up the forest floor even less than oxen, which have to drag timber out on some kind of sled. Though heavy, these tractors are surprisingly maneuverable since both front and rear wheels steer. They have a protected operator's cabin amidship; on one end there is a prehensile extension bearing a chain saw large enough to cut through all but the hugest trees, and mounted so it can cut them off only a few inches above ground level. (This is of course pleasant aesthetically, but it is also claimed that is saves some millions of board feet of lumber each year, and helps in management of the forest floor.) This saw can also cut trees into loadable lengths.

On the other end of the tractor is a huge claw device that can pick up a log, twirl it around lengthwise over the tractor, and carry it to the logging road where big diesel trucks wait to be loaded.

Ecotopian foresters claim that this machinery enables them to log safely even in dry weather, since there are no exhausts likely to set fire to undergrowth. It does seem to be true that their methods disturb the forest very little—it continues to look natural and attractive. Several types of trees usually grow in stands together, which is supposed to encourage wildlife and cut the chances of disastrous insect and fungi invasions. Curiously, a few dead trees are left standing—as homes for insect-gobbling woodpeckers!—and there are occasional forest meadows to provide habitats for deer and other animals. The older trees seed young ones naturally, so the foresters generally now only do artificial planting in areas they are trying to reforest. The dense forest canopy keeps the forest floor cool and moist, and pleasant to walk in. Although it rained for a few hours during my stay, I noticed that the stream passing near the camp did not become muddy—evidently it is true, as they claim, that Ecotopian lumbering leaves the topsoil intact, cuts down erosion, and preserves fish. (I didn't actually see any fish—but then I am the kind of person who seldom sees fish anywhere.)

The lumber camps themselves do not have sawmills, though they possess portable devices with which they can saw rough boards in small quantities for their own needs. The main squaring and sawing of timber, and the production of slabs for pulp, takes place at mills located in more open country, which buy logs from the forest camps. The resulting boards are then sold, almost entirely in the county-sized area just around the mill. Lumber sales are solely domestic; Ecotopia ceased lumber export immediately after Independence. It is claimed that, since the U.S. formerly exported half as much lumber as was used in housing, much of it from the West, some surplus actually existed from the beginning of the new nation. Ecotopian foresters argue that their policies have, since then, more than doubled their per capita resources of timber. There are, however, no present plans for a resumption of export.

Interestingly enough, the Ecotopians themselves have a debate in progress about the huge diesel trucks they use to haul logs. Several forest workers apologized to me that they are still dependent on these noisy, smelly, hulking diesels. Yet there are people all over them at the end of the work day, shining them up—one of the few outlets still allowed in this carless society for man's love of powerful machinery. One truck I saw has lost its bumper, and the replacement is a large, sturdy piece of wood. As they wear out, the trucks will be eliminated in favor of electric vehicles. Meanwhile, people argue hotly over the bumpers—extremist ideologues saying that the bumpers (which are actually stainless steel, not chrome plate) should all be replaced with wood, and the traditionalists maintaining that the trucks should be treated as museum relics and kept in original condition. The factions seem about equally matched, which means that the traditionalists have won so far—since a change on such a "drastic" matter is only carried out if there is a virtual consensus.

Our economists would surely find the Ecotopian lumber industry a labyrinth of contradictions. An observer like myself can come only to general conclusions. Certainly Ecotopians regard trees as being alive in almost a human sense— once I saw a quite ordinary-looking young man, not visibly drugged, lean against a large oak and mutter "Brother Tree!" And equally certainly, lumber in Ecotopia is cheap and plentiful, whatever the unorthodox means used to produce it. Wood therefore takes the place that aluminum, bituminous facings, and many other modern materials occupy with us.

An important by-product of the Ecotopian forestry policies is that extensive areas, too steep or rugged to be lumbered without causing erosion, have been assigned wilderness status. There all logging and fire roads have been eradicated. Such areas are now used only for camping and as wildlife preserves, and a higher risk of forest fire is apparently accepted. It is interesting, by the way, that such Ecotopian forests are uncannily quiet compared to ours, since they have no trail-bikes, all-terrain vehicles, airplanes overhead, nor snowmobiles in the winter. Nor can you get around in them rapidly, since foot trails are the only way to get anywhere.

Has Ecotopian livestock or agricultural production suffered because of the conversion of so much land to forest? Apparently not; vegetables, grains and meat are reasonably cheap, and beef cattle are common features of the landscape, though they are never concentrated in forced-feeding fattening lots. Thus an almost dead occupation, that of cowboy, has come back. And cattle ranches in the Sierra foothills have reverted to the old summer practice of driving their stock up to the high valleys where they pasture on wet mountain meadow grass. Grasslands research is said to be leading to the sowing of more native strains, which are better adapted to the climate and resist the incursion of thistles. Pasture irrigation is practiced only in a few areas, and only for milking herds.

But the true love of the Ecotopians is their forests, which they tend with so much care and manage in the prescribed stable-state manner. There they can claim much success in their campaign to return nature to a natural condition.

The San Francisco Bay area has fermented a lot of intellectual development of roots, regional consciousness, bioregions, and how to live like a native in your own region. As well, a lot of people are beginning to live and act on such consciousness—numerous creeks once buried in concrete culverts have been uncovered and restored, forests replanted, natural food systems reused. Peter Berg, who disseminates *Planet Drum*—a series of information bundles exploring watershed politics and bioregionalism (P.O. Box 31251, San Francisco, CA 94131) is editing a book of people's essays in these areas. The Mussel Group, Box 31251, San Francisco, CA 94131, is developing information on local human/biosystem relationships, priorities for restoring natural systems and non-exhaustive use of labor and materials for manufacturing and agriculture in the region. Peter Warshall, (Box 42, Elm Rd., Bolinas, CA 94924) is editing the bioregion issue (12/76) of *CoEvolution*. Gary Snyder, poet and author of *Turtle Island*, continues to write and talk on watershed concerns. Jerry Yudelson, consultant to the California Office of Appropriate Technology (See A.T. section), has been working on restoration projects. Out of all their work is emerging a sense of what real changes in our surroundings and in our heads can be brought about by becoming aware of the places we inhabit.

The Way of the White Clouds, Lama Anagarika Govinda, 1971, $4.75 from:
    Shambhala Publications
    2045 Francisco Street
    Berkeley, CA 94702
There have been a lot of books written giving a sense of the world from the view-viewpoints of hundreds of different religions and non-religions. Most of them blend into a haze in my memory—a haze of talking *about*. For some probably personal reason this one book stands apart and in a special place. Somehow the words convey more than words, the experiences jibe with my own life, but on deeper and more powerful levels, and what Govinda conveys *feels* real and true on all levels. An autobiography of his travels in Tibet and the effects on him of the places and his experiences on those travels.

Seven Arrows, Hyemeyohsts Storm, 1972, $6.95 from:
    Ballantine Books
    201 E. 50th Street
    New York, NY 10022
A beautiful expression—in words, pictures and allegory—of the forces of people and nature that flow together through a place, forming and evolving together.

Moon, Moon, by Anne Kent Rush, 1976, 400 pp., $7.95, from:
    Random House
    201 East 50th
    New York, NY 10022
        or
    Moon Books
    P.O. Box 9223
    Berkeley, CA 97409
In the couple of days this book has been around, each of us has picked it up, leafed through it and settled down into a particular section. Lee even read aloud Astronaut Jim Erwin's account of his mystical experience going to the moon. It is a beautiful book—full of poems, cosmologies, calendars, histories and images about the moon from every culture. You will want to move slowly and go back often to this loving collection of our long-neglected feminine, intuitive, mothering side. As Mao said, "Women hold up half the sky." (LdeM)

the goddess Nut holding up the sky

Pilgrim at Tinker Creek, Anne Dillard, 1975, $1.95 from:
    Bantam Books
    666 Fifth Ave.
    New York, NY 10019
With both this and *Lives of a Cell*, by Lewis Thomas, I've heard about someone having bought 8 or 9 copies to give out to their closest friends. It is a kind of journal of days spent at Tinker Creek. A new and woman Thoreau? Kind of, but I think Thoreau comes out a slow second.

"I had read that spiders lay their major straight lines with fluid that isn't sticky, and then lay a non-sticky spiral. Then they walk along that safe road and lay a sticky spiral going the other way. It seems to be very much a matter of concentration. The spider I watched was a matter of mystery: she seemed to be scrambling up, down and across the air. There was a small white mass of silk visible at the center of the orb, and she returned to this hub after each frenzied foray between air and air. It was a sort of Tinker Creek to her, from which she bore lightly in every direction an invisible news. She had a nice ability to make hairpin turns at the most acute angles in the air, all at topmost speed. I understand that you can lure an orb weaver spider, if you want one, by vibrating or twirling a blade of grass against the web, as a flying insect would struggle if caught. This little ruse has never worked for me; I need a tuning fork. I leave the webs on the bushes bristling with grass."

As a friend remarked, "she sure makes a lot out of things." There's a kind of hit and miss, sense of chance taking abandon to *Tinker Creek*. Lots of gasps and sudden soarings back in time, out to space and back down to: "In the top inch of forest soil, biologists found 'an average of 1,356 living creatures present in each square foot, including 865 mites, 265 springtails, 22 millipeds, 19 adult beetles and various members of 12 other forms . . .'"

Two of Wendell Berry's books give a powerful sense of these ancient and nurturing roots:

The Long-Legged House, 1965, $1.25 from:
    Ballantine Books
    201 E. 50th St.
    New York, NY 10022
A collection of essays on his reestablishing a homestead in the neglected farmlands of Kentucky, this book is filled with beautiful images of the land he knows:
"The most exemplary nature is that of the topsoil. It is very Christ-like in its passivity and beneficence and in the penetrating energy that issues out of its peaceableness. It increases by experience, by the passage of seasons over it, growth rising out of it and returning to it, not by ambition or aggressiveness. It is enriched by all things that die and enter into it. It keeps the past, not as history or as memory, but as richness, new possibility. Its fertility is always building up out of death into promise. Death is the bridge or the tunnel by which its past enters its future."

Memory of Old Jack, 1970, $2.65 from:
    Harcourt Brace Jovanovich
    757 Third Ave.
    New York, NY 10017
A novel of an old farmer's last day, flashing back through his life and relationships with the people and land of his home. His frustrations with so many of the new generations who have succumbed to the lure of the city life is based in his own experience of strength and love received back from his own hard work and simple life.

HISTORICAL PERSPECTIVES

History only doesn't exist in the present if we call it history and ignore it. Tracing something backwards is a good way to reach a conclusion for the future. A city's growth pattern, for example, can only make sense in the context of what was there when it began, and what influenced some areas to become industrial, others to be lived in by only some people and not others. It is especially important now in the context of needing low impact technology and tools that we keep track of the disappearing, the dying, the passing, the soft-spoken skills and metaphors of older people.

Eagle Bend, Self Portrait, $1 from:
  Eagle Bend Public Schools,
  District No. 790
  Eagle Bend, MN 56446

A history and portrait of the town. Hand made feeling. Range of contributors, children and adult. Model for neighborhood and small town efforts.

Asahel Curtis Sampler, $4.95 from:
  Puget Sound Access
  P.O. Box 4100
  Pioneer Square Station
  Seattle, WA 98104

The Asahel Curtis photograph collection, housed at the Washington State History Society, contains about 60,000 negatives, mostly of Seattle, in the period 1900-1915. This volume, edited by David Sucher (who several years ago compiled the Puget Sound Access Catalog) is a selection of about 100 photos with accompanying text. It is a clearly-designed slide show kind of book, and it should be of interest to Seattle lovers as well as a model for selective historical photo perspectives.

Old Glory, the Amazing Life Games Co. Co., 1973, $4.95 from:
  Warner Paperback Library
  75 Rockefeller Plaza
  New York, NY 10020

The oral history movement? In large book format a survey of grass roots history groups around the country; with detailed information on doing interviewing, historical preservation, researching your local neighborhood, region, state. It is subtitled: a pictorial report on the grass roots history movement and the first hometown history primer.

A Talent for Detail: The Photographs of Miss Frances Benjamin Johnson, 1898-1910, by Pete Daniel and Raymond Spock, 1974, $5.95 from:
  Harmony Books
  Crown Publishers Inc.
  419 Park Ave. South
  New York, NY 10016

A wonderful collection of photos of the South (including Black South), famous people, sailors and factory workers. Johnson understands people. Pouring over this book is a good way of feeling closer to that era.

An Everyday History of Somewhere, as written down by Ray Raphael, 1974, $10 from:
  Alfred A. Knopf
  201 E. 50th
  New York, NY 10022

A very nice informal history of people and places in Northern California. Including natural history. Fine pen and ink illustrations.

What follows is a small piece of a diary by a six-year-old orphan living in an Oregon logging camp at the turn of the century. Opal was obviously a remarkable child—her diary is pure poetry and a delight to read. I'm sure the book will be out in paperback within a year, but I'm not sure you'll want to wait.

Opal, by Opal Whiteley, arranged and adapted by Jane Boulton, 1976, $6.95 from:
  Macmillan Publishing Co.
  866 Third Ave.
  New York, NY 10022

Today the grandpa dug potatoes in the field.
I followed along after.
I picked them up and piled them in piles.
Some of them were very plump.
And all the time I was picking up potatoes
I did have conversations with them.
To some potatoes I did tell about

my hospital in the near woods
and all the little folk in it
and how much prayers and songs
and mentholatum helps them to have well feels.

To other potatoes I did talk about my friends—
how the crow, Lars Porsena,
does have a fondness for collecting things,
how Aphrodite, the mother pig, has a fondness
for chocolate creams,
how my dear pig, Peter Paul Rubens, wears a
little bell coming to my cathedral service.

Potatoes are very interesting folks.
I think they must see a lot
of what is going on in the earth.
They have so many eyes.
Too, I did have thinks
of all their growing days
there in the ground,
and all the things they did hear.

And after, I did count the eyes
that every potato did have,
and their numbers were in blessings.

I have thinks these potatoes growing here
did have knowings of star songs.
I have kept watch in the field at night
and I have seen the stars
look kindness down upon them.
And I have walked between the rows of potatoes
and I have watched
the star gleams on their leaves.

Pioneering Communities

by Grandma Brown

My parents were Americans from several branches of American pioneers and in their youth traveled the Oregon Trail with their parents, at different times, not knowing each other until afterward. They had the knowledge of homesteading and of mutual survival techniques. A man had to know a number of skills: the care of livestock, the maintenance of equipment, building of fences, houses and out-buildings, how to sink a well, when to plant, when to harvest, and many other things. He could well have passed college exams in husbandry as well as give the college a few pointers not included in their courses. Although many of them were somewhat short on sophisticated education, theirs was education of a different sort, based upon experiments of their ancestors in America.

My maternal grandfather chose mountain farming and had an up and down farm at Beaver, Oregon, while my other grandpa chose to live near the sea at Tillamook. He was a carpenter.

My young parents, during their first years of marriage, lived in the deep forest and peeled tan bark. Now this is the taking of bark from certain trees to be used for tanning, but without permanently injuring the trees. They kept two horses, 13 sheep, bees, pigs, a cow, and chickens.

I was the first born, and when I was three we traveled from Tillamook County to Lane County, and my father took a timber claim near Springfield. The trip was made via covered wagon, and I can remember how it rained just about all the way, the horses sometimes walking in water up to their knees, drawing the wagon over graveled roads. We would have to find a barn by nightfall to shelter the team or they would be sick.

The community was well established, but there was one remaining parcel of 137 acres, which my father filed claim to. But there was a sizable stream running along the roadside edge of it and the strip was occupied by a man named Putnam, as well as the rest of his acres along the side of ours. Upon this strip there was a maple grove and two springs, and Mr. Putnam

was charging campers 25¢ a night to camp there. People were litterbugs in those days too, and the grove and the creek were full of pollution.

The whole acreage was one jungle of tall trees, underbrush and foliage, woven together with vines. Space for living had to be cleared. It was an insurmountable job for one man with nothing but a saw and some axes. But we weren't alone. Soon our forest rang with the sound of ax and saw and calls of "Timber." The men of the community made short work of it, and soon there was space for a road, a barn and a house. The logs were trimmed and sent to the government sawmill up on the hill. And it came back neatly sawed into lengths of lumber for building. It was stacked on the property and left to season.

For a while my father helped Mr. Donaldson on his place, but there was need for a man to work at the sawmill. The government furnished but one overseer at the mill, and the rest of the labor had to be voluntary. There were three government houses at the mill, and one was vacant, so we moved up there for a time. My father was doing his part for his community, the other two families for theirs.

A one-room house was built as temporary living space, and we moved down from the mountain. Dad made some chairs and tables, and Mr. Donaldson gave us the stove from the hop house. We had brought beds and some other articles with us from Tillamook. The spring was some distance from the house, and water had to be carried from it until Dad drove down a pipe and installed a hand pump.

The sow had six pigs, all of them females, and Dad took that to mean that his surplus for the community would be pork. Every member of the community raised a surplus to be distributed among the members. Mr. Donaldson had a large orchard with a variety of fruit, and he fattened cattle on the river bottom during the summer. Mr. Carney had sheep; he furnished mutton and wool. So it went.

The timber crew came and the clearing of the land began. Dad had been busy slashing out a lot of the underbrush, but it was necessary for skilled men to take out the big trees. The logs were floated down the river to sawmills downstream, but some of them Dad took up to the high sawmill, and they were cut into lumber for our house. In taking out timber the pioneers were always careful to leave some, so each homesteader had part of his place left in forest. This, too, is better thinned out, the dead and diseased trees used for fire wood. Stumps were blasted out with dynamite, but one must know how to handle that stuff.

There were about 25 families in our community, and each community was determined by the boundaries of its school district, although each ran into the other and exchange went on among people for miles around. The areas of the farms varied. Some had not claimed their 160 acres limit, but each tried to raise as much for his own family as he could and depend on the surpluses for the rest. Surplus and labor were always free. You did not insult a man by offering him money for his help.

This is a shortened version of a
piece sent to Joel and Sherri Davidson of
Living in the Ozarks. They didn't have room
for it, so they sent it on to us. Dulcie Brown
now lives at 2646 N. First, Fresno California
93702

Each two weeks the members of the community met at the school house. The first thing the men held a meeting to assess the progress of the community and to decide the order of work for the next two weeks. Every man would explain his own needs, and volunteers would be assigned to help him in whatever he had to do.

When problems arose there was voting, and usually all members abided by the will of the majority. There were no elected officers, but generally they sought the advice of Mr. Donaldson, who was the oldest and most experienced. When the men had decided exactly what was to be done in the next half month, the young men held their meeting and discussed vital issues of the day, often scheduling debates on vital issues affecting the state or nation.

Noon time lunch was on long tables outside, or, if it was rainy, inside the school house. The ladies then displayed their handiwork for all to admire. After that they discussed problems concerning housekeeping and children.

Evening brought entertainment. Young men played their instruments, someone sang, and children recited poems. During the early evening there was a time devoted entirely to young children, when any one of us could say anything we wanted, tell our problems, or just show off. Each member, big and little, was made to feel his importance to the community as a whole. If a decision went against a member, he was offered opportunities to perform some important service which was designed to restore his confidence. Each family was a unit revolving within a unit of the community.

As girls grew up, they were given opportunities to stay for short periods in homes other than their own to learn different ways of doing things than their mothers did. Or they often worked outdoors gardening or grooming animals. There was a wide range of choices, one of which was to help with birthing and care of infants and mothers. Our midwife was an Indian lady, who was always ready to tell others the necessary things to do. She usually only stayed until the baby was born and mother and baby made comfortable, usually a day or a little longer. Then other women or girls took over. The new mother was always kept in bed 10 days after her baby was born, and that is the natural way to protect her health. Of course all women nursed their babies. But in the rare case when she couldn't nurse, a goat was brought and the baby thrived on goat's milk. I remember when my second brother was born I stood by and watched the midwife take care of the baby. She explained to me everything she was doing, washing the baby, oiling him with olive oil, taking care of the navel and putting on the band around his belly to hold the navel in place and finally handing the squalling little squirmer to his mother for sustenance.

We took Saturday baths in the same tubs Mama washed the clothes in. The hot water was taken from the reservoir on the side of the range. It was my job to fill that reservoir every day, carrying in buckets of water from the pump on the porch. I also carried in tons of wood from the woodshed off the back porch. (It was the cabin Dad built first.)

We had a telephone on which line there were some umpteen subscribers. It sometimes took you a while to get a call through because somebody was always on the line. Early one day in the spring there came an emergency call. One short ring always meant clear the line, an important call coming through. Then the ring. It was ours! Why? Don't ask me. But when Dad answered, there was a battery of receivers down and the call was: San Francisco is burning. There has been a terrible earthquake. Many homeless. What can you give? Wayside (place at the side of the road) what you can and teamsters will pick it up.

It was spring, nothing had been produced yet. All we had to spare were a few bushels of potatoes in the bin that had weathered the winter. Those Dad took to the roadside. After the disaster there were a great number of homeless children, and these were offered for adoption. You had to pledge to treat the child as your own, to send it to school and keep it in good health. You also had to be of good character. We did not put in for adopting, but some others did. Donaldsons had three boys, so did Carneys, and each opted for a girl. Donaldsons got a girl named Jenny, about 15, and Carneys a girl named May, aged about 8. The Carneys showered their girl with everything, and I loved to play with her because she had so many toys. May also had two fathers. Her real dad hadn't been killed, but he put her up for adoption. We all sort of envied a girl who had everything, even two papas.

You might think that people who worked as hard as they did wouldn't have time for fun. But, to the contrary, almost anything was cause for celebration. Weddings called for a chivauri (I am not sure I spell it right) and a dance and a giving of presents. Christmas was a big time, with parties at various houses, exchange of gifts, and a play given in the school house. This usually was children acting out the manger scene. And a big Christmas tree with everybody under 18 getting a big bag of goodies.

In all it was a community well organized and hardly ever a bad dispute. Nobody knew how much money you had; it wasn't important. It was something one forgot until the rare times when it might be needed. But if you didn't have it it wasn't a necessity. And I think that may be why those old days were so good.

OUR WORLD FROM ABOVE

The beautiful jewels of cities at night, of sunset and moonrise on the clouds, of pastel deserts, snow-capped mountains with glaciers and emerald pools of ice-formed waters. The history of the life of our planet in the faint traces of vast floods, river-cut gorges and canyons, layering of rock, the building and destroying of soil and vegetation. The devastation we have brought to places we have loved, and the painful and joyful making of things we cherish. All give new dimension and images to the events that are so closely interwoven with our lives that we cannot conceive of their total nature and form. Seeing from above or afar, and the maps such visions create that guide our future actions and dreams, gives new dimensions to our consciousness of ourselves, our actions and our planet.

Starmaker, Olaf Stapleton, $1.95 from:
   Penguin Books
   7110 Ambassador Rd.
   Baltimore, MD 21207
A deeply perceptive examination of the different patterns and levels of relationships on our little planet, presented "from above," visiting different planets and societies where each relationship is dominant. Gives some beautiful evolutionary glimpses into possible futures.

Cosmic View: The Universe in 40 Jumps, Kees Boeke, $4.50.from:
   John Day Books
   T.Y. Crowell Co.
   666 Fifth Ave.
   New York, NY 10019
From a fly on a hand out into galaxies and then back into the hand and down to inner space, which of course might as well be outerspace.

"Our World from the Air," E.A. Gutkind, in *Man's Role in Changing the Face of the Earth*, Wm. Thomas, editor, 1956, Vol. 1 $4.95 from:
   University of Chicago Press
   5801 Ellis Ave.
   Chicago, IL 60637
Gutkind's pioneering work with aerial images has been instrumental in giving us visual perspective on the patterns of our activities and the changes they have made in our planet.

Powers of Ten, Ray and Charles Eames, 1968, $10 rental from:
   Film Distribution Section
   Division of Cinema
   University of Southern California
   Los Angeles, CA 90007
      or
   Museum of Modern Art
   11 West 53rd Street
   New York, NY 10019
8-minute color film. A linear view of our universe from the human scale to the sea of galazies, then directly down to the nucleus of a carbon atom. With an image, a narration and a dashboard, it gives a clue to the relative size of things and what it means to add another zero to any number. It can be bought for $150 from Pyramid Films, Box 1048, Santa Monica, CA 90406.

ATS II Pictures of the Earth and *Indian Ocean Cloud Patterns*, from:
   National Center for Atmospheric
   Research
   P.O. Box 1470
   Boulder, CO 80832
The first home movies of our planet and the rhythms of weather change through time lapse photography. Other films available.

The Third Planet—Terrestrial Geology in Orbital Photographs, Paul D. Lowman, Jr., $32.00 (plus $10 airmail) from:
   Weltflugbild
   Verlag Reinhold A. Muller
   Feldmeilen
   Zurich, Switzerland

Weltraumblider, J. Bodechtel & H. G. Gierloff-Emden, $15.00 (plus $7.20 airmail) from:
   Paul List Verlag KG, Munchen
   SV Sudwest
   Munchen 33
   Postfach, 780 Germany

The Earth From Space, J. Bodechtel & H. G. Gierloff-Emden, $16.95 from:
   Arco Publishing Co., Inc.
   219 Park Avenue S.
   New York, NY 10003
Planetary systems of weather, water, rock and life becomes much more comprehensible when viewed from above. These collections of photography from space flights are both beautiful and highly informative. Weltraumbilder is the most recent and comprehensive. All three form useful tools for understanding, politics, geology, weather, navigation.

Lloyd Kahn

"Viewed from the distance of the moon, the astonishing thing about the earth, catching the breath, is that it is alive. The photographs show the dry, pounded surface of the moon in the foreground, dead as an old bone. Aloft, floating free beneath the moist, gleaming membrane of bright blue sky, is the rising earth, the only exuberant thing in this part of the cosmos. . . . If you had been looking for a very long, geologic time, you could have seen the continents themselves in motion, drifting apart on their crustal plates, held afloat by the fire beneath. It has the organized, self-contained look of a live creature, full of information, marvelously skilled in handling the sun."

Lives of a Cell, Lewis Thomas

Ecological Surveys from Space, National Aeronautics & Space Administration, available for $1.75 from:
> Government Printing Office
> Washington, DC 20402

This is an introduction to use of satellite aerial photography in ground ((otherwise known as earth) inventories; forestry, agriculture, hydrology, etc. Lots of color photos. Published in 1970, so there have been many advances since then.

The World From Above, Hanns Reich, 1968, $6 from:
> Hill and Wang
> Farrar, Straus & Giroux
> 19 Union Square W.
> New York, NY 10003

Contains the magic and meaning lacking in *Photo-Atlas of U.S.* Beautiful images that coalesce and retain new understanding of the events that we are usually so close to that we cannot see and comprehend. Weather, glaciers, terraced rice paddy, cities, elkherds and bird flocks, swimmers, plowed fields, strip mining, river meanders, bomb craters, desert oasis, and our small earth-hall home.

Photo Atlas of the United States, Photographic International, 1975, $5.95 from:
> Ward Ritchie Press
> 474 S. Arroyo Pley
> Pasadena, CA 91105

First complete photographic atlas of U.S. using satellite photography. Color enlargements of 10 major cities. A valuable concept, but hopefully will be followed by photo atlases with greater sensitivity. Little range of scale is given—no sense of U.S. as part of globe, of detailed close-in enlargements of various regions, of earth and weather, of the real beauty of color that has made every air traveler fall in love with the beauty of our planet. Scale used corresponds more to traditional political boundaries than either to geo-cultural regions or ability to clearly reveal landform patterns.

National Ocean Survey
> Rockville, MD 20852

Aerial photos mostly of coastal areas.

Aerial Photography Division
> **Agricultural Stabilization &**
> **Conservation Service**
> **U.S. Dept. of Agriculture**
> **Washington, DC 20250**

Especially important if you're looking for a photographic description of how things have changed. They have negatives back to 1933 and presently have images of over 80% of the nation. On a local level, you can often get aerial maps or reference to resources from State Departments of Geology, Regional Planning Associations and State Highway Departments. Or buy yourself or a friend a special treat: rent an airplane and pilot and photograph your home from above.

Interpretation of Aerial Photographs, 3rd Ed., T. Eugene Avery, $10.95, from:
> Burgess Publishing Co.
> 426 South 6th St.
> Minneapolis, MN 55415

Thorough coverage of aerial photography —processes used, techniques of interpretation, sources of aerial photographs and maps; uses in agriculture, forestry, landforms and geology, engineering, urban-industrial patterns, and air intelligence and military target analysis. A goldmine of interesting information.

The EROS Data Center
> **Sioux Falls, SD 57198**

The ERTS (now called Land-Sat) satellites launched in 1972 and 1973 have photographed nearly the entire globe from an altitude of about 900 kilometers. The ground resolution of Land-Sat images is about 180-275 meters, compared with Gemini and Apollo from 70 to 125 meters, Skylab's multi-spectral camera at 40 to 100 meters, Skylab's earth terrain camera, 10 to 40 meters, high altitude aircraft cameras 4 to 10 meters, and military satellite cameras, which can obtain a resolution better than 3 meters.

In order to make use of the images effectively, it is recommended you have access to a computer—otherwise it's kind of like the proverbial bird that sings too high to hear. The data produced is staggering. "It will produce 15 million bits of information per second, the equivalent of an Encyclopedia Britannica every couple of minutes."

The ordering of Land-Sat images is complicated. We recommend you write for details. (High flight aircraft—U-2— and Skylab images also available).

Mt. Wilson and Palomar Observatories

The political regions of our country have developed with total disregard for the realities of our land and our regional cultures arising from that land. Our "melting pot" mythology has attempted to erase local and regional cultures—but it has yet to erase the landforms, climate, soils, vegetation and living creatures that constantly bring into being regional personalities and cultures in response to the unique problems, potentials and rhythms of each place. Those regional lives and cultures are essential and will endure beyond any artificial political boundaries.

A look at one of Erwin Raisz's intricately beautiful landform maps of the U.S. (No. 3—$1.00 from Erwin Raisz, 130 Charles St., Boston, MA 02114) gives real meaning to the regions shown here, which respond like a well-fitting shoe to the different landform regions. These regions have shared problems, potentials and lifestyles which sharing among the people of the regions can do much to improve. The life of

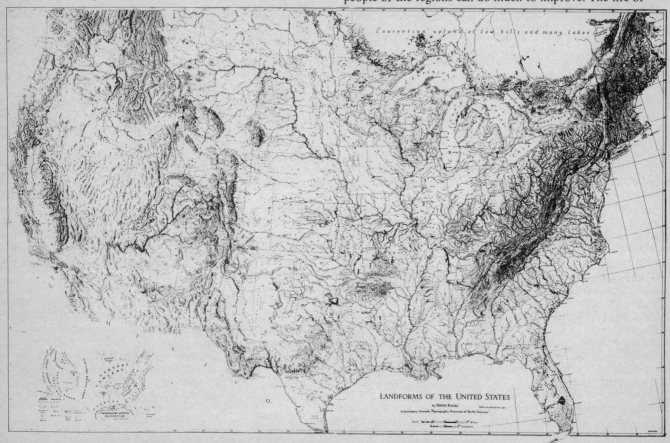

LANDFORMS OF THE UNITED STATES
by ERWIN RAISZ

Regional Perspectives

Maps are useful when things get too big or complex for us to tie together in our own memory and perception. Recently applied tools that permit mapping underwater, at different wavelengths than visible light, or from earthorbit create maps that coalesce together a new feeling/understanding of our places. Get together the following maps, put them all up on a wall, and you're ready for some fascinating travels.

Landforms of the United States, $1 from:

    Erwin Raisz (Map No. 3)
    130 Charles Street
    Boston, MA 02114

The only maps most of us are used to seeing are highway maps that make it look like there's nothing in this country but freeways and road numbers. There may not be, but if you peel off those roads and look at the contours of the land beneath, you end up with the beautiful Erwin Raisz landform maps. You can pour over these for hours—discovering that the hills of northeast Indiana are terminal moraines of glaciers and the old shores of Lake Erie, or follow the cleft of the Hudson River and Lake Champlain all the way from New York to Montreal, or see the cliff over which Niagara Falls stretches for miles across upstate New York. Write for list of other maps.

Portrait U.S.A., for price and other offerings, write:

    National Geographic Society
    17th and M Streets, N.W.
    Washington, DC 20036

Issued as a supplement to the July 1976 *National Geographic*, this is the first color photomosaic of the U.S. Produced from more than 500 separate satellite photos to provide a clear and cloud-free view, it's what we would look like if we had a real big mirror to look into, or were sitting on a chair in high orbit.

Potential Natural Vegetation of the Coterminous United States, $14.50 from:

    American Geographical Society
    Broadway at 156th St.
    New York, NY 10032

An overwhelming 65"x40" eight color map that lays out the location and extent of various plant communities in the U.S. They correspond, of course, with the landform and geology maps, and the population maps correspond to these. Forms the basis for meaningful bio-regions where similar and shared conditions provide a useful basis for a shared culture.

Tidewater, Virginia, is closer to that of New Orleans than to West Virginia. The myths of *Planet Drum* and *Ecotopia* are alive for the people of the Pacific Coast. The dryland farming of eastern Montana has more to share with that of the Texas Panhandle than with western Montana. Regional publications are arising to further the sharing of our lives and the meeting of our common needs. A sense of our regions and their cultures gives us a sense of place and of our roots as well as of where we can find resources to answer our needs.

Atlases such as the *Climatic Atlas of the U.S.* by Stephen Visher can give more detailed regional maps for topography, geology, climate, soils, flora and fauna—but they only bring into finer focus the general regional pattern. Different regions have distinctive features and resources, and much to share with each other, but our lives are nourished and formed dominantly by what is offered and required of us by the region in which we live. Know it well.

Geo-cultural Regions

World Biogeographical Provinces Map, 22" x 38", full color, $3 postpaid from:
CoEvolution Quarterly
P.O. Box 428
Sausalito, CA 94965
Attempts to do on a world scale what *Potential Vegetation . . .* does so beautifully for the U.S. A good first attempt, and, given funding and expertise equal to the American Geographical Society, would hopefully provide a stunning new image of meaningful world regions.

Population Distribution, Urban and Rural, in the U.S. -1970, United States Maps, GE-70, No. 1 (Stock No. 0324-00224), 35¢ from:
Superintendent of Documents
U.S. Government Printing Office
Washington, DC 20402
This map shows population by white dots on a black map on a deep blue background. The U.S. appears as it does

from an airplane at night, with the necklaces of twinkling lights out of the darkness coalescing into the fairyland of urban areas. Shortly after we first saw this, an issue of *Astronomy* appeared with an infra-red satellite photograph of the U.S. on the cover which looked exactly like this population map.

The Floor of the Oceans, $10 from:
American Geographical Society
Broadway at 156th St.
New York, NY 10032

Ocean Floor Maps, inquire for available maps and prices from:
National Geographic Society
17th and M Streets, N.W.
Washington, DC 20036
The maps from the American Geographical Society cost about ten times as much as those from the National Geographic

Society, but *are* incredibly more beautiful and detailed. These maps deal with the two-thirds of our planet that is hidden from our eyes beneath a layer of water as well as an ocean of air. Rivers flow there, and vast mountains and plains reveal the growing pains of a cooling planet. There are deserts and fertile valleys and vast migrations of sand, water, plants, animals, fish, heat and wind. These maps give an amazing view into the geography of these regions.

Bio-Region Maps
When you put these all together, you begin to discover a sense of bioregions—where geological, biological and cultural patterns coincide and co-evolve. These regions form a many times more useful organization for thinking and doing things than do the abstract and historically accidental boundaries of states or federal regions.

MAPS

The four most important federal mappers are the Coast and Geodetic Survey, the Geological Survey, the Forest Service and the Bureau of Land Management. The first, with its coastal charts and its nets of mathematical triangulations, underlies all the others. The Geological Survey is responsible for two current series of maps, both incomplete, and some superseded series too, also incomplete; furthermore, its maps are the underpinning of the famous Army Map Service mapping, the series which for the first time in history was pushed through to completion for every acre of American soil.

The Army series (issued also in a civilian version, handled by the Geological Survey), while admirable in many ways, must be given low marks in certain fields, notably legibility. Why two versions, a military and a civilian? I've seen them both; the difference seems to consist in just one feature: the grid or land net. The military version displays the ten-kilometer military grid, an entirely fictitious grid resembling (but not identical with) latitude and longitude. The civilian version displays the net of townships, a real, not fictitious, grid, inasmuch as it is actually marked out by witness trees, stakes and landmarks.

Many would like to own at least one of the famous moulded plastic relief maps which have been made by an Eastern firm on the basis of the military version of the Army series. They're now available through retailers, after a long period of limited distribution through a military map office only.

The Army maps are almost too stingy in their scale to be of great use to the walker, bicyclist or leisurely motorist. They are at the scale of 1:250,000, yielding a mile which is only 1/4 of an inch long. The one big advantage of this series is that it is complete—has no gaps—a point not to be sneezed at if you have had the common experience of finding that your favorite series has a hole just where you were depending on it to help you.

The Geological Survey also handles its own two series, called the "mile per inch" and the "2000-footer." The first has a scale of 1:62,500, which yields a mile so close to an inch in length that the difference is negligible. This series is printed in sheets about 17x21 inches in size, each covering a quadrangle 15 minutes of latitude and longitude on its sides. The oblong measures about 12x17 miles in area. Each oblong bears the name of some town, mountain or lake within it. Local retailers ask about $1 per sheet; if you're in no hurry you can send off to Geological Survey, Federal Center, Denver, for their index or key maps and their price lists, generally about 75 cents per sheet. The series has extensive and disgraceful gaps.

A more generous scale, 2000 feet per inch, characterizes the other Geological Survey series. Like the mile-per-inch, it shows land forms by means of brown lines called contours. On the whole, it is this series that the Geological Survey is pushing nowadays, while the other series marks time. This is the series to get, if you can afford it. Prices are the same as for the other series, around $1 per sheet. But where a given area will be covered by only one or two sheets in the mile-per-inch series, it will require four to eight sheets for the same area in the 2000-footer series. The oblongs are about 6x9 miles, or 16x23 inches, in area, and the latitude-longitude quadrangle is 7-1/2 minutes on a side. Bulky and unwieldy. (Bob Benson)

MAP SOURCES

U.S. Geological Survey
Map Information Office
Washington, DC 20242
The most widely-used maps, used in most hiking and guidebooks. They also have useful publications, including: *Maps of the United States, Types of Maps Published by Government Agencies, Topographic Maps* (how to read, etc.). Write for detailed information on maps about your area.

U.S. Army Topographic Command
Corps of Engineers
Washington, DC 20315
Maps developed for corps projects, as well as world-wide coverage, and some plastic relief maps.

National Ocean Survey
Distribution Div., C-44
Washington, DC 20235
The new world air charts now show almost all the land areas of the planet (a few Siberian and Antarctic sheets still in the works). Ask for catalog of aeronautical charts and related publications.

Coast and Geodetic Survey
Rockville, MD 20852
Shoreline and river channel maps.

Bureau of Land Management
Dept. of Interior
Washington, DC 20240
Mostly the BLM mapping is in the western half of the U.S., where most of the public land holdings are.

Department of Agriculture
Washington, DC 20250
Both the Soil Conservation Survey and the U.S. Forest Service do extensive mapping. Write to find regional/local offices.

The National Atlas of the United States, 431 pp., 14 pounds, $100 from:
U.S. Geological Survey
1200 S. Eads St.
Arlington, VA 22202
Eight years in the planning. Election districts, agriculture, exploration, battlefields, climate, population. A good reference tool. Get your library to purchase it.

Map Collections in the U.S. and Canada, a directory, ed. by David Carrington, 1970, $8 from:
    Special Libraries Assn.
    235 Park Ave. S.
    New York, NY 10003

There are quite a few good map reading books. Here are some I've used:

Mapping, by David Greenwood, 1964, $3.95 from:
    University of Chicago Press
    Chicago, IL 60637

Nontechnical introduction to mapping in general.

Map Reading, $1.50 from:
    Dept. of Army Field Manual
    Government Printing Office
    Washington, DC 20402

This is good stuff on practical map reading.

Things Maps Don't Tell Us, Armin K. Lobeck, 1956, $6.95 from:
    McMillan Publishing Co.
    866 Third Ave.
    New York, NY 10022

Mr. Lobeck takes some sample map blow-ups and in detail describes how to read the maps through geographic interpretation, a good compliment to more specific map reading books.

Guide to the Cartographic Records in the National Archives, $3.25 from Government Printing Office

If you really get into maps. (Order General Services Division book no. 569-b.)

Oxford World Atlas and *Economic Atlas of the World,* 1972 from:
    Oxford University Press
    200 Madison Ave.
    New York, NY 10016

The *World Atlas,* at $6.95, has got to be the bargain atlas. Very colorful. Stands up well with a spiral binder. The way they have broken up the world is rather awkward but still delightful.

The *Economic Atlas* has over 200 maps illustrating world resources, nation by nation production of goods, etc. Very good for overview.

Geography and Cartography, a Reference Handbook, C. B. Muriel Lock, $32.50 from:
    Shoestring Press
    P.O. Box 4327
    Hamden, CT 06514

With this 750-page annotated catalog/directory to books about geography and maps, atlases and much more in related fields, you can get lost. But what safer way to get lost than in a book about maps.

The annotated entries are sufficient to give you an idea about the content and how it will/won't fit your fancy or need.

Atlas of Oregon, William G. Loy, project director, $24.00 from:
    University of Oregon Press
    Eugene, OR 97403

180 pages of 4-color maps, 700 total, six pounds (or 2.5 kilos—as it is done in the metric system). The atlas is similar to the Washington Environmental Atlas, although the range of subjects is greater, and the scale is somewhat smaller and not quite as useful for detailed planning. The overall picture of the state is about as whole systems as you can get. Might serve as a mantra before environmental design gatherings.

There are historical maps, population density, habit of over 500 species (very small maps), household income, newspaper distribution, power generation, climate, land use, labor and health statistics.

The introduction/overviews to the mapped areas are also well written.

The Acquisition of Maps and Charts Published by the United States Government, $2.00 from:
    Publications Office
    249 Amory Bldg.
    University of Illinois Graduate
      School of Library Science
    Champaign, IL 61820

A guide that can lead you to maps on dozens of subjects, and introduce you to how to order, and defining your needs.

Also a good resource list/bibliography that can lead you still further.

Mapping the World: Portrait of Mother Earth, Erwin Raisz, $3.00 from:
    Abelard-Schuran Inc.
    6 West 57th St.
    New York, NY 10016

An introduction to mapping by that cartographic magician.

Jonathan Carver's North America

![Map of North America with labels including ASIA, Strait of Anian, Lowland, Northwest Passage, Hudson Bay, De fonte's Entrance, L. Winnipeg, R. Bourbon, Oregon R., Shining Mountains, Mississippi R., Minnesota R., Missouri R., Arkansas R., Colorado R., Red R., Rio Grande, Ohio R., Gaspe, Mexico]

Fig. 66. The prevailing idea in the mid-eighteenth century was that North America was a sort of pyramid with all great rivers rising from the Shining Mountains in the center

(From B. De Voto, The Course of Empire, *Houghton Mifflin, 1952.)*

In Chinese the character (symbol) meaning to be lost in the forest relates to a state of non-existence.

Our own language is filled with references to the mind as a place, a place to explore, and where one can get lost, with byways and paths, fields and forests, terrors and rivers.

There are streams of consciousness, centers of attention, right paths and mental reservations.

People get lost in thought, find their way, change directions.

The quality of one's model of the universe is measured by how well it matches the real universe.

A friend of mine was arrested one day because he had lost his way. He was on his way to a large city north of here but suddenly realized he (or another he) had taken himself east toward another, smaller town. He was found lightly hitting his head against a telephone pole in frustration.

He was brought to court to have judgment passed on his STATE of mind. Was he harmful to himself or others; and/or was he capable of taking care of himself.

Another time I saw a person standing a foot away from a very white wall, staring at a patch of light. He stood there for five minutes. He was going nowhere. He had no purpose and was lost in the patch of light, or lost in thought.

We wouldn't think of arresting someone who was lost, but knew *where* he was going, only not *how* to get there, but to be disoriented because your mental compass is broken and you have no way of knowing how to get on to the next thing (no things, just all around, every which way), or why to go anywhere rather than right here—that's when you stand out.

I read a summary of my mental state once, which was surmised during a selective service medical examination. It was quite simply put: patient is in touch with time, place and person. I've learned to fake being a conductor too well.

One can simulate systems or already internal systems inside his self. Models of thinking-feeling-doing are as valid as models of river drainage systems, of aircraft, of space ships, or of universes. (John Lilly)

The brain is being mapped. Neuropsychologists and other brain scientists are like archaeologists or anthropologists beset with the problem of uncovering and describing the intricate network of a dig the size of a cosmic New York City.

Each cell (in the mind) is capable of linking up across special pathways with between 60,000 and 300,000 other cells.

As with the technology of satellite and high aerial photography, the one perspective from above (or in the case of brain science, the one perspective of mapping the *physical* brain) is not sufficient.

There is a necessary interplay between the map and the territory, the census bureau and the residents, the studier and the studied, the high flight photographer, computer programmer and the native or guide to the land itself.

The person who has lived for 50 years in one spot, in his mind, or on a piece of land, can tell others through a special kind of knowledge (knowing that, rather than knowing how) what it's like to live on that land, in their mind.

It seems that no man can effectively illuminate the way for all men. There is more than one road and a great number of sub-paths. On all these, men who can serve as beacons are needed. (John Lilly)

Mental Maps

Mind in the Waters, edited by Joan McIntyre, 1974, $6.95 from:
> Sierra Club Books
> 530 Bush St.
> San Francisco, CA 94108

Maps of a water world forged by sound in the brain of delicate undulating shaped wet beings.

Mental Maps, Peter Gould, Rodney White, 1974, $2.95 from:
> Penguin Books
> 72 Fifth Ave.
> New York, NY 10011

I heard once about a woman who moved to Oregon based on a viewmaster slide of Crater Lake (which was recently polluted) when she was 8-10 years old. Try it sometime: ask people what areas they'd like to live in and why.

I imagine that a lot of the 25% of the nation's energy consumption is from people wanting to be there rather than here, or here rather than there. "We are slowly realizing that people's perception of places is one of the things we must consider as we try to understand the pattern of man's work on the face of the earth."

Mental Maps is a report on studies done in England, the U.S. and elsewhere on how people perceive parts of the world, especially those they have only just heard about.

Galton's Walk, Herbert F. Crovitz, Harper & Row, 1970. **Out of Print**

"Throughout the search for [a] lost name, one can reject names that were not the correct one even though the correct one escapes capture. Furthermore, one could pick the lost name from a list in which it was embedded, if only one were given such a list. An intriguing possibility is this: when the stage has been reached in which one can verbalize some features of a solution—i.e., the solution lies "at the tip of one's tongue"—the solution has already been made (as a lost name was once learned); the problem now is to release it from cognitive inhibition."

A Model of the Brain, J. Z. Young, 1964, $13 from:
> Oxford University Press
> 200 Madison Ave.
> New York, NY 20016

From studies of octopus brain structure some possible patterns or networks that may be applicable to human mental maps.

Embodiments of Mind, Warren S. McCulloch, 1965, $3.95 from:
> MIT Press
> Cambridge, MA 02142

This was the book (even though I've never read it cover to cover) that turned my thinking about the actual life possibility of mathematically mapping the brain. That it was inevitable and happening, but much longer than a watched pot to complete. Very technical and/or abstract.

The Machinery of the Brain, Dean E. Wooldridge, 1963, $2.45 from:
> McGraw-Hill Books
> 1221 Ave. of the Americas
> New York, NY 10036

Now 14 years old, much has happened but this is a good place to go—short of going to technical medical journals—to find out current state of what is known about the mind/brain.

Laws of Form, G. Spencer Brown, 1969, $2.25 from:
> Bantam Books
> 666 Fifth Avenue
> New York, NY 10019

It seems, and mathematicians contend that mathematics deals with fundamental organization and structure of our world and our minds. Yet it has always felt cold and abstract to me. This book is a primer on Zen math, and for the first time gives me hope that the world of mathematics may someday be expressed in its beauty for everyone to understand. Read the introduction—the rest may need a guide. The theme is that a universe comes into being whenever a space is severed or a distinction is made, and by tracing the way we represent such a severance, we can reconstruct with uncanny accuracy the basic forms underlying linguistic, mathematical, physical and biological science.

Brains, Machines and Mathematics, Michael A. Arbib, 1965, $2.45 from:
> McGraw-Hill
> 1221 Ave. of the Americas
> New York, NY 10036

Much good stuff on the complicated passages of electrical impulses through the network of the brain.

The I Ching or *Book of Changes*, Richard Wilhelm/Cary Baynes translation, 1950, $8.50 from:
> Princeton University Press
> 41 William Street
> Princeton, NJ 08540

When we first were trying to decide on a name for the *RAINBOOK*, we thought of calling it the *RAINBOOK of Changes*, because what it represented to us was an account and access to a basic pattern of changes our society was going through. But that was too close to the name of this beautiful and venerated classic to feel right. You can't read the *I Ching*. It's not a book. It's somehow a collection and distillation of powerful and purified multidimensional lenses through which we can review, meditate on and realign our actions to our most deepfelt sense of purpose and existence.

—✂—

*See also pages on Language in Communications section.

Resource Inventories

Although some planning, taking stock, making inventories, has existed for years as a central part of planning and research in local and federal governmental agencies, in recent years several things have contributed to an increase in mapping, land use inventories and environmental impact surveys:
- a federal law, administered by the Environmental Protection Agency, calls for environmental impact statements to be made for projects which will have a major impact on the environment.
- a general trend toward evaluation and accountability.
- the availability of satellite and high aerial photographic images and computer techniques associated with the data collected that allows for tremendous amounts of information to be put into patterns and contexts.
- the increase in the amount of land use planning demanded by local government and citizen groups.
- enriched ideas about the needs of and methods available for making clearer pictures of interrelationships between different disciplines and different physical laws.
- the furthering of ideas about carrying capacity of the land, limits to growth and resource allocation.

As government increasingly gets involved in studying the overall impact of development and growth, it becomes increasingly clear that political boundaries make little sense, hence the development of regional government units, which in many cases relate more closely to natural geo-regions. You can't deal with a river that wiggles by putting it into political straight lines.

As the techniques for measuring the impact of development on the environment become more sophisticated, it also becomes clear that everything is related. You don't throw anything away; you only give it, or throw it to someone (another agency for example) else. Environmental impact statements and planning guidelines are now beginning to encompass both the social and natural world. The measure of "success" begins to include such vague things as happiness. We are probably just beginning to see the growth of cross discipline studies that will entail ecologists working closer with sociologists, and people working in energy relating to people working in land use planning.

There are countless inventories, land use studies, environmental impact statements published monthly. As well as keeping tabs on it through local environmental groups, land use planning agencies, etc., you can get on the EPA mailing list in your region. Write to: Environmental Protection Agency, 401 M Street, S.W., Washington, DC 20460.

Environment, Power and Society, Howard Odum, 1971, $6.50 from:
> Wiley Interscience
> 605 Third Ave.
> New York, NY 10016

Howard Odum, and the energetics team at University of Florida, have done much to advance the idea of net energy accounting, carrying capacity, and the study of environmental impact through a multi-disciplined approach. His 1973 paper, *Energy, Ecology and Economics*, opened things up for a lot of us. Reprinted numerous places, including *Co-Evolution Quarterly*.

Transition, prepared by the Office of Energy Research & Planning, 1975 $6.95 ($9.95 to libraries) from:
> Prometheus Unbound, Specialty
> Books
> P.O. Box 42261
> Portland, OR 97242

A 250-page attempt to give a picture/map of the energy resources, use and flow, of the area known (in the 1970s) as Oregon. A commendable effort.

Design with Nature, Ian L. McHarg, 1971 $5.95 paperback from:
> Doubleday Natural History Press
> Garden City, NY

This book brought city planning into the context of ecological studies. I still, after not picking it up for several years, find it inspiring. The variety of perspectives and maps is lovely.

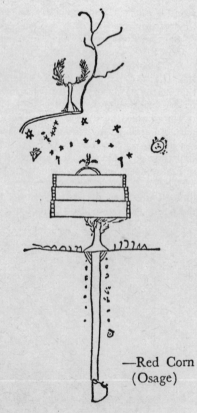
—Red Corn (Osage)

Federal Environmental Monitoring Directory, by the Council on Environmental Quality, 30¢ from:
> Government Printing Office
> Washington, DC 20402

A really well-done guide to federal agencies doing environmental inventory work.

Washington Environmental Atlas, U.S. Army Corps of Engineers (with assistance from the Institute for Environmental Studies), 1975, price unknown from:
> U.S. Army Corps of Engineers
> 4735 E. Marginal Way S.
> Seattle, WA 98134

A 3 foot by 2 foot inventory/atlas, with several hundred contributors. Must be one of the most complete surveys ever done (in mapping format). Our first reaction: think of the money involved. It lays on my floor, something to walk around till it's reviewed. It grows on you. Of course, there may have been a way to do it with less expense, but then again, it's a working tool. The problem with most atlases, like the *NW Atlas*, is the scale is often only of general interest; these maps, on the other hand, are generous enough to be of use in, for example, environmental impact statements, real, critical land use decisions.

Is there a Corps of Engineers prejudice? No, I don't think so. The balance is there, the completeness of criteria, which involves geological, hydrological, biological, archeological, historical and contemporary cultural, environmental use and recreational management.

Ask your library. This should be made available to the public. Hours of fascinating reading. Even has a map locating Bigfoot sightings—right after Fish & Mollusks.

Making the City Observable

It takes a faster breed of cartographer to keep track of the flow of growth and death of cities, the patterns of information exchange, the results of decisions and attitudes, the record of man's relation to certain intense places where communication, service exchange, commerce and transportation are concentrated. As rivers leave canyons and deltas, we leave footprints in our search and finding of the things that we feel, or are made to feel, we need, to survive and pursue happiness.

A city has a money flow
          traffic flow
          rivers of tears
          waste flow
          energy flow
          services flow
A city has a soundscape
          smellscape
          touchscape
          sightscape
          tastescape

In order to see the whole city, one must begin to find patterns, networks, motivations and beliefs. There have been many good efforts recently to see, to comprehend a city.

Making the City Observable, Richard Saul Wurman, 1971
$7.50 from:
  MIT Press
  Cambridge, MA 02142
This study and catalog of tools describes some of the wide variety of planning aids used and dreamt of, things like: synagraphic mapping, computer graphics, sequence experience notation, urban atlases, walk-through models, aerial photos, city photo books . . . Excellent. A new edition has been promised.

Zephyros
  1201 Stanyon St.
  San Francisco, CA 94117
They produce some of the best city environmental education materials in the country. Especially relevant in this context is *Your City Has Been Kidnapped*. Ron Jones also did a good guide on how to research a community called *Finding Community*. (See also "Some Ideas" below.)

World Soundscape Project
  Dept. of Communication Studios
  Simon Fraser University
  Brunaby, BC Canada
Even the best of the cross-disciplined, whole systems approach to thinking, planning and designing often neglect sound. It is another world that, outside of music, is ignored. Our ability to describe sound, and to perceive changes in the sound environment—ask someone on a country road turned highway when the road got noisy—is still in early stages, like mapping the physical world was in the Middle Ages.

GEE! Group for Environmental Education
  1214 Arch St.
  Philadelphia, PA 19107
I think they coined the phrase "Making the City Observable" (and Richard Wurman is at GEE!). They have produced many good materials that can assist one in comprehending the city environment, including *Yellow Pages of Learning Resources* and *Our Manmade Environment*. Write for current publications list.

The Vancouver Book, Chuck Davis, editor, 1976 $10.95 from:
  J. J. Douglas, Ltd.
  1875 Welch Street
  North Vancouver, BC, Canada
This is probably the most comprehensive, full pictured view of a city. (See full review in Communications Section). section.)

Studying Your Community, Roland L. Warren, $3.95 from:
  Free Press
  866 Third Ave.
  New York, NY 10022
A very comprehensive outline on how to do research in your community, with emphasis on subject and area surveys. Somewhat old but good range finder.

"The Urban Observation Program—a HUD-founded city-university experiment that works," in *Nations Cities*, December 1974.
A survey of the urban observatories models set up in several U.S. cities.

Some Ideas

1. The American Institute of Architects has had some interesting workshops in which persons are given some material and told to go to a chosen spot and build a small city.
2. Robert Moran, a conductor, has written musical scores that entire cities play through car lights flashing, radio and television stations simulcasting certain sounds/songs.
3. Have a show and tell which would allow nonperformers, nonartists to bring forth their stories, for example the city as viewed from a bridge tender's eyes, etc.
4. Community novel. Once I helped start a thing we called the home grown library where we had a large book that we called the community novel. People that visited and used the library (which had mostly just locally written stuff) would add to the story.
5. Have an exhibit of photos of the city from different angles, historical photos, aerial photos, maps, models of city blocks.
6. Do a time lapse movie of the city growing over a period of years.
7. What would you call a historical society that collected memorabilia in the present before it became historical?
8. Give people in a workshop situation an outline map of the city, then have them fill it in with landmarks important to them. This can especially be meaningful when the people involved are from different neighborhoods and/or classes. (See "Mental Maps," *Newsweek*, 3-15-76.)
9. Map out some people's routines based on where they move (like the mayor).
10. Conduct a city-wide scavenger hunt for lost objects, lost services, lost emotions or ideas.
11. Draw a map of your city illustrating where humor and sorrow are found.

(Some of these ideas from Zephyros)

Tom Bender

ECONOMICS

The dreams that fueled our recent history and supported the central role of our particular brand of economics have lost their momentum and believability. New dreams, new ethics and new values which can align the framework of a new economics with the fundamental values held (if not always followed) by our society, are beginning to coalesce as we come clear of our past beliefs. The dimensions of what must change and what must take form are becoming visible through the mists of our conventions.

Within this country, the size, economic and political power of our corporations have reached the level where they are al-most totally beyond control of governmental regulation and come closer to the reverse—of regulating the government instead. Our recent past has been one of those rare and unusual periods of history when abundance of resources made rapid growth possible and made acceptable the institutional concentration of power necessary for rapid and massive development. Yet viewed from not too far into our future or from most other periods of history, our recent past must appear as a Mad Hatter's tea party in Alice's Wonderland where all the rules are topsy-turvy and the most insane activities commonplace.

The realities of the activities and effects of our giant corporations are far different than their claims. The Vietnam War, the safe-energy, environmental, consumer and labor movements have dug out a lot of that reality and have also shown that smaller, simpler and less costly alternatives are both available and preferable. Power is a destructive thing—the more one person or group has, the less everyone else has, and the safest alternative to having it all yourself is for everyone to share it equally.

Beware those who yell (or advertise) the loudest—they might be covering their own tracks. A 1969 government investigation of welfare fraud found only 4/10 of 1% of all welfare cases were fraudulent but also found that 28% of farmers and businessmen and 34% of those living on interest payments were guilty of fraud and tax evasion!

CORPORATE POWER

Global Reach, Richard Barnet and Ronald Müller, 1974, $4.95 from:
Simon and Schuster
630 Fifth Avenue
New York, NY 10020
The claims and the realities of multi-national corporations and their destructive effects on both the U.S. and under-developed countries that have resulted in worsening conditions in both areas, while exponentially increasing their own power and wealth. This has the details.

Fear in the Countryside, E.G. Vallianatos, 1976, $14 from:
Ballinger Publishing Co.
17 Dunster St.
Cambridge, MA 02138
American development programs, both in this country and abroad, have almost universally aided the wealthy elite at the expense of the poor. Valianatos documents the growing power of wealthy agricultural landlords and urban elites and the deepening poverty of the small farmers resulting from our "development" efforts in Latin America. He also presents evidence that transfer of agricultural technologies can rarely be successful because of biological and cultural specificity of different regions and that social injustice is a greater cause of world hunger problems than is agricultural productivity.

Gonna Rise Again, 1976, $1.75 from:
Resources for Community Change
P.O. Box 21066
Washington, DC 20009
Economic exploitation of workers has been around for a long time, and in some form is probably going to be around forever. If you want to know its form today, what people are doing to lessen it, what groups and resources are available to help you understand and change conditions—dig in. An important part of the shell game of economics.

What's Happening to Our Jobs?, $1.45 and *Why Do We Spend So Much Money?*, $1.00, available from:
Popular Economics Press
Box 221
Somerville, MA 02143
Both these reports translate into simple and graphic language many of the shady dealings going on behind the walls of the business world that end up with 90% of us getting the short end of the deal. Simple questions most of us have wanted to ask sometime, and answers that may or may not surprise us. Well documented, with lots of true life tales worth passing on.

State Growth Management, prepared by the Council of State Governments, May 1976, free from:
U.S. Dept. of Housing and Urban Development
HUD Building
Washington, DC 20410
All about how to stimulate growth, but contains a lot of information useful for evaluating that whole idea. Tables listing state by state the subsidies and incentives given to promote more frenzied economic activity. Good summary of current mindsets and programs, with a few attempts beginning to question and manage growth. One Massachusetts study concludes that the State itself is a major contributor to costly and inefficient development by encouraging and supporting fringe rather than central development.

The Bell System and Community Telephones, Thomas Brom and Ed Kirshner, 1974, $1.50 from:
The Community Ownership
Organizing Project
349 62nd Street
Oakland, CA 94618
This was a real eye-opener to me. It made clear why I've felt more than vaguely uneasy about Ma Bell and her minions and their incessant demands on our pocketbooks. It describes the effective and economic operation of the few remaining municipally-owned phone systems—Edmonton, Alberta, for example, that earns 25% more revenue than comparable Bell-owned systems. It also explains some of the financial shell games played with the various Bell-owned "subsidiaries" which result in major overcharges to customers and subsidies of certain favored groups. For instance, Bell buys all its equipment at inflated prices from its subsidiary, Western Electric, since only Ma Bell's return on investment is regulated. Revenue from home phone use and local calls supports a limited class of affluent business telephone users who make 2.5 billion interstate calls per year. Training and labor costs are excessive because of Ma Bell's infamous employment practices that result in a 62% yearly turnover of operators—the highest rate in the country. The list goes on and on. Alternatives to the Bell System are explored, as well as the process of getting there.

Yerba Buena, Chester Hartman, 1974, $4.95 from:
Glide Publications
330 Ellis St.
San Francisco, CA 94102.
Yerba Buena gives an excellent picture of the politics of profit behind urban "development" . . . who promotes it, who profits, how finance and city councils are manipulated and controlled, and how the costs are forced onto the poorer members of the community. Factual and strongly documented.

Economics of U.S. Subsidy Programs, Congressional Record, Hearings before the Subcommittee on Priorities and Economy in Government, Jan. 13-17, 1972, from:

U.S. Government Printing Office
Washington, DC 20402

Extensive documentation of special interest government programs, intentional subsidies, hidden subsidies and patterns of economic aid in different sectors of our economy—particularly to those who need it least. Did you know that every dollar of air fares is subsidized by two dollars of our tax money? A very valuable set of documents.

Property Tax Organizing Manual, 1973, $2.50 from:

Movement for Economic Justice
1609 Connecticut Ave., N.W.
Washington, DC 20009

Property taxes have had an unfair impact on lower income residents of almost every community—frequently through underassessment of expensive residential, commercial or industrial property, special tax districts set up to exempt industries from property taxes, or through a variety of loopholes that have worked to the advantage of the wealthy. This manual carefully lays out how property taxes work and how they are cheated on. It then provides step-by-step instructions on how to investigate local tax situations and organize for changes. Useful to understand some of those old hidden subsidies as well as to work for more fair local tax policies. These people also put out *Just Economics,* $10/year, a monthly newsletter on current economic issues.

Phantom Taxes in Your Electric Bill, Richard Morgan, 1975, $2.50 from:

Environmental Action Foundation
724 Dupont Circle Building
Washington, DC 20036

Some utilities end up with a lot of money to invest by collecting taxes from their ratepayers and passing it on to the government late or never. This report details the worst offenders, the games they play and how we pay—to the tune of $1.5 billion a year.

*See the section on Utilities and Energy for reports of corporate misdeeds in that area.

Cost of Energy Slaves

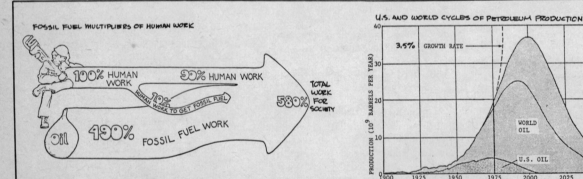

A lot of our present wealth has come from the great amount of work done for us by fossil fuels, which until recently have needed very little of our own effort to obtain. For the work we've spent obtaining fossil fuels, we've been getting back fifty times as much work done for us by those ancient fossils. When we figure that we spend about ten percent of our own work to obtain such energy, we realize that fossil fuels have had the effect of temporarily increasing our "work force" by almost SIX TIMES!

Being able to do so much work cheap—with so little expenditure of our own effort—has had another effect . . . the massive exploitation of other people who don't have cheap energy slaves to work for them. They have had to compete with their own labor against the cheap work of our fossil fuels. As a result, they only get paid the pittance we have to pay for fossil fuels. When we combine this human exploitation with the increased work those fuels do for us directly and our rapid consumption of material resources on a global basis, we should seriously wonder why we aren't richer than we seem!

If we look further, however, and compare how fast we are using up our fossil fuels to how fast the rest of the world is using up theirs, we might have second thoughts about our extravagant lifestyle and spendthrift use of energy. We have been using up our petroleum and coal resources much faster than the rest of the world, and if we keep on as we are we will exhaust them while other countries still have cheap and plentiful energy slaves.

We have enjoyed a powerful worldwide economic and political dominance built upon our energy base and should be wary of similar future dominance by others. It would seem wise to save some of our wealth and the energy it is based on for our future rather than to see how rapidly we can use it up. Reducing our demands now and becoming less reliant upon any use of energy saved from the distant past can ensure us a more positive future. In addition, improving the energetics of our production processes and foreign trade, conversion to income energy use, and realistic appraisal of evolving global political and economic balances are necessary to protect ourselves from costly economic and political errors.

Economic activity that produces unnecessary or useless things certainly can't be counted as contributing to our quality of life, nor can replacement of disposable things that shouldn't have been disposed of. War and military expenditures are our worst example, but we have yet to learn to choose in all things between the desirable and the merely possible. We need to set personal and national economic priorities that reflect basic values that we can be comfortable with before all people.

A balanced society that seeks quality and greatness rather than growth and magnitude operates in totally different ways. Such values are finding voice and feeling right, and their implications for how we work and live are emerging in surprising and positive ways.

WHAT IS WORTH DOING?

Council on Economic Priorities
84 5th Ave.
New York, NY 10011

One of the good public research groups watching corporate practices. Have several reports/studies on: economic impact of the cost of pollution control; overview of social performances of various corporations. Write for publications list and membership/newsletter information.

Priorities, donation requested, from:
American Friends Service Committee
980 N. Fair Oaks Avenue
Pasadena, CA 91103
A well-done newsletter documenting alternatives to a military economy. Recent issues have focused on the unemployment caused by military spending because of its capital-intensity, legislation dealing with the conversion from a military-dominated economy to a civilian one, and the effects of the federal research and development program in commiting future expenditures on useless systems such as the B-1 bomber and the Trident missile submarines. Defense, space and atomic energy receive two-thirds of the federal research funds. *Priorities* presents the sound economics of alternatives.

The Defense Monitor
Center for Defense Information
122 Maryland Avenue, N.E.
Washington, DC 20002
Our journalists should be seeking out these kinds of people in the Postal Service, academia, banking or agriculture —finding people who can propose viable alternatives for public evaluation instead of merely publishing the official policy preferences of top bureaucrats. Legislators should require submission of alternative budgets and priorities by staff people as well as by administrators. This is an excellent model—a newsletter containing evaluation of alternative military priorities, programs and budgets by professional military people who support a strong defense but oppose excessive and ineffective expenditures or forces.

The Buddhist sees the essence of civilization not in a multiplication of wants but in the purification of human character. Character, at the same time, is formed primarily by a man's work. And work, properly conducted in conditions of human dignity and freedom, blesses those who do it and equally their products.

If the nature of the work is properly appreciated and applied, it will stand in the same relation to the higher faculties as food is to the physical body. It nourishes and enlivens the higher man and urges him to produce the best he is capable of. It directs his free will along the proper course and disciplines the animal in him into progressive channels. It furnishes an excellent background for man to display his scale of values and develop his personality.

Since production and consumption are merely a means to human well-being, the aim should be to obtain the maximum of well-being with the minimum of consumption. (From *Buddhist Economics*)

ETHICS AND ECONOMICS

"Buddhist Economics," E.F. Schumacher in *Small Is Beautiful*, 1973, $2.45 from:
Harper and Row
10 E. 53rd St.
New York, NY 10022
This powerful essay, frequently reprinted but still relatively unknown, has laid the foundation for looking creatively at the relation between ethics and values and the sciences and institutions built upon them.

"Energy, Ecology and Economics," Howard T. Odum, available from:
Energy Center
University of Florida
Gainesville, FL 32601
Pioneering exploration of the requirements for living beyond our fossil fuel subsidies, with the general ecosystem principles or ethics involved.

Sharing Smaller Pies, Tom Bender, 1975, $2 from:
RAIN
2270 N.W. Irving
Portland, OR 97210
An overview of the need for institutional change emerging from new energy and economic realities. Explores value changes possible or necessary with these conditions and their implications for economics.

Toward a Steady State Economy, Herman Daly, 1973, $3.95 from:
Wm. Freeman and Co.
660 Market Street
San Francisco, CA 94104
One of few available sources for explorations of the implications of resource limits for economics. Essays on the social dimensions of steady state economics, the entropy law and the economic process, economics of spaceship earth and other useful slices of the transition toward equilibrium.

STOLEN GOODS

We often complain about having to pay too much for things, but do we ever complain because we have to pay too little for something?

Can things cost too little?

When someone stops us on the street and offers us a TV or watch or stereo at a really low price, the first thing that pops into our heads is: "Is it HOT?" Our intuition always warns us that when something costs a lot less than it's supposed to, there is probably something funny going on.

We think about stolen goods when someone offers us a "deal" on the street. But do we think about stolen goods when we find a "bargain" at a supermarket, a discount plaza or an import store? Do we think about stealing from our children when we go to the gas station? Yet we buy gasoline that is cheap because we're pumping out the energy savings of millions of years so rapidly that none will be left for our own future or for our children.

When we buy fresh produce from California in the supermarket, do we realize we are likely buying goods that are produced illegally? Is it less wrong to buy illegal goods from a "Safeway" than on the street? Much of California's produce comes from the Central Valley, where vast corporate farms operate with flagrant disregard of federal and state laws limiting use of irrigation water to 160-acre family farms. And much of the produce is picked by illegal immigrants in violation of immigration, tax and employment laws. Is it stealing when a company that monopolizes food processing sets impossible quality criteria for produce of small independent farmers, then buys their crop cheap because there are no other buyers to whom they can sell?

How do we know if prices for things are low because they are being *dumped*? It's not uncommon for large producers to sell some items below cost to drive out their small competitors who produce more efficiently but can't afford large losses. And how can small farmers compete with corporate farming that *wants* to operate at a loss for tax writeoffs?

Imports also can be too cheap when our trade arrangements and energy sources exploit the workers of other countries (RAIN, May 1976). How would we feel if our country had no source of cheap fossil fuels and another country started to sell fossil-fuel-produced goods in our country so cheaply that we were all put out of work? We would end up having to work for starvation wages to compete with such cheap energy sources and stay alive. Is it right to purchase goods that support such an exploitative relationship?

So what if we do buy stolen goods, or illegally-produced products, or goods that are produced by exploitation? The major problem, it seems, is that when someone loses, someone else gains. *Someone* gets rich off of "stolen goods"—either the buyer or an intermediary or both. When wealth accumulates, power accumulates—whether we speak of large corporations vs. individual Americans or U.S. citizens vs. the rest of the world. And the more that power is concentrated, the less possible it is to sustain the principles of democracy and equality that our country was founded upon and which are necessary to the kind of society we wish to live in. Buying stolen goods contradicts those principles we claim to believe in and follow, and either we must change or they must.

Whether or not we eventually buy a "hot" TV hinges not only on whether we will get caught, but also—on some level— on a realization that supporting a market for stolen goods increases the odds that sometime we may become the source for such stolen goods.

Chickens always come home to roost one way or another. Exploitation of others eventually comes full circle—if not through rebellion, then through disease—if not through disease, then from atrophy. Wealth insulates and isolates, and, removed from the continual probing and testing of real forces of life, our information and judgment fail to keep us within the limits of the game. (Our Drain America First energy policy is a good example of this kind of failure.) While we become wealthy off of other countries, we are in turn exploited and controlled by the power and wealth of our large institutions.

Though we claim and often act otherwise, our purchasing decisions are never based on economics alone. Our so-called economic decisions always occur within limits set by ethics, morals and other social values. We require things to be Union Made. We don't allow child labor. We set the rules on corporate taxes, patents and monopoly that become the rules of the game within which economic trade, survival and success occur. Such ethical frameworks are essential and are more basic than profit or economics because they enable the continued survival and health of the resources, environment, social fabric and personal judgment necessary for our survival and well-being.

The separation of our ethics and our actions has occurred in part because our production and exchange processes are so complex and large that we are isolated and distant from where goods may have been "stolen." Without knowing what occurs or sensing the effects, we have less and less reason to trust our ethical judgment. We're also so wealthy ourselves, as a country, and so unused to doing things ourselves that we often have little sense of value and costs.

"Marked" prices, standardized goods, changing prices, take-it-or-leave-it buying, and prices totally determined by someone else are so universal that we have very little sense of what we're getting for what we pay or what is fair exchange. We don't know *what* we're getting (poly-epoxyl who?), if profit on it is excessive, if taxes were paid, if someone was unfairly paid for making it, if externalized costs were accounted for in its price. And things really *have* been changing so rapidly it's difficult to judge prices. New technical processes produce things more cheaply, but inflation and exhaustion of resources cause prices to swing erratically upwards.

Not only do our economics become confused as a result of all this, but our relationships with other people are harmed. Because we don't know what a fair deal would be, we can only assume that the less we can get something for, the better deal we got. But even then we're uncertain that the other person knows something we don't and we might get taken. And *someone*, it seems, is supposed to get the best deal out of an exchange. Our exchanges rarely give us good feelings towards the people we exchange with. We never end up thankful to other people or wishing to do something nice for them in the future in exchange for what they did or gave us.

Penny Johnson

All these things tie back to our not knowing what's happening, and so do ways of changing the situation. There are lots of things we can do:

▪ Reduce the scale of organizations. A small and knowable scale of production is the best insurance against not knowing what's happening. Present regulations discriminate heavily against small but efficient producers.

▪ Open financial records. Seeing how much a merchant or producer pays and gets for their products pinpoints avoidable expense and profit. More businesses are feeling more comfortable with people knowing rather than wondering. People act differently, too, when they know!

▪ Encourage local auctions, exchanges, flea markets, used goods sales. They will be more and more valuable in the future, are fun, and are good places to learn what things are worth. They have been regulated away in many communities.

▪ Exchange with friends and people you know—and *give* more than required. It will usually come back with interest. Remember the baker's dozen.

▪ Make and do things ourselves instead of purchasing them. Do real and varied work. We can save money, taxes and reduce the GNP while learning the worth of things.

▪ Get poor—live simply—and avoid the rush later. Reducing desires instead of satisfying them helps get us closer to reality and to the worth of things.

▪ Learn and share the energetics and economics of our foreign trade and our national economy.

▪ Regulate foreign trade of items not produced at equal wage rates or with careful energetics. The only trade that is socially affordable is trade of surpluses, not necessities.

▪ Prevent passing the buck, the costs and the damages caused by our activities on to people who don't profit from those activities.

▪ Give legal standing to trees, future generations and our shared surroundings so that passing on of costs to them and exploiting them can be controlled.

The more people know about something, the less chance there is of monkey business. There are ethical dimensions to exchange. Their importance to society is greater than the economic dimensions of exchange, and it is up to us to ensure their observance.

Banking institutions play a pivotal part in the direction and nature of our economy. But not without self-interest. Your money is frequently used to support the real estate and other speculations of the bankers, and the interlinked corporate ties between banks and other businesses often drain wealth out of communities and into the pockets and power of other people and corporations.

WHO'S USING YOUR MONEY?

Redlining is the practice whereby bankers quietly determine that they won't make loans in a part of town where it might be less profitable to them. They thus effectively draw a red line around a neighborhood, creating a self-fulfilling prophecy of deteriorating and vacated slums. Branch banking and non-enforcement of charter regulations allow banks to take money from one area and loan it elsewhere—making loans unavailable in the local community and making the savings of poor people in the city pay for developing rich suburbs. The Central Seattle Community Council Federation showed that for every dollar placed in savings institutions by Seattle city residents, about 30¢ is reinvested in the city, while for every dollar invested by suburbanites, about $2 is reinvested in suburban growth.

In Chicago the problems of redlining became visible some three years ago, and, after many unsuccessful attempts to get banks to change their practices, the city council finally passed an ordinance requiring full disclosure by banks of their loan practices. The city government has been persuaded to deposit its money in non-redlining institutions, and more than $2 million was withdrawn from those banks and reinvested in other institutions who had formed agreements with the community coalition. Chicago now has over $100 million in pledges to move savings from redlining lenders, five of whom have signed greenlining agreements. State, church and retirement funds, or other large blocks of savings can produce powerful leverage on banks in this way.

The U.S. Congress has passed a bill (S-1281) requiring disclosure of lending practices by financial institutions, which will assist individuals and community groups researching redlining practices. It won't help, however, with more subtle variations of redlining such as discriminatory interest rates, excessive downpayment requirements and unusually short loan periods, or with redlining practices by insurance companies. Write your Congressperson for a copy of the law.

The Bankers, Martin Mayer, 1974, $2.25 from:
> Ballantine Books
> 201 E. 50th Street
> New York, NY 10022

Gives a good overview of the manipulations inside our financial system. Talks about how banks are used to the advantage of the rich and how they operate.

"Redlining: Problems and Tactics—The Chicago Experience," Gail Cincotta, *Street Magazine*, Summer, 1975 from:
> Pratt Institute Center for Community
> and Environmental Development
> 240 Hall Street
> Brooklyn, NY 11205

A summary of redlining challenges in Chicago.

Homeowners' Federation
> 10234 Washtenaw Avenue
> Chicago, IL 60642
> and

Housing Training and Information Center
> 4209 W. Division St.
> Chicago, IL 60651

Good contacts for further information on technical aspects of redlining and what can be done at a neighborhood level.

Excellent studies of the Adams-Morgan District of Washington, D.C. are available from:
> Institute for Local Self-Reliance
> (ILSR)
> 1717 18th Street, N.W.
> Washington, DC 20009

Redlining: Mortgage Disinvestment in the District of Columbia, by ILSR, the D.C. PIRG and the Institute for Policy Studies, $1.50.
Provides detailed documentation by zipcode of loan practices of local savings institutions and the failures of regulatory agencies, as well as the actions that can be taken to remedy the problems.

Money, Money, Who's Got the Money?, William Batko of ILSR, $1
Gives a brief overview of DC banking practices that remove money and profits from the District and their effects on economic activity in D.C.

How to Research Your Local Bank, William Batko, 1976, $2 from:
> Institute for Local Self-Reliance
> 1717 18th Street N.W.
> Washington, DC 20009

A manual for cities and community residents interested in examining the actions of local financial institutions and the impact they have on local economic development. Explains where and how to obtain information and what it all means. Specifics on things such as control and ownership—how small banks are not created for the sole purpose of making money but rather to facilitate other business ventures of the bank owners, such as real estate development.

The Adams-Morgan Business Sector: Paying for Other People's Development, Batko, Connor and Taylor, ILSR
A fine study of the detailed economic, employment, environmental and social effects of different banking practices upon a neighborhood. Comparisons show, for instance, that supporting local non-chain stores instead of franchises and shopping centers keeps more money circulating in the community and produces significantly more employment per dollar of sales.

The Banking System: A Preface to Public Interest Analysis, by Black, Canner and King, 1975, $15, executive summary $1 from:
> Public Interest Economics Center
> 1714 Massachusetts Ave., N.W.
> Washington, DC 20036

The U.S. banking system is labyrinthian, and even an analysis of it leaves one's head swimming. Just coping with the magnitude and complexity of banking operations seems to leave few analysts time or space for major insights or suggestions. Part of the problem is lack of information on the *non*-banking activities of banks—their interlocking matrix of control with other corporations and activities. This report gives an overview of banking activities, the dangers of the concentration of economic power they represent, detailed data on holdings of bank trust departments in selected industrial areas and other aspects of intercorporate control.

be glad tomorrow you bought land today...

GRAND CANYON SUBDIVISION

Tom Bender

UNNECESSARY ACTIVITIES?

Standing along a road watching log trucks going both directions loaded with logs (taking trees back to put on the stumps?) or carrying Florida oranges to California and California oranges to Florida, you sometimes wonder how much of the seemingly purposeful activity we see (and pay for) is really necessary. When we analyze a system, almost everything in it seems necessary and accountable—with perhaps some minor adjustments possible. Yet when we look outside that system we often find much simpler and wiser patterns to be possible, such as living near your work instead of developing more efficient transportation or baking your own bread instead of shipping wheat, flour and bread thousands of miles back and forth. Those over-complex systems absorb a lot of energy and money and are a major reason why even with the great wealth of this country we seem to end up poorer and unable to do many things that were affordable before.

One good example is the real estate "profession." They skim off about 6% of the total value of *all* real estate exchanged. When you consider that the average American family moves every five years, that means that in 20 years you've paid one-fourth the value of your home to real estate agents. For a city of 500,000 that means $2.5 million per year paid out to realtors. For what? Studies done by the Florida Real Estate Association showed that most people felt the realtors did not earn their commission, were a hindrance, or could have been profitably done without.

In many cities "multiple listing services" have been set up by realtor groups where everything for sale in the city is listed on cards with photographs and specifications. The commission on sales is then split between the listing agent and the selling agent—with a very small fraction going to the cost of the listing service. But those card files could easily be set up in libraries and banks and shopping centers, and people could easily do for themselves what they pay a couple of thousand dollars to a realtor to do. Combine that with a couple of books like Les Scher's, and you have people able to handle the whole process of buying and selling competently by themselves. What useful services realtors *can* provide can be done on an hourly consulting basis rather than a huge commission.

Finding and Buying Your Place in the Country, Les Scher, 1974, $12.95 from:
Macmillan Publishing Co.
866 Third Ave.
New York, NY 10022

A valuable investment for anyone considering purchase of real estate. Guides like this make the real estate profession and their substantial commissions on real estate sales obsolete. Explains in good detail how to look for property, finding out what's really there, what kinds of legal complications the property may have, evaluating the price of the property, understanding financing options, contracts of sale and what different words do and don't mean, and when you do or don't need a lawyer. Helps the uninitiated (most of us) figure out some of the tricks of the game and keep from being burned.

Don't Go Buy Appearances, George Hoffman, $2.95 from:
Woodward Books
Box 773
Corte Madera, CA 94925

A manual for checking out and evaluating a house before purchase. A lot of good specific advice on how to find out if the furnace boiler is about rusted out, what the electrical capacity of the house is, whether the leaky faucet is a major or minor problem and how to tell quality and what it means in your pocketbook over 40 years. More importantly, how to figure if fixing the problems are major or minor undertakings.

Inexpensive energy to work for us made it possible to do almost everything on a large scale—from schools to transportation systems to corporate industry.

"Bigger seemed better" because it meant that someone else took responsibility for planning and providing things. "Bigger" was part of "more"—a convenient way to think when quantity was more easily available than quality. But bigger means centralization of power and wealth, and the opportunity to profit from others' work. And it means alienation. Smaller means WE have to take responsibility—it also means things are understandable and controllable.

It's been firmly established now that one size isn't best for everything—particularly if that means Biggest. Smaller industries, smaller towns, and even smaller cars are proving more economical, more efficient, and easier to live with. Almost all our systems—taxes, laws, education and finance—are oriented to stimulate growth and favor size. One of our changes is to reorient these structures to provide at least equal opportunity for various scales, and even to favor small scale organizations where socially more desirable. This means such things as giving employment tax credits rather than investment tax credits, leveling or inverting our electric rates that give power cheaper to big users, and favoring locally-owned businesses over chains or franchises.

SIZE and

Size, Efficiency and Community Enterprise, Barry Stein, 1974, $5 from:

> Center for Community Economic Development
> 639 Massachusetts Ave., Suite 316
> Cambridge, MA 02139

Extensive documentation of economies and diseconomies of scale in manufacturing industries showing large firms to be generally economically less efficient than small ones. It also shows how a large number of specialized small firms can enjoy more economies of scale than a large, integrated firm; documents greater inventiveness of individuals than corporations. A wealth of important data and insights into myths and realities of large and small scale business operations.

Returns to Scale and Comparative Efficiency in Investor- and Municipally-Owned Electric Power Distribution Systems, $7 from:

> Leland Neuberg
> Institute of Urban and Regional Development
> University of California
> Berkeley, CA 94720

An economic/statistical analysis of claims by private utilities opposing municipal takeover that municipalized firms are likely to be less efficient and that extensive economies of scale exist in distribution. Results show unit distribution costs decreasing up to 85,000 customers and increasing beyond that, and show total distribution costs for private utilities to range from 5.7% to 11.7% higher than for municipal utilities.

Technology and Employment in Industry, A. S. Bhalla, ed., 1975, $14.95 from:

> International Labour Office, Washington Branch
> 1750 New York Avenue, N.W.
> Washington, DC 20006

This collection of specific, detailed case studies of industries and industrial processes in many countries demonstrates that a considerable range of technologies exists for industry—even in "core" processes. Such alternatives provide significant latitude for different mixes of employment, machinery, materials and energy within economically competitive costs. Options are thus available that can simultaneously reduce unemployment, respond to our increasing capital shortage, accommodate increasing energy and material prices and provide mechanisms for reducing externalized costs such as transportation and unemployment compensation. Lack of awareness of alternatives by business leaders is shown to be a dominant obstacle in businesses adapting cost-effective changes to more job-producing, energy-saving processes.

Small Is Beautiful, E. F. Schumacher, 1973, $2.45 from:

> Harper and Row
> 10 East 53rd
> New York, NY 10022

Schumacher shows that the smaller and more direct ways of doing things both work and feel better, in thinking and in practice. Reports on decentralization attempts in the British coal industry, worker and community-controlled corporations, successful development and application of small-scale manufacturing and farming equipment, and the effects on people and their communities of such smaller patterns. Highly recommended.

For a long time we fell for the magic shell game of urban growth—it always looked like we would profit individually. But it always ended up with us paying and the other guy driving the new Cadillac. Merchants imagined new customers that growth would bring, but not the new competitors that accompanied them. Homeowners saw a larger tax base but not the increased costs of services for larger numbers of people. Shoppers saw the greater variety of large cities, but not the

crime rates, loss of natural areas and higher housing costs. The numbers are clear now—it costs more to live in a growing city or to live in a large city. Some people profit from growth—but not many. You can tell who they are. They're the ones saying growth is good for everyone. More and more communities are beginning to decide HOW they want to live and what kind of growth—if any—is good for that goal, and acting accordingly.

GROWTH

"Santa Barbara—The Impacts of Growth," reprinted in the *Second Alternative Public Policy Reader*, Shearer and Webb, ed., $7.50 from:
> Conference on Alternative State and
>   Local Public Policy
> Institute for Policy Studies
> 1901 Q Street, N.W.
> Washington, DC 20009

A solid and straightforward discussion of the questions people have about growth of a community: Will growth controls raise my taxes? Will growth provide jobs? For whom? —with well-reasoned answers. Gives a good, simple view of the issues involved and some of the realities behind them.

More Is Less, Elizabeth Bardwell, 1973, $1 from:
> **Capitol Community Citizens**
> **114 N. Carrol St.**
> **Madison, WI**

A specific case study done by a community group of the costs of urban growth in Madison, Wisconsin. It analyzes costs of services, amount of open space per capita, noise and pollution levels, manufacturing and industrial statistics, employment levels, etc. over several decades of continuous growth.

Community Environmental Council
> **109 E. de la Guerra**
> **Santa Barbara, CA 93101**

Active and successful community group that stays on top of developments in this this and many other areas.

The Costs of Sprawl, Real Estate Research Corporation, 1974:
> U.S. Government Printing Office
> Washington, DC 20402

Executive Summary (4111-00023) 55¢; *Detailed Cost Analysis* (4111-0021) $2.90; *Literature Review & Bibliography* (4111-0022) $3.25. Also summarized in *Ekistics*, Oct. 1975. Thoroughly documents a wide range of costs for different patterns of community land use from low density single-family suburbs to high density compact planning. Covers capital, land, energy, pollution, water use and auto use costs for different options. Many costs are halved through compactness of land use.

The Costs of Urban Growth: Observations and Judgements, Richard C. Bradley, 1973, $2.32 from:
> Pikes Peak Area Council of Gov'ts.
> 27 East Vermijo
> Colorado Springs, CO 80903

A good comparison of the costs and benefits of living in various sized cities—and in cities growing at various rates. The bigger the city, and the faster it grows, the higher the taxes, the costs of housing and services, and the crime rate. Smaller cities and slower growth were shown to be associated with more open space, hospital beds, library capacity, and school space per person. It's full of good statistics:

"Among the 148 SMSAs with populations larger than 200,000 people in 1970, those that LOST population during the 1960s averaged a 9% increase per capita cost . . . whereas those that GAINED population averaged a 12% increase in per capita costs."

Urban Growth Management Systems, American Society of Planning Officials, Planning Advisory Service Report Nos. 309, 310, 1976, $12 from:
> **ASPO**
> **1313 E. Sixtieth Street**
> **Chicago, IL 60637**

Analyzes an interesting range of thirteen operating growth management systems and surveys legal considerations in growth management, socio-economic and environmental impacts of such activities. Informative on the actual effects and community response to various measures.

Nongrowth Planning Strategies, Earl Finkler and David Peterson, 1974, $3.95 from:
> **Praeger Publications**
> **111 Fourth Ave.**
> **New York, NY 10003**

A concise and right to the point study of growth control for communities. No one has yet dealt with real responsibilities of small regions towards growth, but at least this covers what isn't happening at state and federal levels and why it is pragmatically necessary for communities to act. Analyzes economic costs of non-growth and explores a range of available mechanisms for attaining it.

This book and the ASPO study both discuss the landmark legal victory of Petaluma, California, to control its rate of growth. For more detailed information on the Appellate Court brief in the case, contact City Manager Robert Mayer or City Planner Frank Ray, Petaluma, CA 94952.

GOOD PRIORITIES?

The U.S. expenditures below make up one-third of our GNP. Each of us would have different priorities as to which are more important. But because we consider that some, such as defense and health care, are essential, we have been uncritical of expenditures for them. Others are luxuries which are nice but probably will not be worth their future political and economic costs. Some, such as advertising, are stimuli to increased consumption and become undesirable when conditions supporting growth no longer exist. Many are expenditures on things which are used up and leave no enduring benefit for society. Together they suggest considerable room for economies, new priorities and simpler means of gaining desired benefits.

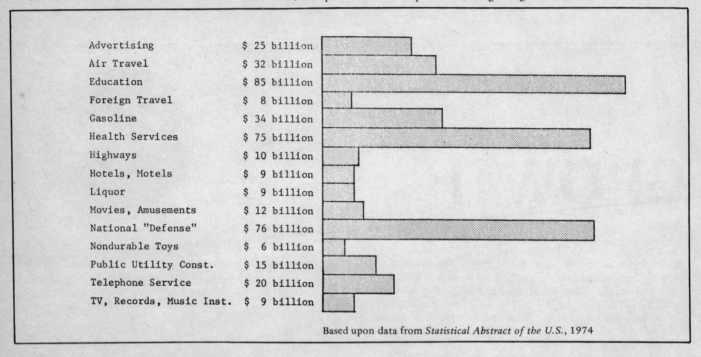

Advertising	$ 25 billion
Air Travel	$ 32 billion
Education	$ 85 billion
Foreign Travel	$ 8 billion
Gasoline	$ 34 billion
Health Services	$ 75 billion
Highways	$ 10 billion
Hotels, Motels	$ 9 billion
Liquor	$ 9 billion
Movies, Amusements	$ 12 billion
National "Defense"	$ 76 billion
Nondurable Toys	$ 6 billion
Public Utility Const.	$ 15 billion
Telephone Service	$ 20 billion
TV, Records, Music Inst.	$ 9 billion

Based upon data from *Statistical Abstract of the U.S.*, 1974

Taxing the Pavement, Not the Earth

One of a number of streams which feed into Johnson Creek

Johnson Creek flows through the southeast corner of Portland. The largest creek in the city of Portland, it floods at least a couple of times a year.

The people who live in the flood plain area have a different view of the creek than those that live on higher banks or hill tops.

Yet another point of view is held by the people who live in the 80-square-mile drainage area, but away from the creek.

The Metropolitan Sewage District (MSD) is one of those multi-government agencies (county, city, federal) set up to deal with wiggly things that don't fit political boundaries, such things as Johnson Creek, which flows through three counties and two small towns.

The MSD has come up with a way of supporting a program of maintenance of the creek. A flood control program that does not call for large stream containment programs—no conduit "packaging" programs—is proposed.

To be financed by a taxation of the human inhabitants of the drainage area, based on the amount of impervious soil they own, the plan would, for example, have people with parking lots pay more than farmers.

Plans also include tax benefits for persons who improve the water flow retardation quality of the land, e.g. construct ponds, plant trees, etc.

What is also noteworth is the change in direction; previous plans have always called for large final solutions, whereas the development of a maintenance program reflects a guardianship kind of relationship.

There are, of course, some loopholes. For example, if land use laws are not also administered and the development (of more slippery cemented drainage areas) outraces the maintenance and cleaning-up program, then larger solutions will look necessary, but only because existing land use ordinances were not recognized as integral to making the "small, less expensive solution" work.   S.J.

The Seven Laws of Money, Michael Phillips,
1974, $3.95.
    Word Wheel
    540 Santa Cruz Ave.
    Menlo Park, CA 94025

The Seven Laws of Money

*Its fragments probe and move around and through the realities
beneath money like Zen koans. Anecdotes, poems, commentaries, how-to information, and accounting of personal experiences all draw to the surface of our consciousness a new awareness of ourselves and how we deal with each other. Seven Laws
has been a seed of the new briarpatch economics emerging
from the cracks of our society.*

"When you open a checking account, open it with the largest amount of money you possibly can. I'm not kidding!
Even if the average balance in your account is only going to
be $50, try to borrow a friend's $10,000 (home down payment) for *one day* so you can use it to open your account.
You don't have to go that far, but anything over a couple of
thousand dollars looks good. You can withdraw most of the
money a few days after the account is opened. Really! The
reason for this is that the bank records your opening balance

on your signature card (and often in other places, too), believing that it is representative of your financial status. I did a
study when I was a banker and found absolutely no correlation between opening balances and the kind of balances that
appeared later on in the same account. It's such a strong tradition to do it this way (at least a hundred years old) that
bankers still judge people by their opening balance. Try it;
the branch manager will smile on you forever more.

"It may seem middle-class to have credit, but if you have it
you need less money. 'Credit' is the ability to borrow, and if
your credit is good you don't need savings—or at least you
need less savings. Savings are generally for emergencies, but
if you have credit you can use it in an emergency instead of
your savings, and pay it back later. For example, if you're
busted in Marrakech and a $500 bribe will get you out, you
can get an "advance" on your American Express card.

"All it takes to establish credit is a little time and a little
stability. You need *one* job, one address, a phone and a checking account for one year. Having decided to establish a good
credit rating and already having a job and an address, wait
four months and then apply for a gasoline credit card. Next
apply for credit at a luxury store (they give credit *very* readily
because their losses on credit are covered by the high mark-up
on their merchandise). After six months apply at Sears or
Macy's or a similar middle-price-range national store. Their
credit is the very hardest to get and can really get you the
rest. Use these credit accounts once or twice and pay
promptly. After from seven to nine months you can apply
for Master Charge or Bankamericard (not both at the same
time). When you get them your credit is really established
(after a few months, you can ask by letter to have your credit
card borrowing amount raised). Now you are free—you can
get a new job as often as you wish and move as often as you
feel like it; your credit is established. Just remember to pay
your accounts promptly, and never have a run-in with a
jewelry store! Most bad credit ratings are put in the credit
rating computers by jewelry stores—the $300-diamond-studded-watch-type places.

"Credit is dependent mostly on stability. Your stability is
measured by the time you stay with a job (they check), the
time you have lived at your present and previous residence,
whether or not you have a phone (bad debtors usually avoid
having their own phone), and by your checking account. Be
sure not to overdraw your checking account more than once
or twice a year; sometimes your bank may keep track of it,
and sometimes the word gets around to other banks.

"Lastly, if you need a loan, shop around. The bigger the
loan, the more important this is. Banks are not monolithic;
each branch is different. Some have loan officers or managers
who are liberal, smart and understanding; others have insensitive bores who retired at age twenty-four when they joined
the bank. Ask around. If you need a loan for a specialized
purpose—say an organic restaurant or to import merchandise
from Zanzibar—find someone who got a similar loan and go
to their lender. Specialized knowledge and good experience
on past loans are what encourage a lender to make additional
loans in esoteric areas."

" There is no tipping in Japan. It made me realize what
tips mean. We tell ourselves that tips are rewards for doing a
good job, a reward-punishment thing. Then why do we only
have tips in job categories where people are expected to be
servile—say taxi drivers and waiters, as compared to plumbers
or doctors? It's because this is a vestige of slavery experiences
and of our contempt for certain ways of earning a living, not
reward-punishment."

EMPLOYMENT ENERGY, and ECONOMICS

Tax Credits for Employment Rather than Investment, by Berndt, Kesselman and Williamson, 1975, from:

> Institute for Research on Poverty
> University of Wisconsin
> Madison, WI 53715

Present subsidies to large-scale, capital- and energy-intensive industry are substantial and contribute to both unemployment and overproduction of goods in an era of limited resources. Employment tax credits rather than investment tax credits assist substitution of employment for capital and energy, while the removal of all tax credits results in less promotion of unnecessary production. This study finds that removal of investment credits lessens capital demand and probably causes a net increase in employment as well as a shift to greater blue-collar employment. Various employment credits with the same cost as present investment credits would provide 0.5 to 1% increases in employment, 1 to 6% less need for capital and 0.5% increase in prices of output (which would be more than balanced by lower unemployment costs).

The Impact of Solar and Conservation Technologies Upon Labor Demand, Skip Laitner, May 1976, from:

> Public Citizen
> P.O. Box 19404
> Washington, DC 20036

An excellent and well-referenced analysis of the employment benefits of alternatives to conventional power generation. Puts to rest the whole debate about energy and jobs with Herman Daly's well-founded remark that the whole purpose of using non-human energy has always been to replace human labor. Goes on to clarify many issues and show employment increases generated through more efficient appliances, comparative job intensities of nuclear and solar resources (solar technologies provide roughly 2.5 times more jobs per unit of energy than will nuclear), and capital savings of solar industries. Every union and every congressperson should see this.

Energy and Employment in New York State, Draft Report, May 1976, available from:

> Legislative Commission on Energy Systems
> State of New York
> 828 Legislative Office Building
> Albany, NY 12224

This analysis shows that New York State has three viable, indigenous alternatives to coal and nuclear energy that can be employed immediately at lower capital and energy costs than the conventional nuclear or coal options while at the same time creating more employment within the state for an equivalent amount of energy produced than either nuclear or coal. These alternatives are conservation, wood and wind. In each case the energy production or savings of the alternative have been compared to the equivalent energy from coal or nuclear for the worker years on a thirty year cumulative basis:

1. Conservation: Up to three times the employment at lower or equal capital costs and much lower energy costs.

2. Wood: From four to six times the employment at equivalent capital costs and lower energy costs.

3. Wind (without storage): One and one-half times the employment at lower capital costs and equivalent energy costs.

4. Wind (with storage): Twice the employment at slightly higher capital and energy costs with available technology.

Solar energy and waste recovery were not studied in detail but appeared to have favorable employment impacts.

The Demand for Scientific and Technical Manpower in Selected Energy-Related Industries, 1970-1985, from:

> National Science Foundation
> 1800 G Street, N.W.
> Washington, DC 20006

A National Science Foundation report on the potential needs for manpower. Based on the assumption inherent in "Project Independence" of the increasing need for locally produced supplies of energy. A limited number of copies is available.

Center for Advanced Computation
University of Illinois
Urbana, IL 61801

Publications of the Center provide interesting data on the shifts in numbers and kinds of employment as well as energy use resulting from reallocation of funds from one kind of priority, such as highway construction, to other uses. Write for publications list. Some have been reprinted:

"Job Impacts of Alternatives to Corps of Engineers Projects," Hannon and Brezdek, *Engineering Issues*, Oct. 1973, pp. 521-31, from:

> American Society of Civil Engineers
> 345 E. 47th Street
> New York, NY 10017

Shows that transfer of funds from ACE projects to national health insurance, social security payments, mass transit development, construction of sewage plants or general tax relief would provide significant increases in employment and that specific Corps projects may not even benefit nearby local communities.

"Options for Energy Conservation," Bruce Hannon, *Technology Review*, February 1974

Provides information on energy and employment intensity per dollar of product for many industries, for different food products providing equal protein and for household expenditures.

Manpower Requirements for Nuclear and Coal Power Plants, free from:

> Critical Mass
> 133 C Street, S.E.
> Washington, DC 20003

Comparison of employment impacts over the lifetime of alternative processes for producing an identical product indicate that coal power will result in 40 percent more employment than nuclear power, while costing less.

Employment Impact Statement, 50¢ from:

> RAIN
> 2270 N.W. Irving
> Portland, OR 97210

A simple step-by-step way to figure the employment impacts of a new industry and the benefits of alternative options.

Our basic reason for using fossil fuels has always been because they allow us to do more with less work. Their increasing depletion means a general shrinking of the boundaries of the excess we can produce and means increasing substitution of human work or employment for such energies. Yet the gap between what is necessary to simply meet our needs and what we have been consuming in needlessly complex production of unnecessary things is so great that what is really required of us is not slavery but merely discretion and wisdom.

The Energy Dilemma—What It Means to Jobs, R. Denny Scott, 1976
> International Woodworkers of
> America
> 1622 N. Lombard
> Portland, OR 97217

It's encouraging to see such good things coming from labor unions. This union is one of the best and knows what's coming down the road for us. This paper refutes claims made that unemployment will result if increased energy supplies are not obtained, examines effects of automation in reducing employment and explores the myth that energy and GNP and well-being are closely linked. It concludes that economic and employment growth can occur in sufficient quantity to accommodate an expanding workforce without a corresponding historical increase in energy consumption.

Chash of Culture: Management in An Age of Changing Values, Carl H. Madden, 1972, $5 from:
> National Planning Association
> 1606 New Hampshire Ave. N.W.
> Washington, DC 20009

An open and serious examination, by the chief economist of the U.S. Chamber of Commerce, of the implications for the U.S. business community of the changes being brought about in our society by our resource limits. Well worth reading by anyone interested in what changes are going to be necessary in business products, practices and goals. Madden does an excellent job of taking things like the Second Law of Thermodynamics and firmly, yet clearly, explaining its ramifications for industry and business.

"Employment and Economic Development," *Ekistics*, Vol. 40, No. 237, Aug. 1975, available in most architecture or planning libraries or from:
> Page Farm Road
> Lincoln, MA 01773

Subscriptions $24/yr. Special issue on accomplishments of employment-intensive economic development processes. Studies of China, Tanzania and Kenya as well as other countries. Development policies planned to meet the needs of the vast majority of people rather than mere rate of growth. *Ekistics* papers tend to be rather abstract and intellectual, but this issue does provide feedback from some rarely-explored aspects of development.

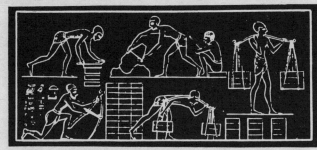

Energy and Labor Demand in the Conserver Society, Bruce Hannon, July 1976, from:
> Center for Advanced Computation
> University of Illinois Urbana-Champaign
> Urbana, IL 61801

Quantifies the substantial number of new jobs created through energy-conserving shifts in the structure of the U.S. economy. As well as showing that a great range of energy-conserving options generate jobs, the study shows that electrification of our energy sources results in a loss of approximately 75,000 jobs per quad of primary energy transformed into electricity. (TB)

EMPLOYMENT BENEFITS OF ENERGY CONSERVATION

Project	New Jobs Per Quadrillion BTU Saved
Changing from ...	
Plane to train (intercity)	930,000
Throwaway to refillable beverage containers	750,000
Car to train (intercity)	700,000
Owner-operator truck to class 1 freight train	675,000
New highway construction to health insurance (federal)	640,000
Car to bus (intercity)	330,000
Car to bus (urban)	210,000
New highway construction to personal consumption	200,000
Car to bicycle	200,000
Plane to car	160,000
Plane to bus	140,000
Electric to gas stove	160,000
Electric to gas water heater	120,000
Electric commuter to car	110,000
Electric to gas clothes dryer	100,000
Frost free to conventional refrigerator	60,000
Plush (25 appliances) to moderately equipped (16 appliances) kitchen	30,000
New highway construction to railroad and mass transit construction	30,000
Present to increased home insulation (oil heat)	15,000
Moderate to spartan (4 appliance) kitchen	10,000

*A lot of what all this means is doing things on a small enough
scale that we can understand what is going on and take a
meaningful part in determining what, why and how things
happen.*

COMMUNITY ECONOMICS

Home, Inc., Scott Burns, 1975, $6.95
from:
> Doubleday and Co.
> 245 Park Avenue
> New York, NY 10017

Our whole way of measuring economic
activity is skewed towards large-scale
production and consumption. If we do
something very efficiently for ourselves,
it doesn't count in our GNP. If we have
someone else do it, even at great expense, the GNP says "Yeh! We're doing
better." And, of course, we only count
what happens from 8 to 5, five days a
week, in "the office." Never counted is
the at-least equal amount of work done
at home, by housewives or housebands.
Buying labor-saving devices for the
home so people are free to "go to work"
so they can pay for the labor-saving
devices so they can . . . is only running
on a treadmill that gives the illusion of
progress because we ignore the value of
homework. Burns explores the economics of the home and shows that
investment in the home in general and
in such things as insulation in particular,
provide a much greater value and return
than almost any industrial investment.
A whole dimension of our economic
system that has been studiously ignored.

The Cities' Wealth by the Community
Ownership Organizing Project, 1976,
$2.50 ($5 for institutions) from:
> Conference on Alternative State
>   and Local Public Policies
> 1901 Q Street N.W.
> Washington, DC 20009

The comprehensive programs proposed,
fought for and to a degree enacted by
the community activist coalition in
Berkeley since 1967 provide an important example for other communities.
Good programs, the real-live politics of
getting changes implemented, the information pried out of the city government
on how things have actually been done
are all extremely useful. They bring together an exciting picture of how an
awakened citizenry has decided they
want their city to be. The difficult
questions of the city as employer—
cutting excessive costs while working
for better conditions for the employees
on the bottom—are dealt with and
examples given of red tape changes that
have been made in the bureaucracy itself.

 AT THE END OF 1972, OUR COLLECTIVE SAVINGS
AMOUNTED TO THE FOLLOWING:

Savings and Loan	$207,300,000,000
Mutual Savings Banks	$ 91,300,000,000
Commercial Banks	$276,100,000,000
Credit Unions	$ 21,700,000,000
Life Insurance Reserves	$203,600,000,000
TOTAL	$800,000,000,000

The figure above does not reflect our personal or commercial
checking accounts, shares of stock or cash equity in our homes
or personal property but only individual or corporate savings
which can be invested for long periods of time.

The greatest majority of these savings are owned by individuals, but, conversely, most of the funds are used to finance
commercial activity only because we are not organized to use
our own money.

If we loaned the above savings to 40,000 potential developing
neighborhoods of 5,000 people each, which would cover the
entire country, this would provide each neighborhood with
$20,000,000 and each family of four people with about
$16,000 in funds with which to finance a place to live. With
this kind of capital base and a little leverage we can go a long
way towards making our neighborhoods better places in which
to live.

The point we are trying to make here is that we are collective-
ly very wealthy, and, if we use our wealth wisely, we can make
our country even better than it is. We have no one to blame
but ourselves for our situation, since we have the money, but
we have not organized ourselves so we can use our savings.
Instead we have turned them over to others to manage for us.

(From *Cooperative Community Development*)

*A Rural New Town for the West Side
of the San Joaquin Valley*, Kirshner,
Baar and Brom, 1975, $3 from:
> Community Ownership Organizing
>   Project
> 349 62nd Street
> Oakland, CA 94618

A growing outcry is likely to bring enforcement of California's blatantly dis-
regarded 160-acre limitation on agricultural use of irrigation water. The result-
ant land reform would bring about the
development of small towns in the Westlands. This COOP study investigates the
development of support services and
community building necessary for successful land reform and shows how an
agricultural based rural community
might be organized and financed with
significant savings (considerably

in excess of 25% of annual income) for
the residents.

Cooperative Community Development,
Joe Falk, editor, 1975, $2.95 from:
> The Future Associates
> P.O. Box 912
> Shawnee Mission, KS 66201

In Kansas City, Joe Falk and the Future
Associates have worked out a very comprehensive program of leveraging community savings held in life insurance
companies, various kinds of banks,
pension funds and individual savings to
secure funds for neighborhood improvement rather than commercial development. They show that more than $210
billion of our savings is available from
those sources.

BIG NAMES—BIG DRAINS

Most banks give preferential loan rates to big-name companies, chains and franchises wanting to open a local outlet, because their big name and big financial base gives them the appearance of being a better risk. And most communities welcome such big names because of the aura of big-time they convey from advertising.

Yet both banks and communities have important reasons to rethink these priorities and to go as far toward banning outside-owned businesses and the institutions, such as advertising, that reinforce such unproductive concentration as they can. For banks it's simple—outside-owned businesses drain money out of a community (see box), while locally-owned businesses cycle and recycle money through the local economy *and* the local bank.

For the community the benefits of local ownership are even greater. A fast-food franchise that drains two-thirds of its cash flow out of a community also drains the life and power and self-confidence out of the town. Yet most communities offer generous tax advantages to such outside-owned enterprises to encourage them to locate there—assisting the very forces that damage the local economy. Such enterprises provide jobs and spend money, as they claim, but compared to the jobs and money benefits of a more locally self-reliant community, *big names mean big drains!*

EXPORTING MONEY

National fast food chains, like chain supermarkets, provide convenience, jobs and tax revenues to their service areas. And, like the supermarkets, they also export capital.

Figures were obtained on the financial status of one chain outlet (a MacDonalds), located in an inner-city area. Corporations cost out their expenses, allocating to each restaurant its proportional share; this breakout is illuminating. If the figures from this one store are representative (and there is good reason to expect that they are, given the industry's standardized operations), then we all deserve a break.

Fully 20.00% of this store's costs immediately leave the community: advertising; rent (paid to a corporate subsidiary); a service fee paid to the corporation; accounting and legal fees; insurance; depreciation and amortization; and debt service. This restaurant, like all other outlets, purchases its food and paper supplies from other centralized corporate subsidiaries. These costs are 41.81% of total expenses. Management costs go toward paying salaries outside of the area and equal 5.62% of expenses. Other expenses, a total of 9.07%, are unclear in their ultimate origin. Only "crew labor" (15.04%) and some portion of taxes (1.93%) clearly remain in the community.

This one restaurant does about $750,000 in sales annually and earns about $50,000 in profits before taxes. Over $500,000 of this money leaves the community; as much as $67,500 more may also be "exported." Were the buildings owned locally, management hired from local residents and supplies purchased locally, some of this drainage from local economies could be effectively plugged.
—William Batko in *Self-Reliance*

Ancil Nance

CONTROLLING MONEY FLOWS

Our focus has so long been toward promoting bigness that it is difficult even to think how communities, states or regions can act to strengthen their economies from within and make them more self-reliant. Starting to do so will open up a flood of ways we can't even think of now, but a number of actions are possible even at this time. Communities can stop giving tax breaks to outside industry. States and cities can't establish trade restrictions, but they can raise sales taxes on everything and use the income to lower property or other taxes for local businesses, in effect making local goods cheaper. A large number of new businesses require some sort of code, zoning or other variances, and outside-owned businesses can be blocked there. All businesses rely to some degree on local good will and are relatively sensitive to local threats of boycott, harassment or bad publicity. Making known the real economics involved within the community can encourage support of local businesses. Use of public media for advertising which inherently favors large, centralized operations can be restricted or banned. (Who would choose a local Sleep-Good Motel when all you hear of is nationally-advertised Road-Sore Inns?) Most local chain or franchise operations are financed locally—making local finance sources aware of the economics and community sentiment can make financing more available for locally-owned operations. Assistance and support services for setting up local businesses can be developed similar to agricultural extension services. The inefficiencies of scale and high overhead of centralized institutions means that such moves toward simpler, more decentralized economies provide a reduction in overall costs as well as an improvement for local economies.

COMMUNITY

TITHING

Tithing is a very different kind of banking—it is simply taking responsibility ourselves for what our money does. In the strictest traditional sense, it means giving one tenth of a year's produce or profits away (originally to the Church). Many people are going back to this practice—no matter how little they have—and are finding the rewards great.

Tithing can be looked at as an investment—whether time, interest or dollars—and its most important benefit may be in learning how to invest wisely and soundly. It could be the beginning of getting away from the abstractions and material rewards of money. For further thoughts on tithing, see the December 1974 issue of
> *New Age Journal*
> 32 Station Street
> Brookline, MA 02147
> ($1, back issue)

Many food co-ops have worked out related plans where they have invested their profits in new enterprises. In Minneapolis, the North Country Co-Op seeded other neighborhood co-ops, a bakery, a warehouse and a restaurant. Austin, Texas, and Iowa City, Iowa, co-ops have done similar seeding—starting related enterprises without keeping control of them like the horizontal and vertical expansion of large corporations.

Eugene Community Sustaining Fund
> Box 340
> Eugene, OR 97401

The Eugene Community Sustaining Fund is a good example of a formalized institutional tithing process. Or you might call it a voluntary tax of conscientious businesses to support community needs out of their profits. About 2% of income is generally contributed, and the funds are used as seed money to start and assist projects of value to the community—sort of a more adventurous and less fossilized Community Fund!

STATE BANKS

North Dakotans, fed up with being at the mercy of out-of-state bankers charging excessive rates for rural credit, set up a state-owned bank in 1919. One of the most profitable banks in the country and presently the only one that is state-owned, it saved thousands of farmers from ruin in the depression and now has about $32 million in loans to farmers, $35 million in housing loans and $27 million in student loans. The bank, largest between Minneapolis and Spokane, relies heavily on deposits of state funds, avoiding the potential misdealings resulting from divvying up state deposits to the profit of private banks and keeping state money inside the state. Public disclosure and public control are two obvious advantages of state banks. Moves to set up similar systems are underway in Washington, Oregon, Massachusetts, Colorado, New Jersey and California. See "Banks of North Dakota," by Derek Norcross, *Parade* Magazine, November 9, 1975.

The Bank Book, **Joan Hedahl and Edward Buckingham, $1.25 from:**
> Colorado State Treasury
> 141 State Capitol
> Denver, CO 80203

An innovative service of the Colorado State Treasurer, providing detailed information to consumers on the services available at every bank in the state and their cost or benefit to users. Further development of such a service should include information on how the banks use the funds of their clients, their non-banking activity and relations to other activities so people can choose to put their money in banks that will use it in ways they consider socially desirable.

CREDIT UNIONS

Credit unions are locally controlled savings and loan organizations set up by a group of people to retain control of how their savings are used. They avoid some of the problems with placing your money in a bank where it is then loaned out on the bank's terms to the "best credit risks" (mostly large corporations). Because each member of the credit union has a vote in policy-making, YOU can borrow and loan money for purposes YOU value.

Savings are insured by the federal government, members keep for themselves the normal bank profit. Members must have a "common bond"—living within a specific area, working for a common employer, or sharing membership in an organization whose activities develop common loyalties and mutual interests.

Although a very beneficial alternative to normal banking institutions, credit unions may have several difficulties. Lack of capable financial management often causes problems, short time limits on loans frequently prevent home mortgages (though at least one credit union set up its own savings and loan to allow home mortgages), and loans cannot be made to non-members or organizations. Many people cannot qualify for affinity requirements and cannot obtain credit union services. And the money belonging to a credit union must be deposited in a normal bank—permitting its use by the bank despite the wishes of credit union members.

Approval procedures are often difficult—the federal government refused to allow a national prisoners' credit union that was being set up because prisoners' savings are put into a fund whose interest goes into the guard's retirement fund! The government claimed the prisoners had no common bond. A feminist credit union *has* been set up in Massachusetts, and local ones are much easier to do.

For more information on credit unions, write:
> **National Credit Union Administration**
> **Washington, DC 20456**

and check with your state credit union office.

FINANCE

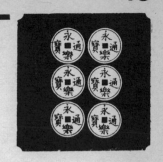

SWEAT EQUITY

Our own work is often the best kind of money possible for financing projects. We don't have to get someone else's approval, and we can use our evenings, weekends and other normally non-income-producing time productively. Building a home ourselves can reduce first costs by at least fifty percent, while using our time recycling materials instead of purchasing new ones can cut costs another 20%. Building a house in sections as money and time become available instead of all at once can avoid costly financing. This is important because financing costs double and even triple what we end up paying for a house. An owner-built house costing $5.50 per square foot for materials would end up costing $33 to $50 per square foot if built as a tract house—once mortgage costs are added in.

Our own work is also more valuable. When we have someone else do work for us, we have taxes taken out of OUR income before we hire them, we have to pay for their profit, and we are usually limited to union productivity levels. For more details see:

The Owner-Builder and the Code, Ken Kern, Ted Kogan, Rob Thallon, 1976, $5 from:
> Owner-Builder Publications
> P.O. Box 550
> Oakhurst, CA 93664

In New York City, a six-story, 23-unit tenement at 251 East 119th Street, in East Harlem, has been rehabilitated by a street gang—the Renigades—into a tenant-owned and managed cooperative. Sweat equity by volunteers to earn their own apartments has allowed projected rents to be $130 per month as opposed to $250 per month for similar one-bedroom apartments done by private contractors. Materials and salaries for 12 gang members who performed most of the work were financed by a loan from the city's Housing and Development Administration. In a similar project on the Lower East Side, in addition to rehabilitating the building, solar collectors have been designed for the roof to supply hot water, and the now-skilled group plans to rehabilitate other buildings and manufacture solar heaters for other locations. For further information contact:
> Pratt Institute Center for Community & Environmental Development
> 240 Hall Street
> Brooklyn, NY 11205

OTHER CAPITAL SOURCES

Sources of Capital for Community Economic Development, Leonard Smollen and John Hayes, 1976, $10 from:
> Center for Community Economic Development
> 639 Massachusetts Avenue
> Cambridge, MA 02139

A very helpful guide for anyone starting out into the maze of finding money to start a community-based business. A key to meanings of jargon and secret passwords, description of an amazing variety of sources for money, what they finance, terms, special loan conditions, etc., as well as a listing of minority-owned and -managed banks and savings/loans and other capital sources.

Public Pension Funds as a Source of Capital for Job Creation, Ed Kirshner, Kenneth Baar and Eve Bach, 1975, $2 from:
> Community Ownership Organizing Project
> 349 62nd Street
> Oakland, CA 94618

Piece-by-piece we discover how pervasively our beliefs in corporate power have focussed all of the energy in our society into their growth. Public pension funds as well as many other major chunks of wealth floating around our society are unquestioningly invested in corporate stock. This paper analyzes the economic and social implications of alternative investment patterns. Investing pension funds in housing (heresy!) rather than stocks is shown to be less risky, to give greater economic return and to have more positive social impacts. COOP also puts out a good quarterly newsletter called *The Public Works*, which covers many of their activities (free).

Community Ownership in New Towns and Old Cities, Edward Kirshner and James Morey, 1975 from:
> Center for Community Economic Development

I really had trouble getting into this at first—it looked like it was going to be another socialistic tract about government ownership. I was wrong—it isn't, and it's good! A lot of really obvious stuff once you think about it—utilities are basically no-risk public monopolies. Public ones have a track record at least as good as investor-owned ones. In both cases the rate payers end up paying for the whole operation. So why should the profits go to outside investors rather than back into reducing costs for the community? They show specifically that if all the land, real estate development and utilities were owned by the community (with revenues subsidizing housing) then up to 100% of new housing would be within the reach of low and moderate income families. They lay out a lot of options and the benefits of each—for new and existing communities, for common mortgages, financing rental housing, leasing of greenbelt land for agriculture, community-owned industrial parks, businesses, utilities, cable TV. Returned profits reduce direct housing costs by 25-50%, depending on options chosen, and incomes required to afford new housing would drop from $18,000 to $7,800 in some cases. Well worth reading.

There are a lot of variations on the theme: cottage industry, "right livelihood," meaningful work, small business. There are examples scattered throughout the book: look for the food co-ops (Agriculture), the Springfield Creamery and tofu/miso making (Eating High and Lightly), bed and breakfasts (Wise Travel) and bicycle repair (Transportation). It's a lot of what we are all about.

Bootstraps means being a contributing part of a local community rather than pulling money out to invest elsewhere. Collective, non-hierarchical decision-making and/or worker control is common. The products tend to be oriented to moving us towards living lightly on the earth—bean sprouts, solar collectors, tipis, house remodeling, herbs. The people involved often work only part-time (and often at home) earning the freedom to paint, write, wander or mind families.

Some other examples:

* Typesetting or typing at home—our own Irish Setter proves that this works.
* Cosmetics and natural soaps. This is one of David Morris's favorite examples.
* Publishing. Magazines are a lot more work than they sound (and are not profitable), but small book presses abound. See the print section.

The Fabric Appliance Company
Rt. 1, Box 150A
Baldwin, WI 54002

Our good friend Kurt Buetow designs and makes wonderful canvas hanging chairs (send for a price list). Also hanging Japanese baths, kites, packs, hammock tents, hanging shelves and other practical esoterica. The chairs don't take that much time to make and sell (mail order and retail) for enough to support his design and homesteading activities.

Cloudburst
2440 N.E. 10th
Portland, OR 97212

"My folks were really amazed when I said I was a garbage person," says Michaela Moore Marcus. "It's very hard work!" She and Dave McMahon run a neighborhood recycling business for 110 families in N.E. Portland based on the ORE Plan system of collecting separated wastes from households.

See Recycling section for more information on the ORE Plan.

Nomadic Tipi Makers
Star Route, Box 41
Cloverdale, OR 97112

Jeb and Caroline at Nomadics are still one of the best examples we know of appropriate small business. They make fine tipis—write for their price and size list—which they are constantly revising (sometimes up and sometimes down) to reflect their true costs. They sell about 400 tipis a year—all mail order—and gross about $100,000. They spend one day a week cutting pieces in the loft of their barn overlooking the ocean and four mornings on mailing. The sewing is contracted out to local farmers' wives—all they need is an industrial sewing machine ($400 investment) and a corner in their homes. It's piecework but they average between $5 and $8 an hour! Their initial investment is quickly paid off and if any of them wanted they could branch out into work on their own. Jeb and Caroline say their sewers make more money than they do because the women do more work.

SOME OTHER RESOURCES:

Small-Time Operator: How to Start Your Own Small Business, Keep Your Books, Pay Your Taxes and Stay Out of Trouble, Bernard Kamoroff, CPA, 1976, $5.95 from:
Bell Springs Publishing Co.
P.O. Box 322
Laytonville, CA 95454

Mother Earth News Handbook of Home Business Ideas and Plans, 1976, $2.25 from:
Bantam Books
666 Fifth Avenue
New York, NY 10019

Large-Scale Sprouting as a Cottage Industry, Michael Connor, 1975, 75¢ from:
Institute for Local Self-Reliance
1717 18th Street, N.W.
Washington, DC 20009

BOOTSTRAPS

Competitive Scale in Manufacturing: The Case of Consumer Goods, Barry Stein and Mark Hodak, 1976, $1.75 from:

> Center for Community Economic Development
> 639 Massachusetts Avenue, Suite 316
> Cambridge, MA 02139

One of the most difficult factors in launching a new business venture by community groups is determining a size of operation that has probability of success but least commitment of financial resources. This study determines the size of new plants that are entering specific markets, calculates the market sizes associated with these new plants, and estimates the least size that is thought appropriate (by others who have done it) for new plants to enter the market for a product. Very helpful data for anyone considering a manufacturing venture.

Testimony Before the Senate Select Committee on Small Business, Dec. 2, 1975, Dr. Barry Stein, 12 pp, inquire for price, from:

> Center for Social and Evaluation Research
> University of Massachusetts
> Boston, MA 02125

A very clear summary of the different economic and community costs and benefits of small and large business, real efficiency of small business and manufacturing, and recommended changes in legal structures and administrative practices by government agencies to encourage more independent, community-sustaining and effective businesses. By the author of the excellent *Size, Efficiency and Community Enterprise.*

The Community Context of Economic Conversion, Barry Stein, 1971, 63 pp., inquire for price:

> Center for Community Economic Development (see above)

Explore the community impact of defense contracts, absentee ownership, and industrial trends, such as the impact on Seattle, Boston and Southern California of depending on aerospace contracts for their main employment base. Presents excellent case for community-owned businesses.

How to Start Smaller Industries, Series 1-6, limited number available from:

> Japan Consulting Institute
> Hibiya Park Bldg., 1-1
> Yuraku-cho, Chiyoda-ku
> Tokyo, Japan

Since 1969 J.C.I. has been putting out a series of booklets outlining how to set up various industrial plants at minimum cost and scale as part of technical assistance they provide on a consulting basis to foreign clients (largely in Asia) establishing industrial plants. Information on each industry includes outlines of the industry, description of the process, construction of the plant, number of employees, necessary expenditures, production capacity, return on investment and locational factors. Toilet-paper plants, sawmills, mosquito coil making, umbrella manufacture, screw making, and 111 more industries.

CECOCO Catalog, $11 airmail from:

> P.O. Box 8
> Ibaraki, Osaka, Japan

A guidebook for rural cottage and small industries—everything from chopstick making machines to agricultural implements. The catalog really gives one a picture of what can be done at that scale. Much that can be applied to this country.

Hoedads Treeplanters Co-op
454 Willamette
Eugene, OR 97401

200 or so belong to Hoedads, contracting their own labor out to timber companies, Forest Service, fire-fighting, etc. Each crew elects a representative to central council; percentage of wages taken out of paychecks to support office, staff. *Not* looking for new members, but a good model for labor-intense work co-ops.

Community Industry in Vermont, Jeremy Ingpen, 1975, $1.00 from:

> The Vermont Alliance
> 5 State Street
> Montpelier, VT 05602

Criteria for economic development and lessons from existing community-sized and -controlled projects. A generally fine discussion of the effects of different kinds of economic development in Vermont and considerations necessary to insure that future development provides benefit for the people of the state and communities.

In the Making
221 Albert Road
Sheffield, York, England

65p single copy, £1.90 subscription (they accept only International Money Orders in UK). "A directory of proposed productive projects in self-management or radical technology"—a typically British publication (with typically British humor) that seems to cover just about everything going on in the field of "jobs without bosses."

Community Development Clearinghouse
Vermont Tomorrow
5 State St.
Montpelier, VT 05602

With help from CETA they are establishing an information clearinghouse for community development. Information to include alternative energy, energy efficient housing, agricultural self-sufficiency.

New Age Journal, $8/year from:
32 Station Street
Brookline, MA 02147

Several good articles on community business have appeared in *NAJ* over the last year or so. *NAJ* No. 2 ($1) is an excellent issue on dealing with money—credit unions, tithing, businesses. *NAJ* No. 11, March 1976 ($1), has a mind-opening interview with New Age Entrepreneur par excellence, Bob Schwartz.

Job dissatisfaction, right livelihood, feeling that what we do and make is both needed and good fills a long empty void inside us with a warm and welcome feeling.

MAKING WORK WORTH IT

Self-Management, Jaroslav Vanek, ed., 1975, $5.95 from:
> Penguin Books
> 7110 Ambassador Rd.
> Baltimore, MD 21207

One obvious way to resolve many of the worker/management problems is to merge them—worker ownership and self-management. Doesn't take care of the producer-consumer problems, but frequently is a good first step. Vanek surveys the theory and reality in practice of self-management, with case studies of small business and national economies from around the world.

Worker-Owned Plywood Companies: An Economic Analysis, Katrina V. Bennan, 1967, Economic and Business State University Press, Obtain through the Interlibrary Loan Department of your local library.

One of the major fears preventing businesses from encouraging labor-intensive processes is the fear of labor/management conflicts and problems of employee boredom and low productivity. One obvious answer is to eliminate the conflict of interests between workers and owners through worker-owned businesses. Bennan's case study shows that they have been and can be well-managed and economically viable, even under difficult conditions of using abandoned plants, obsolete equipment and difficult material supplies that were legacies of past ownership. The firms studied actually had worker productivity 30 to 50% greater than in non-worker owned firms, along with greater flexibility to adapt during difficult times.

Industrial Common-Ownership Movement (ICOM)
> **8 Sussex Street**
> **London SW 1, England**

A group of British companies, most of them small, who are self-governing (including the Scott Bader Company described in *Small Is Beautiful*). They run a non-profit loan group to assist new ventures and put out a series of publications, including one which describes each of the member companies. Write for information and a publications list (include SASE).

Workforce
> **Vocations for Social Change**
> **5951 Canning St.**
> **Oakland, Ca. 94609**

VSC has been around quite awhile now and has spawned innumerable centers through the country. The centers often become general community resource information access centers, not only through employment counseling, but because of the counseling style (lifestyle: what do you really want to do?). *Workforce* has a radical perspective (liberation, struggle, rights), is published bi-monthly, usually with a focus on an area (day care, prisoners, labor, media, education, etc.) Serves as one of the few national links for job openings in collective, alternative political groups, projects. (Usually good source listings). Donation for subscription.

What Color Is Your Parachute?, Richard Bolles, $4.95 from:
> Box 4310
> Berkeley, CA 94704

Emphasizes job hunting and career searching, but also how to figure out what is really satisfying and productive for you to do.

Where Do I Go From Here With My Life? by John C. Crystal and Richard N. Bolles, 1974, 253 pgs., $7.95 soft cover from:
> Seabury Press
> 815 2nd Ave.
> New York, N.Y. 10017

A very systematic, practical and effective life/work planning manual for students of all ages, instructors, counselors, career seekers and career changers. John is preparing a videotape expanding on the subject of "Understanding the World of Work."

Briarpatch Review, $5/year, quarterly, from:
> **330 Ellis Street**
> **San Francisco, CA 94102**

Healthy small business and industry—for right livelihood rather than profit—is the necessary base for developing a more diverse and viable economic structure. Briarpatch is an association of such businesses in northern California that assist each other and share resources and friendships. Putting eco-nomics into practice ahead of the theory.

Job sharing is a concept that seems to be taking hold even in very straight, traditional situations like banks and universities. I've seen articles on it recently in *The Willamette Valley Observer* (April 16), *Ms. Magazine* (May 1976), and the *Oregonian*. Another term for it is part-time—hiring two people to take responsibility for a job. In Eugene two women share a school nurse position by simply dividing up the day. They can cover for each other when they're sick or can work together for busy days like hearing tests. In some jobs that are more flexible time-wise, two people simply divide up the work. As each tends to work more than the required hours, employers often get more for their money—even if they are paying full benefits to each. Much of the credit for the new trend can be given to the women's movement—more qualified women who need flexible hours geared to child care problems. Oftentimes jobs are shared by a couple, which means hours at home can be divided equally. Whatever the reasons, it seems to be a healthy move towards increasing a person's work options.

Flexible Ways to Work
   Doug and Roz Clark
   2683 Alder
   Eugene, OR 97405
and

New Ways to Work
   457 Kingsley
   Palo Alto, CA 94301

These groups offer free educational and counseling resources for employers and potential employees who would like to try job sharing.

4 Days, 40 Hours, Riva Poor, 1973, $1.95 from:
   Mentor Books
   1301 Avenue of the Americas
   New York, NY 10019

Flexible Working Hours, Heinz Allerspach, 1975, $6.95 from:
   International Labor Office
   1750 New York Avenue, N.W.
   Washington, DC 20006
Shuffling around working hours and giving workers some control over when they work is one of the current cosmetic changes being explored to placate basic worker dissatisfaction with the structure of work and production of goods. Both these studies indicate that greater benefits may accrue to the employers than to the employees—though more flexible patterns may benefit both. They won't solve any basic problems, but in conjunction with worksharing may begin to crack the rigidity of U.S. work patterns.

RESEARCH GROUPS

A lot of good people and groups are helping pull together the information, ideas, organization and hard work necessary to build a new economics that is sustainable, equitable and feels good. These are some of them. Help them, and go to them for help.

Public Interest Economics Review, bi-monthly, $5/year from:
   PIE Foundation
   1714 Massachusetts Avenue, N.W.
   Washington, DC 20036
Good perspectives on unemployment, economic priorities, who's doing what economic research, current projects and legal battles. Access to economics networks.

Environmentalists for Full Employment
   1785 Massachusetts Avenue, N.W.
   Washington, DC 20036
Established to demonstrate that a full employment economy can be harmonious with a clean and healthy environment, EFFE has helped coordinate a major conference between labor and environmentalists, publishes a free quarterly newsletter and acts as a clearinghouse on jobs/environmental issues.

Council on Economic Priorities
   84 Fifth Avenue
   New York, NY 10011
Doing research on just that—see Community Research section for details and available publications.

Center for Community Economic Development
   639 Massachusetts Ave., Suite 316
   Cambridge, MA 02139
An excellent group that keeps tabs on the benefits and costs of doing things at a local community level vs. larger scale institutions. Local services, local business, local manufacturing and cooperative or community ownership of enterprises can often yield surprising benefits for the people concerned and for the community. Write for publications list.

Institute for Local Self-Reliance
   1717 18th Street N.W.
   Washington, DC 20009
A strong, experienced group working with development of neighborhood and community economic and social structures. Work on banking, sewage, small business, energy, urban agriculture and other areas. Many excellent ideas for going about developing local small businesses.

Community Ownership Organizing Project
   349 62nd Street
   Oakland, CA 94618
Some of the best research on community economics in the country—how to recover control of our own resources. Write for publications list and see their publications listed above in this section.

Union for Radical Political Economics
   41 Union Square, Room 201
   New York, NY 10003
A national network of radical economists working on development of sound economic analysis which serves the interests of people working for progressive social change. Put out *Review of Radical Political Economics*, and the Boston-area group puts out *Dollars and Sense*, which explains economic issues in simple simple, straightforward terms.

Metastasis
   P.O. Box 128
   Marblemount, WA 98267
Probably the best single source in the U.S. for useful and hard-to-get how-to publications for setting up and operating small enterprises of many kinds. Write for their pricelist.

53

Ancil Nance

COMMUNITY BUILDING

This section is about the process of change. It is about how communities, groups of people, are getting it together to make a difference. Sometimes they plant trees on their block or stop a highway from blustering through their neighborhood. It's about "radical weirdos" and "rednecks" discovering that both want control of lowering utility rates. It's about people focusing on their problems at the grassroots level. It's about using our combined voices and energies for the places we care about. It's happening all over. In China. Probably even next door.

It's also about the networks of information sharing that help it all happen. Words and vibes and openness. WATS lines borrowed from a Congressperson. Gatherings in the woods and at the Sheraton (you should have seen the compost privies in their promenade!). Sleeping bags on the floor. Big pots of pea soup. Nights when we scare ourselves with talk of the inevitable nuclear disaster (or biological catastrophe or famine), balanced by nights when we feel joyful at the instant simpatico of a new friend. Boogeying. Seeing our communities start to change.

"They've All Gone to Look for America," Bo Burlingham in *Mother Jones*, February/March 1976, $8/year from:

**1255 Portland Place
Boulder, CO 80302**

What happened to all the radicals of the '60s? Most of the media hints that we've given up. Put your ear to the ground. This article focuses on ACORN (See Rural Roots), but it hits on some im-important and encouraging notions about the social change movement as a whole:

Midway through my travels, I began to experience a mild intoxication: Was this all some gigantic mass movement on the verge of springing full-born on the national scene, a major force that somehow nobody in Washington or New York had managed to notice? No, but as I pondered what I was seeing, the intoxication stayed: These groups were more numerous, markedly more far-reaching, and seemingly destined to be longer-lasting than any I had seen in the '60s. It is too early to tell whether they can achieve real power and influence, but they definitely have brighter prospects than anyone would have thought a few years ago.

These are politically sophisticated people. In talking with them, I realized that they hold diverse views on the abstract issues which once preoccupied the New Left. They do not, however, regard their differences—whatever they may be—as important. ACORN did not attract them with its line. Rather they came because it worked.

Neighborhood Power, Karl Hess and David Morris, 1975, $3.45 from
**Beacon Press
25 Beacon Street
Boston, MA 02108**

A good, positive overview of the possibilities for urban neighborhoods—the growth of community business, housing, government, production, cooperation. Here are ideas and proposals for making urban communities livable and self-reliant by two who have been involved in the Adams-Morgan area of Washington, D.C. for several years. Small is possible *and* good!

Rules for Radicals, A Practical Primer for Realistic Radicals, Saul D. Alinsky, 1971, $1.95 from:
**Random House
201 East 50th
New York, NY 10022**

There's a fine line between organizing and being pushy. This can help you see the edge. Alinsky's stuff is still a good way into thinking about how to marshall up people's resources.

Cooperative Community Development, Joe Falk, Ed., 1975, $2.95 from:
**The Future Associates
P.O. Box 912
Shawnee Mission, Kansas 66201**

Subtitle: A Blueprint for Our Future. A good, solid "how-to" on organizing a cooperative neighborhood, block by block. Real estate acquisition, rehabilitation, new construction; cooperative purchasing and rental of all kinds of goods and services; creation of neighborhood jobs and other home income producing opportunities; and the creation of a neighborhood capital base through a neighborhood investment fund, volunteer labor bank and credit union, plus good working relationship with local financial institutions. It's all laid out in such loving detail that it's obvious he's had a lot of experience—and faith.

"The irony of all this is that those now making decisions for us all live on a block, in a neighborhood, with their family, so they are also one of us; they just do not realize it and therefore we have not been a factor in their decisions and actions. This approach we are taking should change this situation almost overnight and thus start every organization cooperating with us while they are pursuing their own interests."

**National Center for Voluntary Action
1785 Massachusetts Ave., N.W.
Washington, DC 20036**

The Center is a clearinghouse for information about voluntary action programs (VITA, VISTA, etc.), citizen participation and community technical assistance projects. They can produce from their files very nicely done rundowns on hundreds of groups.

**Organizers' Book Center
P.O. Box 21066
Washington, DC 20009**

This is the place to order hard-to-find books on effective community and poli-

tical action in the broadest sense. Third World and minority are strongly represented as are economic and environmental issues. More Saul Alinsky than Sierra Club in orientation and style. You'll learn a lot just from the catalog, *Books for Organizers*. Highly recommended.

**Conference on Alternative State and Local Public Policies
Institute for Policy Studies
1901 Q Street, N.W.
Washington, DC 20009**

This is a group that has sponsored two gatherings (Madison in 1975 and Austin in 1976) of alternative mayors, legislators and other officials and staff people to discuss tax reform, insurance legislation, you name it. Who's doing what where and how we all can help each other. There are more good people in positions of power than one might think, and they are responsible for some big changes. Here are some of their valuable publications (prices given are for individuals—double them if you are an institution):

Conference Newsletter ($5/yr.)—quarterly report on activities, plus info on recent model legislation—a good way to stay informed.

Second Annual Public Policy Reader ($7.50)—a mammoth (600 pp.) collection of the best and most innovative proposals, bills and ordinances of 1975.

Alternative Legislation Series (50¢ each)—model bills on Cooperative Banks, Utility Regulation, Energy, Health, "Lifeline" Utility Regulation, and Auto Insurance Corporations.

Legislative Handbook on Women's Issues ($2.50), *Public Control of Public Money* ($1.50), *The Cities Wealth: Programs for Community Economic Control in Berkeley, Calif.* ($2.50), and *The Manitoba Auto Insurance Plan* ($1).

**League of Women Voters
1730 M Street, N.W.
Washington, DC 20036**

The League publishes on so many things from polls to budget processes, to parliamentary rules and recycling. I think that's what I like about their publications. They will probably have said something about some part (usually just a small part of a big organizational picture) of your problem. Write for publications list.

National Association of Neighborhoods
    1901 Que Street, N.W.
    Washington, DC 20009
The association is an alliance of over 200 neighborhood organizations and city-wide coalitions. They provide information assistance through workshops and conferences and by publishing a good newsletter ($10/yr.).

SEDFRE
    315 Seventh Ave.
    New York, NY 10001
They publish some good introductory, reminder list type publications on community organizing.

Center for Community Change
    1000 Wisconsin Ave., N.W.
    Washington, DC 20007
The Center is a good source on information about community development corporations, and other governmental policies affecting neighborhoods. Publications include: *Citizen Involvement in Community Development; Community Development Block Grants—a monitoring guide*. Also they publish *Monitor*, which is a good source of Washington, DC, news affecting communities. $10/year.

UPLIFT: What People Can Themselves Do, $5 from:
    National Self Help Resource Center
    1800 Wisconsin Ave., N.W.
    Washington, DC 20007
The National Self Help Center works from a notion of communities and groups creating projects and programs that are more reliant on volunteers than on outside monies, enable people rather than only assist them through a crisis, and programs that grow out of perceived needs.
    UPLIFT is a rundown of several dozen projects in the country they are familiar with.

Citizen Participation in Urban Development, $6.50 from:
    Learning Resources Corporation
    2817 N. Dorr Ave.
    Fairfax, VA 22030
A good introduction to community organizing and participation in planning.

*See also the Economics section for coverage of community economic development.

Balancing the Scales of Justice: Financing Public Interest Law in America, 1976 (write for price and availability) to:
    The Council for Public Interest Law
    1250 Connecticut Ave., N.W.
    Washington, DC 20036
In the past ten years or so, it has become increasingly obvious to many Americans that our system of justice isn't quite as fair as it should be. Partly as an outgrowth of earlier civil rights, civil liberties and legal aid group movements, the new concept of public interest law includes those lawyers and law firms who provide free (or unusually cheap) legal services to folks who have not been able to find representation before. Now the poor, racial and ethnic minorities, the handicapped and children, as well as interests such as environmentalism and consumer affairs, can be heard in court. See this book for an excellent review of the development of the public interest law movement, descriptions of how and for whom specific groups work, how they are now financed and what their prospects are.
If you feel you could use the services of such a law firm, the Council is the place to write.   (Lauri deMoll)
CDC News
    Community Development Division
    American Institute of Architects
    1735 New York Ave., N.W.
    Washington, DC 20036
Free. For the past eight years, community design centers have been providing free (usually) design services for neighborhood groups. Traditionally they have designed tot lots, remodeled drop-in centers and worked as advocates with citizens on neighborhood plans. More and more now they are getting into rehabilitation for energy conservation. The *CDC News* is a periodic update on their goings on. And I just got "Community Design Centers Profile: 1975-76" in the mail today—a complete listing and description of current CDCs. If you have anything to do with architecture/environmental design in the community, you ought to be on their mailing list. Or if your group needs some design or advocacy planning assistance.

National Association of Accountants for the Public Interest
    233 Sansome Street, Room 400
    San Francisco, CA 94104
The accountants, like the architects and lawyers, have started to do free work for folks who are boggled by debits and credits, 501(C)(3)'s and Form 990's. The national organization publishes a newsletter ($5/yr, $15 membership), which can fill you in on what's happening. They can also steer you to the local group in your area.

Arkansas Community Organizers for Reform Now (ACORN)
    523 West 15th
    Little Rock, AR 72202
and
SD/ACORN
    611 So. Second Ave.
    Sious Falls, SD 57104
A truly grassroots organizing group that starts with "curbside stuff" like a need for a stoplight at a busy intersection and moves on to challenge the power structures in the community. In Arkansas they presently have a federation of 70 community groups with 5,000

dues-paying families. The organizers are dedicated and middle-class—the members are the politically and economically impoverished working class. They all carry it off well. Keep an eye on them and learn from them.

Office of Neighborhood Associations
Portland City Hall
1220 S.W. 5th
Portland, OR 97204
and
Portland Alliance of Neighborhoods
2155 N.W. Glisan
Portland, OR 97210

There are over 70 neighborhood associations in Portland. They have grown up in the by now well-known way, through persons getting organized over two or three basic issues: housing, transportation and land use planning.

The Office of Neighborhood Associations serves as a liaison between city governments and the neighborhoods, coordinating budget task force committees who review individual city department budgets, comparing them with the needs of different neighborhoods.

The Portland Alliance of Neighborhoods was formed to increase information sharing between neighborhood groups, and to create a forum for issues that involve more than one neighborhood.

*See the Sharing and Gathering section for examples of community meetings, barter exchanges, craft fairs and the like—putting life into communities!

Earth Station 7
402 15th Ave., E.
Seattle, WA 98112

Earth Station 7 is an example of a resource sharing collection of groups who share an old firehouse. It presently houses a free medical clinic, tool lending library and an environmental education/community design center called

Environmental Works. It is an exciting use of underused city property, and a model of a loose collective of groups with minimum centralized functions.

San Francisco Zen Center
300 Page Street
San Francisco, CA 94102

A prime example of community involvement centered in a badly-deteriorated neighborhood of San Francisco. They have set up the Green Gulch Greengrocer—a corner store to make available to the area organic produce (grown at their Marin County farm) and oven-hot Tassajara bread. The zennies volunteer their time, so prices stay low. They have sponsored a park and neighborhood foundation to help residents rehabilitate the area. The spirit with which all these things are done and its implications for everyday life are well worth becoming aware of. Their newsletter, *Wind Bell*, is available for $4/year (3 issues).

The Black Panther Party
8501 East 14th St.
Oakland, CA 94621

The Black Panthers haven't been getting into the news too much lately—a far cry from the days of the urban riots. But they are alive and well in Oakland working on cooperative housing, sickle cell anemia research, free clothing and food programs, legal and cultural education, and job training for the black community. For details read the Fall 1974 *Co-Evolution Quarterly* that they guest edited, and send for their publications list.

Community Action Agencies operate in both urban and rural settings to provide a service support base for low income and minority communities. They are federally-funded by the Community Services Administration (CSA), the former Office of Economic Oppor-

tunity that did a fancy dance and name change to survive the Nixon years. In the past couple of years of rising fuel shortages, many have been getting into insulation and weatherization programs, and a few have even begun to work with alternative energy technologies. These efforts are now being supported by the new CSA-funded National Center for Appropriate Technology (see the A.T. section for details). For a list of CAAs in your area, write to Community Services Administration, 1200 19th St., N.W., Washington, DC 20506.

Washington County Community Action Organization
546 S.E. Baseline
Hillsboro, OR 97123

A good example of a rural-based community action project in our state. They operate out of a little green house that is bursting with people and energy. Their ongoing services include a rural awareness project, an emergency shelter project, home maintenance and weatherization, youth groups, a translator's bureau for court appearances and the like, Head Start, and consumer advocacy programs for welfare, food stamps and Social Security problems. They operate the Gleaning Project, which in 1975 harvested over $57,000 worth of food from local fields for distribution to over 1,000 elderly, low income and disabled people. The food was the windfall crop which would have otherwise gone to waste. The farmers donate the food, getting a tax break. They have also sponsored a Women's Self-Help Divorce Project, a Natural Food Preservation Project and a food co-op, community gardens, a tax assistance clinic and bilingual (Spanish) community education. Their newspaper, the *Rural Tribune*, is an excellent free 8-page bilingual monthly that is a fine model for communities anywhere.

NEWSLETTERS

Self-Reliance
**Institute for Local Self-Reliance
1717 18th Street, N.W.
Washington, DC 20009**
$6/year, 6 issues. One of the best news-letters around. The information they present comes out of hard work the Institute is involved in (see A.T. and Agriculture sections). Most neighbor-hood associations and groups have not reached full consciousness, and *Self-Reliance* is a good guide for getting there, in getting people to think about growing food, growing businesses, money and energy in their neighbor-hood.

Community Planning Report, $65 ($70 if billed), weekly, from:
**Resources News Service
1046 National Press Building
Washington, DC 20045**
An excellent newsletter focusing on the problems of growth and community, put out by some good folks in Washing-ton D.C. Keeps tab on government hear-ings, new legislation, upcoming gather-ings on the East Coast, new regulations published in the Federal Register, recent rulings in the courts, federal research grants and contracts, and a listing of relevant books and resources. Always full of useful information for com-munities trying to chart a new future.

Working Papers for a New Society,
**123 Mt. Auburn St.
Cambridge, MA 02138**
$10/yr., quarterly. Collections of often quite useful papers for putting together, as the title says, a new society. The Winter '76 issue has an excellent article on the conversion of the British Triumph motorcycle factory to a worker-owned co-op, the history and prospects for ad-free TV, tax reforms, problems of big lumber companies and independent woodsmen in Maine, the effects of the recent Socialist government in B.C., and other good things.

doing it!, $10/year, bi-monthly, from:
**Box 303
Worthington, OH 43085**
Their emphasis is on urban changes. 80 pages describing interesting projects in more depth than we attempt. It feels like it will be useful.

Street: Magazine of the Environment
**Pratt Center for Community and
Environmental Development
240 Hall Street
Brooklyn, NY 11205**
The Summer 1975 issue has an excel-lent summary of housing problems: good articles on "red-lining" (lending institu-tions' practice of refusing loans and mort-gages in deteriorating neighborhoods, thus ensuring their demise), the use of the National Environmental Policy Act of 1970 for *urban* environments, and sweat equity cooperatives to rehabilitate housing. Each article gives address and phone numbers for people to contact. Many of the programs mentioned are federal; others, though specific to NYC, could be adapted anywhere. Lots of good ideas here.

Common Ground
**Cross Roads Resource Center
2314 Elliot Ave. So.
Minneapolis, MN 55404**
$4/yr., quarterly. This 64-page news-print magazine is filled with information specific to the Twin Cities, most of which can apply anywhere. Hospital workers on unionization, high rise and industrial development, and a good, clear "People's Guide to Home Insula-tion" and "Alternative Energy and Who's Doing It." Back issues ($1 each) on Neighborhood History, Parks and Open Space, Community Control, Con-trolling Neighborhood Development, Parade of Neighborhoods, and Art for Our Sake.

Futures Conditional
**Northwest Regional Foundation
P.O. Box 5296
Spokane, WA 99205**
$20/year. The FC packages often con-tain articles and resources useful for community organizing, especially as related to communication experiments. Recently put together a follow-up to the UN Habitat Conference with a series of good articles.

Neighborhood Ideas
**Center for Governmental Studies
P.O. Box 34481
Washington, DC 20034**
$20/year. The center is involved in many projects and one focus is neigh-borhood development. Their newsletter, *Neighborhood Ideas,* is another good source of information on neighborhood ideas around the country. Other pub-lications include *Little City Halls,* 35¢ and *Municipal Decentralization and Neighborhood Resources,* $5.

Shelterforce
**Shelterforce Collective
31 Chestnut St.
East Orange, NJ 07018**
$3/yr. (quarterly). Karl Hess says that the most important part of neighbor-hoods getting it together is dealing with ownership of the land. This is a paper that will keep you up to date with part of that question . . . tenants issues. Covers rent strikes, tenants unions and redevelopment hassles nationwide. Also a good access section on books and re-ports in the field.

ENVIRONMENTAL GROUPS

There is another level of community participation in change: the state and national politics of environmental and consumer issues. Decisions and changes at these levels affect us all. A fight won for the banning of non-returnable bottles or a progressive utility rate restructuring in one state serves as a model for other states. A national decision to delay construction of nuclear power plants until the waste disposal question is solved has immediate ramifications for hometown battles. The National Conference on Alternative State and Local Policies (see Community Organizing at the beginning of this section) is an important resource in these areas. Here are some others to open up the tip of this very large network.

The Grassroots Primer, James Robertson and John Lewallen, ed., 1975, $7.95 from:
Sierra Club Books
530 Bush Street
San Francisco, CA 94108
Is your marsh about to be paved over? Want to outlaw non-returnable containers in your area? Here's a book that can give you a feel for how to jump into the fray. 19 firsthand examples to show you that individuals and groups really *can* make a substantial difference, as well as an excellent how-to guide called "Steps to Power." Included are subjects such as Who's In Charge, Your Constituency, Allies, Opposition, Elan Vital, Handling Hearings, Publicity and so on. It's the most encouraging and positive book I've seen in a long time. And it's a good way to get a feel for what's happening in this whole area.

Not Man Apart, $10/year from:
Friends of the Earth (FOE)
529 Commercial
San Francisco, CA 94111
Bi-weekly. This is my unabashed favorite source of continuing information on environmental goings-on. Legislative updates (with entries starred for special action needed), book reviews, news from different parts of the country, and *Nuclear Blowdown*—a regular two-page spread of goodies from the nuke frontier. Sometimes it gets depressing to read about all the outrageous things the Bureau of Land Management, the Army Corps of Engineers, and the like keep trying to pull off, but we're winning enough battles to keep my optimism

alive. *NMA*'s sense of humor helps too! If you don't have time to do much reading, pick up this one—it'll keep you busy.

FOE is an active lobbying and publishing group—a fine example of effective action combined with public information flow. Write them for publications lists and for their chapter nearest you.

Sierra Club
530 Bush Street
San Francisco, CA 94108
One of the better known of the environmental lobbying groups, Sierra Club is also one of the largest, with 49 chapters and 153,004 members. They have five Washington representatives who lobby on legislation ranging from wilderness protection to energy conservation. They also undertake environmental litigation opposing, for instance, Bodega Bay as a site for a California nuke and the development of a dam for the Grand Canyon. Lumbermen in the Northwest often sport bumper stickers saying, "Sierra Club, kiss my axe," in honor of recently won decisions halting logging at the edges of the Redwoods Park in California and the Boundry Waters Canoe Area in Minnesota, as well as the prohibition of cutting of immature timber in West Virginia's Monongahela National Forest. Other activities to make their viewpoints more visible include sponsoring of conferences, films, advertisements and wilderness outings. They publish beautiful "picture books." My favorite is *In Wildness Is the Preservation of the World* ($4.95)—Eliot Porter and Henry Thoreau make a powerful combination.

Environment Action Bulletin, $10/year, bi-weekly, from:
33 East Minor
Emmaus, PA 18049
Another of Rodale's useful gems. A good balance of information and a good complement to *NMA*.

Environmental Policy Center
317 Pennsylvania Ave., S.E.
Washington, DC 20003
These folks are low-key, hard-working and effective in lobbying for a wide variety of energy and environmental issues. They send out detailed action

alerts to interested citizens to help with letter-writing and call-in campaigns.

Public Citizen
P.O. Box 19404
1346 Connecticut Ave., N.W.
Washington, DC 20036
This is Ralph Nader's famous "Raiders" (or infamous, depending on your perspective). They are a powerful lobbying group with the valuable ability to get wide press coverage of their efforts (though not all of it positive). Their research and lobbying efforts range from tax reform and health care to utility rates and airline passenger rights. They're really more of a "consumer" group than "environmental" but I put them here just to remind you that it's *all* interrelated.

Oregon Environmental Council
2637 S.W. Water
Portland, OR 97201
This group is a good model of a statewide coalition of environmental groups and individuals who have hired a lobbying staff to watchdog land use, energy and the like in the state legislature. They publish *Earthwatch Oregon* ($10/year), a monthly update on issues and legislation at hand.

Northern Plains Resource Council
Stapleton Building
Billings, MT 59101
The issue of strip mining brought together this coalition between normally "straight" Montana ranchers and "long-haired" environmentalists. It is one of the most effective and powerful local lobbying groups going . . . landowners and activists who have come to depend on and respect each other. There's an excellent description of them in the *Grassroots Primer*. Not content just to prevent strip mining for coal, they have started the Alternative Energy Resources Organization (AERO—see the Energy section) to prove that alternatives *do* exist.

For good citizen involvement, participation, or whatever you want to call it, we feel you need what we've been calling feed-forward—that it's kind of dishonest to give people input into a decision-making process if they don't have enough information beforehand as a base from where they can make clear decisions.

Many of the citizen participation systems that have been developed are very one-sided, where people are just asked to comment through various channels, like questionnaires in land use planning, or newspaper balloting.

Not only do the people need an information base, "feed forward," it is also important, and something lacking in many citizen involvement projects, to give the people feedback about their input.

Mapping and Graphing Community Points of View describes one possible way to present information gathered during a community involvement planning process.

The "Access" project in Santa Barbara outlines a way to make information available to a community which will allow them to make proper decisions.

Another problem with citizen participation programs is that they are not what I call iterative, that is they don't have cycles or loops. They usually consist of one feedback process, with no follow-up or further clarification.

P: When we talk, like we are now, we go back and forth; it is a dialogue, and often it involves "meta-communication," like "I don't understand what you said," or "Could you clarify that?" or "Do you mean: ?" These are necessary kinds of questions that help us see if we are really communicating. People in a community dialogue have to agree on terms, what the subject is, what the next step is, and many complicated things that demand cycles, dialogue, back and forth conversation.

S: So where is all this citizen participation stuff going?
P: I think it's going in the direction of a large-scale process that informs people about what the issues are in a community,

CITIZEN PARTICIPATION

Televote
American Institute for Research
P.O. Box 1113
Palo Alto, CA 94302
The televote system is a way to inform citizens about public issues, and in return get informed opinions. Relevant facts and opposing views are sent to all interested citizens; they then have a week to express their opinions by dialing certain numbers on the telephone, including a special televote number which assures that only one vote is counted from each person. Results are processed by computer and delivered to public officials and the media within a day after the televote ends.

Yosemite Planning Team
Golden Gate National Recreation Area
Fort Mason
San Francisco, CA 94123
Here's an example of a federal bureaucracy responding to public pressure in a positive way. When the word went out on the grapevine that a huge new development, including convention facilities and shopping center, was planned for Yosemite National Park, all hell broke loose. Suddenly an advisory committee was set up and a planning team hired to obtain citizen input on the future of the park. 48 public workshops were attended by 5,600 people and a very detailed questionnaire including options to un-develop portions of the park was sent out to 59,000 people. 20,700 people responded, and a new development plan is now in the works. We suggest anyone interested in citizen involvement in any form write for copies of the questionnaire and the summary. They're excellent models. Thank you, Department of the Interior! (LdeM)

Land Conservation and Development Commission
1175 Court N.E.
Salem, OR 97310
The LCDC has coordinated some of the most extensive citizen participation programs in the country. They have been viewed as successful by some, and by others as inadequate. A referendum to do away with LCDC was recently defeated in Oregon. While not having any new technologies to citizen participation, they've had lots of experience.

Information, Perception and Regional Policy
National Science Foundation
Division of Intergovernmental Science and Public Technology
Technology
Washington, DC 20550
This report summarizes the concept, design and evolution of the ACCESS (alternative comprehensive community environ-

in the nation or in the world, and then a way of allowing alternative methods of participation in the decisions about these issues, and it will have to be a process that allows people to step in exactly to the degree that they can or want to.

S: But what about in just, say, the next year or so?

P: More token programs until people will finally stop participating. You'll look in the newspapers and see the possibility of going to ten different workshops to involve citizens in this or that, and give up. Once everyone burns out, after no one wants to attend anymore, the bureaucracies get tired of citizen participation, in the present state of the art, and the courts say, but you got to do it, and then it will all go kapooey and things will change.

The bottom line, though, eventually, is a complete evolutionary leap in how we govern ourselves.

S: I think you've told me before, though, how you don't see that there should be some kind of gigantic centralized citizen participation process, that the varieties are important.

P: We have got to make a large-scale social commitment for allowing, facilitating and supporting diversity. We still see ourselves as separate and unable to work together. We need to recognize our differences so we can see that we're different but not separate.

Like in biological systems which have lots of variety. They can handle a lot of information flowing through them. But if you have a rigid system, then almost anything will make a big difference. If you have a varied, diverse system, then information coming in will be considered and handled by some part of the system, while other parts, the system as a whole, will go on.

This is part of a November 1976 conversation Steve and Rhoda held with Peter and Trudy Johnson-Lenz. See the Information section for other pieces.

COMMUNICATIONS

mental study system) project in Santa Barbara. The project and the report address the problems of making information about community planning available and understandable to the general public. Lots of good "making the city (or system) observable" ideas.

Community Issue Dialogue
Northwest Regional Foundation
P.O. Box 5296
Spokane, WA 99205
NRF has received a large contract from HUD to investigate, develop and test methods for effective large-scale citizen participation. It calls for the first actual use of a balloting process developed by E.J. Corwin, and a version of the *Graphing and Mapping Community Points of View* computer program developed by Peter and Trudy Johnson-Lenz.

Participation Systems, Inc.
43 Myrtle Terrace
Winchester, MA 01890
In 1962 C. Harrison Stevens used networking techniques to win an upset election as a selectman in Bedford, Massachusetts. He has published many reports and a book on citizen involvement, information exchange, citizen feedback systems and networking. They have sheet size summaries of some forms of citizen involvement and do consulting workshops and carry out citizen participation projects in New York.

Journal of Community Communications
LGC Engineering
1807 Delaware St.
Berkeley, CA 94703
Still jockeying for its rightful place, unsure of what community communications is, but a really important area: the place of community communication technology (which they define as many-to-many, e.g. computers, vs. the one-to-many, e.g. broadcast media). $10/year.

"Information and the New Movements for Citizen Participation," Hazel Henderson, in *Annals of American Academy of Political and Social Science*, March 1974, pp. 34-43.
An important treatment of the role of information in citizen participation.

"Many citizen leaders realize that all institutional structures are, by definition, designed to screen out any information they perceive as unwanted or irrelevant so as to better concentrate on the purposes for which they were organized—hence, their capacity for selecting, concealing, distorting and impounding information and the resulting shortcomings of their planning and goal setting processes."

MIT Community Dialog Project
Prof. Thomas B. Sheridan
MIT 1-108
Cambridge, MA 02139

This project studies the facilitation of group meetings using electronic voting aids and other procedures. It evaluates this technique as a function of the topic, participants and moderator of the group. Also into cable TV citizen participation. 43 pages, from Prof. Sheridan.

RED STAR OVER CHINA

It's been clear almost from the beginning that something exciting has been going on in the People's Republic of China. The increased level of travel there in recent years has resulted in a flurry of reports about what has been accomplished since 1949. Almost all of the material written shows that there is much we can learn from their experience: their localized health care program (barefoot doctors, virtual elimination of VD and other diseases), their incredible use of simplified technology, the ethic of serve the people, and their consciousness and self-reliance.

Yet, I was greatly impressed by a talk by Orville Schell at Farallones last summer where he expressed his ambivalence about his three months' work experience in China last spring, first in a remote farm area and then in a Shanghai factory. He had gone speaking Chinese and feeling great enthusiasm for all he had read. He was surprised to find that the *total* selflessness of the people nearly drove him up a wall after a time—they looked at him askance when he asked for a little time alone. It also depressed him to realize that the Chinese are plunging full speed ahead into an industrial society—albeit on their own terms. He felt there was very little of the so-called "ecological consciousness" he had hoped to find. Pollution in manufacturing centers is as bad as many places in the West and growing daily worse. People recycle and reuse things because they cannot afford to waste them. When it is important to have more fertile agricultural land, the river is made to change its course even if it changes the face of a beautiful mountain.

His lesson was clear—we can borrow ideas from the Chinese experience, but we *must* adapt them to our own needs and culture. It'll be some time, I think, before we know enough to understand what all this really means for our own struggles for alternatives to our present way of doing things.

In the meantime, here are some of the books I found most interesting and helpful in my search for some understanding of what was going on there.

The China Reader, 3 Volumes, Franz Schurmann and Orville Schell, Vintage, 1967, $2.95 from:
Random House
201 East 50th
New York, NY 10022
"Imperial China," "Republican China," "Communist China." These books will give you a good overview of China's recent history with a good smattering of political writings and first-hand accounts.

The Crippled Tree, A Mortal Flower, and *Birdless Summer,* Han Suyin, 1972, from:
Panther House Ltd.
P.O. Box 3553
New York, NY 10017
The three-volume autobiography-history from 1885-1948. A half-Chinese, half-Belgian woman growing up in Szechuan Province. Somehow these books gave me as good a feeling as anything I read about how it was "before."

Yo Banfa!, Rewi Alley, 1952 , $1.35 from:
New World Press
135 East 44th
New York, NY 10017
When this New Zealander's efforts to organize factory workers into cooperatives proved too radical (and effective) for the Kuomintang, he joined the communist forces. He's still there today. A good picture of the terrible oppression of pre-communist China.

Red Star Over China, Edgar Snow, 1937, $2.95 from:
Grove Press
53 East 11th St.
New York, NY 10003
This is the classic story of Snow's trips behind Red Army lines in 1936 when they were still a band of "upstarts." He was skeptical when he went and then became very close to them. His succeeding books, *Journey to the Beginning, The Other Side of the River, Red China Today* and *The Long Revolution,* chronicle his continuing friendship with the Chinese. His warm and loving accounts make all the big names into real people.

China Shakes the World, Jack Belden, 1949, $3.95 from
Monthly Review Press
62 W. 14th St.
New York, NY 10011
An American reporter traveling among the peasants and the Red Army during the war with the Japanese and the continuing struggle against Chiang K'ai-shek's Kuomintang. Good reports on peasant-efforts.

Once the fighting was over, it was time to turn full efforts to the on-going struggle of changing people's lives—continuing the real revolution:

Fanshen, William Hinton, Vintage, 1966, $2.95 from:
> Random House
> 201 East 50th
> New York, NY 10022

The best account I know of a small village's efforts to "turn itself over"—dealing with former landlords and spies, dividing up the land (this had to be done several times as their perceptions of "fairness" changed), and consciousness-raising—the continuous process of teaching each other to be effective farmers and comrades. Warmly written. Although I haven't read them, I'm sure Hinton's later books, *Iron Oxen* (1971) and *Turning Point in China* (about the Cultural Revolution, 1972), are equally perceptive.

Prisoners of Liberation, Allyn and Adele Rickett, Anchor Press, 1973, $2.50 from:
> Doubleday
> 501 Franklin Ave.
> Garden,City, NY 11530

Two Americans convicted of spying in the period during the Korean War and sentenced to prison. A fascinating account of the criticism/self-criticism process by which they dealt with their crime (including their distaste for the Chinese as a people—even though they had been Chinese language students) and and their totally changed attitudes following their release after four years. They now work with the AFSC in this country.

Away With All Pests, J. S. Horn, 1969 $3.75 from:
> Monthly Review Press
> 62 W. 14th St.
> New York, NY 10011

This is one of my favorites—if you're only reading one China book, pick this one by an English doctor who immigrated with his family in the '50s. A fine perspective on the process of humanizing health care—one of the more successful of the efforts to truly serve the people.

Here are some more up-to-date things covering specific topics:

Women and Child Care in China, Ruth Sidel, 1972, $1.25 from:
> Penguin Books, Inc.
> 7110 Ambassador Road
> Baltimore, MD 21207

China: Science Walks on Two Legs, Science for the People, Avon Books, 1974, $1.75 from:
> Hearst Corporation
> 959 Eighth Ave.
> New York, NY 10019

Barefoot Doctor's Manual, translation by U.S. Dept. of Health, Education and Welfare, $6.95 from:
> Cloudburst Press
> Mayne Island, VON 2J0
> BC, Canada

Fire in the Lake, Frances Fitzgerald, 1972, $2.25 from:
> Vintage Books
> 201 East 50th Street
> New York, NY 10022

A book about the cultural interfacing of the traditional Vietnamese, modern Communist and our own American societies in Vietnam with very perceptive views of the fundamentally different base from which three cultures arise, act and affect their people. Shows that a range of totally different cultural forms as viable as our own is possible and that new and more desirable forms can be developed.

China Books and Periodicals is the best way to keep up with current writings. They carry all the books here and many, many more, including the writings of Mao and other revolutionaries, Chinese language books, children's books, records and maps. They also carry material on Vietnam and other Third World liberation struggles—including a number of books and pamphlets in Spanish. Write them for their extensive catalogue.

West Coast Center	**East Coast Center**
2929 24th St.	125 5th Ave.
San Francisco, CA 94110	New York, NY 10003

> **Midwest Center**
> 210 W. Madison St.
> Chicago, IL 60606

Well, now that you're all fired up to go, talk to the *U.S. China People's Friendship Association*, National Office, 2700 W. 3rd St., Los Angeles, CA 90057. Find out which of the many local chapters is nearest you—they put together trips regularly in addition to sponsoring discussion groups, speakers, films, etc. They also publish a quarterly magazine that's full of interesting pictures and a wide variety of articles. It's available on many newsstands:
New China
> 41 Union Square West
> New York, NY 10003

$4/yr. ($8 institutions)

RURAL ROOTS

We try to watch for patterns; what is presented in this section seems to illustrate one: New forms (or old forms in new clothes) of communication and growth in small towns, villages and rural routes. The contacts between rural communities, and between city and country, seem to be increasing; problems traditionally thought of as one or the other's are being grappled with as shared plights.

Deadwood • Blachly • Five Rivers • Greenleaf • Creswell • Camas Swale • Tidewater • Mapleton

About 40 miles west of Eugene in the Oregon Coast Range, there has been, as in many other rural areas, an influx of newcomers, in some ways like the old timers and hillbillies. But then again, not the same.

There was a large wave of people who moved out of the cities in the late sixties and early seventies: then they were often greenhorns who lasted only part of a winter, and surely by the time they saw the second winter come on, moved back to the city or warmer climates.

There were others who stayed and now regard themselves as old timers, sometimes aghast at how rough shod and speedy new people appear.

It is often a unique and unstable marriage of cultures. In Deadwood, a recent meeting of people working at the food cooperative discussed the negative feelings some people had about the way the food co-op was run.

The minutes reflect the cultures and tension: "About 45 families have contributed membership dues to the co-op; the total population served by the Deadwood Post Office consists of 40 star route boxes and another 70 post office boxes.

"Geography and age were identified as two distinguishing divisions: Co-op members tend to be younger and live up the creek, while non-members tend to be middle-aged or older and live along the highway. That is only a generalization, however, since some middle-aged or older folks living on the highway participate and some younger folks living up the creek do not.

"Suggestions for possible causes of resentment included:
• Dislike for some mannerisms, style of dress, or general lifestyle on the part of some younger neighbors.
• Unhappiness with the fact that a VISTA volunteer was helping the co-op and was receiving some tax money.
• Dislike of any neighborhood organizations.
• The idea that the bulk-buying food section of the co-op is competing with the Deadwood Store.

• The idea that many of the people who have moved here over the past few years are transient and may not stay in the neighborhood for a long time.

"Some members at the meeting thought that it is important to recognize the strong tradition of individual independence and self-reliance here. Historically, neighbors have helped each other out in time of need, but basically have lived very private lives and prided themselves on taking care of their own needs.

"It was suggested that newcomers to the neighborhood should be very sensitive to this individualism and respect it, even while co-op members continue to form associations of mutual benefit." (*Deadwood Ditto*, March 22, 1976, p. 1)

The Deadwood Cooperative has also recently been the recipient of a $25,000 grant to develop wood products on a small craft/cottage industry level.

Some residents in this coastal area have also recently grouped together over what they feel is a crisis—the use of toxic sprays in reforestation. See the Agriculture section for a discussion of Citizens Against Toxic Sprays. (SJ)

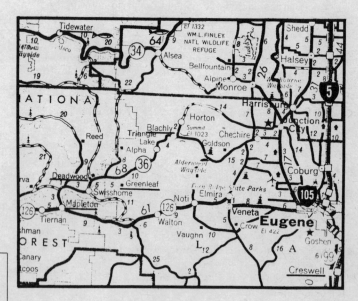

Small Town
P.O. Box 517
Ellensburg, WA 98926
$15 home membership, $25 institutional and professional. A small, but useful, monthly news journal geared toward rural small towns. Articles on land use, planning, historic preservation, community profiles, community health, family farms and small business. Keeps track of recent publications and political goings-on affecting rural communities. Even the letters are interesting. Should be in every Chamber of Commerce. Highly recommended for anyone interested in a sense of community at a reasonable scale.

. . . A REPORT by the census bureau made public last December said that from March 1970 to March 1974 an estimated 5.9 million persons moved out of metropolitan areas, while 4.1 million moved in, a net loss of 1.8 million; although some of the rural growth is just the outer extremes of metropolitan growth, some is growth of small towns far away from large cities. . . .

WHAT'S GROWING IN IOWA?

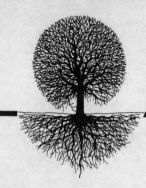

by Craig Mosher

Four hundred kilometers west of Chicago, amidst fertile corn fields, on the banks of the Iowa River, sits Iowa City, home of a growing group of alternative organizations. The University of Iowa adds 21,000 students to the city's 50,000 population and provides a secure state payroll for almost half the employed people in town. There also are several small factories and many farm-oriented businesses here.

Scattered around town and out over the countryside are many communal living groups. Crafts people and artists produce wares to be sold at bi-monthly crafts fairs in town.

Several cooperative day care centers, an alternative elementary school and a free university meet only a part of the need for alternative education. The Crisis Center provides hotline service to people in need, with volunteer and United Way support. A Simple Living group meets weekly. LINK is a monthly-published listing of things people want to learn and teach.

The Iowa Student Public Interest Research Group has been an effective statewide lobby and organizer for environmental and political issues. Two consignment shops, Goodwill Industries and a Free Store, provide free or low-cost used clothing.

A Free Clinic staffed by liberal medical professionals and students provides free medical care several evenings a week. HERA, a radical feminist psychotherapy collective, offers treatment and raises consciousness of the social causes of emotional illness—particularly sexism. The Emma Goldman Clinic for Women is a women's health collective which provides self-help groups, pregnancy screening, abortions, gynecological services and pre-natal classes. All these services are offered in a supportive environment so women learn to care for and control their own bodies as they receive health care. Educational and political programs operate out of the Women's Center at the University, and there is a women's restaurant, struggling to maintain its women only policy in the face of City opposition. A women's work crew contracts remodeling jobs.

Through the valiant efforts of a citizens' advisory committee, the City Council—which has long been controlled by business interests—has allocated substantial federal money to neighborhood community centers and a Citizens Housing Center, which will help low-income folks rehabilitate their own houses. An active tenants' organization helped push these changes through the council.

The largest alternative organization in Iowa City is the New Pioneer Cooperative Society, which operates a natural food store, bakery, Stone Soup Restaurant and co-op garage, a memorial society and a new co-op credit union. New Pioneer began five years ago as a small buying club for people interested in natural foods. They soon had a store front and grew a thousand members. The co-op store sells dry goods, herbs, dairy products, oils, vitamins, a wide variety of books and periodicals and some cooking equipment. Members who volun-

teer two hours per month to help in the store get a 20% discount on purchases and six low-paid staff keep the place operating. The membership is diverse and includes mostly non-students who live and work in Iowa City and the surrounding countryside.

Upstairs from the New Pioneer food co-op is Blooming Prairie Warehouse, which supplies many midwestern co-ops. The warehouse was established about two years ago and has also grown rapidly as more co-ops have sprung up around the state. There are over a dozen food co-ops and buying clubs in Iowa, including two which have just started this year. The warehouse is continually seeking local sources of organically grown food. But some inexperienced local farmers trying to grow organically are very frustrated at the poor quality of their initial efforts. As the co-ops grow and farmers learn, an increasing proportion of our food will come from local sources.

Craig Mosher is a father and partner, furniture and toy maker, teacher at the School of Social Work (University of Iowa), and chairman of the board of the New Pioneer Co-Op Credit Union.

For more information (perhaps a sample copy of their excellent monthly, *Co-Op News*) contact:

New Pioneer Cooperative Society
529 South Gilbert
Iowa City, IA 52240

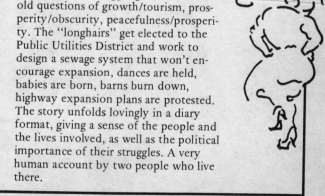

The Town That Fought to Save Itself, by Orville Schell with photographs by Ilka Hartmann, 1976, $6.95 from:
Pantheon Books
Random House
201 E. 50th
New York, NY 10022
The story of a small town just north of San Francisco struggling with the new/old questions of growth/tourism, prosperity/obscurity, peacefulness/prosperity. The "longhairs" get elected to the Public Utilities District and work to design a sewage system that won't encourage expansion, dances are held, babies are born, barns burn down, highway expansion plans are protested. The story unfolds lovingly in a diary format, giving a sense of the people and the lives involved, as well as the political importance of their struggles. A very human account by two people who live there.

*Most of the resources that relate to this section can be found in Economics of Scale, Agriculture and Health.

SHARING AND GATHERING

There is a more or less mathematically correct folk wisdom that nine people working together can lift as much as ten people individually. When you get more out of a whole than you can get from all of its parts, some people call it synergy, others call it common sense.

In *The Pursuit of Loneliness*, Philip Slater talks about Americans' desire to be isolated, or alone, not as hermits, but isolated from the challenge and ambiguity of having interaction with people outside of a chosen few relatives and friends.

The exact cents of an economic exchange allows us distance. We don't have to get along, or be curious about other people's problems, points of view and world. I've noticed over the years that whenever my earnings increase, so increases the number of things I decide, or am compelled (because of lack of time) to pay for, rather than make, do myself, or exchange with others.

When money was short, and non-existent, during the 1930s depression, hundreds of swapping and bartering exchanges sprang up.

* The Ohio plan was a program of the Federal Relief Administration which was a federation of manufacturing facilities run mostly by the unemployed. A large catalog was printed, similar to a Sears Catalog, of goods produced by the federation of manufacturing plants. The difference being that you could not purchase the illustrated goods with money, but paid for the goods with time by working in one of the facilities to produce other goods. In one year the factories produced over $100 million worth of goods.

* The Midwest Exchange operated for several years at Antioch College and was a fascinating merging of education and industry. The students worked their ways through college (still an integral part of an Antioch education) by working in one of several industries based on campus, like printing, art bronze and laboratory research facilities. The goods produced were not very marketable during the Depression, so the college set up the Midwest Exchange. A typical exchange was a deal between the college and an exchange member who ran a nursery and dairy. To the college he delivered eggs, butter, milk and nursery stock; in return he accepted the labor of Antioch students, printing, and the tuition of his daughter at the college.

* The Society of Independent Artists had several grand exchanges in New York. Paintings, for example, were given a number, and each person with a service to barter for a painting was indicated by a symbol—a blue heart for a doctor, silver star for attorney, and so on. By all descriptions, the events were somewhere between flea markets, art galleries and scavenger hunts.

Many skill and service exchanges have arisen in the last three to four years as a response to inflation and the energy crisis. On a large scale, the International Federation of Traders, who deal in huge quantities of goods (like $1 million worth of computer parts for like amount of auto parts), has shown a definite increase in recent years. On the community scale a wide assortment of services have come into being, like service exchanges, skill banks and bartering co-ops.

They are not easy running, well-oiled services. Often the initial efforts are failures because they are volunteer based and lack month-by-month cohesion, but especially they run into difficulties because our sharing skills are rusty. We are not used to the degree of personal interaction and the informality of transactions.

There are many variations on the theme of skill or service exchange. What works one place and time may not work equally well elsewhere. For example, maybe just encouraging flea markets or growers' markets is a way of encouraging exchange, or maybe a tool lending library would be just the right method. Community gardens and food buying clubs are yet another way of getting the sharing flow started.

Always first find out what the native way is. There are probably many specific local reasons why sharing and bartering has or has not taken place.

Fairs and Festivals

Fairs and festivals are effective ways of breaking down our usual forms of entertainment, which so often are focuses on the performances of persons on a stage, in a field or on the air. In the Northwest there were at least half a dozen "Lifestyle" fairs in about a six-week period recently, and that number is probably not too far off the national average. Many communities now have annual Renaissance or craft fairs which are generally joyous, fun occasions.

Northwest Washington Barter Fair
Rural Resources and Information and other groups in northwest Washington have sponsored an annual barter fair where people can trade goods, swap stories, exchange information, buy crafts and compare notes on firewood and how cold it's going to get. Over 3,000 people attended the last one.

Saturday Markets
Every Saturday, rain or shine, between May and Christmas in both Portland and Eugene, 200-plus vendors display their homemade or home-grown products. The markets have become much more than just exciting places to shop; they have become gathering/meeting places for people. And the craftspeople themselves meet each other and begin a process of mutual aid.

For a good booklet on how to put one together, send $2.00 to
Saturday Market
P.O. Box 427
Eugene, OR 97402

Help! For the Small Museum, Arminta Neal, 1969, $9.95 from:
Pruett Publishing Co.
3235 Prairie Ave.
Box 1560
Boulder, CO 80302
The only example I could find of a book dealing with the variety of exhibit and display methods. It is oriented towards the museum world, but does have good ideas and a glossary of manufacturers of exhibit-related goods.

Community meetings have served the function of building federations or coalitions of groups who can benefit from closer ties with each other. For lobbying efforts, resource sharing, implementation plans, or just by facilitating a richer, cross-disciplined approach to problems.

Town Meeting

These have become popular recently, probably in part due to the Bicentennial activities. Programs like Alternative for Washington, Syncon, Feedback (Troy, NY), and Iowa 2000 have promoted the use of town hall meetings, often using new communications technology. They've been an integral part of many New England towns as long as anyone can remember. See also the Citizen Participation section. (page 59)

Salons

You might just call it a hunker down out in the hills, but a salon, as they've existed since around the Renaissance, is ostensibly an agenda-less gathering for the sake of conversation. It's the idea. You don't have to call it a salon. Bringing together people, for example, who haven't met, but maybe know of each other, or each other's work, has few immediate or measurable results. But in the long run (and it's fascinating to watch), something inevitably happens. Take a look at "Salons and Their Keepers" by Stephanie Mills in the Summer 1974 *Co-Evolution Quarterly* (P.O. Box 428, Sausalito, CA 94965).

Eugene Sustaining Fund and Community Meeting
  Box 340
  Eugene, OR 97401

In 1973 some Eugene organizations got together in a series of general meetings to discuss possible avenues of supporting one another. Out of these meetings came the sustaining fund idea. Now over 50 groups ranging from the home fried truck stop to our federal credit union participate by a volunteer tax system. The money accumulated is dispersed by the members to not-for-profit, democratically-run organizations. Write for details (send self-addressed, stamped envelope).

'75 Sense, TV Town Hall
  from: Coos County TV
  Box 641
  Bandon, OR 97411

The Educational Coordinating Council and Southwestern Oregon Community College helped support this successful town hall meeting via television. Write for final report.

Community Meetings

CRIME PREVENTION

Due in large part to monies available through the Law Enforcement Assistance Administration (LEAA), there has been a growth of policing programs directed at mobilizing (softly in most cases) and educating the public about their role in crime prevention.

Block clubs, block parties, security procedures (like engraving goods with drivers' license numbers), and mobile patrols exist in many neighborhoods. In Oakland alone there are some 900 crime prevention block associations.

These programs have their obvious dangers and difficulties, like overzealous block captains seizing power, or people reporting anything unusual, reporting on the weird, unnormal, eccentric behavior of innocent people.

These crime prevention programs in some way do parallel developments in preventative medicine. They emphasize an underlying cause for crime, rather than punishment after the incident.

A result of the rapid growth of urban areas and communication and transportation patterns that allow us to cohabit with a world of friends that are not our neighbors is an anonymity that makes it easier to commit.

I don't think the emphasis even need be on crime prevention, though it's easy to gather people around that issue, for such programs to work. Many people don't feel they have the time or inclination to get to know their neighbors, and minimal and specific mechanisms like block parties, block clubs, may allow us the freedom still to choose who we want to relate to, while giving us a sense of security and comfort that our neighborhood, and not just our house, is our home.

Citizen Involvement in Crime Prevention, George J. Washnix, $14.50 from:
  Lexington Books
  125 Spring Street
  Lexington, MA 02173

A good recent study done by the Center for Governmental Studies.

PEOPLE TO PEOPLE INDEXES

By 1974 or so I had figured out that, like nuclear energy had become a kind of Vietnam war issue, so meetings, conferences and workshops had taken the place of demonstrations.

Conferences all around the country have produced catalogs/directories to the participants, including information about interests, needs, resources and philosophy. The conferences have included such things as the Evanston, Illinois, conference on learning exchanges in 1973; Bend in the River, an Oregon town hall meeting; the Northwest Alternative Agriculture Conference, held in Ellensburg, Washington, in 1974 and spawning another dozen more local conferences; and a potpourri gathering of artists and everybody, called Quick City, held in California in 1972.

The directories serve as a minimum effort, spontaneous network builder, establishing links between people with hardly any centralized coordination.

Performing Arts Index, 1976, 50¢ from:
    Contact Center
    1005 N.W. 16th
    Portland, OR 97210

First there was the Performing Arts Marathon, where people from around this area were drawn together, stretching the definition of "performance," and they danced, sang, talked, puppet-ed, laughed—and then they put together a directory of those performers and many more, along with loads of information useful for performing, for getting the word out, where to perform, legal and funding assistance—and then they put it all together. Has anyone heard of other such directories? $2

Montana Alternative Agriculture Conference
    c/o Jim Baerg
    Box 1311
    Missoula, MT 59801

Conference catalogs take another step forward. This one includes bibliographies, resource lists and other useful tidbits, turning the people to people concept into a handbook.

The Leap Year Papers, 1976, $1.95 from:
    Cascadian Regional Library (CAREL)
    P.O. Box 1492
    Eugene, OR 97401

The Leap Year Conference was a very high gathering of people in the Northwest (it turned out that people in Iowa were meeting at the same time . . . where else?). We met originally to form a federation, but it wasn't time. But it was good to know we were all doing good things in different corners of the region. This is an excellent and well put together report, including a mammoth mailing list (more than just people there) available on sticky labels for $4. Read about the crystallizing process of a network and the how-tos of putting together a conference. Also available is a 90-minute recording of the final general summary meeting.

The Goodfellow Catalogue of Wonderful Things (see Directories and Catalogues) and *The Farms of Puget Sound* (see Agriculture) are fine, fine examples of ways to connect people up with one another, in these cases craftspeople and farm producers, respectively.

Tool Lending Libraries

It would cost an individual around $5,000 to set up a tool bank the size of the one that exists at the Home Resource Center in Portland. Libraries (book ones) were set up when it became evident that individuals could not afford to buy all the books they might need or want, and because the one-time use of many books hardly seemed worth the expenditure. It is also true with tools—there are many useful tools which may only be used on occasion or once or twice in a lifetime.

Oregon Historical Society

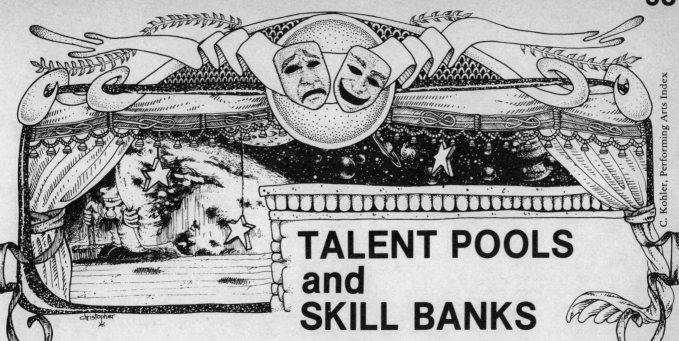

C. Kohler, Performing Arts Index

TALENT POOLS and SKILL BANKS

There has also been a growth of organizations that assist in the coordination of volunteer assistance. I'm still not sure how a parallel growth in unemployment fits into the picture, but many organizations in this country, especially small non-profit ones, are dependent on volunteers.

International Voluntary Services
1555 Connecticut Ave., N.W.
Washington, DC 20036

These people assign "volunteers" (who receive $80-$150/month plus all expenses and travel) on multinational teams in other countries. They need people with degrees and experience in the areas of agriculture, engineering, health services, small business development and other technical fields.

Alternatives for a Statewide Technical Skills Resource Bank for North Carolina, from:

Office of Citizen Participation
401 N. Wilmington St.
Raleigh, NC 27601

The North Carolina office seems to be one of the most effective and far-reaching of the many regional volunteer co-ordinating bodies.

Volunteers in Technical Assistance (VITA)
3706 Rhode Island Ave.
Mt. Rainier, MD 20822

Provides professional and technical assistance to groups and individuals working to solve community problems, mostly in foreign countries. Volunteers are all over the U.S. and provide help in the development of appropriate technologies by mail.

Independent Foundation
1028 Connecticut Ave., N.W.
Suite 618
Washington, DC 20036

A coordinating group for alumni (as they call them) of Peace Corps and VISTA. IF is now in the process of implementing a nationwide skill bank of volunteers starting from this base. There is also a new placement service for environmentally-related jobs overseas sponsored by the Peace Corps through the Smithsonian Institute (c/o Dept. L-1, Washington, DC 20560).

Everything for Everybody
406 West 13th
New York, NY 10014

A personal service bureau with several community centers and a food co-op in New York City. Members benefit by being members of the food co-op, free use of an exchange and barter newspaper, access to a clothing exchange and bartermart, and participation in a small free school. It costs $5/month; $15 for 6 months, $75 for one year and $100 for a lifetime.

Briarpatch Network
330 Ellis St.
San Francisco, CA 94102

Created in 1974, the Briarpatch Network consists of over a hundred individuals and small businesses that have formed a federation in order to sustain and foster a spirit of cooperative business ventures. They share resources and resource persons (including a floating accountant, business manager), and plan to compile a directory to members including their skills and offerings. Send $1 for a copy of their soft and useful magazine.

City Volunteer Corps
City of Los Angeles, City Hall
Los Angeles, CA 90012

In 1975, the program placed 25,000 hours of volunteer time, representing about $110,000 in equivalent man/woman hours. They use a computer program which is now being further developed by the Independent Foundation.

Community Skills Bank
41 Third St.
Ashland, OR 97520

The bank, now operating with over 300 active members, is coordinated by a Vista volunteer, Cathy Ging. As well as serving as an exchange of services and goods, the bank also maintains a community organization directory and a "community memory," the name given for a kind of member-written part of the earth catalog, how-to information is written up in a series of looseleaf books by people just wanting to tell others about a good book, useful warning, tip on a good product, or an answer to someone's question, also registered in the "community memory."

Home Resource Center/Service Exchange
3534 S.E. Main
Portland, OR 97214

The Home Resource Center is an interesting model for a comprehensive neighborhood self help center. As well as a delegate Community Services Administration office, the center maintains a tool lending library and the Service Exchange, where more than 1,000 people are actively involved in exchanging goods for services and services for services.

LEARNING EXCHANGES/ COMMUNITY MEMORY

In *Deschooling Society*, Ivan Illich (1972, $1.25, Harper & Row) proposes a model which could replace schools. He called it the learning web, a network of people and information where learning could take place:

"Someone who wants to learn knows that he needs both information and critical response to its use from someone else. Information can be stored in things and in persons. In a good educational system access to things ought to be available at the sole bidding of the learner, while access to informants requires, in addition, others' consent. Criticism can also come from two directions: from peers or from elders; that is, from fellow learners whose immediate interests match mine, or from those who will grant me a share in their superior experience. Peers can be colleagues with whom to raise a question, companions for playful and enjoyable (or arduous) reading or walking, challengers at any type of game. Elders can be consultants on which skill to learn, which method to use, what company to seek at a given moment. They can be guides to the right questions to be raised among peers and to the deficiency of the answers they arrive at. Most of these resources are plentiful. . . . We must conceive of new relational structures which are deliberately set up to facilitate access to these resources for the use of anybody who is motivated to seek them for his education."

There have been many attempts (at least 75-100) to set up such learning webs, sometimes called learning exchanges.

People Index
Ft. Vancouver Regional Library
1007 East Mill Plain Blvd.
Vancouver, WA 98663
One of the longest running people indexes in the country. There are over 800 people who have filled out a card describing their interests and skills. The cards are filed like book catalog cards and indexed using the same classification system as the rest of the library. They have a good 4-5 page summary of how it works.

The Learning Exchange
P.O. Box 920
Evanston, IL 60204

Chicago area residents can find teachers, tutors, discussion groups, students, speakers and action projects to share their information and talents through The Learning Exchange. There are more than 2,500 listings in topics ranging from appliqué to Virginia Woolf, and in four years more than 20,000 people of all ages and skill levels have been connected up. About half the people charge for their service, others barter or volunteer. Listing and inquiries are free, but a $15 membership means a helpful catalogue, a special phone line and a newsletter. It sounds almost too good to be true, but it seems to be working and, I'm sure, filling a huge gap in many people's lives.

Community Memory: A Public Information Network, Ken Colstad, Efrem Lipkin, from:
Loving Grace Cybernetics
1609 Virginia St.
Berkeley, CA 94703
A short summary of the history of the Community Memory project in the San Francisco Bay Area. For several years Resource One housed an XDS-940 timesharing computer. The computer, which also had terminals in Berkeley and Palo Alto, served for some time as a community bulletin board, on-line social service directory, and generally a public service computer center.

Anyone wanting to know the status of the project, and future plans (as well as reading a very interesting newsletter), should send $1 plus postage for a copy of the *Journal of Community Communications*, 1807 Delaware St., Berkeley, CA 94703.

HELP
284 Illinois Union
University of Illinois
Urbana, IL
An example of a large, university-based and computer-maintained learning ex-

change among students and faculties. It is several inches thick and contains the academic and other interests of several thousand people.

A Register of Faculty Professional Interests at the University of Oregon, from:
Office of Scientific & Scholarly Research
University of Oregon
Eugene, OR 97403
An example of a published directory to, mostly, academic and scholarly interests among faculty members. Designed to create increased flow of ideas between departments.

Neighborhood Information System
c/o Oregon Museum of Science & Industry
4015 S.W. Canyon Road
Portland, OR 97221
Peter and Trudy Johnson-Lenz have developed several community computer programs as part of a joint project with OMSI. The Neighborhood Information System is a program developed for a neighborhood association in Lake Oswego, to assist them with the analysis of information collected for input into the general Lake Oswego comprehensive plan.

The system was developed using APL (an applied language) computer. A significant advantage of APL is the relative ease in which a program can be written, thus saving expense. The program can be used to compile resident directories, skill and service exchange, surveys, resource inventories and mailing lists.

Free University Network
615 Fairchild Terrace
Manhattan, KS 66502
A coalition of over 200 free universities. Very often a free university either is, or helps operate, a learning exchange. They are a good resource for learning. The network publishes a newsletter and directory.

NETWORKS

There are many uses of the word network these days, and if our experienced Washington, DC, groupies are correct, in the next one to two years networks and networking are going to be what people are talking about.

Social scientists are talking about formal and informal networks as a way of describing the ways people interact and communicate; while brain scientists are increasingly using network as a metaphor (and physical actuality) for the mind; while mathematicians work on theories that allow one to predict the consequences of various changes and adjustments in a network; and meanwhile librarians continue to work on "networking" library resources, setting up cross reference and access systems for different libraries.

There is some way we use networks around RAIN which borrows from all the other uses, but is predominantly a pattern of communication by which we shift through information to find the right bits, and through surface realities to find underlying patterns.

Networks of people have a common language, even a private language. You know you are in the middle of a network when (1) it feels like everybody knows everybody else (especially weird and nice when great leaps of time and geography exist between people), (2) when everything is related to everything else, (3) when there are an equal number of people that you know as there are people you know *about*, people that you know so well you refer to them in conversations like old familiar sweaters, (4) when you find out about things before you see them in print, (5) when you know, by some kind of double time mental calculations—within minutes, whether or not someone is part of your network, karass or karma.

* There is a new genus of people, information networkers, who delight in finding the right piece of information for a person that enables him to move a direction of thought or a course of action.
* Conferences, meetings and workshops have created networks or tribes of people with common ground, or reasons to know each other. Conferences like Bend in the River, an Oregon state-wide media referendum organized by Ken Kesey, Brian Livingston and others, and the Alternative Agriculture Conference (November 1974, Ellensburg, Washington), have created coalitions, networks and friendships, with effects as quiet and fundamental as winter shadows. The Toward Tomorrow Fair in Amherst, Massachusetts, and Habitat Forum in Vancouver, B.C., both in summer of 1976, did it too.
* Self-conscious network groups have been formed, like Comnet in Seattle, the Network Project in Maryland, Rural Resources and Information in central Washington, Openings Network in Denver, the Movement for a New Society in Philadelphia, and whatever name Wes Thomas appears under (Communication Technology, 21st Century Media, Synergy Access).
* Magazines, catalogs, People's Yellow Pages, and newsletters, inviting participation and cooperation from readers, forming in the process a cooperative information sharing network, e.g. regional newsletters like *LION, Smallholder, Tilth, Alternative Sources of Energy, Planet Drum* and *RAIN*.
* Couriers and troubadours roam the country picking up and dropping off information like birds out of unconscious consideration carry the seeds of plants. Carried to a refined art by people like Dana Space Achley, with his multi-media presentations of his travels, and Rainbow Flute walking around with his regionally written journal

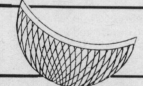

MAKING CONNECTIONS

When I came back into Portland in 1971 after living in the drippy bluegreen Douglas fir covered Cascade foothills, in order to actualize a fantasy I'd been having about a technological greenhouse and information center, I kept running into people who told me I should talk to Jack Eyerly. I even ran into someone else who had also been told he should talk to him.

I had been reading the Morning of the Magicians, *and my first meeting with Jack was colored with a sense of meeting a 400-year-old elf and magician. The basement he and Polly lived in at the time, hanging on a cliff overlooking Portland, was filled with files and papers, memorabilia and strange unexplained still lifes.*

Sometimes Jack talks so slow that while you're waiting for him to say the next thing, which you hope will tie up the previous ten minutes, he somehow manages to squeeze a whole other thought into a word that seems to come out of a chair or one of the many cats in the house.

But who knows? Jack is different to different people. He sometimes seems to talk through you, riding a ridge between just reinforcing what he thinks you want to hear and saying it in such a way that it feels like a yoga position that is slightly stretching the ends of your present idea tension.

Referring people to Jack is an unpredictable experience. To Jack there is a reason why a contact is made, everything fits in somehow, and the person who makes contact, maybe by calling on the phone, may be put on a train that picks up new cars at every crossing until your question looks like a dog disappearing over a faraway sunset-lit hill.

Rhoda and I talked with Jack in November. The following is a partial transcription of that conversation.

To me the people who have carried networking—whatever that is, cooperative information exchange, rural brain, whatever—into an art form are the correspondence artists, and the highest cooperative artist I know lives in Portland. He doesn't have a name; he has about ten, and no one knows his real one.

One of his names is Mr. and Mrs. Blassner. Another is the Nome Twins and Dr. Al Zimmerman. He maintains all these personalities, and writes for occult magazines, carrying on correspondences with himself in the letters to the editor. He also maintains a personality as a research institute in correspondence with some major European research facilities. And it's all pure invention, thought; networking around the world with all these identities, through all kinds of special worlds, with their own languages and events.

He acts as an intermediary crossing point for a lot of different people in given fields of interest, and he sometimes folds one of these fields over on another.

From my perception, there's nothing different between what he does and what you (RAIN, Steve, Rhoda) do, even though you're supposedly responding to things that are more real—place, history, services, the futility of people running around because they don't know where things are, and getting themselves into all kinds of really tragic situations.

I think he's an extreme case, but it's very entertaining. It's a delight he exists. He jolts me . . . I like people who make my thinking change, who wake me up to different relationships.

I guess if I wanted to carry further the art of being a communicator, or connector, in the sense of facilitating communication between myself and the world, and others, and others and the world, and others with others, and all of that, it would be more interesting to move into non-verbal areas.

Written history leaves out the thing most important about how we perceive things. Dance and ritual. When you (Steve) talk about your difficulty in your new house, finding the right seat, where to put your cup of coffee—it may have to do with the way you sit, not the chair or table.

The moment the catalog (this one) is published it's a historical document as opposed to being a life connector to current information. So much so that I think of it as an art form. It does more in what it communicates about how things are related to other things than actually giving life information. It's a view or a map from a point of view.

I know it's my sense of love and trust for the people in a network. I know trust and love are shitty things to deal with and I feel it intensely. I don't have the form for it yet, but I feel connected with others around the world all the time.

There was a very dramatic time in my life when it was maddening to live in such a small world where you only talked about certain things, and your survival is dependent on certain relations. And the pleasure goes out. So I turned myself loose. I wasn't going to seek out any museums (Jack was then a museum director). I salvaged food and all that. I wanted to remove myself from that milieu. The people around me, reinforcing themselves. It was keeping me from thinking. But I found I couldn't remove myself. I would go into a drive-in with hotrods and still meet someone from that group, and I was even fascinated by the encounter. After that I began to relax. I realized it was my affections, caring about certain things was a force, and other people's caring was a force, and

I drew these forces to me and enhanced what we normally call chance. All the clues that we don't have language for we pick up on even if we're consciously trying to avoid it.

I sometimes feel that what I'm trying to do is exert some kind of pressure, trying to make some situation work, and I couldn't articulate it until I ran into this waterwitch, a really good one who can find anything, not just water. His wife had died, and I asked him what he was doing now, and he said he was putting all his energy into making the world better. I started thinking about this old man sitting out there thinking about the world. I think that's what I'm doing when I make connections for people.

I know the first time I saw a person whose life was dedicated to one thing. He was living in a trailer house, living an austere life. I couldn't figure out why I was fascinated by him. His whole life had to do with model airplanes.

I saw that it was possible to focus, while all the other options around me looked like holding patterns. One of the things this person had done was create his own job; others were just doing other people's work.

He wasn't wholly supporting himself—that was important to me. He was on some kind of workman's compensation. That fascinated me—that he was "sick," or disabled, and that allowed him to be more whole.

I knew I wasn't "whole." I wasn't a great athlete, for example . . . with all the options in the world there are some I'd never be. Too short . . . how do you find a place in the world—not just to take a job, but a way to nourish your special flower.

I found that if I accepted the idea that I was disabled, that I lacked all kinds of things that would help me fit in, then I was better off.

I'm constantly in the position of a counselor, merely reinforcing my respect and love and excitement in people just being themselves, as opposed to being something they aren't, including being themselves and being so irrational that they want to try to be something they are not.

There are times, and there are parts of us that don't work well. I think it is important to get past that and reinforce the part that does work. The function of all these directories, and lists, and counseling, and being there on the phone, and offering something; it seems that just offering hope and an example is enough.

The first time I realized that a common role in life was a counselor was when I was a kid. The famous juvenile delinquent in grade school discovered his god in a social worker, someone who would listen to him talk, and he would do the same to me then because I too would listen. I realize though that he was just biding his time. He wasn't getting anything out of the content I exchanged.

There's a great relation between growth and healing. The laying on of hands, giving people comfort and growth, discovery, freshness, and the curiosity that works and engages problems and actually perceives things, rather than this kind of pattern where people reinforce the thing that will at least sustain them—where they get involved in an activity like going to a tavern to bide time so they won't have to confront the possibility of failure or joy.

It seems to me there is essentially something healthy about any organism, and there's lots around it and within it that are unhealthy; things that can kill it, that stop it from being that organism. If you perceive the essential self in yourself and others, then that is what you reinforce, and it doesn't have to do with measuring the quality or quantity, or whether it's big or small. We have to be more accommodating to what is already there.

NETWORKING RESOURCES

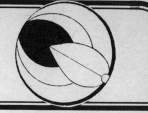

Encyclopedia of Associations
Gale Research Co.
Book Tower
Detroit, Mi. 48226
What on Earth are we doing? Looking through the 14,000 entries is a sound lesson in grouping/community and networks. Daughters of the King, National Jogging Assoc., Better Light, Better Sight Bureau, Grinding Wheel Institute, Wood Tank Assoc., Purple Plum Assoc., Society of Flavor Chemists, Titanic Enthusiasts of America . . . not sure what all filters they use, but it is a large information base; useful for locating interest and information as well as a metaphysical wonder. Vol 1 costs $55, Vol. 2, Geographic and Executive Index, is $38, and the quarterly supplement is $48. Most libraries have copies.

Social Networks, J.A. Barnes, 1972, $1.25 from:
Cummings Publishing Co.
2727 Sandhill Road
Menlo Park, CA 94025
A good introduction to network theories in the social sciences.

Smallholder, $4/year, monthly, from:
General Delivery
Argenta, BC, Canada
One of the best examples of a two-way information exchange network newsletter. Just people sharing what they are learning while farming and traveling through seasons.

Synchronicity, C.G. Jung, 1960, $2.45 from:
Princeton University Press
41 William Street
Princeton, NJ 08540
Synchronicity is the meaningful coincidence of two or more events where something other than the probability of chance is involved.

1977 Meeting on Networks
c/o Christian De Laet
Concordia University
Montreal, Quebec, Canada H4B 1R6
This looks like it's going to be the watershed event for networks/networking. The goal is to bring together the network theoreticians with the "practitioners." The conference proposal itself is a very useful document about networks, and I imagine when the proceedings are published they will serve as a good overview on networks.

Cascadian Regional Library (CAREL)
P.O. Box 1492
Eugene, OR 97401
Cascadian Regional Library was formed in the spring of 1976 by Brian Livingston and Marshall Landman and others during the time they were organizing an annual Northwest-wide, small-scale, alternative communications conference. The goals of the library include maintaining keysorted lists of alternative groups and individuals, sponsoring of conferences, publications of directories and support of regional couriers to connect urban and rural centers. Send $1 for Compu-sort indexing manual and a list of publications, including the *Leap Year Papers*—see Sharing and Gathering.

"A Communications Network for Change in Higher Education" in *On Learning and Social Change*, Michael Rossman, 1972, $10 from:
Random House
201 East 50th
New York, NY 10022
A good summary of that amazing group of networks developed around science fiction and fantasy magazines and books.

The Morning of the Magicians, Louis Pauwels, Jacques Bergier, 1968, $1.25 from:
Avon Books
959 Eighth Ave.
New York, NY 10019
Pauwels and Bergier weave an amazing overview of the history of ideas, finding many missing pictures from the usual historical records, and a good deal of their version of the world is based, as they say, on intelligence being a kind of secret society.

Denver Open Network
762 Lafayette
Denver, CO 80218
The network is a fairly recent example of a loose coalition that shares in loose fashion, with minimum overseeing and centralizing of functions. They publish a newsy newsletter about things going on in the network and in Denver.

*See the Agriculture section for several pages on Food Distribution Networking. And see the Appropriate Technology section for details on that growing network.

Movement for a New Society
4722 Baltimore Ave.
Philadelphia, PA 19143
A network of over two dozen groups around the country seeking a decentralized movement for non-violent revolution. With a foundation in the work of the American Friends Service Committee, these groups were formed several years ago, and represent one of the most evolved forms of tribes of individuals sharing resources and goals. A theoretical guide to their works can be found in *Working Papers for a New Society*, $10/year from 123 Mt. Auburn St., Cambridge, MA 02138.

Yearbook of World Problems and Human Potential, Union of International Associations (and) Mankind 2,000, $65 from:
1 Rue Aux Laines
1000 Brussels, Belgium
1,000 pages. This is a phenomenal work. It is the first comprehensive attempt (real time and not just abstract and theoretical) to match up world problems with groups who say they are attempting to solve them. It is a difficult indexing job to produce and make visible such a complex situation (I mean *all* the world problems and *all* the international groups), and there are articles in the text suggesting ways out, pointing to a new visual way of conceiving of such networks.

The Harmony of Interaction, Anthony Judge, from:
Union of International Associations
1 Rue Aux Laines
1,000 Brussels, Belgium
This is one of the clearest explanations of networking on a global scale. Anthony Judge is one of the primary persons responsible for the *Yearbook of World Problems and Human Potential*. He is one of the few persons addressing the problem of how to make networks visible by uses of new mapping and graphing techniques.
"Detailed maps of networks should be as readily available as local road maps. People should be able to obtain problem atlases and problem globes."
"I would like to suggest that we are at the same stage in our problem mapping ability as we were in the Middle Ages with respect to mapping the physical characteristics of the surface of the earth."

Oregon Historical Society

COMMUNICATIONS

In the beginning was information, communicated to the one great nobody, about nothing, until Wiggle and Mess landed in the middle of nowhere and called it something, and disagreed about how to name it.

An assumption behind this catalog is the primariness of information. It is prior to the food to eat or energy and technology to improve the quality of our lives. It is invisible until you let yourself pretend it is everything.

Information and communications

are often looked upon as a process, or means toward an end, and some of us who treat information and communications as a goal in itself are guilty of just talking.

This section and community building, treat information and communications as an end itself. It is:
* getting the right information to the right persons at the right time
* about coincidences and synchronicity
* about how to keep track of people

and ideas (and not suffer information overload)
* about the flow of ideas into actions
* about: how many times have you asked yourself, "now why didn't I know about this before?"
* of the mysterious way things work and don't work
* finding each other
* the lighted corridors between disciplines where the history of ideas evolves
* friendships and coalitions

"Everything is there: the minute history of the future, the autobiographies of the archangels, the faithful catalogue of the library, thousands and thousands of false catalogues, a demonstration of the fallacy of the true catalogue, the Gnostic gospel of Basilides, the commentary on this gospel, the commentary on the commentary on this gospel, the veridical account of your death, a version of each book in all languages, the interpolations of every book in all books.

"When it was proclaimed that the library comprised all books, the first impression was one of extravagant joy. All men felt themselves lords of a secret intact treasure. There was no personal or universal problem whose eloquent solution did not exist—in some hexagon. The universe was justified, the universe suddenly expanded to the limitless dimensions of hope. . . .

"But the searcher did not remember that the calculable possibility of a man's finding his own book, or some perfidious variation of his own book, is close to zero. . . .

"The uncommon hope was followed naturally enough by deep depression. The certainty that some shelf in some hexagon contained precious books and that these books were inaccessible seemed almost intolerable."

Library of Babel, Jorge Luis Borges

"One-to-one communications media such as telephone and letters create no new links, while one-to-many connections such as television, newspapers and bureaucracies inevitably restrict the flow of information through their offices. Since political and economic power follows the lines of communication, the potential for abuse is tremendous. A large pool of information, freely accessible and amendable through public computer terminals, is one of the few systems proposed for many-to-many communications."

Journal of Community Communications

"Many old maxims point out that talk is cheaper than action. A comparison of the entropy balance and the energy balance on the surface of the earth indicates that the maxims are indeed a reflection of our experience. The amplification of information is easier than the amplification of power."

Scientific American, Sept. '71

"Ambiguity seems to be an essential, indispensible element for the transfer of information from one place to another by words. Where matters of real importance are concerned, it is often necessary, for meaning to come through, that there be an almost vague sense of strangeness and askewness."

Lives of a Cell, Lewis Thomas

Information Mantra

"If, when you get a number on the telephone, you give a message, the message remains the same, even if you give it to a wrong number. The result of such an error in the brain is very different. Supposing some vinegar comes in contact with one of the sensitive end organs of taste in the tip of your tongue and "gets a wrong number"—that is, say, supposing the nerve fibre conducting the impulse provoked by the vinegar, instead of connecting with its proper reception area, becomes in some way cut and grafted onto a nerve fibre leading from the ear to the brain—what do you think you would taste? You would taste nothing. You would hear a very loud and startling noise."

The Living Brain, Grey Walter

"Public channels of communication include newspapers, radio, and television. Private channels are largely conversations and, to a slight extent, personal letters. People find information from private channels to be more significant to them than what is spread in the public channels. There are several possible reasons for this. For one thing, people judge the validity of the information by using their evaluation of the speaker providing the information. If the speaker is credible, so is what he is saying. Another reason that private channels may be favored is that they are specific. If one asks a question of a friend, he does not have to wade through a great deal of extraneous information to obtain the answer. Public channels do not allow for immediate feedback on the value or appropriateness of the information, while private channels do. Finally, private channels may be valued for the affective support they give, as well as for the information they provide. When a person has a serious problem, he may value support and sympathy as much as information in resolving the difficulty."

Robin D. Crickman, in
Community Information Needs

Of every $5 spent in the United States in the early 1970s on goods, services, construction and new machines, more than $1 was allocated to an information service of some kind.

"There are neural centers for generating, spontaneously, numberless hypotheses about the facts of life. We store up information the way cells store energy. When we are lucky enough to find a direct match between a receptor and a fact, there is a deep explosion in the mind; the idea suddenly enlarges, rounds up, bursts with new energy, and begins to replicate. At times there are chains of reverberating explosions, shaking everything: the imagination, as we say, is staggered."

Lives of a Cell, Lewis Thomas

Peter and Trudy Johnson-Lenz live in a small home just south of Portland, Oregon. They are a fairly rare example of a life and work partnership where personal and public commitments are (most of the time) balanced.

Most often from their home, by mail, telephone and computer, they stay in touch with groups and individuals around the country—exemplifying McLuhan's understanding that in the communication era everyone can be a center.

Their work is an important cross-discipline bridge—spanning interests in education (Trudy was an editor of Teacher Paper), *humane application of computer technology, citizen participation, networking, language, social science and spiritual*

awareness. They have developed several community computer programs. Documentation is available from them (695 Fifth St., Lake Oswego, OR 97034). "Graphing and Mapping Community Points of View" ($3) and "Neighborhood Information System" ($3).

They have recently completed a computer program for the Community Issues Dialog Project of the Northwest Regional Foundation.

Rhoda and I visited with Peter and Trudy in November (1976) to talk about the RAINBOOK. Their input is scattered throughout this section and Community Building. The following are excerpts from that afternoon's conversation. (SJ)

BRIDGES, FIELDS and the OMEGA POINT

S: So, how did we get into this information and networking thing?

P: As I've become fascinated with one thing or another, as I've ventured into the interdisciplinary morass where there's all these confusions, and all these things which seem related but not too many people are talking about the apparent relation, I've found myself getting more and more interested in those relationships rather than the specifics. The general rules. I think what it is to some degree is sheer frustration. The more and more I've gotten into specifics of the world, the more I recoil in frustration at its variety—to some ways of understanding what lies underneath it so I can work my way through it so I don't get overloaded with all the details.

It's important to reduce the spurious variety, like there are lots of things that are the same, but people call them different names. They are talking about the same thing. Sometimes because of narrow disciplines. Like all these technical books we have—I have an intuition they're all thinking about the same things, but they've gotten so convoluted in talking to themselves for so long they can't see that.

T: I think, too, the information thing is part of my own spiritual search which is a very intellectual one. I'm not a worshipper. The more I get into information the more I find myself thinking about thinking.

S: It seems I've spent most of my life looking for the *right* person, the *right* piece of information, the *right* resource, and when I look at other people and try to see if they are on the right path, I have to try to see the relative *right* in my own selection process.

P: I think our filter for finding what you call "right" for us is getting more and more refined. The more refined it gets, the more I seem to be able to draw to myself opportunities which are close approximations of what I want. The better I get, the more they *all* look good to me. All the things that come to me look good, so then I've got to narrow it down more. And when I do that I get more in the channel I narrow down my input to. It all just looks overwhelmingly desirous.

I think it's a process that we're all going through now. Complete information overload. A social network is being put together where we're all finding those connections which we need to make with other people in the world and other groups of ideas in the world. The networks are always changing; you may work in one channel for a while, and then you wander along and plug in somewhere else in a different way. And nothing is bad or good. There are places where you can transmit and receive and places where you can't.

R: So how do you relate this thing that you and some people are refining? How does it, or could it, play a part in everyday, common situations?

P: I run through that question a lot. I don't think there's some way I would just scrawl on a piece of paper, or even a little video-holographic presentation to present to a person in a grocery store what they are ready to hear. People can hear only what they want to hear. Our work is always a balance between what we think people are ready to hear, their perceived needs, with another part of ourselves which is always reaching out. Sometimes we act as a bridge or spark. Sometimes we just muck around until we find some resonance.

T: What we do, to share this information, and theories, and what we are learning is similar to what we did today in order to talk about the *RAINBOOK*. We reduce the list of all the things we think about, know about, talk about, considerably. If you were coming here for the first time we would reduce it still farther—and probably not drag out all this stuff (books, files, reports).

P: We have often made mistakes by talking about too much, and made people bored, confused or scared. When Trudy and I came together for the first time we had the incredible experience of finding each other. We shared conversations for a few hours, and in those hours we were testing each other with words and gestures. The more we tested, the more we found it was like being home. It was like having an index you understood.

S: That'd make a great cartoon, "At last, an index I understand." It's like a private language or shorthand.

S: Can someone give me a better idea of the use of the word "network" as it is used in mathematics, and as it's related to your work in "Mapping and Graphing Community Points of View?"

P: Networking is a term that's getting quite popular, in the sense of social and sharing networks, but there's a whole other

group of people who use networks to mean something else, academic mathematicians who have developed mathematical theories about how networks operate.

I worked on a project in California where these mathematical theories were applied to a study of cliques, networks, grouping patterns in a grade school. We were asking questions like: name the three people you play with the most; the three people you like most; the three people you'd like to sit next to most.

Answers to these questions give you a "socio-gram." If you put a dot on a piece of paper for each person and then draw lines corresponding to who they like, you have a socio-gram. It's also called a direct-a-graph because the arrows point in a given direction—like I might choose you, but you might not choose me, so the arrow or line would only go one way.

Graph theory, which is a branch of topology, specifically direct-a-graph theory, is a pretty well-developed mathematics that even has definitions for a clique; they call it a "strong component," which is a group of people in which any one person can be reached from every other person. . . .

T: It's another way of describing a karass.

P: The pure mathematicians are mostly concerned with the dots and arrow only, not what they mean, or how they are applied.

T: They use the same kind of technology, such as the "strong component" definition, in things like cognitive policy models for foreign policies. It doesn't have to be people.

P: So a direct-a-graph is an iconic, visual way of having something to talk about. And it relies heavily on the topological, mathematical graph theoretical constructs that allow the computer to operate. The question is: when you eyeball a direct-a-graph, just what do you have to do in order to, for example, pick out a clique. It is very exhausting work, especially if you are handling a lot of information.

The mathematics of graph theory is a mathematical way of doing that tiring "eyeballing" of the information displayed by a direct-a-graph. If you were to find the cliques by hand (or by eye) you might be asking yourself things like:

pick an element

trace all the arrows from that element

make a list of all the elements that are reached.

so you end up with a bunch of lists

now you say, OK, did you get back to the original element you started from? Whenever you did, then you have defined a clique.

The computer can do this kind of searching quite simply. So in "Mapping and Graphing Community Points of View" and the work we're doing on the Community Issue Dialog Project, we're attempting to devise ways that the computer can make the visual information—made available through using direct-a-graphs—easier to access and accessible to the people participating in the community dialogue.

T: People can only keep about seven things in their mind at one time, and maybe by using certain visual symbols of people's belief spaces or problems we represent something so you can think of more parts at one time and see the interrelationships.

P: In the *Yearbook of World Problems*, and other places, Anthony Judge talks about using a computer to present people with three-dimensional visual indexes to information. So you look at the computer and see some central idea you've thought of, and see the branches from your idea to all the other close, related ideas. And you say, OK, computer, let's drive down this branch here, towards these ideas, and see what we run into. You visually experience going through the network of ideas.

T: If each node in the network were the same, each one, that is, was a holographic representation of the whole network —does this suddenly become a "field." There's a question of what's the relationship between fields and networks. Is a holographic network a field?

S: What's a field?

P: Networks are very rigid structures, with points and lines. A field is more diffuse, more everywhere, more non-local, and non-specific. There're examples from physics like gravity fields, magnetic, and examples from the spiritual world like auras.

S: So what do visual representations of fields look like? What if you rename your paper on "Mapping and Graphing Community Points of View" to "Mapping and Fielding Community Points of View"?

P: Well, it would probably be the omega point.

One of the characteristics of a holograph is that each point in the holograph contains information about the whole image. If you cut a photograph in half, half the photo will be gone. If you do it with a hologram, unh unh, the whole picture is there; it's just a little foggier. So a holographic network would be where all the information is available at any point. If you think the jet plane reduced the size of the earth, this fantasy holographic network would make the world a point, maybe de Chardin's omega point, in which we are all one, within no time and space.

R: I've never heard anything so ridiculous in all my life.

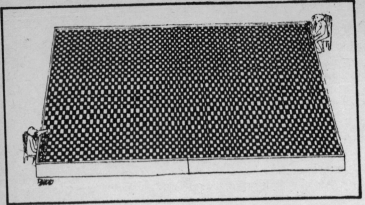

Problem solving is a kind of directed thinking that is somewhere between consciously driving your mental engine so you won't run into others on the same, or intersecting, road or path and thinking creatively, utilizing the most rested, spontaneous, creative, chance-taking frame of mind.

There is much research being done in the area, especially in management or systems science. Some of the theories and concepts may only sound like common sense dressed in new and expensive jargon, but also, as Peter Johnson-Lenz says, it may be a whole new and necessary way of coping with problems we create as we become more conscious of individual and cultural "points of view," and the interrelatedness of disciplines or sciences that have previously been isolated.

Problem Solving

The Universal Traveler, Don Koberg and Jim Bagnall, 1974, $4.95 from:
William Kaufmann, Inc.
1 First St.
Los Altos, CA 94022

This is probably the book most likely to open the door to the possibilities of problem solving kinds of thinking. Its digestible pieces format, full of big graphics, lists, wide-ranging content, could be applied to both persons needing to work in groups, to do group think, to reach a goal, get work done, or solve problems; as well, though it can be used like *What Color Is Your Parachute* to think about how to size up the journey of life like it's a stuck car with the tide coming in.

You could go from this book to most any others listed with clear ideas on how the ideas can relate to you in your own life.

Experiences in Visual Thinking, Robert H. McKim, 1972, $9.95 from:
Brooks/Cole Publishing Co.
Monterey, CA 93940

If I were to recommend two books for follow-up to ideas in this section, it would be this and the *Universal Traveler*. It is filled with exciting discoveries about mental processes, many practical down-home skills for working through abstractions, extensive annotated bibliographies. A work that brings together several fields of study, including systems science, brain sciences and artistic creation.

Strange and Familiar, $6.67 postpaid from:
Synectics Education Systems
121 Brattle St.
Cambridge, MA 02138

When we notice the differences and similarities between two things we are learning there's an odd sensation that accompanies trying to relate "incongruities"—maybe it's the physical effects of stretching the imagination. Many of the 1-2-page exercises in *Strange and Familiar* stretch the imagination: "Which is a better dessert, a sweet lemon or a sour banana? (Circle your choice and tell why you made it.)"

A lot of the exercises in *Strange and Familiar*, as in the rest of several series, expand a theory of teaching by the use of metaphor, improving our ability to make connections. It is an important form of poetic and scientific discipline, exercise and game.

"But if you tame me, it will be as if the sun came to shine on my life. I shall know the sound of a step that will be different from all the others. Other steps send me hurrying back underneath the ground. Yours will call me, like music, out of my burrow. And then look: you see the grain fields down yonder? I do not eat bread. Wheat is of no use to me. The wheat fields have nothing to say to me. And that is sad. But you have hair that is the color of gold. Think how wonderful that will be when you have tamed me! The grain, which is also golden, will bring me back the thought of you." (From *The Little Prince*)

Communication In Organization, Everett M. Rogers and Rekha Agarwala-Rogers, 1976, $4.95 from:
Free Press
866 Third Ave.
New York, NY 10022

This book is a fairly technical or academic analysis of the specific nature of communication that takes place in organizations. A good review of the general concepts, with a section on the place of networks in organizational structure.

How to Solve It, G. Polyai, 1971, $2.95 from:
Doubleday & Company
501 Franklin Street
Garden City, NY 11531

Contains a checkpoint for brainstormers. " 'Inventor's Paradox:' The more ambitious plan may have more chances of success. When passing from one problem to another we may often observe that the new, more ambitious problem is easier to handle than the original problem." (*The Last Whole Earth Catalogue*)

Machine Design, "Creativity by Committee," December 12, 1974, Vol. 46, No. 30, from:
Penton Plaza
1111 Chester Avenue
Cleveland, OH 44114

An example of how brainstorming techniques are being modified to suit contemporary use in various fields.

Diagrams, Arthur Lockwood, 1969, $15 from:
Watson-Guptill Publications
165 West 46th Street
New York, NY 10036

A historical survey of conceptual diagrams/maps. Provides useful models on how to manipulate the concept in graphic form.

By George Bain with acknowledgements to the unknown Pictish artist of the horse on the ancient Invernairie Stone.

A Sourcebook for Creative Thinking, Harold F. Harding and Sydney J. Parnes, eds., 1972, from:
Scribner's Sons
597 Fifth Avenue
New York, NY 10017

A collection from a symposium on creative thinking held at the University of Buffalo, New York, an international research center on the subject.

Change, Principles of Problem Formation and Problem Resolution , Paul Waltzwick, Ph.D., and John Weakland, M.D., 1974, $7.95 from:
W.W. Norton & Co., Inc.
500 Fifth Ave.
New York, NY 10036

Brainstorming, a method of effecting important changes within institutions, often depends on the clear statement of a problem. *Change* documents some of the most paradoxical problems in history and the path to their paradoxical solutions (through paradoxical methods, of course).

The Act of Creation, Arthur Koestler, Hutchinson Press, London, 1966, $2.75, available from:
Dell Publishing Co., Inc.
750 Third Ave.
New York, NY 10017

Presents a cognitive-perceptual model which relates humor to the creative process.

The Psychology of Consciousness, Robert E. Ornstein, 1972, $4.00 from:
W.H. Freeman & Company
660 Market St.
San Francisco, CA 94104

Ornstein sidesteps some of the knots of ontology, teleology, et al. to provide a lucid and intriguing perspective on the puzzle of the way we think.

Training Creative Thinking, Gary A. Davis, 1963, $5.50 from:
Holt, Rinehart & Winston
New York, NY 10017
Documents brainstorming studies carried on largely through industry.

The Journal of Creative Behavior
New York State University College
1300 Elmwood Ave.
Buffalo, NY 14222
Published quarterly. Belongs in the bibliography of well-regarded periodicals on the subject of creative thinking.

Fair Witness, Mesirow & Albright, from:
2136 N.E. 20th
Portland, OR 97212

I've found that some of the most mind boggling uses of video taping is in group and individual behavior feedback. When you first see yourself on tape (especially revealing when it's immediate, I suppose because we remember more about the reality), there's this second or two when you don't think it's you but some slow-moving, animated fake only pretending to be you.

Fair Witness is a communication service for groups, developed by David Mesirow and David Albright, with computer software development by Peter and Trudy Johnson-Lenz.

A group decides it would like to know more about how they work together in meetings, so they record information about how they think meetings should proceed and how they actually do; this information is logged into a computer, programmed to compare how a group ought to work together and how it actually does.

While the meeting is videotaped, a person is recording observations about different behaviors they see. Each observation is assigned a number which corresponds to a place on the video tape computer graphic displays showing when certain behaviors took place. This is compared with the videotapes, which can then serve as "fair witness," proving or disproving the observations of the recorder.

What Color Is Your Parachute?, Richard Nelson Bolles, 1973, $4.95 from:
Ten Speed Press
Box 4310
Berkeley, CA 94704
This and *Where Do I Go With My Life From Here?*, also by Bolles, mainly emphasize job hunting, career searching, but they are excellent models of overviewing life, transforming ideas into actions, and guides or maps to directing our wandering minds toward goals and solutions.

Galton's Walk, Herbert C. Crovitz, 1970, $2.95 from:
Harper & Row
10 E. 53rd
New York, NY 10022
I still return to this book now and then to remember how my mind works, especially its idea of remembering things. Fascinating section on mnemonists (people with super memories).

Yearbook of World Problems and Human Potential, $59.95 from:
Union of International Associations
& Mankind 2000
1 Rue Aux Laines
1000 Brussels, Belgium
This book, or directory, or Thesaurus, or dictionary is at the other end of the spectrum from the *Universal Traveler* It was four years in the making and represents the most extensive work done to date on interrelating worldwide problems with groups working on solutions to these problems. It is as inspiring in concept as in actualization. It may be something you can actually use, but it's as likely that half an hour with it will give you another way of looking at the world. Also contains some good stuff by Anthony Judge on mapping complexity.

The Staff Burn Out Syndrome, $1.25 from:
The Drug Abuse Council, Inc.
1828 L Street, N.W.
Washington, DC 20036
This small booklet hints at something real important. Burning out has become one of those expected, but relatively new, working group routines. People burn out about with the same frequency as meteors hitting the earth and, taken as a wave of movements, especially among small, kind-of-volunteer, non-profit, social change, social crisis, experimentally-managed groups, the waves created by the burnout cycle are one of the basic influences on social change. People burn out, others take over, and the people that burn out show up later, as the same or different people, with new ideas, different outlooks.

"As I suggested earlier, there are physical signs of burn-out and there are also behavioral and psychological signs. For example, the person who used to be a talker now remains silent; he used to contribute to staff meetings but now just sits in a corner and says nothing. Why? He may have become fatigued, bored, resentful, disenchanted, discouraged, confused. He feels futile and fed up and cannot talk about it."

Lateral vs. Vertical Thinking

A few years ago, a now well-known book, *Lateral Thinking in Management*, by Edward de Bono (American Management Association, 1971), outlined the importance of lateral thinking in solving management problems. *Lateral Thinking* was characterized by discontinuity, far-fetchedness, lack of practicality, and the generation of a large quantity of ideas; while *vertical thinking*, derived from the Greeks, emphasizes logical continuity, probability, limitation.

Systems Thinking, ed. by F.E. Emery, 1970, $4.95 from:
> Penguin Books, Inc.
> 72 Fifth Ave.,
> New York, NY 10011

I've found this to be the most accessible introduction to the field of systems science. The materials range from overview to technical and include Ashby's *Self Regulation and Requisite Variety*. It is oriented toward management in business but also includes things like "The Theory of Open Systems in Physics and Biology."

Thinking Straighter, George Henry Moulds, $4.75 from:
> William C. Brown Co.
> 2460 Kerper Blvd.
> Dubuque, IA 52001

Has good analysis of linguistic traps that are laid during social, group and political intercourse.

Thinking With a Pencil, Henny Nelms, 1964, $2.75 from:
> Barnes and Noble Inc.
> 10 East 53rd
> New York, NY 10022

This book has begun to help me overcome the feeling that I'll never be able to do anything but scribble words. Many clues on how to draw simple pictures.

Northwest Regional Foundation
> Box 5296
> Spokane, WA 99205

NRF publishes *Futures Conditional* ($20/year), a good resource for activities in citizen participation, community issues dialogues, group facilitation processes and systems/futures thinking. NRF has hands-on experience in these areas, working on citizen participation projects in the Spokane area.

Society for General Systems Research
> 12613 Bunting Lane
> Bowie, MD 20715

One of the primary groups involved in the study of systems and cybernetics. Their *General Systems Yearbook* is considered a state of the art resource.

COMPUTER CONFERENCING

Computer conferencing is a technique that utilizes the increasing network of computer terminals accessible over great distances by phone lines to facilitate communication among people in, for example, planning, joint proposal writing, inter-group, inter-corporation memo keeping, and problem solving.

Though the technology is still out of reach for many, the altered state of communication the method creates, similar to the Delphi Method, may hold some potential solutions to transportation energy excesses, as well as a possible evolution in our normal ways of talking to each other. Consider:

1) The ideas being exchanged may be considered on their merit alone without the additional input of the speakers' "body language" (which obviously sometimes is equally disadvantageous).

2) Participants may leave the discussion at will and re-enter without losing out on anything, since it is all retained by the computer.

3) A participant, if asked a difficult question, can take his time answering, and even go to the library or bathroom to think about it.

4) The technique allows for people to transmit both public and private messages, so in a sense you can talk to everyone and at the same time whisper something to an individual.

5) You can enter anonymous comments that, if you brought them up in physical conference, might disrupt the flow of the group mind.

*For access to further information about computer conferencing, see the Computer section in Communications Technology.

DELPHI AND COMPUTER CONFERENCING

There are times when directly confronting problems among people in a physical space may only result in further misunderstanding or division.

In a simple sense the delphi method of discussing ideas, reaching decisions, or disseminating information is illustrated by an everyday method of communication. When we write something down, instead of communicating orally, it is often because we either want several or many people to be able to see it, in their own time and place, and because what we have to say can be looked at without all the additional personal information we convey just by being present with another.

The delphi method may be as simple as a kind of chain letter among friends in which an idea, a report or proposal, or a problem or conflict is stated by one person and circulated. The feedback from the original circulation may then be written up, and further circulated until some kind of agreement is reached.

"One of the essential parts of a Delphi Process is anonymity of the participants. If you can just toss an idea into the process people have to just deal with the idea per se, and not who you are, your professional credentials, or whatever. Group dialog processes using electronic voting mechanisms are also anony-

mous. No one knows who pushed which button, but everyone knows what the overall group mind thinks. Anonymity has advantages at times, to bring out people who aren't so sophisticated or don't have an adept or complex, evolved way of relating ideas." (Peter Johnson-Lenz)

The Delphi Method: Techniques and Applications, Harold Lindstone and M. Turoff, Addison-Wesley Books
A comprehensive introduction to the Delphi and related techniques of exchanging information.

The best place to get the most scoop is from:

Futures, $26/year individuals, $39/year institutions, from:
> 300 East 42nd
> New York, NY 10017

The Futurist, $10/year from:
> The World Futures Society
> 4916 St. Elmo Ave.
> Washington, DC 20014

BRAINSTORMING

Apparently it is not good—and indeed it hinders the creative work of the mind —if the intellect examines too closely the ideas already pouring in, as it were, at the gates. . . . In the case of the creative mind, it seems to me, the intellect has withdrawn its watchers from the gates, and the ideas rush in pell-mell, and only then does it review and inspect the multitude. You worthy critics, or whatever you call yourselves, are ashamed or afraid of the momentary and passing madness which is found in all real creators, the longer or shorter duration of which distinguishes the thinking artist from the dreamer."
(From Sigmund Freud, *The Basic Writings of Sigmund Freud*, ed. by A.A. Brill (New York: Random House, 1938), p. 193.

by Anita Helle

Brainstorming began to denote a group thinking process during the thirties. Alex Osborne, of the ad agency Batten, Barton, Durstine & Osborne, pioneered the use of a brainstorming technique, in part as a way of demystifying the creative process. Osborne's approach was "originally a random search method; requiring no advance preparation, it was frequently misdirected, therefore unproductive." In the 1950s, large corporations like Rand and Boeing began to hire so-called "high-creativity" individuals for their "think tanks." *But successful group brainstorming does not, in fact, require highly creative thinkers.* The essence of the brainstorming process lies in the combination of perspectives and talents exercised in a positive atmosphere of trust. (From "Creativity by Committee" by Ronald C. Pellman, in *Machine Design*, December 12, 1974, Volume 46, No. 30.

The object of a brainstorming session is to produce a maximum number of ideas.

SELECT GROUP MEMBERS

Depends, in part, on your purpose

Creativity is not a criterion. The brainstorming process produces ideas for folks like us.

Different interests/experiences should be represented. Invite people with opposing viewpoints. Balance the group in terms of those who are acquainted and those who aren't acquainted. The right amount of tension can result in a state of "creative instability," in which people are stimulated to express themselves, but not inhibited by the expressions of others.

STATE THE PROBLEM

State the problem in a single sentence Write it on the chalkboard or on butcher paper where it will be visible throughout the session.

After the statement has been drawn up by the group, the facilitator should *ask for confirmation*: Is this the way we want to state the problem?

PREPARATION

Determine a location. A relaxed but interesting atmosphere, preferably new to most participants, stands the best chance of encouraging fresh perspectives.

Determine a time. The first and last days of the work week are not usually the best times to get the group's undivided attention. A poll of our office suggests that morning rather than afternoon may be a preferred time for idea-spinning. Many sessions will, by necessity, have to be held during evening hours or on Saturdays.

Should a briefing document be prepared? Is it necessary to provide participants with background information?

APPOINT A FACILITATOR

The facilitator should be a good communicator, able to prevent some members from dominating and some from holding back, able to stimulate and restate ideas without taking sides.

STIMULATE FANTASIES

Encourage wild ideas

Encourage humor

Defer judgment. Approving and disapproving comments are not allowed. Even if someone says "that's a great idea," spontaneity is interrupted. A disapproving statement expressed too early can squelch an idea which might later unfold.

The question of *how to encourage the expression of ideas* demands sensitivity on the part of the facilitator to the size and composition of the group. Here simple how-to-do-it formulas break down, and the importance of choosing a good facilitator is re-emphasized.

Bionics refers to using natural systems as analogies for man-made systems. The notion of radar, for example, was stimulated in part by an understanding of how selective vision operates in frogs. A brainstorming problem might be stated in terms of an analogy which might be easier for group participants to understand, and which might produce fresh perspectives. The food chain relationship between rabbits and predators might become an analogue for the consumer-producer relationship in human systems. (From Gary Davis, *The Psychology of Problem-Solving*, pp. 128-131)

The Map Is Not The

The very meaning of "survival" becomes different when we stop talking about the survival of something bounded by the skin and start to think of the survival of the system of ideas in circuit. The contents of the skin are randomized at death and the pathways within the skin are randomized. But the ideas, under further transformation, may go on out in the world in books or works of art. Socrates as a bio-energetic individual is dead. But much of him still lives a component in the contemporary ecology of ideas.

Gregory Bateson

担 Earth (sign not very well drawn — left lower stroke should be **at** bottom) + the foregoing = level plain, wide horizon.

Every so often when the sun shines around here I'm aware, each time with some amazement, how thick the air is with curlicues and specks—pieces of our fairly orderly world falling apart, drifting about.

And so, too, every so often—sometimes for periods of months—my attention is drawn to the language between me and myself, me and others in the world.

Does the the world change first and pull language after it, or does a new awareness of language suddenly make us see the world differently?

Historically, in the West, language became an overt object of attention to philosophers around the turn of the century. There was a turning away from the Romantic philosophical tradition (represented by Henri Bergson, Friedrich Nietzsche and others). The new analytic philosophy, with centers of gravity in England and Vienna, struck out for a more "down to earth," approachable goal. Philosophers like Bertrand Russell, A. N. Whitehead, A. J. Ayer, G. E. Moore, herded philosophy toward analysis of philosophical language.

By far one of the most complicated and interesting paths was taken by Ludwig Wittgenstein. His books, mostly transcripts of lecture notes, are often painfully—and sometimes unintentionally humorously—complicated.

"Now there is no objection to calling a particular sensation 'the expectation that B will come.' There may even be good practical reasons for using such an expression. Only mark: if we have explained the meaning of the phrase 'expecting that B will come' in this way, no phrase which is derived from this by substituting a different name for B is thereby explained . . ."

At first glance, one of Wittgenstein's underlying themes, "The limits of my language are the limits of my world," sounds like a blatant mental steady state. But, on the other hand (that's one of those expressions?), it is a place to begin; until we know something about it and at least spot the bloomin' borderline between ourselves, the metaphysics implicit in our language and use and the real(?) world, we are perhaps stalking termites with pick-up trucks.

Greatly influenced by the analytic philosophy tradition and occurring almost simultaneously, the science of general semantics begins to grow.

In 1933 Alfred Korzybski published *Science and Sanity*, which was eventually to bring to life a perspective on social/psychological life referred to as general semantics. Like the analytic philosophers, Korzybski was influenced by the swelling awareness of applications of the scientific method—it appeared to be the only way to get *real* results. He attempted to outline a study of man through seeking descriptions and formulas that would point to the relation between language in brain and language in mind.

Korzybski saw the possibilities that are only becoming technically feasible of scientific analysis of language on the surface, as it falls from tongues in relation to the accompanying neurological occurrences.

Very often since, the twenties' semantics has come to mean something more like the study of the ambiguity of language—often as applied in the political sphere—a worthwhile study in its own right, but not nearly as holistic as Korzybski was describing:

"A process accompanying our words which one might call 'the process of meaning them' is the modulation of the voice in which we speak the words; or one of the processes similar to this, like the play of facial expressions."

One of the major influences in the study of language has been the in-depth studies of families of languages. We have always learned a great deal by comparing one language to another; but it's only been recently that elaborate comparisons have been made between languages with little or no direct contact with one another. It is then the culture shock sets in, and language appears like a metaphysical structure that is indeed the limits of *our* world.

Every language and every well-knit technical sublanguage incorporates certain points of view and certain patterned resistances to widely divergent points of view. This is especially so if the language is not surveyed as a planetary phenomenon, but is as usual taken for granted, and the local parochial species of it is used by the individual thinker and is taken to be its final sum.

Benjamin Whorf

 Sun above line of horizon = dawn.

It was found that the background linguistic system (in other words, the grammar) of each language is not merely a reproducing instrument for voicing ideas but rather itself the shape of ideas, the program and guide for the individual's mental activity, for his analysis of impressions, for his synthesis, of his mental stock in trade.

Benjamin Whorf

What this brings to general semantics and analytic philosophy is a wider perspective, for the laws of correct, clear, meaningful maps of the territories are dependent not on simplifying all languages to one that "makes sense" but to create an ever-increasing synthesis of cultural points of view.

 One who binds three planes: heaven, earth and man = ruler, to rule.

The Hopi Indian language is better adapted than our own to the exact sciences. It contains words representing not verbs or nouns, but events, and is thus more applicable to the space-time continuum in which we now know that we are living. Furthermore, the "event-word" has three moods: certitude, probability, imagination. Instead of saying: a man crossed the river in a boat, the Hopi would employ the group: man-river-boat in three different combinations, according to whether the event was observed by the narrator, reported by a third party, or dreamt.

From *Morning of the Magicians.*

Territory

Chinese Written Character as a Medium for Poetry, ed. by Ezra Pound, $1.25:
> City Lights Books
> 1562 Grant Ave.
> San Francisco, CA 94133

"A true noun, an isolated thing, does not exist in nature. Things are only the terminal points, or rather the meeting points, of actions, cross-sections cut through actions, snapshots. Neither can a pure verb, abstract motion, be possible in nature. The eye sees noun and verb as one: things in motion, motion in things."

"All processes in nature are interrelated; and thus there could be no complete sentence (according to this definition) save one which it would take all time to pronounce."

An introductory trip through the difference between a phonetic (English) and a symbol/image language like Chinese.

 Man + fire = messmate.

The Morning of the Magician, by Louis Pauwels, Jacques Bergier, Avon Books, $1.25

"We are not thinking of an organized society, but of the establishment of the necessary contacts between exceptional minds, and a common language, not secret, but merely inaccessible to ordinary men at a given epoch in time. . . . The fate of the world could be discussed openly by ten scientists in the presence of Khruschev and the president of the United States without these gentlemen being able to understand a single word.
. . .

The Art of Awareness, J. Samuel Bois, 1973, $8.95 from:
> Wm. C. Brown Co.
> Dubuque, IA 52001

One of the best interpreters of Korzybski.

Science and Sanity, by Alfred Korzybski
> International Non-Aristotelian
>   Library Publishing Co.
>   Lakeville, CT 06039

The Institute was formed in 1938 by Korzybski. They publish a good journal, the *General Semantics Bulletin*. The last issue had two good articles, one by Gregory Bateson, the other a summary of the work of Wittgenstein.

ETC, a review of general semantics
> P.O. Box 2469
> San Francisco, CA 94126

$6/yr. The other primary semantics review.

Understanding Media, by Marshall McLuhan, McGraw-Hill

Still mind-opening. "Henri Bergson lived and wrote in a tradition of thought in which it was and is considered that language is a human technology that has impaired and diminished the values of the collective unconscious. It is the extension of man in speech that enables the intellect to detach itself from the vastly wider reality. Without language, Bergson suggests, human intelligence would have remained totally involved in the objects of its attention.

"The breaking up of every kind of experience into uniform units in order to produce faster action and change of form (applied knowledge) has been the secret of Western power over man and nature alike. . . ."

The Blue and Brown Books, by Ludwig Wittgenstein, Harper Torchbooks, $1.45
"Philosophy, as we use the word, is a fight against the fascination which forms of expression exert upon us."

Language, Thought and Reality, Selected Writings of Benjamin Lee Whorf
> M.I.T. Press
> 28 Carleton St.
> Cambridge, MA 02142

The basic introduction to comparative language studies; especially fascinating studies of Native American languages.

Water + revolve within a circle = eddy.

"The Aesthetics of Silence," in *Styles of Radical Will*, by Susan Sontag, Delta Books

A good essay on meaning of prolonged, pregnant and necessary silences—lots of overlaps with works of John Cage.

"Everyone has experience how, when punctuated by long silences, words weigh more; they become almost palpable. Or how, when one talks less, one begins feeling more fully one's physical presence in a given space. Silence undermines 'bad speech,' by which I mean dissociated speech—speech dissociated from the body (and therefore from feeling), speech not organically informed

by the sensuous presence and concrete particularity of the speaker and by the individual occasion for using language. Unmoored from the body, speech deteriorates. Silence can inhibit or counteract this tendency, providing a kind of ballast, monitoring and even correcting language when it becomes inauthentic."

The Structure of Magic, Richard Bandler and John Grinder, 1975, from:
> Science and Behavior Books
> P.O. Box 11457
> Palo Alto, CA 94306

Talks about therapy, communication, change in its relation to linguistics. A lot about asking right questions, being able to see below people's "surface structure" which they create or is created by language, to their "deep structure" that is what they are trying to say, mean to say or feel, rather than think.

Reflections on Language, Noam Chomsky, 1975, $3.95 from:
> Pantheon Books
> 201 E. 50th
> New York, NY 10022

A good introduction to the thought of Chomsky, who is a quite readable linguistic philosopher. It seems that often Chomsky's quest is to find the point of departure from naive, non-linguistic thought to sophisticated but more narrow-minded language full thought. Chomsky feels we inherit a cultural/linguistic structure, which is why we take to language like fish to water.

The Concept of Mind, Gilbert Ryle, 1949, $2.25 from:
> Barnes and Noble
> 10 East 53rd
> New York, NY 10022

Ryle is in the thick of language—you've got to be in a story problem, story-within-a-story, frame of mind to read him. He and other linguistic philosophers do not deal with neurological sources of language but rather with the implied logics and world views of commonly-used word structures. At the end of mind-boggling searches like this one is the vast silent cosmic egg, but sometimes before getting beyond language you have to wade through it.

Obviously learning doesn't have to happen in schools. Colleges such as Antioch (Yellow Springs, Ohio) and Bennington (Bennington, Vermont) have known this for years and have compulsory credited work terms for students to get experience outside of academia. In China many, many schools take in work which even the youngest students spend a portion of each day doing to help pay for school expenses. Voc Tech Schools and apprenticeship programs offer a wide variety of ways of learning skills and gaining experience beyond the traditional classroom. It's time for us to loosen up—mix practical work in with "book learning" at all different stages of our lives.

Somewhere Else: A Living Learning Catalog, 1973, $3.25 from:
    Swallow Press
    1139 S. Wabash
    Chicago, IL 60605

This catalog is now several years old, but its range has never been duplicated since. You still might be able to use it, with some frustrations from changes of address, to find some good educational resources and groups.

Taking Off, by Jennifer Eis and Don Ward, 1975, $5.95 from:
    Center for Alternatives In/To
        Higher Education
    1118 S. Harrison Road
    East Lansing, MI 48823

In the past several years a great number of colleges and universities have set up living/learning centers where students can arrange work/study programs in all manner of areas—usually non-academic. The choices range from assisting in a day care center to working in a migrant camp or living with a family in Denmark. The first half of the book is the story of the setting up of one such center at Michigan University. It contains some thoughtful observations about such things as group process and filing systems that would be useful to any sort of non-traditional organization.

The second half is a very thorough listing of programs and contacts all over the world for a wide variety of apprentice, exchange and internship programs. A useful guide for anybody wanting to burst out of the standard academic pattern to experiential learning.

Foxfire Projects
    IDEAS
    1785 Massachusetts Ave. NW
    Washington, D.C. 20036

There are over 20 magazines produced in high schools around the country more or less modeled after the Foxfire, Rabun Gap-Nacoochee high school format: transcribed interviews with people carrying on regional or rural traditions. The concept is broadened to include urban environments with such publications as *Cityscape,* produced by Western High School in Washington, D.C. For listing of all projects, write to IDEAS.

The Wheelwright's Shop, George Sturt, 1923, $6.95 from:
    Cambridge University Press
    32 E. 57th Street
    New York, NY 10022

An autobiographical account of operating a wheelwright shop in England in the late 1800s, but of greater value as a guide to the value of apprentice learning and learning by doing. The book gives a strong sense of how interdependent the designs of things become and how much greater valued are the skills of workers when there isn't so much wealth that everything can be overdone. So many things we do seem rude and awkward that it's good to get a sense of how things become more mellow and well-fitting when enough time has passed to work off the rough edges and find more complete solutions to problems.

*See the Building section for all sorts of apprentice-learning-by-doing programs such as Farallones Institute and the Goddard Social Ecology Program.

Centering, M.C. Richards, 1962, from:
    Wesleyan University Press,
    Middletown, CT 06457

This book has been around for a long time, but I only recently stumbled upon it in Lane's book piles. It deals with the real center of doing anything well—the art of making the potter, not making the pot. It's a modern Western equivalent to Coomaraswamy's *The Indian Craftsman* (Probsthain & Co., 1909, out of print), which deals with the development of a person's skills, faculties and depth through a trade. *Centering* brings alive the old Zen tale of the master who taught his students everything except painting. When their knowledge became balanced, the painting would come.

Innovative Graduate Programs Directory, 2nd Edition, April 1976, cost unknown, available from:
    Learning Resources Center
    Empire State College
    Saratoga Springs, NY 12866

In 1970-71 I published an alternate community weekly newspaper in Miami, Florida. We maintained a post office box and got on many unusual mailing lists. After the paper ceased publication, we kept the post office box and continued to receive mail. In 1974, while working as a researcher and community liaison on a public tv show for older people, I received an announcement in the post office box proclaiming a new master's degree program called Community Information Specialist. My god, I thought, that's what I am—I never knew what to call myself. And off I went.

Now there's an easier way to find a graduate program attuned to the times. This *Directory*. It's not all-inclusive, and the descriptions are incomplete (mostly from the college catalog), but it's a good place to start. The uniqueness of the programs included (in over 200 subject areas ranging from adult education to water resources management) are either graduate credit being given in a new field or external degrees in traditional fields.

While there have been guides to alternate schools and colleges, this is the first listing of experimental graduate programs, most of them on the master's degree level. The directory is arranged alphabetically by name of college or university, with a subject index referring you to the school with a program in that field. (RE)

Learning

Zephyros Education Exchange
1201 Stanyan St.
San Francisco, CA 94117

RAIN sent down a bunch of copies for inclusion in a Z box, and in exchange one day came the three latest Deschool Primers, including *The Best of Zephyros: a zillion unorthodox learning experiences* ($10). I shared the goodies with two friends who got so engrossed neither of them spoke a word for the next 30 minutes. They are all truly maps to community and personal development. SASE for a complete catalog. Some of our favories are:

No Substitute for Madness: a collection of stories, by Ron Jones.

A Child's Garden of Sex, written and illustrated by Jane Speiser, $3. Be happy to have it as an adult.

Your City Has Been Kidnapped, by Ron Jones, $1.50.

Deschool Primer 15, on food, $2.50.

Finding Community: A Guide to Community Research and Action, by Ron Jones, $3.45.

Z Box, $10, twice a year

Teacher Works
2136 N.E. 20th Ave.
Portland, OR 97212

Teacher Works began in 1971, when a group of Portland-area teachers decided to open a teacher center. That ran into problems, and so from 1972-75, Teacher Works orchestrated a national grassroots teacher exchange of curriculum materials. TW members sent in m*a*g*i*c lessons (things that work with kids), which were then printed up and sent back to members twice a year in Teacher Works in a Box. Each sheet bears an anti-copyright: "This material may be reproduced by any means as often as necessary." All 6 editions of the Box are sold out, but *The Best of Teacher Works in a Box* is available for $6.50. It contains 130 lessons, contributed by over 100 teachers, in a convenient 8-1/2" by 11" format.

Teacher Works also wants to spread the idea of a grassroots, decentralized exchange. The TW mailing list was sent to all members so they could start their own local exchanges, and TW has prepared a packet of "how-to" information to get others started (available for $1).

(Trudy Johnson-Lenz)

Seed Catalog, $5.95 from:
Beacon Press
25 Beacon St.
Boston, MA 02108

Whether you're a teacher, hermit, parent, administrator or librarian, you should look this one over. 350-plus pages of materials, organizations, ideas, devices. Emphasis is on the simpler, less expensive teaching tools. And of course they let their prejudices show. Astounding to think of the percentage of groups and materials listed here that didn't exist, say, 6 or 7 years ago. Highly recommended. Even though 2 years old—I'd probably still recommend it even 3 or 4 years from now.

Free Poster Charts and Maps, $2.95
Sources of Free Teaching Materials, $3.95 from:
Mr. Dale E. Shaffer
Library Consultant
437 Jennings Ave.
Salem, OH 44460

20 years ago I received a book called *1001 Free Things*, which started me on a life of mailing for things. It has its ups and downs. The free things are not always really free—it costs us via company expenditure for PR as passed through retail sales. And the pamphlets, charts, posters, would often sound like they would come with brass bands—and instead pieces of dull paper would arrive.

Also there are many good free things, and these guides are obviously well-researched. Good stuff for class supplements, visuals, attention getters, or for us mail freaks lots of things to send ourselves or friends. Most people, I think, would feel they could at least get their money back from buying Mr. Shaffer's guides.

The Whole Kids Catalog, created by Peter Cardozo, designed by Ten Menter, 1975, $5.95 from:
Bantam Books
666 Fifth Ave.
New York, NY 10019

Hundreds of items—mostly access through mail or retail outlets, of things to buy, make, read, cook, think about. The range is from free to expensive (such as movie making equipment): kites, puppets, science, history, photography, carpentry, gardening, pets, etc. Seems like a pretty good image of what a "kid" is—though maybe I'm burning out on access to access with emphasis on buy.

Acclimatization, Steve Van Matre, 1972, $3.95 from:
American Camping Association
Brandford Woods
Martinsville, IN 46151

If you're an environmental ed teacher, a camp counselor or naturalist, read this book or *National Geographic*, April 1974, and then attend Van Matre's workshops. It's about how crawling around in the mud and sniffing leaves can help get kids in touch with nature. I saw and felt it work wonders in Minnesota on squeamish city kids.

*And there's a whole slew of things to give people of all ages a handshake with their built and natural environments. See *Making the City Observable* in the Place section for some clues.

Of course, there is still the whole alternative schools movement: people working towards changing the institutions of learning. Here is the outermost layer of the network and a few of our very favorite resources. They will lead you on the more in-depth stuff.

The New Schools Exchange
Pettigrew, AR 72751

A national clearinghouse for a wide variety of new approaches to alternative and community education. They publish an excellent newsletter ($12/year for 10 issues) full of articles, dialogues and listings of people, places and resources. Also a *National Directory of Alternative Schools* (112 pages) available for $3 (or included in a subscription). They've been around and active for quite a while and always have a lot to say.

Applesauce, $5/yr. from:
National Alternative Schools Program
School of Education
University of Massachusetts
Amherst, MA 01002
A nice newsprint format self-described as "a blend of ideas and happenings in alternative education." The latest issue included a mammoth resource listing complied by Miriam Wasserman and Linda Hutchinson of the Education Exploration Center in Minneapolis. The next issue will focus on vocational education and some curriculum developed by an alternative school for working class women. They are also working on a '76-'77 directory of alternative schools which, judging from their '75-'76 directory, should be worth writing for.

Edcentric, $5/year individuals, $10 institutions, from:
P.O. Box 1802
Eugene, OR 97401
A radical educational quarterly linking educational change to the overall movement for social change. Past issues (60¢ each) have focused on sexism, Chicano education and working class education. Available for $1 are special issues: No. 38 from June 1976 is a good educational resource guide, and No. 37, February 1976, is on public school alternatives. Sample issues available.

No More Public School: A Manual for Innovators, by Hal Bennett, 1972, $2.95 from:
The Bookworks
1409 Fifth St.
Berkeley, CA 94710
I'm more and more convinced that I will not be able to put a child of mine into public school, so I wonder about finding or starting a good alternative. This book gives one ideas, possibilities and courage—particularly for a small endeavor (5-10, 15 kids). He describes it best himself: "This book tells how to take your child out of public school and how to educate him at home yourself. It tells how to put your own school together, which means legalities, curriculum and business stuff and minding the store once you've started. It tells about solutions for when you're in trouble . . . but it does not flirt with dreams for an easy Utopia."

The Parkway Program
Room 308, Stevens School
13th & Spring Garden Streets
Philadelphia, PA 19123
Schools don't have to be in big red brick buildings! Part of the Philadelphia Public Schools, the Parkway Program has classes taught by chemists in professional labs, bankers in conference rooms, and math in movie theaters and city parks. Doubling up on the use of facilities—making public places less specialized—can save energy and materials in countless ways and help make the city more vital. Students in Parkway are chosen by lottery, with equal numbers from each of eight districts. Send $1 for more information.

Rasberry Exercises: How to Start Your Own School (And Make a Book), Robert Greenway and Salli Rasberry, 1970, $3.95 from:
Bookworks
Whenever I'm thinking about alternative learning situations, I go back to this book. It was one of the first written and still expresses best the problems of actualizing the dreams: "It's not surprising . . . that teachers who can be clear about what free schools should *be* often seem at a loss to know what to *do* in them. No money for equipment. Children partaking of new freedoms. Everyone rejecting bad things like *knowledge, authority* and *structure*, and accepting the good things like *freedom, sharing* and *creativity*."

The School in Rose Valley: A Parent Venture in Education, Grace Rotzel, 1971, $1.25 from:
Ballantine
201 East 50th
New York, NY 10022
This is my school! Rose Valley has been going since the '30s—I was there in the '50s. We all wore dungarees, wrote plays and poetry, built tree houses and solar systems, took bird walks and baked bread. The school is always changing, but it's still going strong—nursery age through 6th grade. I'm not very objective about this book. Grace was my science teacher and responsible for a large part of what I'm doing and feeling today. But it's a beautiful account of a very fine model of what used to be called "progressive" and is now called "open" education.   (LdeM)

The Teacher Was the Sea, Michael S. Kaye, 1972, $3.95 from:
Links Books
33 West 60th St.
New York, NY 10023
This is the story of Pacific High School—a live-in community of teenagers building domes, gardening, writing poetry and generally making their way through adolescence. It is interspersed with excerpts from diaries, dialogues from meetings and wonderful photographs. All the agonies of alternative education are in process here—curriculum vs. free form, hiring/firing, student control, discipline, holding in/letting go. I learned a lot about alternative community process from this book. A very personal account.

Farallones Scrapbook, 1971, $4 from:
Bookworks
1409 Fifth St.
Berkeley, CA 94710
An oldie, but goodie, subtitled "A Memento and Manual of Our Apprenticeship in Making Places and Changing Spaces in Schools, at Home and Within Ourselves." I've heard many a teacher exclaim about its ideas—how to build cubby holes and climbing lofts, how to make a beanbag chair, a puppet theater, an inflatable. Useful for innovative classrooms and play areas for all ages and persuasions. And, yes, these are many of the same folks who've gone on to do the Farallones Institute mentioned in several other sections of this book.

DIRECTORIES

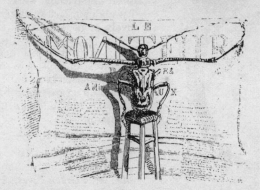

AND CATALOGS

In the last five to six years there has been a tremendous growth of a new kind of publication, the two most well-known examples being People's Yellow Pages (in various cities), and the *Whole Earth Catalog*.

There now exist so many variations on the two themes that distinctions between catalog and directory go haywire.

In recent years libraries have begun publishing community resource directories; journals like *RAIN*, *Workbook* and *Co-Evolution Quarterly* have focused on access to information, or information about information; many magazines now include special access sections; newspapers publish consumer and service directories; conferences and meetings are spawning catalogs/directories to participants, sometimes called people-to-people indexes.

I've collected directories and catalogs for the last five or six years and now find it impossible to keep track of them. Since I helped publish the *Chinook Centrex*, a community resource catalog for Portland, in 1972, there have been at least 15 directories, catalogs or guides to Portland published. (SJ)

SOME OF THE BEST ONES

The Vancouver Book, Chuck Davis, ed., $10.95 from:
J.J. Douglas Ltd.
1875 Welch Street
Vancouver, BC, Canada
The table of contents to *The Vancouver Book* felt oddly like a list I must have made sometime for the ideal cataloging of a city.

The Vancouver Book is a still shot of Vancouver, freezing (most) all the event events, systems, senses and perspectives of a city into lists, descriptions, photos, statistics, addresses and anecdotes.

Included is history (of each neighborhood), climate, soil, trees, birds, archaeology, architecture, lighting, bridges, sounds, maps, tunnels, zoning, garbage, energy, legal resources, health care, magazines, comics, theaters, bowling and cemeteries.

Chuck Davis is a lover both of maps and lists. He is now, I hear, working on a book of maps and, in the introduction, relates this:

"It all started because I'm a list freak. When I was a kid, I remember being more than usually interested in lists. I read, or made up, lists of the longest rivers, the tallest buildings, the oldest people, the widest bridges, and so on. I recall my father once telling me, "Charlie, one of these days you're going to make up a list of all your lists." I wish he were still around to see how his prediction has come true—and in a book, too."

So what do you do with a 500-page book about Vancouver, British Columbia, in Portland, Oregon?

You can think about it. Imagine freezing all the hubbub around you into one large comprehensive mural/aerial photo that allows you to see an entire city from all perspectives (including the turn of a century); maybe while it's sitting still for a minute you'll be able to pick out where you fit in.

The Vancouver Book is some kind of new animal. In my five years of looking at catalogs, lists, directories, almanacs and maps, I've not seen anything that comes as close as *The Vancouver Book* to making sense out of all the parts of a city.

People's Yellow Pages
Vocations for Social Change
Cambridge, Ma. 02139

This is the first PYP published. They have worked through many kinks. It is "alternatives" and social change oriented compared to *The Vancouver Book*, which is more like a picture, a whole picture.

People's Yellow Pages, $3 from:
P.O. Box 31291
San Francisco, Ca. 94131
That they can deal with the Bay Area is beyond me, but they are into their fourth issue, and each one slowly increases the coverage.

B.C. Alternative, $2 from:
Alternative Community Group
1520 West 6th Ave.
Vancouver, BC, Canada
This, along with the *Vancouver Book* (odd they are both from B.C. area), are examples of what is a natural evolutionary trend, the consolidation of phone book type directory with magazine and/or whole earth catalog supplements (or now: *Co-Evolution Quarterly*). Very fine job. Access to British Columbia.

North Idaho Access, $1.94 from:
Box 8367
Moscow, ID 83843
There you go, proving that you don't need cities to have need of a yellow pages; these people have created a lovely guide to services, goods, food, rivers, history, legal aid, libraries, art galleries, and on and on. If you have friends there, if you plan to visit, if you want to know what the beautiful boot filled with mountains is doing . . .

Whole City Catalog, $1.95 from:
 Synapse
 4307 Locust St.
 Philadelphia, Pa. 19104
A catalog librarian's delight. Through layout, simple geographic keys, choice headings, the catalog comes close to making a city observable.

"This catalog provides access to information. It is a community revival manual. Through sharing information, we gain power. By using it, we can return the control of communities to those who live and work within them. Through our lack of awareness and involvement we have lost this control. We have allowed, and in fact encouraged, the institutionalism of our lives. Our direction must now be away from dependence on large institutions and toward direct participation in solving problems and building self-determined communities."

*Here are some unusual twists also covered elsewhere in the book: *Philadelphia Area Green Pages: A Handbook of Tools, Information and Resources for the Greening of Philadelphia* by the Pennsylvania Horticulture Society —see Energy Conserving Landscape. And *Everything for Everybody* for a free-for-all catalog sort of newspaper in New York City. See Sharing and Gathering pages.

Part of the Earth Catalogs
The Vancouver Book is probably the best model of a regional access catalog; also notable are:
 British Columbia Access, Box 5688, Station F, Vancouver, BC, Canada.
 Carologue, access to North Carolina, Box 3337, College Station, Durham, NC 27702.
 New England Catalog, 1973, Pequot Press (out of print).
 Puget Sound Access. No longer in print; may be in a library or somewhere. It's a lovely part of the earth sensing catalog, as you'll see if you find it.

✼✼✼

LIBRARY COMMUNITY RESOURCE DIRECTORIES

There are an increasing number of resource directories being published by libraries, illustrating one of the new focuses of libraries in accessing community resources. Here are a couple of the best we've seen:

Eugene Contact: A Directory of Community Information Resources, from:
 Special Libraries Association
 University of Oregon
 Eugene, OR 97324
This directory seems to me to be a good example of an intermediate step a library can take if it doesn't want to get involved in the role of social service information and referral. Its orientation is on information resources and not services.

Open Dallas, Discover Your City, $2.75 from:
 The Dallas Public Library
 1954 Commerce
 Dallas, TX 75201
The Dallas library is one of the most active community information oriented libraries in the country. Several years ago they published very nice newsprint format access guides and now have published this 280-page directory to Dallas.

Help, for Citizens of Wake County
 Wake County Public Libraries
 Raleigh, NC 27611
This and the Kalamazoo County directory are representative of comprehensible guides to social services and organizations.

Directory of Community Resources in Kalamazoo County
 Kalamazoo Public Library
 315 South Rose St.
 Kalamazoo, MI 49006

Some Other People's Yellow Pages

Ann Arbor People's Yellow Pages
Community Switchboard
621 E. William
Ann Arbor, MI 48108

Kansas City People's Yellow Pages
3950 Rainbow Blvd.
Kansas City, KS 66103

Los Angeles People's Yellow Pages
P.O. Box 24 B15
Los Angeles, CA 90024

Madison People's Yellow Pages
Communications Network
953 Jenifer Street
Madison, WI 53703

Montreal People's Yellow Pages
EGG Publishing
P.O. Box 100, Station G
Montreal, Quebec, Canada

Morgantown People's Yellow Pages
Alternative Vocations and Lifestyle Center
West Virginia University
Morgantown, WV 26506

North Carolina Carologue
P.O. Box 3337
Durham, NC 27702

Ogden, Utah, People's Yellow Pages
P.O. Box 9064
Ogden, UT 84409

Santa Cruz People's Yellow Pages
Basement Roots Library
314 Laurel St.
Santa Cruz, CA

Seattle People's Yellow Pages
Metrocenter
909 4th Ave.
Seattle, WA 98104

Syracuse People's Yellow Pages
Syracuse Peace Council
924 Burnet Ave.
Syracuse, NY 13203

Tucson People's Yellow Pages
New West Trails
745 East Fifth St.
Tucson, AZ 85719

Tulsa People's Resource Catalog
P.O. Box 3243
Tulsa, OK 74101

Washington DC Gazette Guide
1739 Connecticut Ave., N.W., No. 2
Washington, DC 20009

People's Yellow Pages are often very locally oriented, and so many may not have responded to a mailing we did to locate existing resource catalogs.

The following cities have had, may still have, People's Yellow Pages. Write to Steve Johnson, c/o RAIN, if you want address:

Minneapolis, Buffalo, Boulder, Cleveland, Cincinnati, St. Louis, Berkeley, New Haven, Honolulu, New York City, Atlanta; Portland, Oregon, and Portland, Maine; Milwaukee, Wisconsin; Chapel Hill, North Carolina; Bellingham, Washington; Bristol, Connecticut; Ithaca, New York; Venice and Lakeside, California; Tempe, Arizona, and Providence, Rhode Island.

Service Maps

I've seen two examples of publishing a resource directory in a map format and found it an intriguing concept.

A Map of Berkeley, California, published by Idea-Research-Information-System; and *Youth Services Resource Guide*, 2929 S.E. Powell, Portland, OR 97202.

Newspaper Directory

For several years now the *Portland Scribe* has published the "City Survival Page," a one-page listing of 250 or so groups and services. A useful format and resource to consider, especially if you are in a small town or might not be able to come up with a whole book. (*Portland Scribe*, 215 S.E. 9th, Portland, OR 97214.)

Guides to the City

Guides often associated with business organizations, like Chambers of Commerce, have been published for quite some time. They very often emphasize the well-known and -worn cast of usual highlights and restaurants and shops. There have been some better ones published. A good job was done by the Citizens' Planning and Housing Association of Baltimore: *An Informal Guide to a Livelier Baltimore*, $2.50 from: 330 North Charles Street, Baltimore, MD 21201.

Dumping Places

There are at least two examples of dumping places in the country, both of them extinct now. The concept is still something to think about. Both "Dumping Place" and "New Life Environmental Design Network" served for a while as distribution points for other people's flyers and brochures. Rather than doing a magazine, editing, reviewing and all that, these collectives served as centralized distribution points, therefore allowing people to speak with the format, graphics, color of paper they wanted, but with distribution and packaging handled by the collectives.

See *Women and Health* for a good example of one being done by the Boston Women's Health Book Collective.

WANT TO DO ONE?

1) Grab some things with indexes (such as a Sears catalog, phone company yellow pages, Dewey Decimal catalog, other People's Yellow Pages, Whole Earth Catalog). Make a list of which things you want to find out about.

2) Take stock of what you do know, with help of friends and a map of the area you're working with.

3) Find out what resource guides exist. Check with local United Good Neighbors—is there a social service coordinating agency? Hotline and crisis centers often have extensive file systems. Think of the various agencies that may have compiled lists for "in office" use. (It is best to assume there is a list, maybe partial or outdated, for most any subject you're trying to access.) Easter Seal Society, Welfare, Community Health Nursing Associations, Legal Aid, are all likely to have lists and/or directories.

4) Library. That is where you'll find lots of what you need. Make a list of periodicals/newspapers in your area by checking in the library (double check by touring any bookstore, etc.) If possible, subscribe to several and clip and index. And don't forget newsletters. Many are free or near free and will help keep you up to date.

Also at the library, go through reference book section finding such things as state manufacturing guides, checklist of state publications, other national and local directories. (If your library is small, ask the librarian about the state library or inter-library loan.)

5) City-County-State Government phone directories break down bureaucracies into individual job titles. This can be a great aid to finding out who knows what.

6) Outline what radio and television programs (obviously the news) are likely to point you to other resources.

7) Use mailed questionnaires only when necessary. They are not always productive, and it is important to be exposed in person to surprises—finding gate keepers who know the city like the back of their hand (or just one subject or geographic area).

8) Use public transportation. Map out some routes. Take tape recorder. Try for example recording every sign you see. Take it back to friends and see what they know about the places.

9) Bookstores. Check them out. Especially in recent years, there have been many city guides published, e.g., guides to restaurants, second hand stores, places to go. . . .

10) Universities. Often directly through departments, or action programs (like University Year in Action) there's much compiled information about your region. Find out about special study areas and what research might be going on related to your accessing search—especially contact: sociology, urban affairs, population research, educational activities offices.

11) Federal Information Centers. Every contact I've had with this network of federal employees has been positive. Somehow have managed to find people who love to figure out the bureaucracy. (Also get a copy of U.S. Government Organization Manual, U.S. Government Printing Office, Washington, D.C. 20402. $5.75).

12) Polk City Directory. Used to be before phones they published the only directory to businesses and residents. Still useful. Listings tend to be more extensive than phone book. (Available in libraries).

13) Historical Societies. In order to know what a thing is you should know what it has been. Nothing stays the same.

14) Planning Agencies. Especially in recent years most areas have comprehensive planning associations. They and county/city bureaus of planning are likely to have a valuable, pretty unique collection of local environmental and urban resources, often in map and geographic or subject area studies.

15) Bulletin Boards. Figure out where some important ones are. Laundromats, schools, and watch the printed bulletin boards—the various advertising & classified advertising vehicles.

16) With you and by the phone, keep track of specialties' private languages, e.g. abbreviations.

17) Ask people if they've seen anyone walking around with index cards who seems to know a little about everything—and who just keeps showing up.

Putting Together a People's Yellow Pages, 50¢ from:
Vocations for Social Change
353 Broadway
Cambridge, Ma. 02139

CATALOGS

Alternative America
Richard Gardner
Box 134
Harvard Square
Cambridge, MA 02138

Richard Gardner has been trying his best to keep track of non-profit, social change, alternative groups in the country for several years. This book is a newsprint version of the mailing list he has accumulated of about 5,000 groups in the country.

Source Catalogs
P.O. Box 21066
Washington, DC 20009

The Source Collective now renamed Resources for Community Change published a couple of the most successful national access catalogs:
Communications, $1.75.
Communities/Housing, $2.95.
Health, $5.95.
These are excellent resources.

Gay Yellow Pages
Renaissance House
Box 292, Village Station
New York, N.Y.
$5/$10 for 4 issues. Quarterly.

Organic Directory, $2.95 from:
Rodale Press
Emmaus, PA 18049

Health Food/natural food outlets, organic growers, etc.

National Directory of Hotlines & Youth Crisis Centers
National Exchange
51 37th Ave. N.E.
Minneapolis, MN 55421

$3.00. There are hundreds of them. (Last one I saw was two years ago, so may be outdated)

New Directions for Veterans
P.O. Box 865
Lawrence, KS 66044

In process. Sections on education and learning. Changes needed in the VA, men's consciousness, spiritual growth, veterans in prison, a nationwide skills-ideas-friendship exchange network. Write to Lawrence Morgan.

Prisoner's Yellow Pages
Outmates
P.O. Box 174
Storrs, CT 06268

By state hundreds of groups working with prisoners. Literature, job assistance, etc.

Northwest Trade Directory, 1976, $3.10 from:
118 N. Bowdoin Place
Seattle, WA 98103

This is an excellent model of a way to make a network of concern or interest, an economic structure visible. The information about food co-ops, small scale trading and trucking groups, and organic food growers was gathered the hard (easy and rich) way by several people journeying throughout the northwest. The colors, indexing and format are also a delight.

Alternative Celebrations Catalogue, 3rd edition, 1975, $3.75 from:
Alternatives
1924 E. Third
Bloomington, IN 47401

The catalog is a directory to small scale, often non-profit making crafts people, and resource listings of places and ways to celebrate holidays while spending less money and resources. A starting point for simplifying life style. Inquire about newsletter and resource packets.

The Mariner's Catalog, Vol. I ($4.95), Vol. II ($4.95), Vol. II ($5.95), Vol. IV (1976, $6.95) from:
International Marine
21 Elm St.
Camden, ME 04843

Whole Earth Catalog of the sea. Even if you're landlocked. The catalog is more than just hardware; it is history, shores, lore. Indexing/design ideal for either browsing or research. Ask also about other publications.

People's Almanac, David Wallechinsky and Irving Wallace, 1975, $7.95 from:
Doubleday & Co.
245 Park Ave.
New York, NY 10017

This may be the fattest paperback in existence (1500 pages, over 2 inches thick) . . . Adolph Hitler owned 8,960 acres in Colorado. . . . The traditional listing of countries round the world also lists large corporations: International Telephone & Telegraph, population 438,000. . . . Also lists who rules, followed by who *really* rules. . . . They have thought of many unanswered questions and answered some of them. . . . A listing of neglected scientists. . . . Sports oddities. . . . It seems like another Whole Earth outgrowth and is maybe a new genre in itself. . . . Nearly a month later I'm still finding different pockets, unusual slants and inventories. They expect to update: People's Almanac, P.O. Box 49328, Los Angeles, CA 90049.

The Goodfellow Catalog of Wonderful Things and *The Goodfellow Newsletter*
P.O. Box 4520
Berkeley, CA 94704

The catalog is a lovely book; the crafts look loved and individual (though I've had no experience ordering). Prices surely comparable to other handcrafted items. The newsletter is designed to keep people up on other craft news around the country, fairs and shows, especially in California, but also national. Letters, book reviews, craft grants. $4.50 a year.

Land-sailing boats from The Sailing Boat.

Old Glory, The Amazing Life Games
Co., 1973, $4.95 from:
Warner Books
75 Rockefeller Plaza
New York, NY 10019
A catalog of the oral history movement.

The Jewish Catalog, Michael Strassfeld,
1973, $5 from:
Jewish Publications of America
1528 Walnut St.
Philadelphia, PA 19102
A very interesting guide to Jewish culture and religion, with articles as well as access.

The Energy Primer, 1975, $4.50 from:
Portola Institute
540 Santa Cruz Ave.
Menlo Park, CA 94025

Comprehensive, fairly technical book about renewable forms of energy—solar, wind, water and biofuels.

Spectrum, An Alternative Technology Equipment Directory, 1975, $2 from:
Alternative Sources of Energy
Rt. 2, Box 90A
Milaca, MN 56353

A catalog-style sourcebook on a.t. products available from manufacturers. The first of many such catalogs. See the Appropriate Technology section for complete coverage.

New Women's Survival Sourcebook,
Susan Rennie and Kirsten Grimstad,
1975, $5 from:
Alfred A. Knopf
201 East 50th
New York, NY 10022
A very large blend of the *Whole Earth Catalog* and People's Yellow Pages. This is an update from their earlier *Catalog* (1973).

Women Behind Bars, $1.75 from:
Resources for Community Change
P.O. Box 21066
Washington, DC 20009
This is a good hybrid of catalog, organizing manual and directory to groups doing it.

Oregon Women's Resource Guide,
1976, $3 from:
Continuing Education Publications
P.O. Box 1491
Portland, OR 97207
A useful model of a guide that includes some article/essay information as well as a directory to women's resources.

Last Whole Earth Catalog, 1971, $5
from:
Box 428
Sausalito, CA 94965
It is never old hat, I was recently reminded, when I looked through it and realized how many, many things I first found out about in the *WEC*. And—*Whole Earth Epilog* (1974, $4)—summing up and catching up with several years of non-publishing of the *WEC*. And still keeping up is *Co-Evolution Quarterly*, $8/year from the same address. See review in A.T. section.

Real Time, Nos. 1 and 2, John Brockman and Edward Rosenfeld, $3.95
each from:
Anchor/Doubleday
245 Park Ave.
New York, NY 10017
Two very good indexes to ideas and publications on the outer reaches of psychic science and exploration.

Explorers Ltd. Sourcebook, Alwyn T.
Perrin, ed., 1973, $4.95 from:
Harper and Row
10 East 53rd
New York, NY 10022
This is the *Whole Earth Catalog* for resources about recreation, nomadics, adventure, boating, maps, fishing, weather. Many points for the easy reading format.

Canadian Whole Earth Catalog
You'll probably have to find this in a library or used book store. If you do, hang on to it. The ones done on shelter, food and health were probably the best single access resources in those areas.

The Performing Arts Index, 1976, 50¢
from:
Contact Center
1005 N.W. 16th
Portland, OR 97210
An amazing collection of 750 listings of performers, instructors and support services for dance, music, poetry and theater. Frustrating 'cause it's so quickly out of date (the drawbacks of print!) but a model for other places. It's funded each year by a Performing Arts Marathon—24 hours a day for over a week— What a good time! Put together by Tode Oshin and Wayne Waits.

Intermedia
Century City Educational Arts
Project
10508 W. Pico Blvd.
Los Angeles, CA 90064
Harley Lond keeps on top of a weird, ever-changing world of artists, filmmakers, correspondence artists and others who escape classification. *Intermedia* is published quarterly with some articles and lots of good access.

Image Bank
I only got to see this directory for five minutes, long enough to know there can't be too many others like it. Imagine a directory to people and images they either have or are looking for. Buckles the imagination. Sorry, but it's out of print.

---

*_The Grassroots Primer_ (Sierra Club Books) has a good and detailed description of environmentally-related groups. See review in Community Building.

*There are a whole bunch of catalogs connected with Learning. *Somewhere Else, New Schools Exchange, Seed Catalog, Whole Kids Catalog*. See the Learning section for the complete scoop.

SELF-PUBLISHING

The Publish It Yourself Handbook: Literary Tradition and How To. $4.00, Edited by Bill Henderson.
    Pushcart Book Press
    Yonkers, N.Y. 10701

In December, 1972, a group of authors demonstrated on New York's Fifth Ave. protesting the inefficient distribution methods of commercial publishers. The authors sold their own books from push-carts.

A unique collection of the history of print-it-yourself, famous and not-so-famous persons and groups. Includes the experiences of Anais Nin, Leonard & Virginia Woolf, Stewart Brand. . . . It is more a history and experiential text than how to, though scattered through-out and the last 20 pages is how to do it.

News Print Co-Op
    c/o Theatre Project
    45 West Preston St.
    Baltimore, MD 21201

Not really a regional magazine but an interesting concept in print distribution. People pay very cheap amounts for space (quarter of tabloid seems about average) wherein they can advertise, print their poetry, their small magazines, flyers, etc. The co-op, a person at this point, does layout and design. Might be a model for times when paper and ener-gy get short. Send $1 for sample.

Alternatives in Print, $9.45 from:
    Glide Publications
    330 Ellis St.
    San Francisco, CA 94102

Along with COSMEP, this is a biblio-graphic search and find compilation of small press publications, usually not listed in *Books in Print*, etc.

COSMEP (Committee of Small Maga-zine Editors and Publishers)
    P.O. Box 703
    San Francisco, CA 94101

Especially a network for publishers of literature in its various facets and dis-guises. The COSMEP newsletter tries to keep track of small magazines and book publishers. For $20 membership now you can also get their series of booklets on: distribution, library and booksales, printing, promotion, finances and mis-cellania, production/design. All of these are useful, quite good introductions. COSMEP also produces extensive mail-ing lists for small publishers, including bookstores, libraries, etc.

Dustbooks
    P.O. Box 1056
    Paradise, CA 95969

For about 10 years Len Fulton and friends have kept track of the rich de-luge of self-published books, small cir-culation magazines, basement literary and low budget publishers. Most of the work focuses on literature, poetry, arts, so should be supplemented with things like the *Alternative Press Index, RAIN, Co-Evolution Quarterly*, etc.

Resource books include: *Internation-al Directory of Little Magazines and Small Presses* ($5.95); *Small Press Rec-ord of Books* ($4.50); and, to keep on a regular basis, *Small Press Review*, $6/yr. individual, $10 institution.

These are all information access resource magazines which we find useful time and time again. Be sure to also check out these favorites reviewed elsewhere: *Co-Evolution Quarterly* (p. 9, 90), *Self-Reliance* (p. 57, 5) and our very own *RAIN* (p. 9, 243).

Workbook, $7/year students, $10 individuals, $20 institutions, monthly, from:
    Southwest Research and Information
        Center
    P.O. Box 4524
    Albuquerque, NM 87106

Workbook is an information access journal similar in format to RAIN, but dealing principally with social injustice and reform—prisoners, women and gay rights, privacy of information, farm workers and union organizing, as well as more general topics.

Mother Jones, $12/year from:
    1255 Portland Place
    Boulder, CO 80302

I really like this magazine. At first I didn't because it seemed like another "with it" new age bandwagon slickie. But now I look forward to it each month. It's fairly politically oriented—I wept this month on the story of the assassination of Chilean Orlando Letel-ier and Ronni Moffit of the Institute for Policy Studies. It also has movie reviews, RAIN-type blurbs, exposés on economics, nuclear power and in-surance, and interviews with the likes of Robert Pirsig, Robert Altman and Barry Commoner. Denise Levertov is their poetry editor. They seem to be tapped into some networks I haven't seen much on before now. Single issues are $1.

doing it! Bi-monthly, $10/yr, from:
    Box 303
    Worthington, OH 43085

This fat (80 pp.) new magazine looks like a good one. Their emphasis is on urban alternatives. Some articles are on groups which are becoming old hat, like Briarpatch, New Games and the Insti-tute for Local Self-Reliance (each time you say it more people find out about them), but lots of new things (for us) too—a community loft in NYC and the "grey rabbit" bus lines. Articles cover things in much more depth than we at-tempt to do, while access info is given.

NATIONAL RESOURCES

New Age Journal, monthly, $6/year from:

    32 Station Street
    Brookline Village, MA 02146

East-West Journal, monthly, $9/year from:

    29 Farnsworth St.
    Boston, MA 02210

Two journals serving the recent ground-swell of interest in spiritually-oriented activities. *New Age* focuses more on practical, active manifestations of right livelihood, while *East-West* focuses more on the spiritual communities. Both give access to groups, events and other goings-on.

Mother Earth News, $8.00/year, monthly, from:

    P.O. Box 70
    Hendersonville, NC 28739

Seems like most everyone knows this one, maybe not on the level of Mary Hartmann or frisbees, but *TMEN* has reached out more successfully to the multitudes, rather than just a small counter-culture mob, than most any other "alternatives" journal. They usually have a good access section.

The Elements, $7/year individuals, $15 institutions, monthly from:

    1901 Que Street
    Washington, DC 20009

Published by the Transnational Institute (another arm of the Institute for Policy Studies), *The Elements* is concerned with the use and misuse of resources worldwide—energy, food and metals as they relate to weapons, fertilizers and international economic cartels.

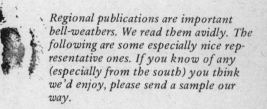

Regional publications are important bell-weathers. We read them avidly. The following are some especially nice representative ones. If you know of any (especially from the south) you think we'd enjoy, please send a sample our way.

Regional Publications

Maine Times
    41 Main St.
    Topsham, ME 04086

Weekly, $12/yr. We've been reading the *Maine Times* for several months now and find it to be a delightful mix of environmental, entertainment and local news of what's happening in Maine. Even the display and classified ads are enjoyable—how many publications carry advertisements for wood stoves and sewerless toilets? In all, very well done.

High Country News
    140 N Seventh St.
    Lander, Wyo. 82520

$10/yr. A unique blend of environmental issues affecting Idaho, Montana, Wyoming, Utah and Colorado, and sensitivity to defining an area's common concerns, traditions, unique life support systems.

Blair and Ketchem's Country Journal
    139 Main St.
    Brattleboro, VT 05301

$10/yr. (12 issues). I don't think it's just my love for New England that makes makes me enjoy this magazine so much. And it isn't just the beautiful photos (many of them in color) or the fine drawings. The articles are right-on: country vets and doctors, grape vines as air-conditioners, wildflowers, garden tools, guinea fowl, cross-country skiing and log cabins. But it's more than that.

A sense of place and roots . . . the spirit of regional self-reliance and cooperation . . . that's getting closer. It's not your usual back-to-the-lander at all. It's a bit fancier than that—done by people who have been living this way for generations. A must for anyone in the Northeast. Of interest for anyone involved in *place*. (LdeM)

Earth Journal
    Minnesota Geographic Society
    1501 S. 4th St.
    Minneapolis, Minn. 55404

A bi-monthly with some emphasis on the North Country. From geography to the tao and back to plants and geography; living on a small planet. $3/yr, 75¢ an issue.

Seriatim—Journal of Ecotopia, $9/year in the Northwest, $12 elsewhere, quarterly from

    Seriatim
    P.O. Box 117
    McMinnville, OR 97128

Seriatim does exist now, and the first issue contains 96 pages of articles by or on Ernest Callenbach, Joel Schatz, logging, the ORE Plan, energy conservation, natural farming, etc. It doesn't seem to bring much new light on the topics it covers or open new territories, but hopefully that will happen as it develops.

Colorado Express
    Box 18213, Capitol Hill Station
    Denver, CO 80218

Published semi-annually. $10 for 2 years. $3.00 each. A cataloging format with outdoor mountains and rivers emphasis. Most issues continuation of access to wilderness equipment. Guide to restaurants in Colorado, VII. Issue No. 1 was catalog of food, transportation, care and recreation in the Denver/Boulder area.

North County Anvil
    Box 37
    Millville, MN 55957

Articles, photos, poems, book reviews, with emphasis on the North Country—but much application elsewhere. More political and rural and funkier (on newsprint for example) than *Earth Journal*. Things like: alternative sources of energy persons: Don & Abby Marier; threshing in Wisconsin, survival program for unemployed; Wounded Knee, art and community. $4.50/yr., 6 issues.

INFORMATION ACCESS AND RESEARCH

SOME SOFT AND SLOW RULES

* There is a list or bibliography about everything until you make a new one.

* A resource person or gatekeeper is worth a thousand books.

* If you have a reason to find it, and the research is not just academic, you will find what you are looking for.

* All research is based on asking the right question to the right person at the right time.

* Most disciplines and specialties are cross-referenced, and all you have to do is find your way into the network.

* The book you are thinking of doing already exists.

* Listen to the language.

* Research is not finding everything that has ever been written about something but just learning how to think about something.

* If you think you have created a new kind of service, or a solution to a problem, someone else thought that awhile back or is just now thinking it.

GENERAL REFERENCE/ RESEARCH BOOKS

Guide to Reference Books, Constance M. Winchell, 1967, $15 from:
  **American Library Association
  50 East Huron St.
  Chicago, IL 60611**
This has long been the basic reference text for librarians. Very complete, not for beginner or casual researcher.

NACLA Research Methodology Guide, $1 from:
  **North American Congress on Latin America
  P.O. Box 226
  Berkeley, CA 94701**
      or
  **P.O. Box 57
  Cathedral Station
  New York, NY 10025**
This is a guide focused on doing research of American power structure.

Where It's At, Jill Hamber, $1 from:
  **New England Free Press
  791 Tremont St.
  Boston, MA 02118**
Similar to the NACLA research guide with more focus on community organizing.

Introduction to Reference Work, William A. Katz, 1974, $9.95 from:
  **McGraw-Hill
  1221 Ave. of the Americas
  New York, NY 10036**
There are two volumes to this work. I've only seen number one, which stands out from the other guides by having more annotated descriptions of reference works. For the averagely serious researcher.

Finding Facts Fast, Alden Todd, 1972, $2.50 from:
  **William Morrow & Co.
  105 Madison Ave.
  New York, NY 10016**
      For price and sensitivity to a range of users, this is one of the best introductions to reference tools. It reminds you of common sense routes to information resources, picking out the most widely useful texts. You'll need other access tools when really digging into local resources, but for what generally can be found in many libraries, this is a good guide.

HOW TO KEEP TRACK OF INFORMATION

After five years of trying to keep track of information, using most every form of filing system I've come across (I try to reorganize at least every three months, with the feeling this one is the one that will work), I've given up. There seem to be only a couple of ways that really help: (1) use the information, and then what you need will always be retrievable, and (2) publish a newsletter like RAIN which can function as a filing system.

Most anyone who gets involved in information exchange (though they may be consciously calling it something else) and community organizing inevitably find themselves scribbling down names of contact people, information resources, ideas and lists of things to do.
    Most all systems of keeping track of information have built-in difficulties and limitations. The most effective system will grow out of your work. Don't set up an elaborate system as a first job. Let it sit for a while, and a pattern will probably emerge.

SOME IDEAS

Notebooks: Rainbow Flute and Randy Skoog, two Northwest courier types, keep notebooks. Rainbow Flute's is a kind of regional novel or journey in which people convey messages to others by writing in the notebook. The overall, time-lapsed effect is beautiful; to see messages back and forth, in each person's handwriting and layout. Randy's contains sections of most used references (addresses of contacts, etc.) as well as current notekeeping.

Keyword record keeping: Rhoda taught (is teaching) me this technique of keeping track of conversations. Rather than attempt to copy things verbatim, listen to the language and pick out key phrases. It reminds me of the Poe project which was an attempt to devise forms to fill out for the dissemination of information about scientific research; based upon the notion that a large percentage of what we say is redundant filler while our mind is thinking, and transitional phrases. So don't listen to things like, "Well, then, I think we ought to . . ." or "I was thinking the other day . . ." or "People have always . . .", etc.

Three by five cards: For most information tracking you might as well start with four by six, since this will allow you to make changes. After some playing around with keysort cards (see below), I keep coming back to simply card index files, I think because my focus of attention changes, and a card index file is a cheap investment and easy to change. Small metal tabs that come in many colors, which can be used to interfile information you may want to retrieve separately, are a good investment.

One useful technique I have used with card index files is to prepare separate lists that in effect can cross-reference the information. For example, on the card index file you may file by the name of the person, but what if that person is with a group that you are searching for a contact within and you can't remember the name of the person? If you number each card and then prepare a list of group names with corresponding numbers you can retrieve it easily.

Keysort cards: In a keysort system, one card is made for each item in a collection. All the elaborative information is on the card, and the cards are indexed by means of notches around the edge of the card. A code is set up prior to entering information, and each subject heading is represented by a hole in the card. The terms under which the item is to be indexed are decided upon and the holes which represent each term are notched. When a needle is passed through the deck of cards, notched items will fall to the table or floor.

There has been much experimentation with keysort cards, in the design of subject headings, for example, using modified zipcodes as a way of setting up geographical indexes. People have also experimented with making their own keysort cards, rather than buying them from manufacturers.

Jaybird, a central Washington rural resources network, in collaboration with Bob Wallace, developed some cards using recycled data processing cards. Jaybird distributes these cards to thirty or so groups in the Northwest, giving each group a small, cheap information center on rural resources and alternative, small-scale food groups in the Northwest.

By several reports, keysort cards work effectively up to 3-400 records. Beyond that it is difficult to keep control over the cards. They are always "out of order," and, especially when used under crisis and fast retrieval situations, the file turns into a crazy juggling act.

Map and file: The Recycling Switchboard in Portland used a keysort card system up to a couple of years ago, when they found it did not quite serve their purpose. They most often needed

Bob Hope has a house full of his files of old jokes. He moved out into another house when the files took over his old one. He never throws anything away.

On March 21, 1947, the New York Police Department received a call from someone who said he thought a man was dead in an old-fashioned brownstone mansion on New York's fashionable upper Fifth Avenue. Upon entering the mansion, police were overcome with the stench of garbage and confronted by piles of trash. One man, Homer Collyer, was found dead. The police tunneled their way through layers of garbage and, nineteen days later, found Collyer's brother. It took the New York Sanitation Department five months to shovel out all the junk, including twelve tons of old newspapers, seventeen pianos, the useless parts of thirty abandoned automobiles, magazines dating all the way back to the 1890s, and the remains of meals of two lifetimes.

From: *The Incredible Collectors*, Bill Carmichael, 1973, $1.25 from:
Warner Paperback
75 Rockefeller Plaza
New York, NY 10019

F. Scott Fitzgerald went through a period in 1935-1936 when he made lists of everything he could think of in an effort to give his life a semblance of order—lists of popular songs, of girls he had known, of the kings of England and France.

to know where a recycling center was in relation to the person calling in for information. A map with variously-colored dots for kinds of centers and services seems to work. A map in relation to a list or card file is a good way of beginning to visualize a network of people and information.

Optical coincidence, uniterm, peekaboo: There are a variety of simple systems (which again can be bought or hand made) that work on the principle of subject heading cards for each area you are concerned with, on which numbers assigned to individual entries are cited, by merely a list of the numbers, a matrix of numbers and letters (allowing more entries on any one subject card), or by, in some cases, actual citing of the documents by lining up punched-out dots. (This has, I hear, even been expanded to a method involving laser beams.)

SOME RESOURCES

Methods of Information Handling, Charles P. Bourne, 1963, $17.75 from:
John Wiley and Sons
605 Third Ave.
New York, NY 10016
A good overview with emphasis on small-scale record keeping.

Information Storage and Retrieval Systems for Individual Researchers, Gerald Jahoda, 1970, $12.75 from:
Wiley-Interscience Books
605 Third Ave.
New York, NY 10016

The Resource File, from:
Information and Referral Services
Administration on Aging
U.S. Dept. of Health, Education and Welfare
Washington, DC 20201
Part of their "Interstudy" research on information and referral services in the country.

Indecks
Arlington, VT 05250
The primary distributor of keysort cards systems. They will do special orders and have a funny newsletter.

Community Information Specialist Program
University of Toledo
Toledo, OH 43606
Lynn Cooper and Sally Taber recently did an interesting paper on cheap filing and indexing systems. The paper may be modified and eventually be put out by the National Self Help Resource Center.

INTERESTING AND USEFUL TOOLS
(Look for them in the library)

There are four basic publishers of reference books in the U.S.:

Gale Research Company
1400 Book Tower
Detroit, MI 48226
They publish such wonders as *Encyclopedia of Associations*, *Directory of Special Libraries and Information Centers*, and *National Directory of Newsletter and Reporting Services*.

H.W. Wilson Company
950 University Ave.
Bronx, NY 10452
Wilson publishes some of the more esoteric ones, as well as *Readers Guide to Periodical Literature* and *Biography Index*.

American Library Association
50 East Huron St.
Chicago, IL 60611
They publish many reference guides aimed at librarians, but also reference works generally applicable like: *A Multimedia Approach to Children's Literature*, *Reference Books for Small and Medium-Sized Libraries*, *A Guide to Selection of Computer-based Science and Technology Reference Services in the U.S.A.*

R.R. Bowker
1180 Avenue of the Americas
New York, NY 10036
They publish *Library Journal, Publishers Weekly, Books in Print, Audiovisual Market Place, Bowker Annual of Library and Book Trade Information*, and *School Library Journal*. Some of these are regulars around the RAINhouse. *Books in Print* we use most often for its list of publishers (also to do this book!) A set costs $69.95, so talk a friendly bookstore into giving you their old set when they get their updated one each year. *Publishers Weekly* is a good, though sometimes exhausting, way of finding out what's being printed in the U.S. Usually only has well-established publishers. $25 a year—this is the only magazine we *subscribe* to.

◆◆◆

Oxford English Dictionary
Oxford University Press
1600 Politt Drive
Fair Lawn, NJ 07410
$75 for a compact edition with magnifying glass. Tracing word definitions by usage as well as definition doesn't always give you that sense that some dictionaries do that definitions all just lead from one to another in a circle with no end.

Thesaurus of English Words and Phrases, Peter Mark Roget, $15 from:
Grosset and Dunlap
51 Madison Ave.
New York, NY 10010
Most of the time I use the *Thesaurus* I don't find the exact word I'm looking for, but am reminded of what I'm looking for. Great for brainstorming games.

Thomas Register of American Manufacturers, $39.75 from:
Thomas Publishing Co.
E. Lawrence Ave.
Springfield, IL 62703
If you are looking for things that are produced, this is a good place to begin.

American Doctoral Dissertations, Mary McNair, Dissertation Abstracts International, from:
University Microfilms
300 North Zeeb Road
Ann Arbor, MI 48106

SPECIAL LIBRARIES, CLEARINGHOUSES, INFORMATION SERVICES

National Technical Information Service
U.S. Dept. of Commerce
Springfield, VA 22151
The central source for the public sale of government-sponsored research. With over 700,000 titles, 60,000 news reports annually. There are weekly abstracts that summarize research activities in several areas and semi-monthly topical announcements in other areas.

State and Local Environmental Libraries, joint publication of U.S. Environmental Protection Agency and National Oceanic and Atmospheric Administration, from:
401 M St., S.W., Room 2903
PM-213
Washington, DC 20460
A 24-page list that unfortunately fails to include much annotation. It is an impressive list on non-usual small libraries and collections.

American Library Directory, from:
R.R. Bowker and Co.
1180 Ave. of the Americas
New York, NY 10036
Lists 25,000 libraries in the U.S.

Directory of Special Libraries and Information Centers and *Research Centers Directory*, from:
Gale Research Company
1400 Book Tower
Detroit, MI 48226
Exhaustive, fully annotated directories to research. Because of the publishing lag, of course, some information may be outdated, and you may want to consult Library of Congress or NTIS for more on-line, real time information.

The National Referral Center
Library of Congress
Washington, DC 20540
The referral center is an excellent source of information, ranging in format from bibliographies they produce, called LC tracer bullets (model bibliographies, containing people as well as books) and going from the general to the difficult. A referral service to assist the science and technology community and publisher of several directories, including: Physical Sciences, Engineering, Social Sciences and Federal Government. All good resources.

Environmental Information Sources Handbook, Garwood R. Wolff, editor, $25 from:
Simon and Schuster
1 West 39th St.
New York, NY 10018
This is a well-indexed, wide-ranging source book on groups, publishers, research facilities in the environmental sciences.

ACCESS TO GOVERNMENT INFORMATION

Superintendent of Documents
U.S. Government Printing Office
Washington, DC 20402
The USGPO publishes thousands of documents every year. You can get on a free mailing list to receive announcements of reports and publications of general interest by writing to the office. An exhaustive and difficult to access monthly catalog, with an annual accumulated catalog, is also available. A good brief guide to government periodicals is also available from them or any Federal Information Center.

Federal Information Centers
They exist in most major urban areas, and my experience has been that they go out of their way to help. Look under U.S. Government in the phone book. In Portland, Coral Buchler and her assistants have become legendary. The Portland office answers some 600-650 questions a day, and not just as related to government, for, as Coral Buchler explains, "People just don't know where to look for information."

Federal Executive Boards
As part of the movement toward regional government administration, and because of the increasing complexity of federal government, executive boards made up of representatives of local government offices have been formed. They have now taken charge of making the bureaucratic structure more accessible to the public and are beginning to publish directories.

Federal Register and *Congressional Record* (available from USGPO)
Both provide access to the daily occurrences in federal government. They make for fascinating reading if you can figure out a way to wade through them. *The Congressional Quarterly Service*, a private publishers, provides weekly and annual summaries of events which may be a way to plow through it.

The Federal Register reports on activities of all government agencies; while the *Record* is a verbatim report of what takes place on the Congressional floor.

Monthly Checklist of State Publications $8.00/year from:
U.S. Government Printing Office
Washington, DC 20402
This is an extensive but incomplete way of locating publications put out by state governments.

Catalogue of Federal Domestic Assistance, from:
Executive Office of the President
Office of Management & Budget
Washington, DC 20503
This is the guide to monies available through government agencies and how to apply.

GAO Monthly List of Reports and *GAO Reports* are free to non-profit organizations, libraries, students, newspapers and local-state-federal gov. officials, and $1 each to the general public, from:
U.S. General Accounting Office
Distribution Section, Room 4522
441 G Street, N.W.
Washington, DC 20013
The GAO, an independent agency of the federal government's legislative branch, has traditionally been called Congress's "watchdog" for its economy, efficiency and effectiveness reviews of executive branch programs. Most of their work originates through requests of congressional committees, individual members or of their own initiative. The Office of Special Programs, directed by Monte Canfield (formerly of the Ford Foundation Energy Policy Project), coordinates GAO's activities in energy, food, materials and regulatory reports reviews. OSP's objective is to focus GAO's attention on pertinent issues facing Congress in these areas and to educate GAO in methods of targeting and analyzing issues. OSP also analyzes government policy on critical issues in reports or issue papers to Congress, such as "The Liquid Metal Fast Breeder Reactor: Promises & Uncertainties," OSP-76-1, July 31, 1975. The most unique and useful characteristics of *GAO Reports* are 1) their layperson language—there is little jargon, and what there is is clearly explained in footnotes or glossaries; 2) their very complete references, including understandable maps, graphs and tables; and 3) their balance of both pro and con views on often controversial issues. An added bit of spice is the inter-agency letters and memos which ever so gently try to persuade GAO to say something else, say it more euphemistically, pat someone on the back in their reports, or not say anything at all.

Freedom of Information Clearinghouse
P.O. Box 19367
Washington, DC 20036
Write for their report on the Freedom of Information Act—what it is and how to use it. There's an incredible amount of useful information hoarded in the federal vaults, and the FIA is a great burglary tool for prying it out. It's also useful to find out who's been snooping on you and what they know, and to see how well the government has been doing its job.

Washington Information Directory, $18 from:
Congressional Quarterly, Inc.
1414 22nd Street, N.W.
Washington, DC 20036
If you want access to Washington, DC, from afar, this book is invaluable. 800 pages of listings of Congressional committees and their staffs, communications and media people, educational and cultural groups, labor and minority organizations. A resource to help you weave your way through the public and private web that is the nation's capitol.

CITY/COUNTY AND STATE AGENCY DIRECTORIES
It is not a widely-known fact that there are such things because they were designed for use by the governments. But when our only access to the elaborate bureaucracies is what appears in the form of phone books, these directories become a vital tool for locating individual departments, and, equally important, they give you a more complete picture of government.

Perhaps if we put enough demand for better access someone will come up with directories designed for public access. In fact, there have been attempts. The City of Portland published a *problem-oriented* directory to services—which until you see it you don't realize what a difference it makes, e.g. rather than dept. of this or that, you find: acupuncture, assumed business names, cable TV, copyright, etc.

Also, the Dept. of Commerce (State of Oregon, Salem 97310) published a problem area indexed directory.

Community

Studying Your Community, Roland L. Warren, 1965, $3.95 from:
> Free Press, Macmillan Co.
> 866 Third Ave.
> New York, NY 10022

Although this introduction to researching your community is relatively outdated and has references to non-existent forms of government, it still serves as a good way into how to begin. The format is basically rundowns of the questions that need to be asked in housing, recreation, health, communication, community planning and politics.

Finding Community: Guide to Community Research and Action, W. Ron Jones, 1971, $4.95 from:
> John Wiley & Sons
> 605 Third Ave.
> New York, NY 10016

This is similar to "Studying Your Community," based on research that involves surveys and studies that have been made well-known by PIRG groups.

Organizing and Conducting Community Surveys and *Interview Techniques and Procedures*, from:
> Community Resource Development
> Colorado State U.
> Fort Collins, CO 80521

These are the best guides I've seen for conducting surveys on the political/educational field. The books that have been published by IDEAS on how to conduct Foxfire-style interviews are something else, but would serve as a good complement.

A Clear View: Guide to Industrial Pollution Control, James Cannon, $4.00.
> Inform Books
> 25 Broad St.
> New York, NY 10004

As William Ruckelshaus says in the introduction: "in order for a citizen to meaningfully participate in government decision-making, he or she must be informed and must have access to decision-makers. This book imaginatively addresses both needs. It places great emphasis on the responsibility of a citizen to become knowledgeable prior to meaningful participation." Introductory material chapters; especially good ones on researching; lots of follow up access; a good guide for volunteer, citizen action groups.

PUBLIC INFORMATION/ RESEARCH

There are several private, non-profit organizations working at a national level to investigate the impact of U.S. corporations and governments on the environment and the public. By making the results of their research available to the media and the public, they aim to put on the pressure required to change products, relationships and modus operandi. *It is important to note, however, that the pressure must be indirect, as these groups, being non-profit (tax exempt) as of this time are prohibited by law from lobbying.*

Center for Science in the Public Interest
> 1757 S Street, N.W.
> Washington, DC 20009

CSPI is a good example of a group which does research and provides information to push and pull the "powers that be" to move things along. Their major areas of concern are food and energy. They have put together publications on the energy and nutritional content of food, personal energy accounting, asbestos and aerosol cans. They publish *People and Energy* ($10/year), a monthly newsletter about citizen involvement in energy, as well as a general CSPI newsletter. Their advocacy pro-

jects include pushing the Federal Drug Administration to label wax-coated fruit and ban inadequately tested food colorings. They just put up a solar collector on their roof, so they're doing more than just talking. See Agriculture and Energy sections of this book for more complete descriptions of their publications.

Science for the People
> SESPA
> 16 Union Square
> Somerville, MA 02143

With chapters throughout the country, this consortium seeks to lay out ethical considerations in scientific research, as well as general implications of directions of various disciplines. The magazine is mostly essay style discussions of issues. from a radical perspective. They welcome manuscripts. Memberships are $12 ($15 to institutions), with some one-by-one sliding scale rates. They have also edited an excellent book called *China: Science Walks on Two Legs* (1974, $1.75 from Avon Books, The Hearst Foundation, 959 Eighth Ave., New York, NY 10019), on the application of science to the daily lives of the most populous nation on earth.

Consumer Federation of America
> 1012 14th St., N.W.
> Washington, DC 20005

This is a federation of over 200 national, state and local organizations working for the passage of consumer protection laws, national health insurance, unit pricing and energy policy. A March 1976 listing is available for $2. *You've Got to Move* is their monthly newsletter. Other booklets include: *How to Prepare a Lifeline Proposal* (75¢) and *How to Prepare a Candidate Survey* (25¢).

Concern
> 2233 Wisconsin Ave., N.W.
> Washington, DC 20007

A group of women whose primary effort is to develop public awareness of environmental issues. A series of semi-annual ECO-TIPS reports on findings on detergents, polyvinyl chlorides, returnable bottles, airborn lead and more.

Research

Caveat Emptor, $8/year from:
    P.O. Box 336
    South Orange, NJ 07079

It's sort of embarrassing to admit it, but I'd never seen this fine consumer magazine before last week. It's been around quite a while. All kinds of issues are covered by columnists such as Herb Dennenburg (former insurance commissioner in Pennsylvania and now TV consumer reporter), Ralph Nader, Nicholas von Hoffman and Michael Jacobson. Good reading. Buyer beware.

Consumer Reports, $11/year, monthly, from:
    Orangeburg, NY 10962

A fine example of a myth-testing organization that makes a lot of useful information available to people on comparative merits of various products. We often have different priorities and come to different conclusions, but they continue to raise questions that poke at both old and new myths—"Is brown rice really better than Wonder Bread?" (They say no.) A valuable resource to scan at a newsstand or library for occasional excellent insights.

Environmental Action Foundation
    724 Dupont Circle Building
    Washington, DC 20036

An excellent source of soundly documented information for community action on electric utilities, nuclear power, solid waste and materials con-servaton, transportation and the supersonic B-1 bomber. Recent publications include:

Taking Charge: A New Look at Public Power ($2.50), which contrasts public and private utility companies, showing that public systems have provided substantially lower rates and better service. Explains how citizens can take over their private utility.

Countdown to a Nuclear Moratorium ($2), a collection of articles by the nation's leading nuclear critics.

Bottles and Sense ($1.50), outlines the economic, environmental and employment advantages of the returnable bottle container.

Vermont Tomorrow
    5 State Street
    Montpelier, VT 05602

A good example of a citizen action group doing research and public education focusing on local needs. Their emphasis is on food and energy self-sufficiency. They are presently working on a series of *Citizen Guides to Community Development*. The first, on Food and Agriculture ($1), covers food and grower's co-ops, farmers' markets and community gardens and restaurants, with a good resource section at the end. Future guides are planned dealing with housing, transportation, economic development and energy.

Public Interest Research Groups

PIRGs, as they are called, exist in many states in the country now, inspired by Ralph Nader in the late '60s. His model, which has since taken root with some slight variations, is to have students contribute $1 of their student activity fees to run a student research and advocacy group. PIRGs are generally run by a student board who hire administrative staff, with much of the leg work being done by students who receive academic credit. The studies have traditionally been consumer- or environmentally-oriented.

For the latest news on the front and a list of PIRGs in your area, write to Public Citizen, 1346 Connecticut Ave., N.W., Washington, DC 20036.

There has also been a growth of groups that are doing research into power structures, the complicated relationships between government, military and industrial boards of influence, and government by personal interest.

Pacific Northwest Research Center
    University Station, Box 3708
    Eugene, OR 97403

They publish a good newsletter with emphasis on power structure in Oregon. $5 for ten-month subscription. They have available a good example of a power structure matrix showing the relationships between government, military and industrial boards of directors in Oregon.

Public White Papers
    Seattle Community Information
    Project
    P.O. Box 12002
    Seattle, WA 98112

At least partial credit for the recent decision by the Seattle City Council to set up an energy conservation office rather than invest in two nuclear power plants goes to these people. When a consultant's work on the viability of energy conservation got buried in the huge environmental impact statement on Seattle City Light's plans to invest in nuclear power, these people highlighted the findings in a White Paper sent to all the people who had the original E.I.S. They also sent it to some other influential people so they could put some pressure on. Put powerful information in the right hands and you can almost accomplish miracles.

MICROCOMPUTER RESOURCES

by Bob Wallace

SMALL-SCALE

Computers are becoming inexpensive. Electronics manufacturers have fabricated entire computer central processors (the "brain" of a computer system) on a single quarter-inch square chip of silicon, costing $20 to $40. In response to this, computers have become a hobby. There are an estimated 15,000 people with home computers now, and an assortment of magazines, books, kit manufacturers and software companies who cater to this new hobby.

Why have a computer? The main applications so far of interest to appropriate technology people are mailing lists, limited typesetting for magazines and newsletters, "community memory" information banks, energy calculations (design of wind and solar power hardware, simulation of world energy dynamics), games (from Star Trek and Pong to educational simulation of ecosystems), music and video synthesis control, bookkeeping for food co-ops—there're lots of things computers can do.

To use a computer, you need the hardware and the software to do the applications you're interested in. A useful computer system costs (*very* roughly) $1,000 to $3,000. The expensive parts are memory (ranging from a $40 audio cassette recorder to disk systems costing several thousands) and good quality printing if you are doing typesetting or word processing. A computer must be programmed; that is, given a detailed set of instructions telling it what to do, step-by-step. At this stage, there isn't much in the way of "canned" software to do a specific task like mailing lists or bookkeeping. Also, most of the hardware manufacturers are new and don't give much support. This means (this year at any rate) you need to know a little electronics and a little programming to use microcomputers; probably the equivalent of a year course—or several books—in each.

COMPUTER OVERVIEW

Platform for Change, Stafford Beer, 1975, $14.50 from:
> John Wiley & Sons
> 605 Third Ave.
> New York, NY 10016

Lays some conceptual guidelines for computer base control in governmental systems that would be real time and be capable of keeping up with change.

Computer Power and Human Reason, Joseph Weizenbaum, 1976, $9.95 from:
> W.H. Freeman and Company
> 660 Market St.
> San Francisco, CA 94104

Rusty Whitney, our wise friend at the Oregon Museum of Science and Industry's software group, recommended this. I have not read the whole thing, but it seems like a good interactive/interdisciplinary approach to understanding computers.

Privacy Journal, an independent monthly on privacy in the computer age, $25/year from:
> P.O. Box 8844
> Washington, DC 20003

The flow of information pouring into increasing numbers of data banks, and increasing number of data banks that are being intertwined—it's like the weather: easy to talk about, hard to do anything about. These people are following the developments of data banks, invasions of privacy, abuse of computers and legislation and laws pertaining to information storage and access.

Magazines are a good way to learn about the field; find out what manufacturers are offering kits, and get a feel for the hobby.

Byte Magazine
> 70 Main St.
> Peterborough, NH 03458

$12/year, monthly. This was the first hobbyist magazine and has many good tutorial articles on hardware, software and applications. Perhaps more hardware oriented than the other mags listed.

Interface Age
> 6515 Sunset Blvd., Suite 202
> Hollywood, CA 90028

$10/year, monthly. Also has many good articles on all aspects of the computer hobby. Perhaps more on innovative applications and new products.

Dr. Dobb's Journal (of Computer Calisthenics and Orthodontia)
> Box 310
> Menlo Park, CA 94025

$10/year (10 issues). This is *the* magazine for microcomputer software. Includes actual programs for "Tiny Basic" (a stripped-down processor for the popular Basic computer language), and interesting rumors. Into sharing information; non-profit (and no advertising).

Population Graph—Map, U.S.A.
Laboratory for Computer Graphics and Spatial Analysis

Making the City Observable
Richard Saul Wurman

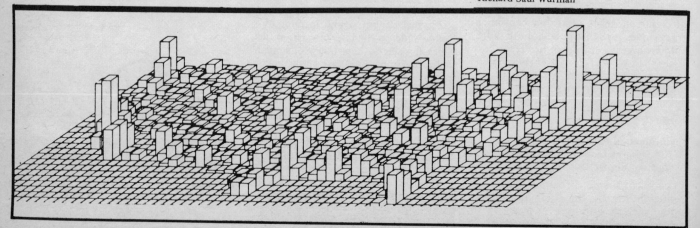

COMPUTERS

People's Computer Company (PCC)
   P.O. Box 310
   Menlo Park, CA 94025
$6/year (6 issues). Educational uses of microcomputers, creative and fun applications, games, cartoons, letters, socially relevant computer uses. Also non-profit. Great for kids.

Creative Computing
   P.O. Box 789-M
   Morristown, NJ 07960
$8/year ($6 student), 6 issues. Also into educational and social issues of computers; futures, philosophy, fiction, art, games. *PCC* and *Creative Computing* complement each other.

There are some new magazines coming out: *Microtek, Personal Computing*, and *Kilobyte.* Sound like they'll be good too.

There are lots of books dealing with computers and microcomputers; I just want to list a couple that are very good and not well known:

Computer Lib/Dream Machines, 128 pp., $7 from:
   Hugo's Book Service
   Box 2622
   Chicago, IL 60690
This is an excellent and fun book, written by Ted Nelson. Half of it explains the basics of computers—how they work, what they can and cannot do, computer languages, data structures—all the basics. The flip side describes some fascinating innovative projects, such as video synthesis, non-linear text processing, artificial intelligence, and many more.

An Introduction to Microcomputers, 350 pp., $7.50 ea. Volume I and II, from:
   Adam Osborne and Associates
   2950 7th St.
   Berkeley, CA 94710
Volume I tells all about microcomputers, from the ground up. Volume II compares the various microcomputer "chips" on the market. No programming knowledge needed; a little electronics background would be helpful for some sections.

Andrew Clement
   Humane Computing
   789 West 18th Ave.
   Vancouver, BC, Canada V5Z 1W1
Andrew worked with a group called Infact, doing a community memory computer project for Vancouver in conjunction with the Community Information Centers. He's now traveling around the country, gathering information about humanistic computer projects for a directory.

Lee Felsenstein
   LCG Engineering
   1807 Delaware St.
   Berkeley, CA 94703
Publishes the *Journal of Community Communication*, and working on a community memory system which will travel around in a van, called "the cruncher." Also designed some of the more popular computer kits.

Boston People's Computer Collective
   Bill Mayhew
   Children's Museum
   Jamaica Way
   Boston, MA 02130

Group trying to increase layman's awareness of computers in society. Offering courses on societal implications of computers and the computer as tool and toy. Also working on a traveling interactive computer exhibit. (Children's Museum has PDP-11 running UNIX).

Barry de Ville, Dymaxion Research Ltd.
   Box 1053—Armdale
   Halifax, Nova Scotia

Research, design, and implement data systems with conviviality and integration in mind. Specialize in: cataloging and retrieval of visuals; social surveys; community consensus polling; and technology impact studies. Designs alternatives, offers hardware access, and provides totally integrated systems.

Richard B. Koplow
   Resource Access Center
   3010 4th Ave. S.
   Minneapolis, MN 55408

Resource Access Center is an educational project seeking to provide hardware and software competence for community service users—agencies and individuals—or potential users of data processing equipment. Programs such as Model Community Service Bureau, Youthiac, and Bit Users Association, bring together professionals and students from grade school through graduate level, providing academic credit for design and implementation of hardware and software useful to community agencies. Project is only now becoming operational, beginning with bookkeeping, typesetting and survey processing systems; mailing sorts, community memory, public access to governmental records and possibly time-sharing to follow.

Bob Wallace
   New World Computer Services
   P.O. Box 5415
   Seattle, WA 98105

That's me. I'm getting my computer system working and will be writing microcomputer software for mailing lists and other networking. I'm also writing software which should make it easier for other people to write software. I'm no longer doing *Comindex*, the directory of alternative computer projects (subscribers will be getting a copy of Andrew Clement's survey when/ if it comes out).

HUMANISTIC COMPUTER USES

Peter and Trudy Johnson-Lenz
695 5th Ave.
Lake Oswego, OR 97034
See interview at the beginning of this section for a detailed discussion of their projects and interests.

The Life Support Systems Group Ltd.
2432 N.W. Johnson
Portland, OR 97210
With a mini-computer this group is attempting to apply computers to community development.

Oregon Museum of Science & Industry
Software Development Group
4015 S.W. Canyon Rd.
Portland, OR 97221
The facility serves as a research and education facility for crazy and bright high school age students; their software programs are distributed around the world. They offer very inexpensive computing for non-profit groups in Portland and are presently developing several community computer programs in conjunction with Johnson-Lenz.

COMPUTER CLUBS

Computer clubs are springing up around the country. The most comprehensive list is probably the one published in People's Computer Club newsletter, Volume 4, Number 6.

Northwest Computer Club
P.O. Box 242
Renton, WA 98055
Meets once or twice a month at Pacific Science Center, Seattle. Publish a good newsletter, $5/year.

The Digital Group
P.O. Box 6528
Denver, CO 80209
Active amateur computer group. Monthly newsletter, $12/year. Into hardware/software support for 8008 and 8080 systems; plans for cassette, CRT, calculator, Mark-8 modifications, 1K operating system, ham radio support. Some boards and kits. Classified ads. Excellent info.

Amateur Computer Society Newsletter
Stephen B. Gray
260 Noroton Ave.
Darien, CT 06820
For people building their own digital computer. Short notes on kits, surplus parts, swaps, letters, etc. More on surplus computer conversion and building from scratch. $5 for at least 8 issues; comes out every 2 or 3 months. 34+ back issues available. 6 pages per issue.

Information

COMMUNITY RESOURCE CENTERS

A center is a point equally distant from all points on the circumference of a circle, or a sphere; it is also a place that actions, forces and people go to or come from.

There are all kinds of centers, like: Center for Short-Lived Phenomena; Center for Being; Center for the Visual Environment; Center for Community Change; Center of Concern; Community Design Center; Center for Research and Development; Center for Science in the Public Interest.

Of course a center is not always called a center; it may be called a clearinghouse, council, switchboard, organization, association or coalition.

And a center may just be a very busy person.

Centers come about for a variety of reasons. Sometimes a critical mass is reached among groups or individuals working in a field of interests, or a forest of concerns, and a gathering, dialogue, negotiating and resource sharing begin to take place.

Some centers are more self-conscious centers, attempting to serve a community in a well-rounded communication and information access capacity, providing individuals and groups with, for example, everyday survival information, access to office equipment, space or communication tools.

There are notable models of centers throughout the *RAINBOOK*, but here are some that may give you a sense of the range of options.

Resource One, Community Memory
For several years the Community Memory Project in San Francisco demonstrated the potential of computer-based public access communication media, with a small network of public terminals. They provided community groups with cheap computer access time and an on-line directory to resources.

For a summary of the project, send $1.00 to: Loving Grace Cybernetics, 1609 Virginia St., Berkeley, CA 94703.

Public Citizen Visitors Center
1200 15th St., N.W.
Washington, DC 20005
Ralph Nader's version of a Chamber of Commerce or Welcome Wagon. They provide information that makes Washington, DC, and federal government activities, accessible to visitors and the general public.

Center for Urban Education
0245 S.W. Bancroft
Portland, OR 97201
CUE has played an important role in Portland in making the city more visible, the media accessible, bringing historical

Centers

roots to the surface and bringing the academic field of urban studies into the community. Their programs currently consist of: urban monitoring project, communicating with the media workshops, community policy workshops and an ethnic heritage study of Portland neighborhoods.

Concilio Campesino Del Sudoeste
P.O. Box 62
San Miguel, NM 88058

The 2,000 mostly Mexican-American residents of this 5-town area in the Lower Mesilla Valley speak little English, have no phones or cars and are not reached by a local newspaper. The Concilio, a broadly-based membership organization, engineered $50,000 worth of volunteer labor to build a community center, got a resident elected to the County Commission, and are now setting up a skills bank and a seller-trade directory for the community. Their tack is to use the organic communication network already in the area—priests, bartenders, beauticians, shopkeepers.

Neighbors West/Northwest Office
Northwest District Association
817 N.W. 23rd
Portland, OR 97210
I've spent many hours in our local neighborhood office, which houses four separate neighborhood groups, partially houses the neighborhood newspaper, and is one of the four neighborhood offices in Portland, given staff and office support from the city government.

The space is not much larger than the inside of a mobile home and always seems disorganized, but somehow manages to stay wired together. The disorganization, I think, is a measure of growing effectiveness of the office as a neighborhood communication center.

Vocations for Social Change
353 Broadway
Cambridge, MA 02139
VSC offices sprang up all around the country either as a direct result of being in touch with the original VSC office in Oakland or as a project of the American Friends Service Committee. Things tend to go hand in hand. If you publish a People's Yellow Pages, or community resource catalog, as the Boston VSC has, you inevitably turn into a center, where

people turn for help, or vice versa, if you open a center first, you will find yourself needing to publish lists, directories and catalogs of community resources.

The National Self Help Resource Center
1800 Wisconsin Ave., N.W.
Washington, DC 20007
They are probably *the* source of information on community resource centers. In the summer of 1976 they sponsored a community resource centers institute, where representatives from a phenomenally rich variety of community resource centers passed a resolution to form a national coalition. For information on the coalition, write to above address.

They also produced a very useful notebook that outlines how and why to set up a center. An excellent resource list. Copies free while they last.

Performance Guidelines for Planning Community Resource Centers, from:
Community Development Division
American Institute of Architects
1735 New York Ave., N.W.
Washington, DC 20036
A good graphic guide for the process of setting up and operating a community resource center.

"Towards a Network of Community Information Exchanges," in *Let the Entire Community Become Our University*, from:
Social Innovation
1506 19th St., N.W.
Washington, DC 20036
Chandler Harrison Stevens has done some of the most intriguing studies and actual experiments in community communications.

I would rather be a node in a network than a cog in a machine.

*See also Community Building for resource centers.

How Do You Start a Neighborhood Center?
National Federation of Settlements and Neighborhood Centers
232 Madison Ave.
New York, NY 10016

COMMUNITY INFORMATION EXCHANGES

An important distinctions needs to be made between what we call "community information exchanges" and what are often referred to as "community information centers." A "center" may offer information to citizens, but an "exchange" sees every citizen as a potential information *producer* as well as an information *consumer*. This view needs to be emphasized because it rejects or replaces the paternalistic view that an individual should be subordinate within society's communication hierarchies.   (Chandler H. Stevens)

Community Information and Service Centers
U.S. Dept. of Commerce
Office of Telecommunications
Washington, DC 20230
These studies headed up by Cleve Hopkins spell out a strategy for the implementation of community communication centers facilitated by new technologies.

"Telecommunications technology may provide new opportunities to decentralize delivery of social services and to improve communication between residents and their local governments. A CISC is a place where citizens, using automated telecommunication technology, can receive answers to questions that arise from their relations with local government."

San Francisco Information Clearinghouse
944 Market St., Room 608
San Francisco, CA 94102
The clearinghouse is a coalition of forty community organizations that operates without any outside financial assistance and assists groups in the coalition and others, through information referral, technical assistance, workshops and joint planning and action. A community congress sponsored by the group pulled together over 1,000 people involved in community organizing work.

LIBRARIES

Libraries on the local level have difficulty getting financial support just for maintenance costs, with most all expansion or research and development monies coming from the federal government. The primary money from the federal government is provided under the Library Services and Construction Act, which passed both houses of Congress in spite of a veto from President Ford, for a total of $56.6 billion in 1977. Most of this money will go towards new construction, maintenance of state library systems (with their focus on providing service to people where no local library resource exists, and for services to the blind and handicapped).

Part of the 1977 funding (about $3 million) will go towards a planned White House conference on library and information science.

There are many issues facing libraries, including copyright problems inherent in library networking, in which information may be transferred from library to library by photocopying and telefacsimile type technologies, allowing libraries to avoid copyright laws and reduce expenditures, while increasing the resources of smaller libraries (in fact, eventually making any library or center equal to any other).

Librarians like Sanford Berman, who publishes the *HCL Bulletin*, have been involved in examining the assumptions in classification systems and other forms of implicit and explicit censorship.

Groups like the Social Responsibilities Round Table have formed in the 1970s over issues of censorship, a consciousness of the importance of being the information-tending shepherds for society, too much focus on middle class America, while not assisting the disadvantaged and minorities.

Like teachers before them, librarians are now abundant and forced to seek innovative ways of employing themselves, which has resulted in rambling free-lance librarians, involved in community research, or information consulting for individuals or businesses. (An interesting article on the subject appears in the *Wilson Library Bulletin*, February 1975.)

Libraries are networking, furthering the traditional interlibrary loan services towards the use of computer technology, telefacsimile, video and other information exchange technologies. Up to 1975 the Ohio College Library Center was the only on-line network covering a large area. The Washington State Library, University of Chicago and Northwestern University, and University of Iowa are approaching that goal.

In addition, certain key projects have shown the example, like the DIALOG computerized retrieval service in the public libraries of Santa Clara and San Mateo counties.

The Western Interstate Commission for Higher Education is coordinating a group representing eleven different states and several bibliographic centers (such as the Northwest Bibliographic Center at the University of Washington) in a plan for a centralized computerized information and retrieval system.

Library Journal
  R.R. Bowker
  1180 Ave. of the Americas
  New York, NY 10036
The *Library Journal* reviews books pertaining to library and information science, as well as general books for library collections, and keeps track of many of the developments in the area.

They also publish an annual that contains all the basic information you'd need to know about operations of libraries (statistics, finances, etc.).

American Society for Information Sciences
  1155 16th St., N.W., Suite 210
  Washington, DC 20036
The ASIS seems to be the information science group that works most closely with librarians. They publish a newsletter and several useful reviews of information science and technology developments.

Wilson Library Bulletin
  950 University Ave.
  Bronx, NY 10452
More article-essay-conceptual pieces on state of affairs in library world.

American Libraries
  American Library Association
  50 E. Huron St.
  Chicago, IL 60611
The magazine for librarians talking to librarians.

Community Information Specialist Program
  Dept. of Library and Information Services
  University Hall, Rm. 309
  University of Toledo
  Toledo, OH 43606
This is the first successful library graduate school program to emphasize community information access. They are drawing people both from the library world and social services. An exciting program that should have great influence on libraries and library schools in the future.

Starting soon, under the gentle guidance of warm information addict and magician Terry Crowley, the Department will begin republishing *Ganglia*, a newsletter that came out of Rutgers University until recently. It is the only newsletter devoted to the field of community information resources and librarians.

Revolting Librarians, Celeste West and Elizabeth Katz, 1972, $2 from:
  Booklegger Press
  555 29th St.
  San Francisco, CA 94131
The best summary of the changing world of libraries, including articles on the Sensuous Librarian, the Unsinkable Miss Philpott, Libraries to the People, Tribal Processes and A Dewey Decimal Mind.

"Libraries in America's Future," a special issue of *Library Journal*, January 1, 1976
300 pages devoted to the present state and future of libraries; including articles on social responsibility, the urban library, libraries and media, and processing for the people.

COMMUNITY INFORMATION PROJECTS

One of the most interesting developments in recent years is the appearance of community information projects. The following short piece is an excerpt from a speech given by Charles Wm. Conaway, at the Buffalo and Erie County Public Library, which I think points out the needs and possible resources of a library in community information retrieval.

INFORMATION. By "Information," I mean facts and opinions. Note very carefully, I'm talking about the substance—the information itself—not the package in which it happens to be stored (i.e. books, articles and maps) that librarians have been traditionally satisfied to deal with; nor am I speaking about the non-print media here. Librarians are becoming resigned to dealing with these non-traditional forms. I'm concerned with the substance, the information contained in these packages, not the packages themselves.

I want to specifically point out that our highly refined bibliographic and indexing systems used in even the most modern libraries are designed to retrieve containers of information, not information. This is an extraordinarily difficult handicap for the information profession to work with; and, unfortunately, no remedy seems just over the horizon, even though there is some interesting work being done toward information retrieval.

NON-CONVENTIONAL. By "non-conventional" information, I mean that which librarians have not traditionally provided in the past. I see at least two reasons for this:

First, our patrons haven't demanded it—but remember that our clientele is changing and is no longer limited to the traditional elites of the educated, the economically secure, and the generally self-sufficient middle class that we have served in the past. Non-conventional information is certainly justified now on the basis of potential demand. And,

Secondly, as librarians, there are some subjects that we just don't think are seemly or important; or that we think are appropriate for us to deal with in our roles as librarians. That is to say, there are conflicts between our values and those of the citizens whom we are expected to serve. (Examples: abortion, draft resistance, political activism, prison reform, popular music, homosexuality, environmental protection, drugs, radical feminism, welfare rights, senior

citizens, venereal disease, and many others). What are your privately-held views about these things? How do they differ from your library's clientele? With the public that do not use your library? What are the consequences of these differing values? Think about this sometime—sometime soon! And a lot!

Of particular importance, we should be aware that no library, no matter how large the system to which it belongs, can hope to provide all this information from within its own collection. But one of the most important kinds of information a library can have is the information about where information may be found. Of all the non-conventional information reservoirs a library can develop, I believe this to be the most important. If we don't have what is needed, who does? And how can we get the information seekers to it? Librarians must become knowledgeable and effective "referrers." Notice the word "refer." Reference librarians refer information-seekers not only to packages of information (books, etc.) held in our libraries—but also to people who contain information. Like any other question negotiation there must be feedback on the success of the referral.

Information for the Community, Manfred Kochen and Joseph C. Donohue, eds., 1976, $10.95 from:
American Library Association
50 E. Huron St.
Chicago, IL 60611
This is the best all-around summary of urban information needs and the role of libraries in meeting those needs. Contains a very good article on community communication patterns, and a summary of urban information needs study by Brenda Dervin.

The Library as a Community Information Referral Center, from:
Appalachian Adult Education Center
Morehead State University
Morehead, KY 40351
This is an excellent introduction to the subject, clearly, in few words describing the need and rightness of having community information in libraries. Also contains the outline for a good problem oriented index to information.

Libraries and Neighborhood Information Centers, Dorothy Ann Turick, ed.
American Library Association
50 E. Huron St.
Chicago, IL 60611
This book has been partially supplanted by the ALA's publication of *Community Information Needs* but still has good information on some of the particular attempts at implementing community information projects in libraries.

COMMUNITY INFORMATION PROJECTS IN LIBRARIES

Community information projects, and library outreach, are of great variety, ranging from the library in a small town in Oregon that loans sewing patterns to a library like the Dallas, Texas, library, with its computerized helper called CAT.

Detroit Public Library
TIP (The Information Place)
5201 Woodward Ave.
Detroit, MI 48202
The Neighborhood Information Centers project supported by HEW called for the implementation of information centers in five public libraries: Atlanta, Cleveland, Detroit, Houston, and Queensborough. Detroit and Houston, it appears, have been the most successful. TIP provides people with information about the community, ranging from abandoned houses to food cooperatives to zoning appeals. The information and referral service is now available at most branch libraries as well. They have some very good materials which will explain more.

INFER
Enoch Pratt Free Library
400 Cathedral St.
Baltimore, MD 21201
INFER is an information and referral service in the central Enoch Pratt Library and its branches. The INFER program operates in cooperation with other county libraries, including the Baltimore County library with its own successful community information project HELP. They currently answer about 200 calls a month.

Dallas Public Library
1954 Commerce Street
Dallas, TX
From available evidence, this is one of the best community outreach programs around. Several years ago they published some nicely done newspaper tabloid resource guides to such things as environment and education. They have since cooperated with the local Chamber of Commerce to publish a book-length guide to Dallas, that is one of the few examples of a hybrid catalog or guide to the city and social service directory.

They also have a computer terminal with a software program called CAT that can search the files of 3,500 organizations, services and resources in the Dallas area.

Helpfile
Kalamazoo Public Library
315 South Rose St.
Kalamazoo, MI 49006
After setting up a file of organizations in the library, they followed the referral service with a directory to community resources which assists the referral service by giving people a general guideline to resources available.

Wake Information Center
Wake County Public Libraries
616 Tucker St.
Raleigh, NC 27603
They now serve close to 1,000 people a month via telephone, walk-in, appointment and letter. They have published a directory called *Help*.

Government Information Division
Edmonton Public Library
Sir Winston Churchill Square
Edmonton, Alberta, Canada
This is an important model. The division is responsible for an estimated 10,000 volumes, acquiring them at a rate of approximately 100 items per month. The goal is to make government information, especially information pertaining to community planning, more available to the public. As well as a centralized resource center for planning information, the staff publishes special issue leaflets, describing key issues and giving resources and references; coordinates workshops and attempts to package and display government and planning information in ways that will make it more accessible.

Baltimore County Public Library
320 York Rd.
Towson, MD 21204
They have previously published a successful, freely-distributed guide to social services in the Baltimore area and recently distributed a nice leisure time activity guide to the area in cooperation with the *Baltimore Sun*. A good way to get out 375,000 copies.

The Library Hands-On Book, 1974-75, copies available free while they last from:
Jovanna J. Brown
Dean of Library Services
The Evergreen State College
Olympia, WA 98505
A model resource on how to access a library. Written and illustrated with great wit, this information packet speaks in a personal manner to the library user about such exotic subjects as the vertical file, LC classification and interlibrary loan, as well as demystifying reference, acquisitions and cataloging. The text describes not only what services are available but why the library functions the way it does. This is one library that wants to make the riches it has to offer easily accessible to its patrons.

Interstate Library Planning Group Directory
c/o Marion Otteraaen
Longview Public Library
1600 Louisiana
Longview, WA 98632

A very unique attempt at breaking down the library resources of the 12 county area around Portland/Vancouver. It is a subject indexed guide to librarians who would be willing to share their avocational expertises. The subject range is intriguing, including: costume history, nutrition, open space schools, urban geography, videotapes, violin, energy, and over 100 other subjects.

HOMEGROWN LIBRARIES

In the meanwhile, pretty far from the traditional sense of library individuals and groups are creating their own kinds of libraries. Tool lending libraries are showing up—even as programs within public libraries (Corvallis, Oregon). Individuals like Joyce Schowalter of Ellensburg, Washington, Johan Matheison (calling the service Tool Shed); small groups like RAIN, the Basement Roots Library in Santa Rosa, California, have their own specialized libraries that are used by appointment, for special use, with unique resources— things like letters, Xeroxed reports, lists, catalogs, file cards, looseleaf files and some books.

Earth Books Lending Library
Sweet, ID 83670
Lewis and Sharon Watson created this unique lending library in response to holes in state library systems and agricultural extension information. They now own several hundred titles, loaning them out for 50¢ a month, which can go towards purchase of the book. For $5 you join and get catalog and access to their Country Contacts Directory.

Rural Library
Toppenish, WA 98948
Bart Alexander has operated an informal library for several years, similar to the Tool Shed in Creswell, Oregon, with his focus being on collecting rare 19th century, pre-industrial era farm books.

Women's History Research Center
2325 Oak St.
Berkeley, CA 94708
They maintain an international woman's history archive of the present women's movement and a topical research library. 2,000 topical areas. A catalog (200 pages) of their current holdings.

Collectors Network
R.G. Benedict, Coordinator
c/o University of Nevada Library
Reno, NV 89507
Mr. Benedict collects and helps maintain special collections of alternative, or ephemeral, literature, which is now available in 32 libraries in the country. He publishes a good newsletter called *Top Secret*.

Everyday Information Needs

People need information to survive that runs the gamut from the startled nerve of a burned finger telling the brain to move, to the need to know how to find one's way through a city: its transportation, services, communications and other complicated systems, to information that produces joy or understanding or a caring or kindred soul.

There's a delicate mathematical and spiritual world being woven by the blurring of several fields of interest: mathematics, systems science (cybernetics), brain sciences, neurolinguistics, and visual thinking or modeling techniques for communicating the new information.

In the "real" world there is a related blurring taking place between library and information sciences, education and social services.

I talked with a person a while back who represented an odd stage in that development. He was director of a group called Community Resources for Career Education. He was continuing work he had started earlier while working for an industry-supported, non-profit agency which had set up a referral service for teachers to locate community resource persons to speak to their classes.

When I met him he was assisting in the development of a community resource identification and retrieval system using a computer software program being developed at Boeing.

We talked about the development of information and retrieval systems in education, and how for several years educational facilities had been the recipients of research and development support for the development of such systems, especially community colleges, with their focus on career education, which has become the byword in education, as a response to the cries for relevant education. Looking forward, though, he could see that development and research in information and retrieval systems was turning toward the social service and community development world, so the system he was developing was not "community resources for career education," but a "community resources delivery system."

Libraries, like educational institutions, have had a similar problem with support, having difficulties getting local support budget bonds passed. The response in some cases has been to appear more relevant, either to a particular community (very often the business community) or to the general or disadvantaged public through various kinds of outreach programs.

The programs that libraries implement often overlap with social service goals, as their implicit goal of "continuing adult education" runs into another hot spot in education, adult, continuing or community education. John Berry points this out in a special *Library Journal* article on library futures:

"We find public libraries discovering that independent agencies provide the same information service they are starting. They have competed with the United Way, with private industry, with other social agencies for service options. Even in this issue of *LJ* there is an implied competition between public libraries and institutions of higher education to decide which will provide for the need to know that growing interest in informal, continuing education will bring."

The information needs, especially in urban areas, of people are increasing because a complicated system creates variety, overlapping concerns, many alternatives and constant change and movement.

Information for the Community, Manfed Kochen, Joseph C. Donohue, 1976, from:
    American Library Association
    50 E. Huron St.,
    Chicago, IL 60611
Of the several books on the subject, this seems to me to be the best one. Chapters on information services, a history of infor-

mation and referral, and a good summary of the key work of Brenda Dervin in the field, called "The Everyday Information Needs of the Average Citizen."

The Production and Distribution of Knowledge in the United States, Fritz Machlup, 1968, $3.95 from:
    Princeton University Press
    41 William St.
    Princeton, NJ 08540
This study is now 15 years old, but I don't think there's been another comprehensive look at the various information-producing industries, covering education, communication, data processing and research and development.

Planning Community Information Utilities, H. Sackman, B.W. Boehm, from:
    HFIPS Press
    Montvale, NJ 07645
This is the basic description of the present situation, need and future for a computer-based community information utility that would plug in the various information producing operations into a utility similar to the telephone or electric company.

INFORMATION AND COMMUNICATIONS BIBLIOGRAPHY

Fuller, R. Buckminster. *Utopia or Oblivion*. Bantam Books: 1969. $1.25.

Simon, Herbert. *The Science of the Artificial*. MIT Press: 1969. $1.95.

Bertalanffy, Ludwig von., ed. (and others). *General Systems Yearbook*. Society for General Systems Research. Annual.

Wiener, Norbert. *The Human Use of Human Beings*. Avon Books: 1954. $1.65.

Platt, R. John. *Perception and Change*. University of Michigan Press: 1970. $7.95.

Boulding, Kenneth E. *The Image*. University of Michigan Press: 1956. $1.95.

Brockman, John. *By the Late John Brockman*. MacMillan & Co.: 1969. $6.95.

Lilly, John C. *Programing and Metaprograming the Human Biocomputer*. Julian Press: 1967. $4.95.

Emery, F.E. *Systems Thinking*. Penguin Books: 1969. $2.65.

Jolley, J.L. *Data Study*. McGraw Hill Book Co. 1968. $2.45.

Ashby, Ross W. *Introduction to Cybernetics*. Barnes & Noble. 1968. $4.75.

Attneave, Fred. *Applications of Information Theory to Psychology*.

Bateson, Gregory. *Steps to an Ecology of Mind*. Ballantine. 1972. $1.95.

McCulloch, Warren. *Embodiments of Mind*. MIT Press. 1965. $3.95.

Wiener, Norbert. *Cybernetics*. MIT Press. 1965. $2.95.

Saracevic, Tefco.(editor). *Introduction to Information Science*. R.R. Bowker Company: 1970. $26.95.

Walter, Grey W. *The Living Brain*. W.W. Norton & Company: 1963. $1.95.

Scientific American. "Information." September 1966. $2.50.

Tribus, Myron & Edward C. Melrvine. "Energy and Information." *Scientific American*, September 1966. $2.50.

Weizenbaum, Joseph. *Computer Power and Human Reason*. W.H. Freeman and Company: 1976. $9.95.

Wilden, Anthony. *System and Structure*. Barnes and Noble: 1972. $23.75.

INFORMATION and REFERRAL

There are over 3,000 service agencies in the United States whose primary, or near primary, goal is information and referral, referring individuals or agencies to other individuals or agencies, keeping the information about the information manageable. There are several key issues that are materializing.

• There's a question about whether referring people to other people or information should be an advocacy role. Should the information counselor or broker act as an active guide through bureaucracies and red tape, or merely refer people to somewhere else without being involved in the actual transaction.

• Information and Referral agencies have traditionally been service oriented; that is, they make referrals to other existing services, usually those that are funded by government, United Way or other traditional and well-established social service organizations. People are therefore perhaps helped, but usually temporarily, enabled to survive a crisis only, and not routed to a permanent way out.

• The directories, and indexing of information itself used by social service agencies, produced by information and referral groups, is itself controversial. Similar to some of the disputes in the library world over how to categorize information, with the myriad of implicit world views in categorizing, indexing schemes such as the Library of Congress or Dewey Decimal systems. The social service directories, and probably soon the computer-based retrieval systems, are an essential part of information and referral, but the orientation is toward inner agency referral.

The United Way has recently swept the field clear for the acceptance of their community resources classification system, and it is predominantly service, rather than problem, oriented.

The difference is subtle and important. When we start from a base of services, we are looking at what solutions to problems have been institutionalized; while if we ask ourselves what the problems are, we are forced to find resources that may exist in any field, we are forced to be multi-disciplined; we would have to cross dangerous governmental bureaucratic borderlands and be in that mess the real world is in where everything is interrelated.

Alliance of Information and Referral Services
    5020 North 20th St., Suite 201
    Phoenix, AZ 85061
AIRS is the national coordinating group of information and referral specialists. They publish a newsletter and assist in the preparation of I&R standards (how to referral, volunteer standards, classifications, etc.).

Administration on Aging
    National Clearinghouse on Aging
    U.S. Dept. of Health, Education &
      Welfare
    Office of Human Development
    Washington, DC 20201
A major group working on information and referral. Much of the I&R growth in this country is related to the needs of people at both ends of the scale; on the one hand, the late sixties saw an increase in hotlines, contact centers and youth programs—all in some way started by that phenomenon we call running away—and on the other end, senior power, with the development of programs aimed at assisting older people with their free time, which is often eaten up by Social Security, welfare and other forms of public assistance.

Especially good publications from the Administration on Aging are the studies done by Nicholas Long, under a Title IV grant, called Interstudy. The reports include: *I&R Services*, an annotated bibliography; *I&R Centres*, a functional analysis; *I&R Services: the Role of Advocacy*.

Community Information Centre (CIC)
    1946 West Broadway
    Vancouver, BC, Canada

CIC is the central hub of a network of very fine neighborhood information centers scattered throughout the city of Vancouver. They provide info on services and events by telephone referral, displaying of public notices and reference materials; they provide free meeting space, phones, office equipment and clerical assistance for community projects; and they help people wend their way through the maze of agencies by helping them fill out forms and giving practical or moral support in making legitimate claims for services. A visit to CIC is a marvel—volunteers busily answering phones, file drawers and card catalogues clicking, and bulletin boards crammed with interesting notices. These people know an amazing amount about their city and have worked out an effective and efficient means of making that information available to people who need it.

Multnomah County Programs & Services
    Office of County Management
    426 S.W. Stark St.
    Portland, OR 97204
The catalog is an attempt at cataloging the services provided by Multnomah County government, with a focus on accountability. Each description contains problem statement, objectives, productivity indicators and program costs, which may sound rather dry, but

I feel it is a tool for the public by which they can better understand the structure of county government and relationships between costs and benefits. Write to Don Eichman for more information.

United Way of America
801 North Fairfax St.
Alexandria, VA 22314
United Way has prepared the standards for I&R that most agencies are referring to and using.

Directory of Human Services, Washington County, Oregon
    Washington County Community
      Action Organization
    546 S.E. Baseline
    Hillsboro, OR 97123
An exhaustive, county-wide inventory of services, groups, and organizations. Unlike your basic urban area social service directory because 1) it's about an area both urban and rural, 2) it includes most everything under the sun, 3) has a unique indexing system (developed by the University of Southern California), and 4) Jim Long, chief cataloger, offers workshops—even in grade schools—on how to use the catalog and how to access community information in general.

The *Directory* also graphically illustrates the need and uses of computers—if it takes 300 pages to cover a modest (but lovely) county in Oregon, what's the state or ultimate cosmic catalog look like? $4.95, includes quarterly updates.

When you watch tv, listen to the radio, or read newspapers, you get ads and news. How does that information get there? News people decide what's newsworthy. Companies selling products have advertising budgets to purchase space and time.

It's the Christmas season as I write this. Commercial tv advertising goes berserk. It is one of the most offensive assaults on the senses ever masterminded. But that's how big business lets you know its's there.

When a new product appears on the market, media blitzes assure consumer awareness. Combine that with knowing where you can find that product—your supermarket, or department store, etc. The mass marketing of products.

Or news and information. Wire services, newspaper chains, broadcast groups and networks, and media conglomerates determine the uniformity of what information gets printed, published or aired in this country.

Where is the space—where are the avenues—the vehicles—for the distribution of new and controversial ideas? What about highly localized interests and special concerns? And did you ever see an ad for Dr. Bronner's soap?

When Steve and I sat down to talk about this section, we came up with a list of key words and concepts we think about and use, as prompters to other people about how information gets communicated.

There are direct *one-to-one and one-to-a-few* methods that involve human interaction—telephoning, letter writing, chain letters, conversations, round-robins, door to door.

There are *places* where people get together—public spaces, hospitality spots, community resource centers, churches and synagogues, community schools.

And *gatherings* of people—potluck dinners, block parties, town meetings, salons, classes, conferences, fairs.

There are *people vehicles*—messengers, gadabouts, couriers, troubadors, minstrels, grapevines, guilds and co-ops.

Small print vehicles—newsletters, handbills, flyers, posters, grocery sacks, match books, bumper stickers, buttons.

Public displays—kiosks, booths, billboards, benches, bulletin boards, neon signs and standing in one place long enough.

Commercial mass media—publishing houses, daily newspapers, radio, tv, movies.

While you're collecting information, what are ways of keeping track, or methods of *record keeping*?—memory, notes, scraps of paper, minutes, notebooks, journals, scrapbooks, lists, files, index cards, key sort systems, computers.

If you want to get the word out about something, where do you start? Well, what is your message? Who are the publics you want to reach? How do you package your information to reach your audience?

How do you know when to use door to door? or print up and post flyers? or do a mass mailing? or prepare a press release or hold a press conference? or even buy an ad?

Do you need to know *about* media in order to *do* the media? I'm not sure. But if you want to know how to use media *effectively*, and to understand its affect on you, then yes.

You can have all the new ideas and information in the world, but if you don't know how to package it appropriately, so that people understand it and pay attention to it, then what have you got?

There are ways to translate commercial mass marketing and promotion techniques to the nonprofit sector and community level. Whether you call it public relations, PR, publicity, promotion, advertising, marketing, networking, or hype—

Do you know how to get the word around in your community?

FRAME OF REFERENCE

Communications: Challenge/Response, by Horizons '76, American Revolution Bicentennial Administration, 1976, 25 pp., 75¢ from:

U.S. Government Printing Office Washington, DC 20402

Fine overview; highlights the innovative ways some groups and communities are using media to communicate public information.

The Image: A Guide to Pseudo-Events in America, by Daniel Boorstin, Harper Colophon, 1961, 315 pp.

A small gem; for mind set and frame of reference. Recommended to me in 1968 by Larry Mans, this book greatly influenced my understanding about the creation and distribution of information in and on American culture. Discusses the differences between news gathering and news making, heroes and celebrities, travelers and tourists, dreams and illusions, and the arts of self-deception. Interesting chapter on recommended reading. Boorstin is currently Librarian of Congress and better known for his books, *The American Experience.*

Subliminal Seduction: Ad Media's Manipulation of a Not So Innocent America, by Wilson Bryan Key, New American Library, 1974

Devastating theories, pretty well documented; illustrated. (Recommended by Joe Bakan)

The Selling of the President 1968, by Joe McGinnis, Trident
The way Nixon got there. Good introduction to the workings of high-powered media campaigns.

Two periodicals: Advertising Age and Public Opinion Quarterly
Especially interesting reading is *Ad Age*'s annual report of how much money American corporations spend yearly on advertising. Check your library.

Early Foundations: Public Opinion by Walter Lipmann, 1922 (recommended by Paul Ashdown), and *Crystallizing Public Opinion* by Edward Bernays, 1923.

HOW-TO

There are many definitions of public relations. Some call it the art of attracting attention. Others say it's the art of using radio, television, newspapers and magazines to inform and influence people. Still others say it is the means of communicating to the public what you or your group is all about. Public relations may be hard to define, yet you know it when you see it.
Reaching the Public

Getting Into Print, 1974, Pub. No. 484, 25¢, *Breaking Into Broadcasting*, 1976, Pub. No. 586, 25¢, *Reaching the Public*, 1976, Pub. No. 491, 30¢ from:
The League of Women Voters
1730 M St., N.W.
Washington, DC 20036
For under $1 you can get a good feel for how to get the word out. Excellent resources.

A Handbook on Free Access to the Media for Public Service Advertising, by the Public Media Center, 1974, free, see p. 110 for address.
Basically geared toward energy activists, particularly how to combat image advertising by oil and nuclear power interests.

If You Want Air Time, 15¢, from:
The National Association of Broadcasters
1771 N St., N.W.
Washington, DC 20036

The Organizers Manual, by the O.M. Collective, Bantam, 1971, $1.25
Has a 40-page section on mass education and communications: reaching

people (leaflets, newsletters, posters, etc.), canvassing, information centers, speakers bureaus, mailing lists, mobile units, coffee houses, films, guerilla theater and zaps.
Published at the height of the Vietnam and urban conflicts and written from a radical perspective, but still a useful handbook.

How to Make the Media Work for You, Catherine Samuels, 1974, $3 from:
Women's Action Alliance
370 Lexington Ave.
New York, NY 10017
Primarily written for use by women's groups, but also serves as a good introduction.

Mediability: A Guide for Non-Profits, Len Biegel and Aileen Lubin, 1975, $8.95 from:
Taft Products, Inc.
1000 Vermont Ave., N.W.
Washington, DC 20005

How To Be Heard: Making the Media Work for You, Ted Klein and Fred Danzig, Macmillan, 1974, $9.95
Both books contain useful information relevant to small groups, though seem to be addressed towards larger nonprofits, like charities.

There are several "definitive" professional guides to public relations and publicity. Check with your local library and PR people for recommendations.

Public Relations Society of America
845 Third Ave.
New York, NY 10022
Association of professional PR people.

National Public Relations Council (NPRC)
815 Second Ave.
New York, NY 10017
Assisting the larger, more traditional nonprofits. Publications list.

Public Advertising Council
1516 Westwood Blvd.
Los Angeles, CA 90024
Public service advertising group

INNOVATIONS IN ACCESS

FREE SPEECH MESSAGES
Phil Jacklin
Committee for Open Media
San Jose State University
San Jose, CA 95192
Issue oriented spot messages, or "guest editorials," on the air in the Bay Area since 1972.

PUBLIC SERVICE ART SPOTS
Televisionaries
Los Angeles County
Dept. of Parks & Recreation

Cultural Arts Section
155 W. Washington Blvd.
Los Angeles, CA 90015
30 and 60 seconds in length, a way to present the work of independent film and video makers on tv, where the aesthetic experience is the public service.

AN OP ED PAGE FOR TELEVISION
John Reilly
Global Village
454 Broome St.
New York, NY 10012
212/966-7526
The idea for guest editorials to be placed *opposite* the *editorial* page in newspapers originated at the *New York Times* in 1970. As a way to slot independent video and film documentaries on television, John Reilly proposes that public tv stations initiate a "Video Op Ed Page."

Petition to Institute a Notice of Inquiry and Proposed Rulemaking on the Airing of Public Service Announcements by Broadcast Licensees, June 1976, 46 pp., cost unknown:
Media Access Project (MAP)
1912 N St., N.W.
Washington, DC 20036
202/785-2613
Harvey Shulman
MAP, on behalf of 71 citizen groups, has petitioned the FCC to put some teeth into public service announcements (PSAs): to define them, the criteria for airing, plus a study on licensee and network practices with regard to PSAs.
MAP recommends that broadcast stations air at least three PSAs (minimum 90 seconds) each consecutive two hours and that at least 25 percent of all aired PSAs be local in origin.
The petition itself is a highly readable document about public service advertising—what it is, federal law, station practice, the role of the Advertising Council, which groups gain access and why.

TRY CABLE
Local origination channels often have "message wheels" that carry public service announcements. To assist community groups and government agencies, the State of Oregon Extension Service prepared a booklet indicating which cable systems in the state accept public service advertising.

Cable TV Service in Oregon, '75-'76, free from:
Extension Communications
Ad S 422
Oregon State University
Corvallis, OR 97331

WORKSHOPS
PR workshops for nonprofits are most often sponsored by local chapters of the Public Relations Society, or broadcasters, either at no or low cost.

COMMUNITY ORGANIZATIONS

Audiopool
   Double Helix
   390A Euclid
   St. Louis, MO 63108
   314/361-7111
   John Mondello
Once you know you want it, where do you learn how to do it? Audiopool is one community's answer—a community access studio begun in Dec. 1975.

Provides two kinds of services: 1) *Program Production*—staff will prepare public service announcements ($15 per 30 seconds) as well as produce public affairs and cultural programs. 2) *Studio services*—on a membership basis; provides training and production workshops; a *community newsroom* operates for the production of news reports for air on local stations.

Double Helix has applied to the FCC for licenses to operate nonprofit, non-commercial radio and tv stations in St. Louis.

Center for Urban Education (CUE)
0245 S.W. Bancroft
Portland, OR 97201
503/221-0984
Steve Schneider at CUE (funded by the Ecumenical Ministries of Oregon) has been conducting community access to media workshops for several years.

As a tool for these workshops, and to address the specific need to know the individuals to contact in the media, CUE prepared in 1972 what I believe to be the first and only annotated city guide to newspapers and broadcast stations, detailing deadlines, editors, public service directors, audience/format, geographic area covered, etc. The third revised edition of the guide has been expanded to include statewide information (*1977 Oregon Media Guide*, $1.50).

Urbanarium, Public Communication Service
   Rochester Institute of Technology
   One Lomb Memorial Drive
   Rochester, NY 14623
   716/464-2337
   Gene DePrez
Conducts a wide range of seminars in media tools and access. A unique feature of the program offers technical assistance to community groups in developing communications projects.

BROADCASTERS

Public Media Center (PMC)
2751 Hyde St.
San Francisco, CA 94109
415/885-0200
A public service advertising organization dedicating its energies "to the task of representing the unrepresented—to the task of providing media access to those who have important, often vital information or concerns to share with the public but who have been denied access to the communications media in this country because of a lack of funds, a lack of professional skills, or because their message was deemed 'too controversial.' "

In addition to assisting local Bay Area groups, PMC has developed, produced and distributed national media campaigns for Amnesty International, Environmental Action Foundation, Food Day, the United Farm Workers, and on the dangers of nuclear power.

PMC's work is professional and creative and has received good response from the commercial media.

CLASSIC MODERN COMMUNICATIONS PHILOSOPHY

One can no longer speak of art without speaking of science and technology. It is no longer possible to discuss physical phenomena without also embracing metaphysical realities. The communications of humanity obviously are trending toward that future point at which virtually all information will be spontaneously available and copyable at the individual level; beyond that a vast transformation must occur. Today when one speaks of cinema one implies a metamorphosis in human perception.

This transformation is being realized on the personal level as well as on the global front of the industrial equation itself, where it can be realized only through the synergetic efforts of all men applying all disciplines. While personal films, videotapes and light shows will continue to expand human communication on one level, organizations . . . are suffusing art, science and the eco-system of earth itself at that point where all converge within the purview of modern technology.

Not only do computer, video and laser technologies promise to transform our notion of reality on a conceptual level, they also reveal paradoxes in the physical world that transcend and remake our perception of that phenomenon as well.

Gene Youngblood, *Expanded Cinema*, pp. 415-419

Harold Innis, *Bias of Communications*, Univ. of Toronto Press, 1951.

Norbert Weiner, *The Human Use of Human Beings: Cybernetics and Society*, Doubleday, 1956.

Daniel Boorstin, *The Image: A Guide to Pseudo-Events in America*, Harper Colophon, 1962.

Marshall McLuhan, *Understanding Media: The Extensions of Man*, Signet, 1964.

Jacques Ellul, *Technological Society*, Vintage, 1967.

Lewis Mumford, *The Myth of the Machine: Technics & Human Development*, Harcourt, 1967.

Buckminster Fuller, *Utopia or Oblivion*, Bantam, 1969; *Ideas & Integrities*, Collier, 1969.

Edward Hall, *The Silent Language*, Fawcett, 1969. *Dimensions of Meaning*, Doubleday, 1969.

Herbert Schiller, *Mass Communications & American Empire*, Beacon, 1969.

Edmund Carpenter, *They Became What They Beheld*, Dutton, 1970.

Thomas Kuhn, *The Structure of Scientific Revolutions*, Univ. of Chicago Press, 1970.

Gene Youngblood, *Expanded Cinema*, Dutton 1970.

Ben Bagdikian, *The Information Machines*, Harper & Row, 1971.

Brenda Maddox, *Beyond Babel: New Directions in Communication*, Beacon 1972.

Herbert Schiller, *The Mind Managers*, Beacon, 1973.

Tony Schwartz, *The Responsive Chord*, Anchor, 1974.

Edmund Carpenter, *Oh What a Blow That Phantom Gave Me*, Bantam, 1974.

Bill Kuhns, *Post-Industrial Prophets*.

Edward Hall, *Beyond Culture*, Anchor, 1976.

Free For All/cpf

BROADCASTING

COMMERCIAL TV

One of my earliest memories/recollections of television is coming home from school in the early afternoon to find my mother tuned to the Army-McCarthy hearings.

Of course, there was also Howdy Doody, Miss Frances' Ding Dong School, Milton Berle, Hopalong Cassidy and the Lone Ranger.

I grew up with tv growing up. As it made the transition from live shows to pre-recorded tape. And the addition of a public noncommercial network.

I am an avid tv watcher. Commercial programing, commercials and news keep me up to date on what's happening in America and the way some people look at this country and the world. Mush.

You don't have to buy what that little black box tries to sell you.

Violence/soap operas/heartburn & hemorrhoids/cartoons/commercials/sitcoms/football/prime time/TV Guide/ and the weather.

If you don't like what you see, or would like to see a wider variety of programing, write the networks, contact your local broadcasters, and let them know what you think.

But it is important to know how to speak the language of broadcasters before you get in touch. So first connect with the groups helping to make people aware of the broadcasting industry and the method of regulation by the federal government.

HISTORY AND AWARENESS

A History of Broadcasting in the United States. Vol. I—A Tower in Babel, Vol. II—The Golden Web, Vol. III—The Image Empire, Erik Barnouw, Oxford University Press, 1966, 1968, 1968, 1970. The most complete single work on the subject. Also by Barnouw, *Tube of Plenty: The Evolution of American Television*, Oxford, 1975, 518 pp., $14.95. A popular approach, loaded with pictures.

Mass Communications & American Empire, Herbert Schiller, Beacon Press, 1969, 170 pp. A critical, chilling study of what's happened to our air waves. This book had a profound effect on my thinking about communications in the 20th century.

Equal Time: The Private Broadcaster and the Public Interest, Newton Minow, Atheneum, 1964. Chair of the FCC during the Kennedy Administration; referred to television as a "vast wasteland" in his address to the 39th annual convention of the NAB in May 1961.

Due to Circumstances Beyond Our Control, Fred Friendly, Vintage Books, 1967. By a former president of CBS News.
News from Nowhere, Edward Jay Epstein.
The TV-Guided American, Arthur Asa Berger, Walker Publishing Co., 1976, 194 pp.
Channeling Children: Sex Stereotyping in Prime Time TV, 83 pp., 1975, $2.50 from Women on Words & Images, Box 2163, Princeton, NJ 08540.
Man of High Fidelity: Edwin Howard Armstrong, a biography by Lawrence Lessing, J.P. Lippincott, 1956.
No Lamb for Slaughter, Edward Lamb.
Prime Time, the Biography of Edward R. Murrow, Alexander Kendrick, 1969.
Network Project Notebooks, See page 115.

GOVERNMENT

Federal Communications Commission (FCC), Washington, DC 20554. Has a variety of free publications available. Write the public information office.
Communications Act of 1934, USGPO, $1.25.

INDUSTRY

National Association of Broadcasters (NAB), 1771 N St., N.W. Washington, DC 20036, 202/293-3500.
Broadcasting Magazine, 1735 DeSales St., N.W., Washington, DC 20036. The industry's weekly. Indexed in the Business Periodicals Index (BPI).
Broadcasting Yearbook, by the editors of *Broadcasting Magazine*. State-by-state directory to radio and tv stations in the U.S.
TV Guide, Triangle Publications, Radnor, PA 19088. Walter Annenberg, president. The largest circulation weekly in the world.
TV Factbook
ABC, 1330 Avenue of the Americas, New York, NY 10019.
NBC, 30 Rockefeller Plaza, New York, NY 10020.
CBS, 51 W. 52nd St., New York, NY 10019.

GROUPS

Action for Children's Television (ACT), 46 Austin St., Newtonville, MA 02160. Peggy Charren. Can put you in touch with local groups; publications, newsletter.
American Council for Better Broadcasts (ACBB), 111 King St. St., Madison, WI 53703.
Citizens Communications Center, 1914 Sunderland Place, N.W., Washington, DC 20036. Frank Lloyd. Public interest communications law firm. A key resource.
Council on Children, Media & Merchandising (CCMM), 1346 Conn. Ave., N.W., Washington, DC 20036, Robert Choate. The man who told you about the sugar in the cereal being advertised on Saturday mornings.
Grey Panthers Media Watch, 1841 Broadway, Rm. 300, New York NY 10023.
GWARM, Gay & Women's Alliance for Responsible Media, Box 48, Brooklyn, NY 11202. Robin Souza.
Media Access Project (MAP), 1910 N St., N.W., Washington, DC 20036. Harvey Shulman. Public interest communications law firm.
National Association for Better Broadcasting (NABB), Box 43640, Los Angeles, CA 90043.
National Black Media Coalition (NBMC), 2027 Mass. Ave., N.W., Washington, DC 20036, 202/797-7473. Pluria Marshall.
National Citizens Committee for Broadcasting (NCCB), 1028 Conn. Ave., N.W., Washington, DC 20036, 202/466-8407. Where you can find former FCC Commissioner Nicholas Johnson; NCCB publishes *access*, the magazine of the media reform movement, $24/year.
National Council of Churches, 475 Riverside Drive, New York, NY 10027. Dave Pomeroy.

National Latino Media Coalition, 1699 Lexington Ave., New York, NY 10029, 212/427-1080. Julio Rodriguez.

National Organization for Women (NOW), 5 S. Wabash, Chicago, IL 60603. Has a National Media Task Force; prepared a *Broadcast Media Kit* ($3 members, $5 non-members).

Prime Time School Television (PTST), 100 N. LaSalle St., Chicago, IL 60602. Helps you know how to use commercial tv educationally in the home.

United Church of Christ, Office of Communication, 289 Park Ave. South, New York, NY 10010. Rev. Everett Parker. Pioneer advocates for citizen access to the broadcast and cable media.

PRINT

access, see NCCB.

FCC Actions Alert. Free from the FCC to public interest groups wishing to keep up to date on Commission activities and to give them an opportunity to make comments.

Parties in Interest: A Citizens Guide to Improving Television and Radio, Robert Lewis Shayon, 1974, 28 pp., free from Office of Communication, United Church of Christ.

How to Protect Your Rights in Television and Radio, Ralph Jennings and Pamela Richard, 1974, $5.95 from United Church of Christ Office of Communications. Information on license renewal process and how to challenge a renewal request, how to enter a rulemaking, request for comments, fairness doctrine complaints, cross-ownership complaints. Believed to be the best resource.

Media Access: Your Rights to Express Your Views on Radio and Television, Andrew Shapiro, Little Brown & Co., 1976, $8.95. Discusses the legal responsibilities of broadcasters in regard to citizen participation, including the fairness doctrine, personal attack rule, political-editorial rule, equal time rule, complaints, political broadcasts.

How to Talk Back to Your Television Set, Nicholas Johnson, Bantam, 1970 (out of print).

TV Action Book, Jeffrey Schrank, 1974, McDougal Little & Co., 128 pp., cost unknown. Workbook for monitoring the media in your community.

The Family Guide to Children's Television: What to Watch, What to Miss, What to Change, and How to Do It, Evelyn Kaye, Pantheon, 1975.

The Target List, 1976, 31 pp., $2 from National Correspondence Group, Box 1039, Palo Alto, CA 94302. Access to corporations who advertise on tv; whether you like or don't like the shows they sponsor, this book will tell you how to get in touch with them. Also publishes a newsletter, *Viewer's Disgust.*

"Access to Television & Radio" in *Freedom of the Press vs. Public Access,* Benno Schmidt, Jr., Praeger, 1976, $6.95. Sponsored by the Aspen Institute Program on Communication and Society and the National News Council.

Citizens Groups & Broadcasting, Donald Quimary, Praeger Special Studies Program, 1975. A scholarly study of the citizen broadcast reform movement—the impetus behind it, history of early groups, followed by a case study of three groups: the Greater Cleveland Radio and Television Council, Action for Children's Television, and the Citizens Communication Center.

PUBLIC BROADCASTING

Public Television: A Program for Action, the Report and Recommendations of the Carnegie Commission on Educational Television, Harper & Row, 1967.

There used to be what was called educational radio and television. It metamorphosed into public broadcasting in the late '60s/the fourth network/set up and financially assisted by the federal government/noncommercial/high culture/still educational/instructional/NOVA/Masterpiece Theatre/All Things Considered/The Great American Dream Machine/Sesame Street/Zoom.

Most public stations are licensed to educational institutions, others to private nonprofit community foundations whose boards of directors are similar to those of art museums.

Volunteers provide a lot of support; listener subscribers about one-third of a station's income.

Noncommercial tv stations are often "instructional" during the day to serve school systems, and become "public" in the late afternoon.

Commercial broadcasters say classical music is an unprofitable format, so public radio fills that gap by programing primarily classical music.

Do you watch public tv? Listen to public radio?

Corporation for Public Broadcasting (CPB)
1111 16th St., N.W.
Washington, DC 20006
202/293-6160

An independent agency, set up by an act of Congress, funded by the government and private foundations and businesses. Publishes the informative newsletter *CPB Reports,* edited by Karen Frank, available for free. CPB's *Report of the Task Force on Women in Public Broadcasting,* 1975, is also available at no charge.

National Public Radio (NPR)
2025 M St. N.W.
Washington, DC 20036
Public Broadcasting Service (PBS)
475 L'Enfant Plaza West S.W.
Washington, DC 20024
202/488-5000

NPR and PBS are affiliations of public radio and tv stations, and also provide program services. Both have available lists of existing stations.

National Association of Educational Broadcasters (NAEB)
1346 Connecticut Ave. N.W.
Washington, DC 20036
Publishes the bi-monthly *Public Tele-* communications Review (PTR), $18/yr., and the useful annual, the *NAEB Directory of Public Telecommunications.*

National Federation of Community Broadcasters (NFCB)
1716 21st St. N.W.
Washington, DC 20009
202/232-0404
See community radio.

Catch-44
WGBH
125 Western Ave.
Boston, MA 02134
A true innovation—the first and longest running access program on public tv.

WGBH Television Workshop
and
The Television Laboratory
WNET
304 W. 58th St.
New York, NY 10019
Facilities supported by public tv stations set up for independent video makers to explore experimental video art and commentaries.

RADIO

Rock and roll made me aware of radio. Radio travels with you in your car. Muzak in elevators. See "No Soap, Radio."

What originally began in the late '40s as a way to improve tv program reception to rural areas having difficulty receiving signals (due to geography or distance) or without broadcast stations at all, bloomed in the late '60s and early '70s as a way to initiate new tv stations, due to the limited number of broadcast tv frequencies made available by the FCC.

The idea and technology for unlimited channels instigated many notions—not only could cable rebroadcast distant signals—channels could be set up for community originated programing, news, weather, college courses, etc. You would be able to vote, shop, bank all via the cable.

In 1972 the FCC Third Report and Order called for the establishment of three access channels—public, educational, government—to be set up on already existing and all new cable systems in the top 100 markets by 1977. Systems outside the largest markets with over 3500 subscribers were required to program one local origination channel.

The advent of small format, inexpensive video porta-paks was also part of the cable access picture and the Alternate Media Center was set up to assist cable operators in setting up these channels and video access centers.

Cable was big business, a new industry, and it was booming. But the economic situation of the mid-'70s—inflation, recession and high loan interest rates—brought about a great outcry by cable owners regarding the new cable regulations—they were in a financial crunch—and the date for establishing access channels was postponed.

But some cable operators remained committed to the idea of community access to cable and scattered around the country public access programing is flourishing, either on access or local origination channels.

Alternate Media Center (AMC)
144 Bleecker St.
New York, NY 10012
212/598-3338
George Stoney, Red Burns

AMC set up the country's first cable public access channels and published *The Access Workbook* (1973, 300 pp.), the definitive work on how to do it and worth every penny of the $35 cost if you're planning to go into the business; available with it, or as a single copy for $3 is *The Public Access Experience: Profiles of Six Centers* (1973, 48 pp.), which describes the beginnings of the first access channels.

CABLE

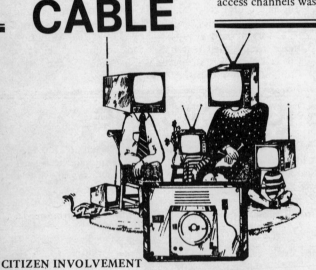

CITIZEN INVOLVEMENT

Center for Community Access Television at Amherst, Box 138, Amherst, MA 01002, 413/549-2800. David Skillicorn.
Eastern Queens Community Cable TV Association, 217-62 Corbett Rd., Bayside, NY 11361, 212/229-1222. Don Hanwood.
Schenectady Access Cable Council, 165 Eastern Parkway, Schenectady, NY 12309. Stephanie Stewart.
Squirrel Hill Citizens Cable TV, Box 8194, Pittsburgh, PA 15217.
Milwaukie Committee for Cooperative Cable Communication Systems, 3367 N. Hackett Ave., Milwaukee, WI 53211, 414/962-2100. Bettie Eisendrath.
Santa Barbara Community Cable TV Project, 119 E. De La Guerra, Santa Barbara, CA 93101.
Citizens for Community Cable, c/o Hawaii Council of Churches, 200 N. Vineyard Blvd., Rm. 403, Honolulu, HI 96817.
Sea-King Media Access Group, c/o American Friends Service Committee, 814 N.E. 40th, Seattle, WA 98104.

PUBLIC ACCESS CHANNELS & CENTERS

Warner Cable of Somerville, 58 Day St., Somerville, MA 02143, 617/628-4050.
Public Access Productions, Cable Ch. 7, Box 572, Vineland, NJ 08360.
Manhattan Cable TV Public Access, 120 E. 23rd St., New York, NY 10010, 212/260-3900.

Community Cable Center of Washington Heights-Inwood & Marble Hill, 4790 Broadway, New York, NY 10034.
Reading Community Video Workshop, Berks TV Cable Co., 112 Muhlenberg, Reading, PA 19602.
Orlando Public Access Workshop, 1111 Virginia Dr., Orlando, FL 32803.
Broadside Video, Elm & Millard, Johnson City, TN 37601
Video Access Center, Cable Ch. 7, Box 146, Columbus, IN 47201, 813/372-8784.
TV Grant, Box 351, Janesville, WI 53545.
Madison Community Access Center, 305 W. Dayton St., Madison, WI 53703, 266-4480.
Dekalb-Sycamore Community Access Center, Community CAble 8, 512-1/2 E. Lincoln Hwy., Dekalb, IL 60115.
General Electric Cablevision Corp., 602 W. Glen Ave., Peoria, IL 61614, 309/685-7671.
Austin Community Television, Capital Cable Co., 208 S. Palestine St., Austin, TX 78701.
Theta Cable Television, Box 25990, Los Angeles, CA 90025, 213/829-2676.
Community Video Center, Mission Cable, 6225 Federal Blvd., San Diego, CA 92114.
Bakersfield Community Video Access Center, Bakersfield Cable TV, 1615 V St., Bakersfield, CA 93301.
Community Action Television, Viacom Cablevision of San Francisco, 1175 Potrero Ave., San Francisco, CA 94110, 415/285-3800.
Public Access to Cable Television (PACT), LVO Cable of Hayward, 24800 Industrial Blvd., Hayward, CA 94545.
Acorn Community Television, 828-C Adeline St., Oakland, CA 94607, 415/444-3068.
Marin Community Video (MCV), 65 Tamal Vista, Coop Shopping Center, Corte Madera, CA.
Community Media Center, 299 Stockton Ave., San Jose, CA 95112, 408/287-5729.
Videolani, Oceanic Cablevision, 851 Cooke St., Honolulu, HI 96813.
Neighborhood Cable Television Center (NCTC), 3315 S.W. Kelly, Portland, OR 97201, 503/228-3532. John Platt.
CIRCT—Center for Innovation & Research in Cable Television, 117 N.W. 5th, Portland, OR 97209, 503/223-3419.
Viacom Cablevision, Box 2340, Lynwood, WA 98036.
Cowlitz Cableview, 11th & Douglas Streets, Longview, WA 98632, 206/425-7310.

SATELLITE

Public access to communications satellites is very new and exciting. The extension of a communications technology, up to now available only to the military, government and commercial industrial interests, to community oriented groups is happening now. Let's hope it will contribute to helping us talk to the person next door.

This is no minor undertaking on the part of organizations wishing to develop low-cost means of long distance communication and information exchange. The planning is crucial and the dollars necessary to put it into effect are substantial. The larger nonprofits, such as universities, medical institutions and public broadcasters, are working through the Public Service Satellite Consortium. Smaller, grass roots and lesser funded groups are being assisted by the Public Interest Satellite Association.

Easy Reading: chapters on satellite communications in *Beyond Babel* and *Mass Communications & American Empire*. Also see, *Satellite Spies*, by Sandra Hochman, Bobbs-Merrill, 1976, $8.95.

National Aeronautics & Space Administration (NASA)
 Experimental Communications
  Program
 Washington, DC 20546
 202/755-8571
 Wasyl M. Lew, Experiments Manager

Public Service Satellite Consortium (PSSC)
 4040 Sorrento Valley Blvd.
 San Diego, CA 92121
 714/452-1140

Public Interest Satellite Assn. (PISA)
 55 W. 44th St.
 New York, NY 10036
 212/730-5172
 Andy Horowitz
 Publications include: *Should People Fight for Satellites?* (free), *Communications Satellites: Now You Can Have Them Too* (free), *A Global Survey of Communications Satellite Systems* ($2), *A Study of the Communications Needs, Uses and Costs of Non-Profit Organizations* ($7.50).

Carl Clark
 23 Seminole Ave.
 Baltimore, MD 21228
 301/747-1395
Carl is a great information/communications experimenter. He is currently directing a health satellite project that will set up emergency medical training and information in Appalachia.

EASY READING

A Short Course in Cable, 1974, 13 pp., single copies free from Office of Communications, United Church of Christ, 289 Park Ave., South, New York, NY 10010.

Wired Nation. Cable TV: The Electronic Communications Highway, Ralph Lee Smith, 1972, Harper Colophon, $1.95. Background, history, issues and expectations.

Cable Handbook, 1975-76: A Guide to Cable and New Communications Technologies, ed. Mary Louise Hallowell, $6.95 plus 40¢ postage and handling from: Communications Press, 1346 Connecticut Ave., N.W., Washington, DC 20036. Mid-70s state of the art; extensive resource citations.

Social Services and Cable TV, Peg Kay and the Cable Television Information Center, funded by a grant from the National Science Foundation, July 1976, U.S. Government Printing Office, cost unknown. Up to date and complete; includes history, review of the literature, extensive bibliography; sets forth many examples of social services already implemented on the cable.

Design Study for Urban Telecommunications Experiments, Summary Report, Paul Bortz, Principal Investigator, 1975, 170 pp., cost unknown, from Denver Research Institute Industrial Economics Division, University of Denver, Denver, CO 80210. Discusses interactive programing for home subscribers and interactive information services in public places.

On the Cable: The Television of Abundance, Report of the Sloan Commission on Cable Communications, 1971, 256 pp., McGraw Hill, $2.95.

Cable Television and the FCC: A Crisis in Media Control, Don R. LeDuc, Temple University Press, 1973, 289 pp., $10. Law and regulation. Excellent bibliography.

Cable Television: A Guide for Citizen Action, Monroe Price and John Wicklein, 1972, 160 pp., $2.95 from United Church of Christ.

The Cable Book: Community Television for Massachusetts? 1974, $3 from Urban Planning Aid, 639 Mass. Ave., Cambridge, MA 02139. Valuable introductory resource for citizen involvement.

Cable Television in the Cities: Community Control, Public Access and Minority Ownership, Charles Tate, ed., 1971, $3.95 from the Urban Institute, 2100 M St., N.W., Washington, DC 20037.

GOVERNMENT

Federal Cable Bureau, Federal Communications Commission, Washington, DC.

State Cable Commissions. Some states have set up cable authorities to regulate the growth and operation of cable systems: Alaska, Connecticut, Delaware, Hawaii, Massachusetts, Minnesota, Nevada, New Jersey, New York, Rhode Island, Vermont.

Municipal Cable Officers. There is usually at least one person in city government assigned to keep track of cable development, and many cities have established cable authorities or commissions.

INDUSTRY

National Cable Television Association (NCTA), 918 16th St., N.W., Washington, DC 20006, 202/466-8111. Free resource packets. Publishes the annual *Local Origination Directory*, $4.

State Cable Associations

Broadcasting Cable Yearbook, by the editors of *Broadcasting Magazine*, 1735 De Sales St., N.W., Washington, DC 20036. State by state directory of cable systems, and software and hardware suppliers.

NW Cable Network, c/o Sharon Portin, Viacom Cablevision, Box 2340, Lynwood, WA 98036. Regional association of local origination managers.

GROUPS & ORGANIZATIONS

Cable Television Information Center, 2100 M St., N.W., Washington, DC 20037. Extensive publications schedule.

Cablecommunications Resource Center, 1900 L St., N.W., Washington, DC 20011, 202/296-5810. Jim Welbourne. Particularly interested in assisting minority ownership of cable systems. Publishes the bi-monthly *Cablelines*, $5/yr.

Publi-Cable, c/o State College, Kutztown, PA.

N.J. Cable Video Information Project, Urban Communications Teaching & Research Center, Livingston College, Rutgers University, State University of N.J., New Brunswick, NJ 08903, 201/932-4096.

MIXED MEDIA

DIRECTORIES

There's no one great all-encompassing directory. But the following will send you in the right direction.

A Guide to Independent Film & Video, Hollis Melton, ed., 1976, 87 pp., $4 from:
Anthology Film Archives
80 Wooster St.
New York, NY 10012
The final issue of the Bulletin for Film and Video. Leans towards film resources; the category breakdown and lack of index make the information difficult to access.

American Film Institute Guide to College Courses in Film & Television, Sam Grogg and Victoria Venker, eds., Acropolis Books, 1975, $4.50.

Aspen Handbook on the Media, 1975-76, William Rivers and William Slater, eds., 1975, 182 pp., $3.95 from:
Aspen Institute
Program on Communications & Society
360 Bryant St.
Palo Alto, CA 94301
Good general resource to established media organizations and publications.

International Video Exchange Directory, annual from:
Video Inn
261 Powell St.
Vancouver, BC Canada
A vehicle for the direct exchange of tapes and information among small format video producers and noncommercial users of video. It is not a list of everyone doing video but of those interested in exchange. Only those listed receive a copy of the directory.

Media Report to Women Index/Directory, Donna Allen, ed., $6 from:
3306 Ross Pl., N.W.
Washington, DC 20008
Most comprehensive annual of women's media groups. This is special. It also serves as a yearly index to the excellent monthly, *Media Report to Women*. Just reading the range of articles covered in the magazine indicates the range of concern and movement of women in media.

Northwest Alternate Communications Directory, 1976, $1 if available from:
Cascadian Regional Library
Box 1492
Eugene, OR
Brian Livingston has organized several media conferences in the region, and this directory grew out of the 1975 gathering. An excellent model for other regions and cities.

New Woman's Survival Sourcebook, Kirsten Grimstad and Susan Rennie, eds., Knopf, 1975, $5
The Communications, Arts and Literature Sections can direct you to hundreds of examples of women communicators.

Source Catalog: Communications, 1971, $1.50 from:
Source Collective
Box 21066
Washington, DC 20009
Not for current use but as early '70s state of the art.

UK Video Index
Centre for Advanced Television Studies
15 Prince of Wales Crescent
London, England

Video Resources in New York State, 1975, $3 from:
Publishing Center for Cultural Resources
27 W. 53 St.
New York, NY 10019
Exemplary.

STATE OF THE ART

The following references offer an historical overview.

A Resource for the Active Community, 1974, 125 pp., free from:
Canadian Radio Television Commission
100 Metcalfe
Ottawa, Ontario, Canada
Exciting report, detailing citizen participation in Canadian radio, television, cable.

Access, free from:
Challenge for Change/Society Nouvelle
National Film Board of Canada
Box 6100
Montreal, Quebec, Canada
Early '70s periodical, now publishing occasionally, about people access to media in Canada. Excellent format.

Network Project Notebooks
101 Earl Hall
Columbia University
New York, NY 10027
Produced 1972-74. While the Project no longer functions as a group, the *Notebooks* are still available and are an excellent introduction to government and corporate decision making and use of new communications technologies. Write for availability and price.

Radical Software, from:
Raindance Corp.
51 Fifth Ave.
New York, NY 10003
Ira Schneider, Beryl Korot
While this magazine was published there was nothing like it, and since it ended, there's been nothing to replace it. Write for availability of back issues and cost. Ira and Beryl have recently written *Videoart: An Anthology*, Harcourt, Brace, Jovanovich, 1976, $9.95.

"Television Bibliography" free from:
Rand Publications
1700 Main St.
Santa Monica, CA 90406
Extensively annotated, describes Rand's many books and papers on new communications technologies projects.

TeleVisions Magazine, from:
Washington Community Video Center
Box 21068
Washington, DC 20009
Though now publishing irregularly, back issues are available and are an excellent resource for mid-'70s video and tv information. The summer '76 issue (IV, 2, $1.50) had an excellent spread on small format video on television. Cost of previous volumes varies, write for current prices.

Thesaurus: Mass Communications, by Jean Viet, Unesco, 1975, cost unknown, from:
Mass Communications Documentation Center
UNESCO
Maison des Science de l'Homme
Place de Fontenoy
75 Paris-7° France
The language of mass communications, tri-lingual (English, French, Spanish). Fascinating reading.

HOW-TO

Community Media Handbook, A.C. Lynn Zelmer, Scarecrow, 1973, $7. How to set up a media access center. Excellent.

Doing the Media: A Portfolio of Activities and Resources, Kit Laybourne, ed., 1972, out of print, with plans to publish a revised edition. Contact: Center for Understanding Media, New School, 66 W. 12th St., New York, NY 10011

Producing Slide Tapes, Stephen Lewis, 1975, $3 from: Slide Tape Collective, 36 Lee St., Cambridge, MA 02139.

Video

Electric Journalist: An Introduction to Video, Chuck Anderson, Praeger, 1973, $6.50. Also by Anderson, *Grass Roots Video*, 1976.

Guerilla Television, Michael Shamberg and Raindance Corp., Holt, Rinehart & Winston, 1971, $3.95.

Independent Video, Ken Marsh, Straight Arrow Books, 1974, $7.95.

Introducing the Single Camera VTR System, Mattingly and Smith, $8.95.

Petersen's Guide to Video Tape Recording, Charles Bensinger, 1973, $2 from: Petersen Publishing Co., 6725 Sunset Blvd., Los Angeles, CA 90028. Best bet.

Spaghetti City Video Manual: A Guide to Use, Repair and Maintenance, Parry Teasdale and Videofreex, Praeger, 1973, $4.95.

Video & Kids, Peter Haratonik and Kit Laybourne, eds., Center for Understanding Media, Gordon & Breach, 1974, $3.

Video Primer, Richard Robinson, NY Links, 1974, $7.95.

Video Tools, CTL Electronics, 86 W. Broadway, New York, NY 10007.

Making the Media Revolution: A Handbook for Video Tape Production, Peter Weiner, Macmillan, 1973, $8.95.

Videotape Book, Michael Murray, Bantam, 1975, $1.95.

PERIODICALS

Not listed elsewhere. Frequency of publication and cost of subscriptions change; check with them directly.

access, 1028 Conn. Ave., N.W., Washington, DC 20036.

Afterimage, Visual Studies Center, 4 Elton St., Rochester, NY.

The Animator, Northwest Film Study Center, Portland Art Museum, S.W. Park & Madison, Portland, OR 97205.

AV Communications Review, Assn. for Educational Communications and Technology, 1201 16 St., N.W., Washington, DC 20036.

Avalanche, Center for New Art Activities, 93 Grand St., New York, NY 10013.

Canyon Cinemanews, Industrial Center, Rm. 220, Sausalito, CA 94965.

Cineaste, 333 Sixth Ave., New York, NY 10014

CLIENT: Communication Law Information, Edited Notes by Topic, University of Wisconsin-Madison, Dept. of Communication Arts, Vilas Communication Hall, 821 University Ave., Madison, WI 53706, Don R. LeDuc, Erwin Krasnow, eds.

Columbia Journalism Review, Columbia University, New York, NY 10027.

Communications Tomorrow, World Future Society, 4916 St. Elmo Ave., Washington, DC 20014, Wes Thomas, ed.

CVRP Patch Panel, California Video Resource Project, San Francisco Public Library, Civic Center, San Francisco, CA 94102.

Educational & Industrial Television, CS Tepner Publishing Co., 607 Main St., Ridgefield, CT 06877.

Film Quarterly, University of California Press, Berkeley, CA 94702, Ernest Callenbach, ed.

Filmmakers Newsletter, Box 115, Ward Hill, MA 01830, Suni Mallow, ed.

Inter-Media, International Institute of Communications, Tavistock House East, Tavistock Square, London, England.

Journal of Communication, Annenberg School, Box 13358, Philadelphia, PA 19101.

Journal of Popular Culture, Bowling Green University, Bowling Green, OH 43403, Ray Browne, ed.

Jump Cut, Box 865, Berkeley, CA 94701 (film).

Mass Media Booknotes, Dept. of Radio-TV-Film, School of Communication and Theater, Temple University, Philadelphia, PA 19122, Christopher Sterling, ed.

Media & Methods, 134 N. 13th St., Philadelphia, PA 19107.

Media Mix, 145 Brentwood, Palatine, IL 60067, Jeffrey Schrank, ed.

Media Report to Women, 3306 Ross Pl., N.W., Washington, DC 20008, Dr. Donna Allen, ed.

Midwest Video News, WIDL Video, 5875 N. Lincoln Ave., Chicago, IL 60659.

Musica, Box 55, Troutdale, OR 97060, Indi Allen, ed. (women's music).

Paid My Dues, Women's Soul Publishing, Box 5476, Milwaukee, WI 53211 (music).

Super 8 Filmmaker, 3161 Fillmore St., San Francisco, CA 94123.

Videocassette & Cable TV Newsletter, Martin Roberts Assoc., Box 5254, Beverly Hills, CA 90210.

Videography, 750 Third Ave., New York, NY 10017 (best video source).

Video Info, 16-18 rue Saint Victor, Paris, France, Boris Tirfoin, ed.

film/video/multi-media/independent
production/access facilities/showcases/
workshops/classes/distribution/images/
people

❖ NORTHEAST

University Film Study Center
Box 275
Cambridge, MA 02138

Slide Tape Collective
36 Lee St.
Cambridge, MA 02139
617/492-2949
Catalog of noncommercial slide
shows, production, published
booklet *Producing Slide Tapes.*

Urban Planning Aid
639 Mass. Ave.
Cambridge, MA 02139
617/661-9220
Bob Matorin
Community organizing, publishing, video tape library and duplication.

Somerville Media Action Project
(SMAP)
16 Union Square
Somerville, MA 02143
617/625-7882
Media center, cable access

Rounder Records
186 Willow Ave.
Somerville, MA 02144
Collective

Maine Film Alliance
c/o Abbott Meader
Rte. 3
Oakland, ME 04693

Community Media
Goddard College Summer Program
Paul McIsaac
Box M-4
Goddard College
Plainfield, VT 05667

Stand Communications Center
246 Main St.
Derby, CT 06418
203/735-6203
Cable radio, video.

❖ MIDATLANTIC

April Video
Gone but not forgotten

New Day Films
Box 315
Franklin Lakes, NJ 07417
Distribution

Downtown Community TV
Center
153 Centre St.
New York, NY 10003
212/966-4510
Jon Alpert
Production, workshops, Chinese
neighborhood.

Electronic Arts Intermix
85 Fifth Ave.
New York, NY 10011
212/989-2316
Video distribution, catalog, production facilities.

Media Studies
Master of Arts
Center for Understanding Media
New School for Social Research
66 Fifth Ave.
New York, NY 10011
John Culkin, Peter Haratonik

Anthology Film Archives
80 Wooster St.
New York, NY 10012
Jonas Mekas
Exhibition, library.

Global Village
454 Broome St.
New York, NY 10012
212/966-7526
John Reilly
First video production group in
U.S.; video study center.

Association of Independent
Video & Filmmakers
75 Horatio St.
New York, NY 10014

Women's Interart Center
549 W. 52nd St.
New York, NY 10019
212/246-6570
Workshops, video, film, photography, video newsletters, feminist
film and video festival.

Museum of Modern Art (MOMA)
Dept. PI
11 W. 53rd St.
New York, NY 10019
212/956-7296
Film and video exhibition.

Associated Council of the Arts
1564 Broadway
New York, NY 10036
212/586-3731
State arts agencies directory, $3.

Port Washington Public Library
Video Project
745 Main St.
Port Washington, NY 10050

Television Commercial Library
Dept. of TV & Radio
Brooklyn College
Brooklyn, NY 11210
From the golden age of television.

Media Bus
(aka Videofreex, Lanesville TV)
Box 418
Lanesville, NY 12450
914/688-7084
Skip Blumberg
Media center, van, tv station,
wrote *Spaghetti City Video
Manual.*

Woodstock Community Video
Box 159
Woodstock, NY 12498
914/679-2952
Ken & Elaine Marsh

Everson Museum of Art
401 Harrison St.
Syracuse, NY 13202
315/474-6064
Richard Simmons, video curator
Exhibition

Synapse
316 Waverly Ave.
Syracuse, NY 13210
315/423-2041
Video production facilities

Experimental TV Center
164 Court St.
Binghamton, NY 13904

Media Study
207 Delaware Ave.
Buffalo, NY 14202
716/847-2555
Gerald O'Grady

Portable Channel
The Community Video Center
8 Prince St.
Rochester, NY 14607
716/244-1259

Ithaca Video Project
328 E. State St.
Ithaca, NY 14850
607/272-1596

Film & Video Makers Travel Sheet
Film Section, Museum of Art
Carnegie Institute
4400 Forbes Ave.
Pittsburgh, PA 15213
412/622-3212

Independent Film & Video Preview Network
c/o Pittsburgh Filmmakers
Box 7200
Pittsburgh, PA 15213
412/681-5449

National Endowment for the
Arts
Washington, DC 20506

American Film Institute
The Kennedy Center
Washington, DC 20566

❖ SOUTH

North State Public Video
Box 7
Carrboro, NC 27510
919/929-7888
Production

Charleston Communications
Center
153 King St.
Charleston, SC 29401

Video Center
Florida State University
University Union
Tallahassee, FL 32306

Richard Loveless
University of South Florida
College of Education
Tampa, FL 33620

Alabama Media Project
Box 1984
University, AL 35486
205/758-2301

Louisville Communications
Center
125 Cagle St.
Louisville, MS 39339

New Orleans Video Access
Center (NOVAC)
1020 St. Andrew
New Orleans, LA 70130

Louisiana Society for the Arts
Box 401
Abita Springs, LA 70420
Only self-distribution net in U.S.,
Filmmakers Directory.

Rice Media Center
Box 1892
Houston, TX 77001
713/522-7997
Jim Blue

❖ MIDWEST

Antioch Video
Yellow Springs, OH 45387
513/767-7331, x 494
Library, tape duplication, catalog

Input Community Video Center
1015 W. Mitchell
Milwaukee, WI 53204

Community Video Exchange
814 W. Wisconsin Ave.
Milwaukee, WI 53233
Video tape library and training
program.

Wisconsin Public Library
Video Program
3030 Darbo Dr.
Madison, WI 53714
Kandy Brandt

Film in the Cities
490 N. Robert St.
St. Paul, MN 55403

Walker Art Center
Film Dept.
Vineland Place
Minneapolis, MN 55403
612/377-7500
Exhibition

Southdale-Hennepin Area Library
Media Lab
7001 York Ave. So.
Edina, MN 55435
Don Roberts

University/Community Video
Center
Studio A, Rarig Center
Univ. of Minnesota
Minneapolis, MN 55455

WIDL Video
5875 N. Lincoln Ave.
Chicago, IL 60659
312/271-4629
Business, mobile studio, equipment catalog.

Videopolis
3730 N. Clark
Chicago, IL

Communications for Change
22 W. Erie St.
Chicago, IL 60610
312/565-1785
Tedwilliam Theodore
Video intervention, workshops

MIXED MEDIA CENTERS

American Library Association
Video Cable Communications
    Section
50 E. Huron
Chicago, IL 60611
Cable Packet, check on current
cost.

On the Wall Productions
3457 Shenandoah
St. Louis, MO 63104
314/771-5405
John Mondello
Multi-media production group.

Commedia
6170 McPherson
St. Louis, MO 63108
314/863-3861
Eric Von Schrader
Media van.

Tulsa Public Library
400 Civic Center
Tulsa, OK 74103
Tom Ledbetter
Cable government access channel

❖ APPALACHIA

Broadside Video
Elm & Millard
Johnson City, TN
Media center; video ethnography
series

Elizabethtown Communications
    Center
105 N. Mulberry
Elizabethtown, KY 42701

Appalshop
Box 743
Whitesburg, KY 41858
Media center, recording studio,
films, catalog

❖ ROCKY MOUNTAINS

Denver Community Video Center
1459 Ogden
Denver, CO 80218
303/832-3603

Rocky Mountain Film Center
University Film Studies
Univ. of Colorado
101 Hellems Bldg.
Boulder, CO 80302
303/492-7900
Virgil Grillo
Exhibition

The Mediaworks
Box 4494
Boulder, CO 80306
303/494-1439
Michael Haldeman
New Periodicals Index, workshops.

Media Exchange of Telluride
Box 984
Telluride, CO 81435

Grass Roots Network
Box 2006
Aspen, CO 81611
Video

❖ CALIFORNIA

Hippovideo: Foundation for
    Multi-Media & the Arts
1290 Wilshire Bldg.
Los Angeles, CA 90017
213/482-4747
Boyd Clopton, Jack Paritz
Production

TVTV
Top Value Television
Box 48-455
Los Angeles, CA 90048
First small format video group to
break into network programming

Olivia Records
Box 70237
Los Angeles, CA 90070
213/389-4243
Feminist collective

Environmental Communications
64 Windward Ave.
Venice, CA 90281
213/392-4964
Slide collections, catalog

Positive Media in America
139 Wadsworth Ave.
Ocean Park, CA 90405
213/392-8756
Paul Holman
New age media communicators

Long Beach Museum of Art
2300 East Ocean Blvd.
Long Beach, CA 90803
David Ross, video curator
Exhibition, production facilities.

Kern County Library System
Video-Mail Service
1315 Truxton Ave.
Bakersfield, CA 93301

Insight Exchange
Box 42584
San Francisco, CA 94101
Exhibition

Bay Area Video Coalition
50 Oak St.
San Francisco, CA 94102
People

California Video Resource Project
San Francisco Public Library
Civic Center
San Francisco, CA 94102
Roberto Esteves

Optic Nerve
141 10th St.
San Francisco, CA 94103
Production group.

Media Alliance
13 Columbus Ave.
San Francisco, CA 94111
People

La Mammelle
Box 3123
San Francisco, CA 94119
Gallery, programing

Pacific Film Archive
University Art Museum
Berkeley, CA 94720
Edith Kramer
Exhibition

Canyon Cinema Cooperative
Industrial Center, Rm. 220
Sausalito, CA 94965
415/332-1514
Distribution, catalog

❖ NORTHWEST

InnFo
Box 266
Astoria, OR 97103
503/325-5938
Paxton Hoag
Business, multi-media.

Northwest Film Study Center
Portland Art Museum
S.W. Park & Madison
Portland, OR 97205
503/226-2811
Bob Sitton
Exhibition

Jack Eyerly
1990 S.W. Mill St. Terr.
Portland, OR
503/223-7898
West Coast media arts connector,
extensive archives (see networking
interview this section)

The Video Access Project
(Creative Outlet, CIRCT)
N.W. Artists Workshop
117 N.W. 5th, Rm. 215
Portland, OR 97209
503/223-3419
Bob Phillips, Elaine Velasquez,
Charles Auch

Northwest Media Project
Box 4093
Portland, OR 97208
503/283-4363
Association of independent video
and filmmakers.

Rhoda Epstein
1955 N.W. Hoyt, No. 10
Portland, OR 97209
Information networker, extensive
archives.

Fair Witness
2136 N.E. 20th
Portland, OR 97212
David Mesirow
Video and computer feedback for
small groups.

Coos County TV
Box 2483
Eugene, OR 97402
TV Town Hall; publication.

Medium/Rare
107 Cross Place
Eugene, OR 97402
Tripp Mikich
Multi-media.

and/or
1525 10th Ave.
Seattle, WA 98122
206/324-5880
Ann Folke

Media Shop
1505 10th
Seattle, WA 98122
206/322-8110
Business, equipment, workshops.

New Directions Radio
NW Alternative Ham Network
c/o Randy Brink
Rt. 2, Box 301-B
Port Orchard, WA 98366

Spokane Community Video
W. 1919 2nd Ave.
Spokane, WA 99204
509/624-3694
Don Jensen, Chris Venne
Production group

Video Inn
261 Powell St.
Vancouver, BC, Canada
604/688-4336
Ross Gentleman
Library, exhibition, directory

❖ CANADA

Canadian Broadcasting League
Box 1504
Ottawa, Ontario

Canadian Communications
    Research Information Center
222 Queen St.
Ottawa, Ontario

Canadian Radio-Television
    Commission
100 Metcalfe
Ottawa, Ontario

Interchurch Broadcasting
315 Queen St. E.
Toronto, Ontario

International Communications
    Institute
Box 8268, Station F
Edmonton, Alberta

National Film Board
Box 6100
Montreal, Quebec

❖ ENGLAND

Center for Advanced Television
    Studies
15 Prince of Wales Crescent
London, England

Inter-Action
14 Talacre Road
London, England
Multi-media van; publishes media
how-to handbooks

Swindon Viewpoint
14 Victoria Road
Swindon, Wiltshire, England
Only community television station
in all of Great Britain. A second
station is starting at the new city
of Milton Keynes.

NO SOAP, RADIO

Two elephants were sitting in a bathtub. One elephant said, please pass the soap. The other elephant replied—no soap, radio.

Vaudeville Joke

If you're driving across the great width and breadth of this country, perhaps you like to tune into radio and pick up some of the local sounds—or play around the dial and see what faraway vibrations the air waves bring you.

Chances are you'll pick up plastic homogenized radio—just like you pick up Denny's and Exxon.

Even if you have FM in your car, you're still likely to be treated to top 40 rock, easy listening, and network news—from coast to coast and border to border.

You'll also be subjected to loud commercials and raucous dj's.

And even if you're a fan of public radio—well, you'll miss the commercials, but you'll still hear the same middle classical music and the same network shows as back home. "All Things Considered" (National Public Radio's network news) may be a considerable improvement over commercial network news programs, but it doesn't fill the gap for local news and information.

But here and there across the land (and across the border in Canada too) there are sounds going out into the aether that fit no mold, that are created by the nature of the location they call home, and the folk doing it.

What I'm talking about is—well, it's really hard to define. I could say community owned/noncommercial/listener sponsored/volunteer operated/independent noninstitutional/low budget/educational (but that conjures thoughts of Boards of Education programming)/public access (but there are all degrees of access and each station defines it differently)/alternative/creative/imaginative/fat free/experimental/process radio/community/unlikely/personal/literate/attitude radio/activist/amiable/edible (to suit your tastes)/live and handmade.

They're *not* canned, prepackaged, computerized radio stations.

They are the only place on the dial—AM or FM—where you can hear sounds that you won't hear anywhere else, a blend of music—jazz/baroque/blues/gospel/ragtime/country/rock/reggae/big band/opera/electronic/soul/avant garde/folk music from around the world/classical of all variety/in studio live performances—mixed with—local community news and public affairs/radio drama/poetry/book readings/calendar announcements/discussion/by kids, for kids/interviews/documentaries.

And the voices—female as well as male, black as well as white, and oriental and spanish and native american indian, eskimo and . . .

You can usually find these stations on the educational portion of the FM band, 88.1-91.9. Even if you don't know what number on the dial they are, it's pretty easy to pick them out amidst the rest. They sound different. Listen.

Sex & Broadcasting: A Handbook on Starting a Radio Station for the Community, Lorenzo Milam, 3rd revised edition, 1975, 352 pp., $5 from:
**Dildo Press
2516 Maple
Dallas, TX 75201**
This self-published book is *the* source for inspiration, history and how-to. What you need to do a community radio station is: an available frequency in a town or city, a group of people to work together, patience, craziness, and some money. The way to gain real time experience is to volunteer at an already existing station.

How to do a community radio station is more than knowing how to get a license or understanding the engineering. It is people. It is personal. It is art. Lorenzo is a storyteller, and this book a literary surprise. Not for radio crazies only.

You do not have to be dull to instruct and inform and enlighten people. Your best, most exciting source of programs will be the thousand thousand people in your area who have never never had a broadcast station come to them and offer them time for free to talk, to be interviewed, to sing. . . .

A radio station should be the place in the community for concerned and talented and plain-home-folk individuals to have a chance to express themselves. In the place you live right now, there are hundreds of secret talents: there is someone who collects (and loves) old jazz; there are politically aware people—who can speak to reality, and raise so many consciousnesses in the process. There are readers—who can do fine 30- or 40-minute readings from novels or plays or poetry or children's books.

There are individuals, walking down the street right now, right there: live, loving people who can play the guitar or the kazoo or the harp—people who would be delighted to know that there is one door to the aether which is open and free to them: a door to all the hungry minds and souls of so many people who will, at last, know (through your station) that they are not alone. . . .

You have the chance to destroy the cruel walls built by the media barons to keep out the dispossessed, the thoughtful, the wondering. Your frequency can be the one place in your community of men where the angry, and the frustrated, and the knowing and the creative and the perceptive and the hopeless and the lost: The one place that they can know that they are free to speak their piece—without censorship, without fear, without cost." (pp. 233-234)

**National Federation of Community Broadcasters (NFCB)
1716 21st St. N.W.
Washington, DC 20009
202/232-0404
Thomas J. (Tom) Thomas, Director
Theresa (Terry) Clifford, Development**
NFCB is a participatory organization representing some 35 community-based public radio stations. It operates a cooperative program exchange among its members, provides a wide range of assistance on station operations such as fund raising, legal problems and program development, and handles individual and joint concerns before national agencies such as the Federal Communications Commission.

Most services are restricted to member stations, which support the organization's work. NFCB helps new groups get started, though, and sponsors national and regional conferences which are open to non-members.

Associate membership is available at reduced rates and the monthly *NFCB Newsletter* goes to all who contribute $15 or more. The newsletter will keep you up to date on Federation activities, community radio concerns and station goings-on.

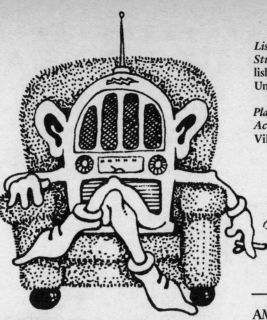

The Possible Tape Exchange (PTE)
705 N. Lincoln
Urbana, IL 61801
Bill Thomas
This is the Radio Program Service of the NFCB which makes available programs from community radio stations at some of the best prices around. Bill has been the guiding light behind this operation since it was just a "possible."

National Alternative Radio Conference (NARC)
In July 1972, eight community radio stations convened for the KRAB Nebula Media Conference, so named after the first community station, KRAB in Seattle. The mid-'70s saw a burgeoning of community radio activity and in June 1975, 150 community radio people gathered in Madison, Wisconsin, and called it NARC.

They met again in June 1976 in Telluride, Colorado, under the sponsorship of the NFCB. NARC looks like it's going to be an annual occurrence. This is the place to meet people actively involved in community radio. Contact the Federation for date and place.

Program Guides
All community radio stations publish program guides, most of them monthly. They detail the schedule of what's being aired.

So if you want to get an idea of the kinds of things being done by these stations, program guides are an excellent source. The Pacifica stations "Folios" initiated this service. In some communities, the program guide has taken on the appearance of a brief tabloid newspaper (containing paid advertising to cover expenses of producing the guide) which gives station personnel, volunteers and listeners an opportunity to talk radio.

Program guides are available with station subscriptions/memberships. For sample copies, send 50¢ to cover cost and postage. See station list for addresses. Those stations with call letters are on the air.

A LITTLE HISTORY

The Pacifica stations, started by Lew Hill in the late '40s with KPFA-Berkeley, were the first listener supported radio stations. In addition to KPFA, the

Pacifica Foundation holds licenses for KPFK-Los Angeles, WBAI-New York City, KPFT-Houston (currently renegade), and the newest, WPFW-Washington, D.C.

Lorenzo Milam had a different idea for ownership of noncommercial broadcast stations—that they should be licensed to the communities they were broadcasting from. He started KRAB-Seattle in 1963, followed by KBOO-Portland (originally a KRAB repeater), KTAO-Los Gatos, KDNA-St. Louis.

The first half of this decade saw a great deal of activity in community radio, due in part to a listing of Lorenzo's book, *Sex & Broadcasting*, in *The Last Whole Earth Catalog*, as well as the growing number of people gaining experience at the existing community radio stations going off to start their own.

Not much has been written *about* community radio in the conventional sense. Lorenzo's book is the only kind of handbook on how-to community radio. The other works are about the Pacifica Foundation stations.

Two people getting graduate degrees in communications, Tobi Kantor and Charles Oppenheimer, are currently researching and writing masters' theses on community radio.

Monopoly Steals FM From the People, by the Provisional Committee for Democracy in Radio, 1946.

The Exacting Ear: The Story of Listener Supported Radio, by Eleanor McKinney, Pantheon Books, 1966

Listener-Sponsored Radio: The Pacifica Stations, by Gene Stebben, unpublished PhD dissertation, Ohio State University, Columbus, OH 1969

Listener-Supported Radio: A Case Study, by Robert Lee Maril. Unpublished PhD dissertation, Washington University, St. Louis, Missouri, 1973

Playing in the FM Band: A Personal Account of Free Radio, by Steve Post, Viking, 1974. About WBAI.

Tobi Kanter
c/o Granfalloon
Box 18470
Denver, CO 80218

Charles Oppenheimer
3316 Burgoyne Dr.
Dayton, OH 45405

AMAZING FACTS

Alaska state law requires the Alaska Educational Broadcasting Commission to help citizens establish educational broadcast facilities, especially in areas where there are none (*How To K-2*) ▪ KBOO-Portland broadcasts live the week-weekly City Council meetings (and gets $1000 a year from the city) ▪ Stand-Connecticut (formerly pirate radio) operates a cable radio station while waiting to hear from the FCC on their application for a broadcast license ▪ Three groups (New Wave, Double Helix, Fessenden Fund) have UHF-TV applications pending ▪ WYSO-Yellow Springs is licensed to a college but cooperatively run with the community and has set up studios in nearby Dayton ▪ KBBF-Santa Rosa is the country's first bilingual (Spanish/English) radio station ▪ KBDY-St. Louis is licensed to a neighborhood association.

KLCC Almanac

COMMUNITY RADIO STATIONS

NORTHEAST/MIDATLANTIC
Monticello Public Broadcasting, Brighton Road, Monticello ME 04760
WCUW, 950 Main St., Worcester, MA 01610, John Levin
Duxbury Community Radio, 450 Lake Shore Dr., Duxbury, MA 02332
Stand Community Radio, 246 Main St., Derby, CT 06418, 203/785-6203, Ron Baktis
Community Progress, c/o Ludwig Spinelli, 270 Orange St., New Haven, CT 06511
WBAI, Pacifica, 359 E. 62 St., New York, NY 10021
Office of Newark Studies, 909 Broad St., Newark NJ 02102
WPFW, Pacifica, 1030 15th St., N.W., No. 522, Washington, DC 20005, Greg Millard
CKNR, 1342 King St., E., Kitchener, Ontario, Canada
CINQ, CP 65, Station G, Montreal, Quebec, Canada
Radio Jonquiere, c/o 112 Rue de la Fabrique, Jonquiere, Quebec, Canada

SOUTHEAST
WVSP, Box 365, Warrenton, NC 27589, Valeria Lee
WAFR (90.3), Community Radio Workshop, Box 1166, Durham, NC 27702, 919/688-5976
Charlotte Community Broadcasting, 1218 Myrtle Ave., Charlotte, NC 28203
WRFG (89.3). Radio Free Georgia, Box 5332, Atlanta, GA 30307, 404/523-3471, Larry Lee
WDNA (88.9), Bascomb Memorial Broadcasting Foundation, Box 330069, Miami, FL 33133, 305/666-9422, Holt Maness
Nathan B. Stubblefield Foundation, Box 82155, Tampa, FL 33682, Arny Shlansky
Green County Development, Box 531, Eutaw, AL, Louis Barnett
Benton-Tippah Broadcasting Assn., 318 Terry St., Ripley, MS 38663
WLNK, Golden Triangle Educational Media Corp., 102 N. 5 St., Columbus, MS 39701
Nora Blatch Educational Foundation/New Orleans, c/o Walter Brock, KCHU, 2516 Maple, Dallas, TX

MIDCENTRAL
WYEP (91.5), Pittsburgh Community Broadcasting, 4 Cable Place, Pittsburgh, PA 15213, 412/687-0200, Tricia Capitolo
WEVL (90.3), Southern Communication Volunteers, Box 2118, Memphis, TN 38101, 901/722-8666, Dennis Batson
WFAC (91.5), Columbus Community Educational Broadcasting, Box 8147, Columbus, OH 43201, 614/224-WFAC, Jeff Burmeister
WAIF (88.3), Step Child Radio, 2525 Victory Parkway, Cincinnati, OH 45206, 513/961-8900, Nan Rubin
WYSO (91.5), Antioch College, Yellow Springs, OH 45387, 513/864-2022, Joanne Wallace
Grand Rapids Public Broadcasting, Grand Valley State Colleges, William James College, Allendale, MI 48401
Community Radio Project, 1130 W. 17, Bloomington, IN
WORT (89.7), Back Porch Radio, Box 3219, Madison, WI 53704, 608/249-0111, Don Steenweg
Fresh Air, 3104 16 Ave., So., Minneapolis, MN 55407, Bryan Peterson
KAXE, Northern Community Radio, Itasca Community College, Grand Rapids, MN 55744, 218/326-9427, Suzi McClear
WDTH, 130 Humanities Bldg., University of Minnesota-Duluth, Duluth, MN 55812
Open Media Corp., Box A3463, Chicago, IL 60690, 312/251-3652, Mitch Lieber
Prairie Air, 705 N. Lincoln, Urbana, IL 61801, 217/367-7261, Bill Thomas
KBDY, Montgomery-Hyde Park Neighborhood Advisory Council, 2505 St. Louis Ave., St. Louis, MO 63106, 314/231-9321, Jeff Fobes
Double Helix, 390A Euclid, St. Louis, MO 63108, 314/361-7111, Bob Zeffert
KOPN (89.5), New Wave Corp., 915 E. Broadway, Columbia, MO 65201, 314/443-5611, Steve Dreher
Sunrise Communications, 545 S. 29 St., Lincoln, NE 68501, Ron Kurtenbach
Ozark Access Center, Box 506, Eureka Springs, AK 72632

TEXAS
KCHU (90.9), Agape Broadcasting Foundation, 2516 Maple, Dallas, TX 75201, 214/742-6262, Dennis Gross
KPFT, Pacifica, 419 Lovett Blvd., Houston, TX 77009, 713/529-4951, Steve Heimel
KAZI, Austin Community Radio, c/o Dr. John Warfield, 5505 Pendleton Lane, Austin, TX 78723
San Antonio Community Radio, 408 S. Texas Bldg., San Antonio, TX 78205, 512/224-5456, Henry Morales

COLORADO
KOTO (91.7), San Miguel Educational Fund, Box 703, Telluride, CO 81435, 313/728-4333, Jerry Greene
Granfalloon, Box 18470, Denver, CO 80218, Tobi Kanter
Bilingual Communications Center, 1100 14 St., Denver, CO 80201, Don Gardenas
KGNU, Boulder Community Broadcasting Assn., Box 1076, Boulder, CO 80302, 303/442-6253, Jerry Bellas

SOUTHWEST
Listeners Community Radio of Utah, c/o Paul Wharton, Box 1222, Salt Lake City, UT 84110
Community Broadcasting Foundation of Phoenix, Box 2734, Phoenix, AZ 85002, Scott Campbell

CALIFORNIA
KPFK (90.7), Pacifica, 3729 Cahuenga Blvd., Los Angeles, CA 90038, Will Lewis
White Ash Broadcasting, 1759 Fulton St., Fresno, CA 93721
Great Silence Broadcasting, Box 37, Pacific Grove, CA 93950
KPOO (89.5), Box 11008, 532 Natoma, San Francisco, CA 94101, Jahid Songhai
KPFA (94.1), Pacifica, 2207 Shattuck Ave., Berkeley, CA 94704, 415/848-6767, Randy Thom
KKUP, Box 547, Cupertino, CA 95014
Reginald A. Fessenden Educational Fund, 131 Wilder, Los Gatos, CA 95030, Jeremy Lansman
KUSP (89), 'Pataphysical Broadcasting, Box 423, Santa Cruz, CA 95061, 408/476-2800
Public Communicators, 787 E. San Antonio, San Jose, CA 95112, Phil Jacklin
KBBF (89.1), Bilingual Broadcasting Foundation, Box 7189, Santa Rosa, CA 95401, 707/545-8333, Dick Mahler
North Coast Broadcasting, Box 644, Mendocino, CA 95460, Karl Toubman

NORTHWEST
KBOO (90.7), The KBOO Foundation, 3129 S.E. Belmont, Portland, OR 97214, 503/234-5431, Carol Mazer
KLCC, Lane Community College, Box 1-E, Eugene, OR 97401, Barbara Stern
KAOS, The Evergreen State College, Olympia, WA, Bob Costello
KRAB (107.7), Jack Straw Memorial Broadcasting Foundation, 1406 Harvard, Seattle, WA 98122, 206/325,5110
CFRO (102.7), Vancouver Coop Radio, 333 Carrall St., Pigeon Park, Vancouver, BC, Canada, 604/684-8494
Aurora Community Broadcasting, Box 1900, Downtown, Anchorage, AK 99510
KTOO (104.3) Capital Community Broadcasting, Box 1487, Juneau, AK 99802, 907/587-1567, Bruce Theriault
KRBD, Rainbird Community Broadcasting, Box 17, Ketchikan, AK 99901, 907/225-4636
Rangell Broadcasting, Box 282, Rangell, AK 99929
Petersburg Community Radio, Petersburg, AK

Carrier Current Neighborhood Radio

- you know your audience
- inexpensive to set up ($1,000)
- localized channels of information are likely to be more trusted
- requires no licensing by the FCC
- decentralization of access to media

When I talked with Peter Haratonik of the Center for Understanding Media in 1975 about my interest in community radio, he said, you should get in touch with Dan Mack. I did and discovered that Dan was talking about a more localized medium than I was.

Dan wanted to put a radio station in apartment buildings on a block in New York City. Low power, low cost AC carrier current radio. An inexpensive, accessible communications vehicle, well suited to dense urban neighborhoods with high concentrations of minorities having special needs that are not able to be met by local broadcast media—the elderly, ethnic groups, foreign language groups, and groups with specialized environmental, political and social concerns.

Dan is now setting up such a station in the middle of a housing project—Douglas Houses on four city blocks on Manhattan's Upper West Side. The studio will be located in the Trinity Lutheran Church. The people living in this project are primarily poor blacks and hispanics.

In December 1976 I talked with Dan about the hows and whys of AC carrier current radio. He says he'll know a lot more about this in six months (by the time this catalog is out) and you can write him:

Dan Mack
225 W. 106 St., Apt. 16K
New York, NY 10025

D: What we're going to do is run phone lines to each of the ten buildings in the housing project. And put an amplifier at the end of each of our lines, a line amplifier. And then hook into the electrical system in each of these places. So basically you run a line to a transmitter into the electrical system. But we're going to then run a line from a transmitter to another house, to an amplifier to an electrical system. To amplify our signal for going that distance.

So we're going to know definitely who our audience is because we're only broadcasting to the people in an immediate area. One of the advantages of this is that you know who you're broadcasting to. So really it's narrowcasting. You know your audience.

It decentralizes the whole process of radio and media, because people who are listening are neighborhood people and are able to come into the church, which is already a kind of a central point in the neighborhood, and participate in the programing themselves. In addition to that we're going to have phone-in access so if people don't want to leave their homes, they can call in.

Another thing is there are studies feeding into this, showing that people—particularly people in poorer urban areas—are more suspicious of outside information than they are of inside information. That is, channels of communication into ghetto areas are very delicate things. People are distrustful very often of federal or city or state programs that come in. So starting IN the middle of something with a communications system like this, we're going to see what happens.

We're already working with CETA people in the neighborhood, we're working through the church, there's a police station right across the street. We're plugging into as many existing community organizations as possible. Not going to be brand new, it's going to be an extension of all the other services there. Making sure that it delivers services and provides services that are not duplicated other places in the city.

The studio's going to be in the church. Basically you need the transmitter and then some sort of board or console which you can buy used (or build yourself). With about $1,000 worth of investment you can get the station on the air. The transmitter I think cost us $480 brand new. (Low Power Broadcasting, 520 Lincoln Hwy., Frazer, PA 19355) Then, of course, it can go up to any amount of money after that, depending on the quality of the accessory equipment.

R: Explain to me why you don't need an FCC license for this, or how this gets to be allowed. I mean, do you have to have FCC approval to be doing this? Do they have to know what you're doing?

D: Under Section 15 of the FCC law you don't need a license. You're technically not broadcasting through the air. You're broadcasting through an electrical system in a house. Although, in effect, you are broadcasting because the electrical system radiates your signal. But it's very low power. We're only having a 5 watt station, going with a 5 watt transmitter.

R: And it's only going to who's hooked up. Will people who are not hooked up outside of the buildings be able to pick up the station?

D: Maybe. I don't know until we actually hook it up and see. There are some very funny things that happen with magnetic radiation. Other people may be able to pick it up. I was told that the University of Washington has an AC carrier current station that can be picked up 300 miles away because their transmitter's right near their generating station at the University and there's this tremendous boost in power that takes place when they plug into that system and is picked up 300 miles away.

The other thing to consider in urban areas, or even in rural areas, is using what they call the side bands of FM stations. There are two or three additional bands for which you need special receptors for your radio. But I know here in New York, for instance, there are some Chinese language stations that are renting FM sidebands from some of the FM stations. The people who want to receive these stations buy special adaptors for their FM radio and they broadcast just to the Chinese community.

Sub carrier and AC carrier current are two different ways of doing similar things. Although AC (AM) carrier current is going through the electrical system of somewhere, and FM sideband, or sub carrier, is again radiating through the air, is broadcasting. So that would be the next step up if you have a geographically diverse group of people that you want to broadcast to.

TRANSPORTATION

We are only beginning to realize that transportation represents a *cost* of society and is therefore something to be minimized rather than maximized. What we really want is to be in good places, with good people, doing good things, and feeling good about it. These things can usually be gotten more easily directly than with transportation.

What do we gain? Apparent freedom, individually—but only apparent. At rush hours, in parking lots, in real time options, the pedestrian or cyclist has an enviable freedom. The hours we have to spend earning the money to pay for our transportation habits are not a freedom. And one of the most real costs of our vast transportation system is that it makes possible and encourages the centralization of power in a few hands. It

is not the two-thirds of Americans that have never been in an airplane that benefit from air travel—it is the corporate businessmen who are thus able to keep together oversized conglomerate industries. It is the management and major stockholders of General Motors that benefit from our car buying, far more than we do. Subsidized transportation allows the centralizing power of advertising and the larger economic base of big industry to force small local firms out of business—often with an increase in both costs and prices as well as loss of power and control by individuals. Reducing transportation and full-costing to users of transportation helps localize the scale of production systems and reduces economic and environmental costs in the process.

The automobile is a useful and good luxury, and in small doses is likely to continue as a desirable element in our transportation system, but less transportation and a smaller proportion of it based on automobiles seem a clear advantage once the full costs are known. Few Americans have ever experienced a good public transit system—so common in other countries. Fewer still have lived where land use patterns provide good surroundings while eliminating the need for commuting, chauffeuring and parking lots. It's not outrageous to claim that our quality of life can improve with a 90% reduction in transportation, and a two-thirds reduction seems likely over the next 20 years.

REDUCING THE NEED FOR TRAVEL

Energy and Equity, Ivan Illich, 1974, 95¢ from:

> Harper and Row
> 10 E. 53rd Street
> New York, NY 10022

A penetrating analysis of the social and economic costs of modern high-energy transportation. Illich shows that:

The typical American male devotes more than 1,600 hours a year to his car. He sits in it while it goes and while it stands idling. He parks it and searches for it. He earns the money to put down on it and to meet the monthly installments. He works to pay for petrol, tolls, insurance, taxes and tickets. He spends four of his sixteen waking hours on the road or gathering his resources for it. And this figure does not take into account the time consumed by other activities dictated by transport: time spent in hospitals, traffic courts and garages; time spent watching automobile commercials or attending consumer education meetings to improve the quality of the next buy. The model American puts in 1,600 hours to get 7,500 miles: less than five miles per hour. In countries deprived of a transportation industry, people manage to do the same, walking wherever they want to go, and they allocate only three to eight percent of their society's time budget to traffic instead of 28 percent.

"City Planning in China," Graham Towers, *Architectural Design*, July 1973, $48/yr. from:

> 7/8 Holland Street,
> London, W8, England

Once again the Chinese seem to be on the right track. Planning for social, not technical ends. Jobs located where the people are, transportation needs minimized and rural resources valued rather than expropriated. Look for the article in most architecture and planning libraries.

In 1972, the Organization for Economic Cooperation and Development (OECD to its friends) did a world survey of traffic-free zones.

"In Vienna, shop owners reported a 25-50% increase in business in the first week after the traffic ban went into effect last December. In Norwich, all but two shops in the exclusion area did more business. Some increase has been reported to be between 15 and 35 percent; Rouen, in France, between 10 and 15 percent.

In Tokyo, of 574 shops surveyed, 21% showed an increase in sales, 60% showed no change and 19% reported a decrease. Seventy-four percent of the merchants interviewed pronounced themthemselves in favor of the scheme."
(Thanks to *Cyclateral Thinking*)

A TALE OF TWO CITIES

Most cities have enacted zoning regulations in recent years that largely prevent people from working in their homes, living over their store or walking to work. "Rational" planning sets up isolated zones of just industry, just businesses and just homes. A nice theory, but the results are staggering. It's like having two towns. Everyone gets up in one town, then everyone moves to the second town, works, then moves back to the first town, leaving the second one vacant. Absurd! We now have enough toilets and sewers and restaurants and furnaces and light fixtures and telephones to service two cities, plus freeways and autos and parking lots for going back and forth, and even police to watch over the empty cities when people are in the other one. Odd? And expensive. We basically duplicate our total urban structure because of our zoning fantasy.

All our earth was once a paradise . . . and paradise begins at home.

The words and sketches of early travelers and settlers are filled with amazement at the beautiful, life-filled places —some of the same places which now stand as barren rubble and pavement. Energy and money spent traveling to good places to escape the ugliness of our cities is energy and money enjoyed once and used up, in the process often destroying these good places.
Energy and money spent making where we live beautiful gives us a paradise we can enjoy every day and one which remains for the enjoyment of our children and others.

It has always seemed a shame that our culture didn't follow the European or Latin American tradition of building our homes around courtyards. The outside walls buffer the noise and smells of even the most urban areas so that the inner garden or court—no matter how simple—stays peaceful and private.

*See also the sections on Shelter and Community Building for more ideas on how to make where you *are* paradise. Actually, that's what this whole book is about.

Energy Conservation through Automobile Parking Management, Newsletter Number 6 of the Energy Conservation Project, May 1976, free from:

> Environmental Law Institute
> 1346 Connecticut Ave., N.W.
> Suite 620
> Washington, DC 20036

The Energy Conservation Project is preparing a series of handbooks addressed to state and local officials, legislators and interested citizens setting out alternative legal strategies for conserving energy (available Spring 1977 from Ballinger Publishing Co.). This issue from one of these books, *Energy Conservation and Urban Transportation*, provides a useful exploration of legal ways to reverse the subsidy to automobile transportation and sprawling urban patterns that people have felt helpless trying to control. Valuable information on effectiveness and problems of existing projects that are trying various strategies of taxing, residential parking permits, parking bans, zoning, subsidy elimination, and redesign of parking facilities.

ADAPTING EXISTING TRANSPORT

"Community and Self-Help Transport," Brian Richards, *Architectural Design*, May 1976, monthly, $48/year from:
> 7/8 Holland St.
> London, W8 England

Also available in most architectural libraries or through interlibrary loan. Richard's frequent contributions to A.D. on transportation give some of the best coverage around of expanded transportation options. This article covers subsidized city taxes in Munich, jitneys or shared cabs, dial-a-ride experiments, mini-buses, and problems and potentials of other options in use or experiment around the world.

"Let's Get the Railroads Moving Again," Orren Beaty, *Not Man Apart*, October 1975, from:
> Friends of the Earth
> 529 Commercial
> San Francisco, CA 94111

A good overview of the history of our railroads and their demise. Then some sensible proposals for their rebirth. Required reading for train freaks.

Alternative Sources of Energy, No. 23, $2 from:
> ASE
> Route 2
> Milaca, MN 56353

Twelve pages of reports on low-cost, low-energy transportation—including a bicycle that runs on abandoned railroads, bicycles, mo-peds (which I haven't seen since I used to assemble them at Sears 20 years ago), mini-trucks and use of methane and propane as auto fuels.

Transportation Policies and Energy Conservation, Ralph Rechel, 1975, $3.50 from:
> The Conservation Foundation
> 1717 Massachusetts Avenue, N.W.
> Washington, DC 20036

A survey of federal and state subsidies, regulation and participation in various modes of transportation and potential policy options for a more effective and balanced transportation system.

Neighborhood Transportation System, from:
> Marin County Transit District
> Civic Center
> San Rafael, CA 94903

Although never put into operation, this is a very nice proposal for a ride-stop system where drivers get coupons from hitchhikers picked up at special stops. Feasibility all mapped out.

How to Convert Your Auto to Propane/Methane, Jerry Friedberg, $2 from:
> Arrakis Propane Conversions
> Rt. 2, Box 96C
> Leslie, AR 72646

It costs about $70-$140 for everything needed to convert *any* vehicle to propane (prices vary with the size of the engine). Jerry says he's driven cross-country several times and found LP everywhere, though not as conveniently as popping into the first gas station. This 15-page booklet has easy-to-read instructions, and he'll sell you 1/3 off standard retail prices on needed equipment.

ELECTRIC TROLLEYS

Barry Commoner, in his February 16, 1976, *New Yorker* article on energy, compared the energetics and economics of various transportation systems and offered some useful observations:
* Railroads are presently the most energy-efficient vehicles. Improvement in energy use requires use of waste heat, which is very difficult in a mobile vehicle. This indicates the value of electrification with use of waste heat from the power plant for space heating and other uses.
* Electrified railroads and electric buses offer particular advantages for stop and go operation because their electric motors can be reversed for use as brakes, returning power to the lines.
  These and other advantages of electric trolleys over diesel buses have led several cities to revive and modernize their trolley systems, and have brought citizen pressure on other cities to do the same.

Citizens for Better Transit
8311 S.W. 3rd Avenue
Portland, OR 97219
This is one such group that has amassed considerable information on the issues involved.

CO-OP RENTALS

Availability of public transit or choosing to live near where we work means that most of the need for automobiles can be eliminated in the city. Payments, parking and insurance for vehicles to have them available for weekend jaunts or evening trips add up quickly for the amount of use. A better option in many areas would be a cooperative neighborhood vehicle rental—where you could get a vehicle right for your needs each time—whether hauling firewood or trash or going to a concert. The profit margin on business-oriented car rentals is excessive and the real cost of a neighborhood rental would be much less, particularly if combined with business rentals to balance demand peaks. It also would eliminate much of the hassle of maintenance, insurance and always having the wrong vehicle for your needs. Any takers? Know of any existing?

AIR SHIPS AND SAILING SHIPS

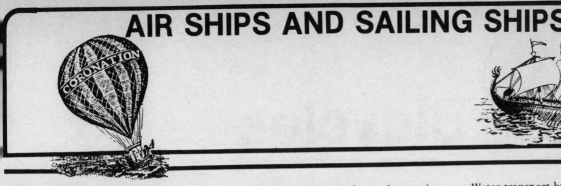

Attention has recently been turning to forms of water and air transportation that don't require the massive fuel subsidies of our present ships and planes. Advancement in understanding of aerodynamics of sails and of the planet's wind systems offer improvement in cruise time of sailing ships. Design of low-power electric winch systems to replace the large crews necessary to operate the sails allow greater potential cargo space. Putting these and other advances together, the School for Naval Architecture at the University of Hamburg, Germany, has been refining designs for "Dyna-Ships," which promised, even before recent fuel price increases, to give a 30 percent greater return on investment than comparable conventional ships. For more details, see: *Energy for Survival*, Wilson Clark, 1975, $4.95 from Doubleday & Co., 45 Park Ave., New York, NY 10017.

"Return of the Tall Ships," James McCawley, *Rudder*, 1971.

"The Sailing Ship in the Fuel Crisis," Basil Greenhill, *The Ecologist*, Sept. 1972. (Gatesby, Molesworth St., Wadebridge, Cornwall, GB)

Lighter-than-air craft are also getting renewed attention. Balloons are now used in some forestry applications. Goodyear Corporation has proposed greater use of cargo-carrying dirigibles in this country. And the German firm WDC has been testing a modern lighter-than-air craft over Accra, Ghana, to prove that the ship, costing only one-eighth of a comparable jumbo jet, is a superior means of transporting crops, minerals and people in areas not serviced by a network of roads.

Airships: An Illustrated History, Henry Beaubois, 1973, $35 from:
Two Continents Publishing Group Ltd.
30 E. 42nd Street
New York, NY 19917
A fancied-up, profusely illustrated coffee table book, but gives fascinating coverage of the evolution, design and details of lighter-than-air craft. Also contains an overview of current experimental projects in various countries that were presented at the London and Paris conferences in 1971 and 1973. A good introduction to lighter-than-air craft.

Water transport by barges has never really lost its cost advantages for moving bulk materials. Canal cruising has also been a favorite peaceful vacation in England, the Netherlands, Finland, Germany and other areas. The *Mariner's Catalog Number Four* ($6.95 from International Marine Publishing Company, 21 Elm Street, Camden, ME 04843) as well as previous catalogs contains an incredible wealth of resources for anyone interested in ships, water and ocean life. Number Four also contains a review of *Canal Enthusiasts' Handbook No. 2* from David and Charles, North Pomfret, VT 05053 ($10.95), which they recommend as *the* source for anyone interested in canals and canal transportation.

Lighter than Air Society Newsletter
1800 Triplett Blvd.
Akron, OH 44306
Active memberships, including the newsletter, are $6/yr. 1977 will be the 24th volume of the newsletter.

$8 a Gallon for Gasoline?

How many of us would still consider the automobile a wise transportation choice if gasoline cost $8.00 a gallon? Most of us would scream highway robbery and foam at the mouth in rage—but that is what gasoline would cost right now if automobile transportation wasn't guilty of some of the most massive tax evasion and taxpayer subsidy in history. Even including the cost of car payments, insurance and repairs in addition to the cost of gas and oil, we are paying less than half of the true cost of automobile travel. As a result of not paying the full cost, we use and waste more of it than we would if we paid the real bill.

The additional $7.50/gallon above the present cost of gasoline and gas taxes represents the user taxes that would be required to pay some of the most obvious costs presently avoided by highway users. Half of it is the cost of congestion, traffic accidents, and air pollution directly resulting from but not charged to the automobile. The other half is coughed up by everyone who pays property taxes—in the form of higher taxes resulting from streets and highways not being included on the tax rolls. A recent study of New York City showed that such tax losses there exceeded $1.14 billion per year.

Paying $7.50 per gallon as a gasoline tax wouldn't mean any increase in costs—it is merely the amount that we (or someone else) are *already* paying in hidden subsidies to the automobile. Having to pay the full costs would obviously curtail much of our excessive highway building and use of automobiles and trucks. If we paid the *total* cost of automobile travel at the gas pump each time we chose to use the auto instead of having most costs paid separately in monthly payments, insurance, property taxes, etc., we would be more aware of what we really pay for this service. All included, we would have to pay more than $15 per gallon of gas—which would make the cost of a bus or train ticket seem the real bargain it is!

Automobiles will become an increasing burden as the cost of fuels and maintenance of our massive highway system increases, and beginning now to pay the real costs would provide an effective stimulus towards less expensive land use and transportation patterns.

For more details on the societal cost of the automobile to New York City and its region, see *Societal Cost Accounting: A New Tool for Planners*, by Brian Ketcham, 1976, available from Citizens for Clean Air Inc., 25 Broad Street, New York, NY 10001.

Bicycles

It's happened quietly, but bicycles have become a major means of transportation in this country. They're out-speeded, out-noised, out-priced, out-spaced by automobiles, so aren't so visible (thank goodness!). But they've become the dominant means of transportation in many U.S. cities (usually college towns), where piece by piece a whole bicycle transportation system has been put together—bicycle paths and bicycle lanes, parking areas, bicycle trips for traffic signals, sales and repair shops, trailers for bicycles, bicycle storage on buses, trains and mass transit systems. You don't need to go to Amsterdam anymore to see a different world of transportation— go to Martha's Vineyard; Madison, Wisconsin; Santa Barbara, California; and Eugene, Oregon.

Bicycling Science: Ergonomics and Mechanics, by Frank Whitt and David Wilson, 1974, $4.95 from:

> MIT Press
> 28 Carlton St.
> Cambridge, MA 02142

The bicycle of today is the simplest, quietest, most efficient and least lethal of modern vehicles. This is an excellent book for the person who wants to know how and why they work so well: power required, muscle efficiency, gradient resistance, drag coefficient values, quantitative measurement of the rolling resistance of pneumatic tires, and more, much more.

Energy Use for Bicycling

> Oak Ridge Ntl. Laboratory
> Environmental Program
> P.O. Box X
> Oak Ridge, TN 37830

"If 10% of the urban auto travel conducted during daylight and in good weather for trips of 5 miles or less were shifted to bicycles, the savings in 1971 would have been 180 trillion BTU, 1.8% of total urban automobile energy use." Report No. ORNL-NSF-EP-65.

Bicycle Transportation, by Nina Dougherty and William Lawrence, Environmental Protection Agency, 1974, $.94 from:

> Supt. of Documents
> U.S. Government Printing Office
> Washington, DC 20402

Just about everything you wanted to know about bicycles as alternative transportation: energy efficiency, use statistics, problems and programs (both in the U.S. and abroad). Also an extensive bibliography. Good, hard data.

Give Way: A Report on Cycling in Britain, Richard Feilden, $3.90 from:

> Friends of the Earth, Ltd.
> 9 Poland Street
> London, W1V 3DG, England

It's always useful to see what's happening in other parts of the world. This report has lots of statistics and discussions of different cities' solutions to bikeway planning.

The Story of the Bicycle, John Woodford, 1970, 175 pages, $5.95 from:

> Universe Books
> 381 Park Ave. South
> New York, NY 10016

This little book concentrates on the interaction between the bicycle habits and customs in England in the late 19th century. Read how cyclists led the campaign for smooth roads; the differential gear and the pneumatic tire, essential in cars, were invented for early pedal-powered vehicles; every part and feature to be found in modern bicycles was in use by 1905; the bicycle lent impetus to feminism, and women in the 1890s were especially supportive of the first equal-wheeled, chain-driven "safety bicycles."

Alderson's history is well-written and lavishly illustrated with etchings and woodcuts of the time. (Bart Jones)

The 1976 Bicycle Bibliography, David J. Luebbers, 148 pages, from:

> Route 3, Box 312
> Columbia, MO 65201

Notes on books, documents, magazine and newspaper articles on bicycles and bicycling. Very complete—includes many little-known gems. (Bart Jones)

In San Diego it costs 25¢ in addition to regular fare to get your bicycle across bridges that don't allow "non-motorized units."

BIKECONOMICS

A sharp pencil can show some surprising benefits by switching from cars to bikes for much of our transportation. A bicycle may cost $100, while an auto will likely cost at least $4,000. Count in operating costs, insurance, etc. if you wish—it figures out that most people using autos spend 15-20% of their disposable income on the auto, and a total of 30-40% once hidden subsidies are included. That would buy a lot of bicycles, bus tickets and a few trips to Hawaii or Europe in addition! If you look at the situation of many American homeowners with thirty-year mortgages on their homes in addition to auto expenses, the economics comes out even stronger—the savings from avoiding automobile costs can be used to pay off the mortgage more quickly, saving interest payments equal to or greater than the actual value of the house. Riding a bicycle may be worth $30,000 to $40,000 to you over a 20-year period. That doesn't sound so dumb!

Ed Robbins

by Bart Jones

Repair

Five repair manuals, all with sound, usable mechanical information, in order of increasing completeness and technicality:

Bicycles: All About Them, McPhee Gribble Publishers, illustrated by David Lancashire, 1976, 32 pp., $1.50 from:
Penguin Books
72 Fifth Ave.
New York, NY 10011

Mostly basic mechanics, also history and riding techniques, presented "to appeal to 7-12-year-olds and to anyone else who isn't too grown up." Lots of brightly-colored pictures.

This is a good place to bring up two important topics that this book and many others neglect:

OILING:(p. 15): Greased ball bearings (in hubs, crank, most pedals, headset) don't need oil. The grease will last from 6 months to 8 years, depending on how well the bike is treated (never leave it in the rain!) and how much it's used. After about 2000 miles, the bearings need overhauling and new grease.

The only bicycle parts that need frequent lubrication are the chain—especially the chain—and any gear changers (10-speed derailleurs or internal 3-speed hubs).

If you insist on oiling your bearings, use only one or two drops and be sure to do it every month. Oil, WD-40, etc., will dissolve most greases, and then the bearings will be dry. One of the surest ways to ruin a bike is to let a kid loose on it with an oil can. After half a quart of oil, the bike works beautifully; a few weeks later it's a frozen-up piece of junk in need of a major overhaul. Go easy, or not at all.

TIRE REMOVERS (p. 16): Be sure to use something with a rounded end. Old spoons or pencils (if strong enough) are fine. Nicest of all are the special tire levers with a slot on the other end to tuck under a spoke.

Screwdrivers, a common choice, will just make more holes in the inner tube. Use something else.

Anybody's Bike Book, Tom Cuthbertson, revised edition, 1971, 178 pp., $3.95 from:
Ten Speed Press
Box 4310
Berkeley, CA 94704

Detailed instructions, funny drawings. Invites you to jump in and learn by being always clear that it's o.k. to be ignorant.

Richard's Bicycle Book, Richard Ballantine, 1974, 295 pp., $3.95 from:
Ballantine Books
201 E. 50th
New York, NY 10022

Requires some basic mechanical knowledge or experience in using tools. Use it with caution, since the author often states as fact his opinion or bias. Heavily Manhattan-centered. (I've never known a bicycle to get so skungey so quickly as Ballantine assumes; and not all car drivers are out to get you.)

Drawbacks aside, the instructions are clear and easy to follow. This book is especially good at explaining how things work.

Part of *Richard's Bicycle Book* discusses history, philosophy, riding techniques (especially in New York), and designing cities for bicycles and people. Five pages are devoted to the "transportation dreamworld" of Stevenage, England, where pedestrians and vehicles of all kinds move safely and smoothly at their different speeds.

How to Fix Your Bicycle, Helen Garvy, drawings by T. White, 1972, 48 pp., $1 from:
Shire Press
P.O. Box 40426
San Francisco, CA 94110

Requires either basic mechanical knowledge, lots of patience and common sense or a slightly mechanical friend. Low-key style (the author left her ego out of it, unlike the preceding two books): good instructions and drawings. Assumes you can learn: "Don't be afraid of your bike. You should be able to take most of it apart and get it back together like it was, especially if you are neat and careful and watch what you are doing."

Glenn's Complete Bicycle Manual: Selection, Maintenance, Repair, Clarence W. Coles and Harold T. Glemm, 1973, 339 pp., $5.95 from:
Crown Publishers
419 Park Ave. South
New York, NY 10016

Very complete, detailed instructions for anything you're likely to find on a bicycle. Useful mainly for bike shops.

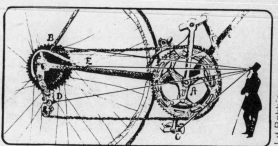

Ed Robbins

We didn't know much about repairing bikes (though now I'm inspired to learn) so we asked our friend Bart Jones to do this section for us. Bart is a member of the Bicycle Repair Collective (1912 S.E. Ankeny, Portland, OR 97214), which besides fixing bicycles teaches bike repair. He has been a bicyclist all his life and a professional bike mechanic for five years.

ORGANIZATIONS

Urban Bikeway Design Collaborative (UBDC)
    W20-002 MIT
    Cambridge, MA 02139
        or
    UBDC—West Coast
    P.O. Box 2983
    Stanford, CA 94305

The people at UBDC have obviously done a lot of research and gained a lot of experience in bikeway design—more importantly, they are bike riders themselves. Besides putting out a number of excellent publications (see below), they also sponsor a yearly design competition for bicycle safety, education and design feats. If I were planning to activate biking systems and facilities for my community, I'd go to them first as references and professional help. Some of their publications:

Cyclateral Thinking, Douglas B. Smith, Ed., Summer 1975, $3. Sections by different people on community planning, funding, bicycle education, design problems and case histories of different bikeway systems. No definitive solutions but lots of examples and ideas. Its bibliography is the best I've seen and includes many more things than we have here.

Cyclateral Thinking is also the name of a wonderful hand-drawn newsletter published by John Williams, an irreverent planner from Canada. It's available from UBDC for $3 for 6 issues per year.

Sprocket Man, 50¢
This is a very good, commonsense comic book on bike safety put together for the Stanford Dept. of Public Safety. A very nice use of the comic book medium 'cause it makes you read it from cover to cover and you even *learn* something.

Living Systems
    Rt. 1, Box 170
    Winter, CA 95694
Besides their work in energy conservation and passive solar design (see those sections), Living Systems, specifically David Bainbridge, has done some good stuff for bicycles in Davis. *Bikeway Planning and Design* is a 9-page primer available for $1. And a new book (including a 10-page bibliography) will be available from them soon.

Citizens Bicycle Advisory Committee
    400 S.W. Sixth, Suite 546
    Portland, OR 97204
A citizens group meeting monthly to advise the City of Portland on spending $50-$60,000 each year on improving bicycle riding conditions. Maps of Portland are available.

Metropolitan Association of Urban Designers and Environmental Planners (MAUDEP)
    c/o Carl Berkowitz
    Box 722
    Church St. Station
    New York, NY 10008
Publishes newsletter, the *Bicycle/Pedestrian News*, and sponsors national and international conferences on planning and design.

Philadelphia Bicycle Coalition
    3410 Baring Street
    Philadelphia, PA 19104
A calendar, a bike-route map for Philadelphia (one in progress for the region), a campaign to get Bicentennial tourists to bike around the city, and a list of people willing to teach bicycle repair and maintenance. Also the Ben Franklin Brigade—a network of citizen groups in Philly federated with similar groups in other cities—is working towards a "park and pedal" transportation system. Cars, buses, boats and trains should be equipped to carry bikes; theft-proof parking devices should be supplied at public buildings, transit nodes and tourist sites, and bike lanes should be established on roads and bridges. Send a SASE for more information.

Attention: Bicycle Scholars
Writing a paper on the bicycle movement? On bikeway planning or mixed-mode transportation? The Coalition has put together a "study kit" designed to assist students, instructors, librarians or citizen groups currently at work on a bicycle project. The kit includes back issues of the Coalition's seasonal newsletter, *Bike On!*, ten issues of Friends for Bikecology's poster-newsletter, *Serendipity* (published quarterly during the early 1970s; our limited supply of these remaining issues offers an excellent history of the bicycle movement), a copy of the Coalition's commuter bike map for Philadelphia along with guidelines on how a bike map is produced, a reprint of Stewart Wilson's *Scientific American* article "Bicycle Technology," and, finally, a miscellany of letters, editorials and graphics reproduced to meet your needs (please specify your area of interest). To order the kit, send your name and address along with a $10 check to the Philadelphia Bicycle Coalition, 3410 Baring Street, Philadelphia, PA 19104

(Thanks to the Philadelphia Bicycle Coalition)

ALABAMA

Alabama Bicycle Council
c/o Philip C. Davis
3024 Pelzer Ave.
Montgomery, AL 36109

CALIFORNIA

Bicycle Facilities Committee
Clifford L. Franz, Chairman
L.A.W., Inc.
110 Bloomfield Road
Burlingame, CA 94010

California Assoc. of Bicycle
Organizations
John Forester, President
782 Allen Court
Palo Alto, CA 94303

East Bay Bicycle Coalition
John Carroll, Chairperson
P.O. Box 23934
Oakland, CA 94623

San Francisco Bicycle
Coalition
701 Ulloa St.
San Francisco, CA 94127
Attn. Darryl Sktabak

Santa Clara Valley Bicycle
Assoc.
Bob Shanteau, President
P.O. Box 662
Los Gatos, CA 95030
408/969-2778

Western Wheelers
c/o Carol Peterson
P.O. Box 183
Menlo Park, CA 94025

COLORADO

Bicycles Now!
c/o Dr. Fred Wolfe/DRCOG
1776 S. Jackson St., Suite 200
Denver, CO 80210
303/758-5166

Sangre de Cristo Cycling
Assoc.
3601 Azalea
Pueblo, CO 81005

CONNECTICUT:

Connecticut Bicycle Coalition
c/o Mrs. Lewis A. Dibble, Jr.
510 N. Church St.
Naugatuck, CT 06770

DELAWARE

Delaware Friends for
Bikecology
2117 Meadow Lane
Wilmington, DE 19810

GEORGIA

Southern Bicycle League
c/o J. Berryhill
242 Superior Ave.
Decatur, GA 30030
404/377-4707

ILLINOIS

League of American Wheelmen
19 S. Bothwell
Palatine, IL 60067

INDIANA

Zero Auto Growth
P.O. Box 44666
Indianapolis, IN 46204

KANSAS

Bi-State Ad Hoc Committee
for Better Bicycling
P.O. Box 2203
Shawnee Mission, KS 66202

KENTUCKY

Bluegrass Wheelmen
c/o Donald H. Burrell
882 Maywick Drive
Lexington, KY 40504

Louisville Wheelmen
c/o David Dunn
122 S. Hite Ave.
Louisville, KY 40206

MARYLAND

Baltimore County Task Force
on Bikeways
Baltimore County Office Bldg.
111 W. Chesapeake Ave.
Towson, MD 21204

Citizens for Bikeways
110 E. 25th Street
Baltimore, MD 21218
Attn. Joe Gardiner

Oxon Hill Bicycle Club
P.O. Box 18081
Oxon Hill, MD 20021

MASSACHUSETTS

Boston Area Bicyclists Assoc.
Building W20-002
84 Massachusetts Ave.
Cambridge, MA 02139

Bicycle Repair Collective
51 S. Prospect
Amherst, MA 01002

MICHIGAN

Ann Arbor Bicycle League
c/o Ecology Center
417 Detroit St.
Ann Arbor, MI 48104

Detroit Bike Paths
c/o Tom Holleman
Harrington Road
Rochester, MI 48063

MINNESOTA

Gopher Wheelmen
c/o Chris Kvale
1924 South 8th St.
Minneapolis, MN 55404

MISSOURI

Ecobike
c/o Jack Ashmore
5531 Locust
Kansas City, MO 64110

MONTANA

Bikecentennial 76
c/o Dan and Lys Burden
317 Beverly Ave.
Missoula, MT 59801

Friends for Bikecology
c/o Colleen Martin
1411 Ave. C
Billings, MT 59102

NEW JERSEY

Citizens for N.J. Bikeways
555 Mt. Prospect Ave., 5D
Newark, NJ 07104

NEW YORK

American Bicycle Hall of
Fame
c/o Dr. Roland C. Geist
260 West 260th St.
New York, NY 10471

Bikeways for Buffalo
c/o Joan Smith
309 Highland Ave.
Buffalo, NY 14222

Mohawk-Hudson Wheelmen
Patricia Gerfin
1087 Wendall Ave.
Schenectady, NY 12308
518/346-1801

Transportation Alternatives
20 Exchange Place, Rm. 5500
New York, NY 10005

OHIO

Bike for a Better City
Timothy Bristol
72 West Norwhich
Columbus, OH 43201
614/294-6003

Mattilou Catchpole Sierra
Club Bicycle Coalition
992 Quilliams Road
Cleveland Heights, OH 44121

OREGON

Alternative Transport Project
P.O. Box 1135
Eugene, OR 97401

The Bicycle Lobby
Sam Oakland
Rm. 405 Small Park Hall
Portland State University
Portland, OR 97200

The Bicycle Repair Collective
1912 S.E. Ankeny
Portland, OR 97214

Citizens Bicycle Advisory
Committee
City of Portland Bureau of
Planning
424 S.W. Main, Rm. 205
Portland, OR 97204

Oregon Bicycle Transit Study
Dept. of Urban Planning
University of Oregon
Eugene, OR 97403

PENNSYLVANIA

Bike, the Bicycling Community
of Bethlehem
Hans Wuerth
P.O. Box 1151
Bethlehem, PA 18018

East Coast Bicycle Congress
5300 Akron St.
Philadelphia, PA 19124

Philadelphia Bicycle Coalition
John Dowlin
3410 Baring St.
Philadelphia, PA 19104
215/382-6693

RHODE ISLAND

Yankee Pedal Pushers
c/o Ted Lotring
70 Benevolent St.
Providence, RI 02906

SOUTH CAROLINA

Coastal Cyclists
19 Chalmers St.
Charleston, SC 29401
Attn. Leah Martin

TEXAS

Citizens for Environmental
Coalition
1200 Bissonnet
Houston, TX 77005
713/524-0607

VERMONT

Vermont Bikeways Coalition
c/o Ben Bosher
68 Buell St.
Burlington, VT 05401

VIRGINIA

Bike Commuters of EPA
c/o Nina D. Rowe
3612 N. John Marshall Dr.
Arlington, VA 22207

WASHINGTON, D.C.

Washington Area Bicycling
Assoc.
1346 Connecticut Ave. N.W.
Room 323
Washington, DC 20036
202/223-0003

WISCONSIN

Central Cycling
c/o Ed Deuerlein
4746 N. 29th St.
Madison, WI 53209

Cyclateral Thinking

U.S. BICYCLE ACTIVISTS

Though much of our need for transportation can be beneficially eliminated and much more simplified, there still remain times when travel can be wise and valuable. We need to learn to discriminate between travel that is wise and simple and a good experience for all concerned and travel that degenerates into an exploitative tourism. Wise travel must include sharing and giving, not just looking and taking. Wise travel must be based on respect and reverence for the ways of others and for their places. Many communities and people are learning that distinction, the problems caused by tourism, and developing more fulfilling ways of traveling.

Wise Travel

Ready to cover some ground? Here is a sprinkling of publications that provide good examples of books for traveling by bike—nationally, regionally and around a city:

Discovering Santa Barbara . . . without a car: a guide for people using bicycles, buses, the train, horses, or walking, by Ken Kolsbun, Bob Burgess, 1974, 67 pp., $2.50 postpaid from:
> Teddy Bear Farm
> P.O. Box 863
> Santa Barbara, CA 93102

Model for other cities: bicycle tours with specific themes—"Mom and Pop" stores, Historic and Unique Trees, Food & Resource Value Trees, Buildings of Aesthetic & Historic Interest, Where to Rent, how to use bikes, plus local public transportation. Fits comfortably in hip pocket.

Amtrak has announced that *folding* bikes can be taken free on all its passenger trains, including the Metroliner. Regular bikes can only be taken on trains with baggage cars. There's a $2 handling fee, and check ahead to be sure there's a baggage attendant at any of the smaller stations.

American Biking Atlas and Touring Guide, by Sue Browder, 1975, $5.95 from:
> Workman Publishing Co.
> 231 E. 51st St.
> New York, NY 10022

If you're ready to take off on your bike—short trip or long—this is your book. 150 different tours laid out, ranked as to difficulty and carefully mapped. Not good if you're only interested in one specific area, but there's a good ride or three in each state. And—neato!—the pages are perforated so you don't have to carry the whole thing in your pack.

Bike Tripping, Tom Cuthbertson, illustrated by Rick Morrall, with a "Frame" section by Albert Eisentraut, 1972, 177pp., $3.95 from:
> Ten Speed Press
> Box 4310
> Berkeley, CA 94704

Riding skills for commuting, recreation, racing, touring and "the fanatic fringe" (ch. 13)—would you believe ice riding? Eisentraut's 37-page chapter on "The Frame" contains a wealth of information not easily available elsewhere. This book is especially useful for people new to bicycling; experienced riders will enjoy it too.

(Bart Jones)

East Coast Bicycle Trail Guidebook, 1976, $4.95 from:
> East Coast Bicycle Congress
> 5300 Akron St.
> Philadelphia, PA 19124

The trail traverses the densely-populated corridor from Boston, Mass., to Richmond, Va. (where it joins the Trans-America Trail), yet it is a collection of quiet back roads, historic towns and even a ferry ride or two. They have really scoped out the most beautiful parts of the eight-state region, missing the worst of the megalopolis by many miles. The trail and the book were put together by the scores of cyclists and organizations who have formed the East Coast Bicycle Congress to develop and refine an exciting system of bike routes up and down the east coast. The Guidebook has a large index map and 21 detail maps, along with service listings and general information.

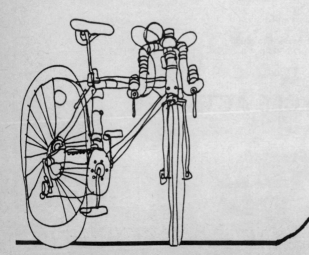

THE EAST COAST BICYCLE TRAIL
BOSTON TO RICHMOND

BED AND BREAKFAST

Motels are becoming less and less desirable solutions to travel accommodations. Although they provide low hassle, easy access and predictable places to stay, that same predictability means no experience worth traveling for—if you've tried one you've tried them all!

Guest houses or "bed and breakfasts" provide the varied experience and the human contact that standardized motels lack. Whereas an investment of $7,000 to $13,000 per room is required for motels, it requires almost no capital investment for people to rent out one or two extra rooms in their homes. At the same time, such accommodations cost travelers less and spread out the income within the community. Guest houses allow better off-season use of the facilities, more individualized accommodations and entail much less risk and impact where tourism levels are likely to decline or fluctuate.

In almost every European city travelers arriving at the railroad station will find an information booth that directs them to the kind of accommodation they want in the part of town they wish. Guest house switchboards operated successfully at Expo in Montreal and Spokane. The small town of Inverness, California, at the edge of the new Point Reyes National Seashore, has proposed a bed and breakfast switchboard as an alternative to ugly and expensive commercialized accommodations that couldn't be supported by local water and sewage conditions. Guest house guidebooks are another way to give people access to what is available in an area. Present ones, such as *Europe on $5 a Day*, have been very profitable as well as useful to thousands of people.

INNS

Another long-lost joy of traveling is staying at inns rather than hotels. Inns are not quick stop-overs for hurrying travelers but are to be enjoyed themselves! Often in beautiful settings, always with unique, cozy, personal rooms, fine home cooking and personalized hospitality, small inns treat guests as *guests*. Distractions such as TV and telephones are usually absent, but you may be treated by the owner's violin instead.

For a listing of places in Northern California see "The Friendly Inns of the Mendocino-Sonoma Coast" in *Sunset Magazine*, October 1975, or:

The Inn Book, Kathleen Neuer, 1974, $4.95 from:

> Pyne Press
> 924 Nassau St.
> Princeton, NJ 08540

The Recommended Country Inns of New England, Suzy Chapin and Elizabeth Squire, 1975, $3.95 from:

> Pequot Press
> Chester, CT 06412

Their definition of a country inn is that it "must have lodging, as well as good food, and it must be open essentially year 'round." This book discusses almost 200 places from Connecticut to Maine, many of which are run by families. It includes prices (some as cheap as $12 for a double), menus, photographs, and what look to be careful directions for getting there. Enjoy.

Country Inns and Back Roads (10th edition), Norman T. Simpson, 1976, $4.95 from:

> Berkshire Traveller Press
> Stockbridge, MA 02162

This one covers more ground—the whole country and even a few in Canada. Some are restaurants, some are hotels. The chatty descriptions are illustrated with nice sketches, but one drawback is a lack of prices.

Lover's Guide to America, Ian Keown, 1974, $8.95 from:

> Macmillan Publishing Co.
> 866 Third Ave.
> New York, NY 10022

This hardback by a big publisher has a whole different feel than the other two (hooray for small presses!), although it does cover much more of some areas, like the South and the Southwest. It's just that the places mentioned in Oregon are fancy and not at all to my liking, which makes me skeptical of their recommendations. They do have prices and descriptions (no pictures), so you should be able to tell what you're getting into.

In Scandinavia dormitories at universities are frequently turned into low-cost hotels during summer tourist seasons. Hostels for all ages with simple dorm space provide extremely cheap and low-impact ways of travel. Both are beginning to appear in the U.S. Campgrounds are often even less expensive, although few exist yet in the middle of U.S. cities as they do in Europe. For membership information and guidebook to youth hostels write:

> American Youth Hostels
> National Campus
> Delaplone, VA 22025

A final note: Found a Holiday Inn ad in *Newsweek* that brags about "152 reasons why the best surprise is no surprises"—including no surprises in the lobby, the food, the carpet or the prices. At least they know what they're dishing out. What ever happened to the famed American spirit of adventure?

Maraka

Taking Pictures
and
Taking Souls

Drinking wine one recent evening with Florian Winter, an Austrian visiting us on a global survey of renewable energy developments for the U.N., we got into talking about the destruction of European cathedrals by tourism.

Each person came, he said, and took away a little of the cathedrals—in their camera, in their mind, or in the conversation—and now nothing remains.

In that absurdity there is truth.

All places live through the reverence with which we hold them—without which they crumble to pieces, unloved, unmaintained, abandoned and destroyed. That reverence is the glue that in reality binds the stones and the blood that in truth sustains the life of a place.

For the life of a place lies in its relation to the people that share it. And it is that reverence first which is taken away, piece by piece, flashbulb by flashbulb, postcard by postcard, tour group by tour group. Without this reverence, a place has nothing to give to those whose lives it must sustain, and they in turn lose their nourishment and fall into the same dereliction as their cathedral.

It need not be so, for the visit of a pilgrim differs from that of a tourist. A pilgrim brings love and reverence, and the visit of a pilgrim leaves behind a gift of their reverence for others to share.

We scorn the people of other cultures who are angered when we wish to photograph them and cast aside their belief that we take away part of their soul.

Yet we do.

For what we seek—with photographs or our presence—is sought because it is that which we lack, and that lack and our presence only prove them right and us wrong. By our taking we diminish us both.

And we lessen the soul of all places to which we go, and ourselves as well, when we take without giving and come to them without reverence to life and to land, to people and to place, to ourselves and to the creation of which we are part. That is the destruction of which tourism is part and from which tourism arises, and it is there that we again can find the healing power for our land and our lives. (TB)

Costs of Tourism

Impacts of Tourism on Prince Edward Island, Executive Summary $1.50, Analysis and Recommendations $2.50, from
Queen's Printer
Box 2000
Charlottetown, PEI, C1A 7N8, Canada

The economic impact of tourism on PEI is significant and seemingly positive. Tourists spend more than $23 million a year, and, subtracting the dollars that immediately go off the Island to pay for imported goods and services, they leave behind more than $20 million.

The story doesn't end there, however, as tourism has been depositing such amounts of money on the Island for a number of years and the environmental impact section of the study didn't mention any mountains of cash lying around disrupting the Island's ecology. In fact, the money does leave the Island again—in the expenditures of the Islanders for goods and services imported from elsewhere. And there basic questions appear, for the social and economic impacts would be very different if the Islanders provided goods and services for each other rather than providing tourist services for outsiders and then using that income for purchasing goods and services from outside.

In spite of its $20 million per year "input," tourism, when combined with off-Island purchases, may cause a net economic loss to the Island through establishing unfavorable trade arrangements with other areas. The economic impact of tourism is more than the money income it brings—it must include the unequal value of city money vs. country money, city prices and wages vs. country prices and wages, and energy slaves vs. people's work which occur in large-scale systems. The odds are that PEI, like most rural areas, doesn't come out ahead on such exchanges, which almost universally work to the benefit of the urban industrialized areas that control the economic systems.

In addition, the effects of tourism on the internal economy of the Island itself are not explored in the study. Who gets the money? What changes are there in the relative wealth of people on the Island? Who owns the tourist facilities? What effect does tourism have on in-migration? How many people come to PEI for summer jobs, taking money away; or stay, splitting the pie into smaller pieces? How much does the Island have to spend on tourist infrastructure—roads, sewers, power plants, motels and police—and is that the kind of surroundings the people of the Island want to have?

Whether we think about Prince Edward Island or America Island or Earth Island, the questions of who benefits and who pays are basic. The report implies that encouragement of tourist patterns that bring the greatest expenditures are best and should be encouraged. Yet the people of PEI take vacations, too, and for them the best vacation at least cost is as much a benefit as it is to the tourists coming to PEI. For society as a whole as well as for the people who pay, the less work, dollars, or energy necessary to satisfy our needs, the better. It would seem that a wise society would ask for a fair return for everyone's work rather than trying to milk each other for the highest possible prices. The absurdity of that approach is apparent in the strategies proposed for PEI to encourage "paying" visitors at the expense of friends and relatives which are of more than economic benefit to the Islanders.

The social impacts of tourism are equally neglected in the PEI study, which examines only surveys of residents' attitudes towards tourism—a process of relatively little use unless the residents have a real feel for what options and alternatives are available to them and what the costs and benefits of each might be. Believing that tourism "gives" them $20 million a year, frequently being personally dependent on tourism income and having little awareness of the indirect and delayed effects of a tourist economy upon their lives, few people can be expected to express what intuitive reservations they might have. Even well articulated attitudes towards tourism express only a small part of the social impacts of the industry. This is particularly true when tourism's significance lies as much in its being a disruptive economic wedge diverting people from a local, self-reliant social and economic pattern into one tied into urban and international operations as it does in the activities of the tourists themselves.

Omitting examination of social impacts implies that there are no significant social effects of different sources of people's livelihood. Yet, if people are dependent upon an institution for their income (as with tourism on PEI), can they fairly evaluate and regulate that institution? If people are largely self-reliant, either individually or as a community, do they develop a deeper and more rewarding understanding and relation with the ecological and cultural webs that support and nourish them? Do the trappings of wealth, such as television, fancy clothes and houses, and big cars create different social impacts than the leisure to enjoy other people, to have satisfying places to spend time, and to enjoy the dignity and self-confidence of forming one's life and surroundings that a slower, less materialistic way of life may offer? Is the additional effort necessary to obtain fair representation in the operation of large scale economic and social patterns greater than the benefits received?

To be of real value, a study of the impacts of tourism needs to explore and lay out meaningful options in addition to a thorough analysis of the impacts of tourism itself. Such options need to include the implications of alternative means of livelihood—small scale, self-reliant patterns of fulfilling the Island's own needs as well as options for livelihood other than tourism within larger economic patterns.

Options for modifying tourism in socially responsible ways need also to be examined. Making clear on what grounds and in what ways visitors will be accepted can strongly affect tourism patterns. Promotion of at-home vacations, local resorts and improvement of communities can reduce the need and desire to travel. Inns and guest houses can replace motels; franchise businesses can be banned on both economic and social grounds; "working" vacations, person-to-person visits, bans on non-resident cars, and dozens of other measures can be developed to allow tourism to operate at a scale and in ways that provide opportunity for visitors and Islanders to enjoy and benefit each other on a non-exploitive and non-dominating basis.

There needs to be a right for people to maintain a society based on deep and loving relations between people and between people and land; based on the ability to relate to people according to what they contribute to your life rather than to your pocketbook; and based on chosen rather than imposed economic and social patterns. True accounting of the operation of such a society as opposed to that of an economic-exchange based society would probably show it to be less costly to operate as well as providing more satisfaction, well-being and happiness for all concerned. That kind of social accounting rather than superficial economic analysis is necessary to evaluate the fundamental changes that tourism brings to PEI or any other place.

See also:
"Tourism and Development: The East African Cause," John S. Marsh, Vol. 5, No. 1, December, 1975 of
Alternatives ($4/yr, quarterly)
Traill College, Trent University
Peterborough, Ontario
Canada

Tourism & Socialist Development, I. G. Shivji, 1973
Tanzania Publishing House
Dar Es Salaam
Tanzania

Tom Bender

SHELTER

Our headlong rush to surround ourselves with the fruits of our mechanized industry is losing its momentum. We are beginning to realize the abysmal effects such surroundings have upon our personal growth and the quality of our lives, and the true costs of ignoring everything but material possessions. We are learning again to value simplicity, people, fairness, our own dreams, the heritage left us by other generations, and the natural world we've banished from our cities. Quality and meaningfulness, not power, are becoming our guiding ethic, and our "economics" that gives us less for more is being replaced by ways to live better and more simply. A new way of building and living is emerging. The models exist, the economics have shifted, our heads are getting clear. It's time to make our places ones we can love.

Architecture for the Poor: An Experiment in Rural Egypt, by Hassan Fathy, 1973, 272 pgs., $5.95 from:
> University of Chicago Press
> 5801 Ellis Ave.
> Chicago, Ill. 60637

Earth plus water equals mud; mud, hands & sun equals brick; brick plus local craftsmanship plus cooperative building ("barn-raising") equals housing, community & rural rehabilitation. Use of indigenous materials, native traditions in design, and a de-professionalized, non-homogenizing architecture work to create a humane environment. How to make mud bricks, catch the wind for natural ventilation, and ancient vaulting techniques. An outstanding documentation of the value of traditional building process, which Fathey has used to create a whole community at less than one-sixth the cost of "modern" methods.

Low-Cost, Energy-Efficient Shelter, edited by Eugene Eccli, 1976, $5.95 from:
> Rodale Press
> Emmaus, PA 18049

Combines good experienced advice on when and when not to build yourself, financing different building options, dealing with codes, neighbors and contractors, along with solid information on lowering first-cost of a home, reducing energy use and employing income energy sources. Not a primary reference in any of these areas, but gives good overall guidance and access to some hard-to-find aids: Cinva-Rams, super-sealants, pre-cut homes, or cellulose fiber insulation. A valuable resource to bring together the various aspects that must be considered for low-cost shelter.

"Low Energy Housing," Andrew MacKillop, *The Ecologist*, Dec. 1972, £3/yr. (monthly) from:
> *The Ecologist*
> Gatesby, Molesworth St.
> Wadebridge, Cornwall, England

Analyzes material and energy consumption of conventional construction and low-cost, low-energy alternatives. Shows potential savings of 90 percent in material and construction energy use through simpler processes.

The Owner-Builder and THE CODE
Ken Kern, Ted Kogon and Rob Thallon, 1976, $5 from:
> Owner-Builder Publications
> Box 550
> Oakhurst, CA 93664

Building codes in this country have enraged almost every person who has had the audacity (or wisdom) to try to build his own home. They also represent major hidden costs for everyone who buys a new home. *The Owner-Builder and THE CODE* documents the origins of present codes in the self-interests of building groups and their impact on housing costs.

It also covers the efforts of United Stand, residents of Mendocino County, California, whose homes were red-tagged for demolition and who have since spearheaded efforts at code revision. California is now in the process of developing a new rural building code and health code to permit more sensible and economical homes and sewage systems, which is likely to trigger similar changes in other states. *The Code* documents the big first step in those changes and will be useful in assisting code changes elsewhere. Provides comparative costs of owner-building, tract housing and custom building along with square foot costs for a number of owner-built homes.

Freedom to Build, John F. C. Turner and Robert Fichter, 1972, $2.95 from:
> The MacMillan Co.
> 866 Third Avenue
> New York, NY 10022

The greatest resource many people have for obtaining an adequate home is their own time and effort put into building it. Owner-building is a basic and widespread phenomenon, yet rarely included in "industry" statistics. *Freedom to Build* outlines the range and value of owner-building, institutional barriers and ways to encourage sweat-equity construction.

Turner's more recent book, *Housing by People* (£2.25 from Marion Boyars Publishers Ltd., 18 Brewer St., London W1R 4AS) goes more deeply into the implications of who makes housing decisions and the relative social and economic benefits of owner-building vs. commercial or public housing.

"Indigenous Building and the Third World," Cain, Afshar and Norton, *Architectural Design*, April 1975 $48/year from:
> Architectural Design
> 7/8 Holland St.
> London WB England

Six case studies of traditional building practices, showing their environmental and social functions, thermal performance, structural wisdom and economic advantages. Quite useful in gaining a deeper understanding of the value of many indigenous ways of building. Building layout, sun-dried brick, mud vaults and domes, microclimate, wind catchers, palm frond construction and water supply.

SIMPLE BUILDING

Handbook for Building Homes of Earth, free from:
> **Office of International Affairs**
> **Department of Housing and Urban**
> **Development**
> **Washington, DC 20410**

A real bargain, even if you had to pay for it. Goes on your bookshelf right next to Middleton's *Build Your House of Earth*. Simple, clear, how-to information for building earth homes—soil testing, site preparation, details of adobe, pressed block, rammed earth, earth roofs and floors, and surface coatings. Excellent illustrations. Better how-to than Middleton's book but fewer design examples and case studies of problems. It's a strange route that highway engineer's soil mechanics takes back into knowledgeable building of earth homes! More details on oil-stabilized earth floors and some other techniques can be found in the earlier *Earth for Homes*, 1955, from the same office.

Build Your House of Earth, G. F. Middleton, 1953, $3.95 from:
> **Compendium Pty. Ltd.**
> **Centreway, 259 Collins St.**
> **Melbourne, Australia**

Comprehensive, clearly written and well-illustrated manual on rammed earth and adobe construction, based on widespread experience in Australia. Formwork, stabilizing earth, keying for plaster, dampproofing, windows, specifications, cost schedules, and a lot of practical questions and answers. Good photos of beautiful earth buildings.

The Adobe News, bimonthly from:
> **P.O. Box 702**
> **Los Lunas, NM 87031**

Network journal for people working with adobe and other earth construction.

Alternative Cements in India, Robin Spence, May 1975, and *Lime and Alternative Cements*, Oct. 1974, both from:
> **Intermediate Technology Publications**
> **9 King Street**
> **London WC2E 8HN England**

Inquire for current prices and other publications. These reports from ITDG initiate a program for finding appropriate alternatives to expensive and often scarce Portland cement. Use of natural cements such as pozzolanas, lime and small-scale production of cement is investigated. Capital costs of small vertical kiln plants are less than large rotary kilns, they have better heat efficiency, provide more employment, and are more flexible to schedule and quality changes. More work needs to be done in this area, but these reports give an excellent coverage of present knowledge.

Construction with Surface Bonding, B. Carl Haynes, Jr. and J.W. Simons, U.S. Dept. of Agriculture, Ag. Information Bulletin No. 374. Contact:
> **B. Carl Haynes**
> **Environmental Engineering Lab**
> **Richard B. Russel Agricultural**
> **Research Center**
> **P.O. Box 5677**
> **Athens, GA 30604**

Use of fiberglass-reinforced cement plaster on both sides of concrete block walls built without mortar joints has been shown to be easier to build and stronger than conventional block and mortar construction. Such walls are strong enough for two story construc-

tion. They also are finding use in low cost containers for solar heat storage and low cost, water-filled Trombe wall passive solar heat storage systems such as designed at Max's Pot (See page 143) in Texas. This bulletin gives details for construction techniques, which differ somewhat from normal processes.

Stone Masonry, Ken Kern, Steve Magers, Lou Penfield, 1976, $6 from:
> **Owner-Builder Publications**
> **Box 550**
> **Oakhurst, CA 93644**

First of a new series of guides for beginning builders being prepared by Kern's press. Beautifully illustrated with clear photographs, this volume covers the basics of stability; choosing, fitting and shaping stone; laid, faced and formed stonework; and details of steps, arches, fireplaces, scaffolding and other operations. At the same time, it gives a sense of the beauty of different kinds of stonework and how to think ahead to how what you're doing will turn out. A beginner's, not a stonemason's, guide, but good for that purpose.

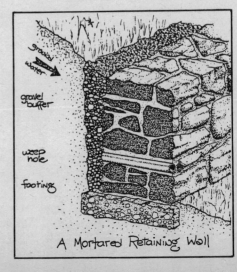
A Mortared Retaining Wall

Build Your Own House in the Old Ohana Style, Suzanne Stewart, 1974 $7.50 from:
> The Hawaii Community Design Center
> 2480 Koa Ave., L-29
> Honolulu, HI 96815

A good, simple, step-by-step guide for building a $7.50/sq. ft. owner-built house house suitable for the Hawaiian climate. The design, unlike many "low cost" houses, feels comfortable. Good how-to drawings include details for making doors, shutters and cabinets. Plans are also available.

Pole Buildings in Papua New Guinea, Peter Lattey, 1974, 41 pp. from:
> Forest Products Research Center
> P.O. Box 1358
> Boroko, Papua New Guinea

Use of simple round poles rather than sawn lumber conserves resources where you're not cutting down 800-year-old forests, but it requires good, simple design. This booklet reviews constructed designs for 30-ft. hessian cement-covered geodesic domes, market halls, bus stops, community halls, health centers and homes, along with design details, plans, photos of completed buildings, and information on structural trusses, cement roofs and rural wood preservation. Donation to cover printing and postage would probably be appreciated.

FHA Pole House Construction, 1971, from:
> American Wood Preservers Institute
> 1651 Old Meadow Road
> McLean, VA 22101

Pole house construction offers a low-cost way to build on sloping sites without major disruption of the site. This booklet contains guidelines for pole construction to meet FHA requirements. Covers soil and site conditions, embedment tables for different loads and soils, connection and framing, useful life, construction economics and new innovations.

Hand-Hewn, William C. Leitch, 1975, $4.95 from:
> Cronicle Books
> 870 Market Street
> San Francisco, CA 94102

Hand-Hewn contains an excellent and comprehensive bibliography to log construction (a world in itself), with best resources listed for each step of the construction process. Details on chinkless construction and photographs of many design and construction ideas for outbuildings, doors, windows, roof construction and insulation.

Wood-Frame House Construction, L. O. Anderson, 1971, $2.75 from:
> Craftsman Book Co. of America
> 124 South La Brea Ave.
> Los Angeles, CA 90036

Provides a solid understanding of conventional construction for the lay person. Good large detailed drawings explain how and why things go together—an understanding, not a how-to guide, but very useful.

Soil Cement: Its Use in Buildings, 1964, $6 from:
> United Nations, Sales Section
> New York, NY 10017

Prepared by the Inter-American Housing and Planning Centre, National University of Columbia, Bogotá. Information regarding types of soils used, lengthy instructional data, models, results of experiments.

The Use of Earth Covered Buildings, 1976, National Science Foundation NSF/RA-76006, limited number of free copies available from:
> RANN Document Center
> National Science Foundation
> 1800 G St., N.W.
> Washington, DC 20550

Proceedings of the July 1975 Fort Worth, Texas, conference on underground buildings. Most comprehensive and up-to-date source available on underground building. Down-to-earth information on legal, economic, insurance, structural, psychological, historical and energy considerations. Life cycle costs show underground building is increasingly viable as energy costs to operate buildings increase. Very comprehensive bibliography, list of people actively working on underground building, etc.

Underground Society and Newsletter, contact:
> Thomas Bligh
> Dept. of Civil Engineering
> University of Minnesota
> Minneapolis, MN 55455

Ongoing developments in underground building—coming out of the 1975 Texas conference.

The Indian Tipi, Reginald & Gladys Laubin, 1971, $1.65 from:
> Ballantine Books
> 201 E. 50th St.
> New York, NY 10022

THE best source on construction, use and history of the American Indian tipi. Tipis—different kinds, designs, making them, living in them, pitching them, their history and transportation, along with old photographs, special uses, and tipis in the modern world. See "Bootstraps" section in Economics for a place to buy a tipi.

Lodge Owners Quarterly, $2.50/year from:
> P.O. Box 122
> Whites Creek, TN 37189

All about tipis for new, old and potential tipi-ers. Construction tips, lodge pole transportation ideas, dates and reports on encampments and powwows.

Domebook II, Lloyd Kahn, 1971, $4.50 from:
> Mountain Books
> Box 4811
> Santa Barbara, CA 93103

With update information in *Shelter*, this remains the basic introduction to making your own domed shelters. Calculation of strut lengths, joints, caulking, case studies of different domes that have been built—transparent, wood shake, individual, and communal.

How to Build a Low-Cost House of Stone, Lewis & Sharon Watson, $3 from:
> Stonehouse Publications
> Box R
> Sweet, ID 83670

Detailed account of use of the Flagg-Nearing technique of portable forms to build a 3-bedroom country home in Idaho at a cost of $2000 for an 1100-sq. ft. house. You'll probably need more information for carpentry and finishing work, but the stoneworking technique is simply explained.

HOW-TO

There is a plethora of how-to books on various building trades—most cover similar ground. These are some of the best.

The Owner-Built Home, Ken Kern, 1972, $6.95 from:
Charles Scribners Sons
597 Fifth Ave.
New York, NY 10017

Revised and expanded, Kern's book gives probably the best available introduction to a wide range of sensible, low-cost techniques of building—adobe, pressed block, rammed earth, stone, masonry, concrete, wood, pole-framed, plastic and salvage materials. This is combined with Kern's often ingenious design ideas, compilation of research from many building research institutes and overall design considerations. The introduction gives sensible axioms of low-cost building: pay as you go, supply your own labor, use your own best judgment, use native materials, design and plan your home yourself, use minimum but quality hand tools, and assume responsibility for the construction yourself. Eccli's book covers economics and energy considerations better, this covers best the options on what and how to build.

A Manual on Building Construction, Rev. Harold K. Dancy, 1948, £1 from:
IT Publications
9 King St.
London WC2 England

Originally a guide for constructing church missions in Africa, this manual contains a wealth of information on building from scratch—on-site brickmaking, manufacturing doors and windows (from trees still on the hoof) and making roofing tiles. Details on a lot of building processes uncommon in the U.S.—grass roofs, mud roofs, mud domes, preparing paints and finishes, as well as design for tropical conditions, business and labor details.

Low-Cost Homes for Rural America: Construction Manual, U.S. Dept. of Agriculture Handbook No. 364, $1 from: from:
U.S. Government Printing Office
Washington, DC 20402

Comes with house plans for $1 more. Clearly illustrated, step-by-step house construction with many useful designs and plans. Insulation standards need updating and structural sizing isn't included—otherwise good source for conventional designs.

Your Engineered House, Rex Roberts, 1964, $4.95 from:
M. Evans & Co.
216 E. 49th St.
New York, NY 10017

Probably best available source for efficient use of resources in designing and building a home. Design to use full standard sizes of lumber, efficient plan arrangement and plumbing design, window placement. Needs to be balanced by creative design, but very valuable resource to help you put your bucks where you want them rather than where you shouldn't have to.

The Last Whole Earth Catalog ($5), and The Whole Earth Epilog ($4), from:
Box 428
Sausalito, CA 94965

Excellent resources on adobe construction, stone, timber, woodworking and other aspects of building. Look here for the cream when you can't decide which of many available resources to turn to.

Simplified Engineering for Architects and Builders, Harry Parker, 1967, $12.50 $12.50 from:
Wiley-Interscience
605 Third Ave.
New York, NY 10016

Reference bible for structural calculations.

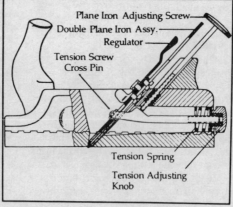

Basic Construction Techniques for Houses and Small Buildings, Bureau of Naval Personnel, 1972, $4.50 from:
Dover Publications
180 Varick St.
New York, NY 10014

Solid, simple, and thorough—everything from logging operations, heavy construction, drawings and specifications to plastering and painting. Good detailed explanation of roof and rafter framing.

*Many of the major changes occurring in building are linked with other areas—see the sections on Waterless Toilets, Home Insulation, Energy-Conserving Landscaping and Direct Solar Heating for closely-related developments.

Wiring Simplified, H. P. Richter, 1975, $1.39 from:
Park Publications
Box 8527
Lake St. Station
Minneapolis, MN 55408

Modern Carpentry, Willis Wagner, 1973, $10.96 from:
Goodheart-Wilcox Co.
123 W. Taft Dr.
South Holland, IL 60473

Carpenters and Builders Guide, $7.50 from:
Theodore Audel & Co.
Bobbs-Merrill Co.
4300 W. 62 St.
Indianapolis, IN 46268

Detailed practical guide for dealing with most any carpentry problem. Clearly illustrated step-by-step methods.

Woodcraft Catalog, 50¢ from:
Woodcraft Supply Corp.
313 Montvale Ave.
Woburn, MA 01801

A connoisseur's guide to woodworking tools—if you think you need Cadillacs. You'll have to pay for it. Sometimes, though, you want to find out if the tool or the person makes the difference. From here you can get and try out Swiss carving tools, Japanese saws, shipbuilder's adze, bark spuds, broad axes, German/French/English/American drawknives—you name it. Next time you will make it yourself. The catalog is a learning experience in itself.

Minnesota Woodworkers Supply Co.
Industrial Blvd.
Rogers, MN 55374

Woodcraft supplies tools, Minnesota Woodworkers supplies all sorts of hard-to-find specialty hardware—plans, upholstery supplies, lamp parts, furniture trim, carvings, hinges and locks, veneers and inlays.

Home and Workshop Guide to Sharpening, Harry Walton, 1967, $2.50 from:
Harper & Row
10 E. 53rd St.
New York, NY 10022

It may seem unnecessary to mention this, but it can turn night into day and make many jobs easier with hand tools than with power tools. A must.

SPIRIT and SPACE

It often seems that spiritual concerns are something foreign and far-removed from the pressures of everyday life—and they usually have been in our culture. Yet the whole purpose of all our frenzied activity is to somehow make us happier. And the most important thing about getting happier is feelings—about ourselves, towards others, about our world. Funniest thing, once we remember why we're doing things—good feelings and feeling good—we suddenly realize that reverence and respect and love in how we do things are more important than frenzy and quantity. More and more that is happening in how people are making the places where they live.

Mud, Space, and Spirit, Gray, Macrae & McCall, 1976, $7.95 from:
   Capra Press
   631 State Street
   Santa Barbara, CA 93101
This book is a record of owner-building in New Mexico—of people making adobes and adobe homes with their own hands and hearts. The results speak for themselves, through good photographs and essays. Contains good bibliography on adobe building.

The Return of the Gods, Ulli Beier, 1975, $14.95 from:
   Cambridge University Press
   32 E. 57th Street
   New York, NY 10022
A small book for the price, but about the work of Susanne Wenger, which deserves to be known. Wenger, a European artist, became involved in repair of shrines of the Yoruba religion in Nigeria, and the building of new shrines as she became more involved in the religion. The shrines she has built are powerful and are sacred—a rare creation in today's culture. Her respect, as an outsider, for the native religion has helped restore a vestige of its power before the impact of unholy Western culture and shows that new and powerful sacred places *can* emerge today.

Shelter, Lloyd Kahn, 1973, $6 from:
   Random House
   201 E. 50th St.
   New York, NY 10022
An amazing kaleidoscope of images, ideas, techniques and tips for beautiful owner-built shelter from the past and present and from all over the world. Shows what can be accomplished where people put a lot of love and energy into their surroundings. Guaranteed to expand anyone's concept of what can be built.

Handmade Houses, Art Boericke, Barry Shapiro, $5.95 from:
   The A&W Visual Library
   95 Madison Ave.
   New York, NY 10016
A very beautiful book filled with color photographs of individualistic and spirited rural homes on the North California coast. Hand-crafted, lovingly and creatively designed, and often breathing new life and beauty into the cast-off materials of a wasteful society. Tea-houses suspended over rivers. Picture-window privies in the forest. Home in a redwood stump. Bathing beneath a huge overhanging boulder. Much better book than its imitators, and available now in paperback.

Environmental Design Primer, Tom Bender, 1973, $5.95 from:
      Schocken Books
      200 Madison Ave.
      New York, NY 10016
Schocken Books has just come out with an edition of the *Primer*. They call it a book of meditations on ecological consciousness—which in some ways describes it better than I could. It has a lot to do with moving our heads into the right space before making our places, and a lot to do with the sacredness of all we do. Sections on feng-shui, ornament, topological design, death and other strange and sundry things. It's pretty much the groundwork behind "Living Lightly," and "Sharing Smaller Pies."

REBUILDING

Things usually change so gradually that we have to keep our eyes open if we want to know when we're suddenly into a new ballgame. Everyone who has been angered by the demolition of beautiful historical buildings to make way for parking lots and fast food chains will be happy to know that we seem to have passed from conditions that encourage such waste to conditions that encourage restoration, renovation, preservation, caring and adapting. Even small buildings are now being disassembled rather than demolished, old neighborhood buildings and homes are being fixed up and upper stories reoccupied. And suddenly a rash of new resources appears for renovation and reuse of old buildings.

Economic Benefits of Preserving Old Buildings, National Trust for Historic Preservation, 1976, $5.50 from:
> The Preservation Press
> 1729 H Street, N.W., Suite 300
> Washington, DC 20006

Escalating construction costs have made the rehabilitating of old buildings economically advantageous. The U.S. General Services Administration has testified to Congress that saving an old building employs five times as many people as building a new one of the same size—a figure verified by labor organizations. Preservation results in economic use of energy and materials, and many old buildings were designed expressly for natural daylighting, ventilation and thermal control that are again becoming desirable. These conference proceedings detail the experiences of many architects and developers spearheading rehabilitation practices— economics, financing problems, structural and architectural restoration, and adaptation to new uses. Their successes offer handsome evidence of the value of preservation, though warning notes are sounded against the transitory value of chic "formula" antiquing and commercial/nostalgic restorations.

Reusing Railroad Stations, by Educational Facilities Laboratories and the National Endowment for the Arts, 1974, $4 from:
> EFL
> 850 Third Ave.
> New York, NY 10022

Over 40,000 railroad stations have been built in this country since 1830. 20,000 still stand, but few will see another passenger train unless massive increases in ridership and financial support for rail travel again develop. Many fine and useful buildings have already been lost to the wrecker's ball because of an inability to assemble new occupancy, financing and interest in rehabilitation. This study documents the availability of fine and usable structures, the apathy and antagonism of many railroad companies, and, more heartening, a wide range of successful conversions to other uses—art colleges, shopping centers, homes, offices, nursery schools and even a bank.

The Restoration Manual, by Orin Bullock, Jr., 1966, $12.95 from:
> Silvermine Publishers, Inc.
> Norwalk, CT 06850

The sleuthing involved in analyzing and restoring old buildings is almost as esoteric as collecting Nepalese snuff jars, but it is frequently necessary and useful for restoring the beauty of fine old buildings buried under a patina of misuse, vandalism and destructive "modernization." A whole new world of beauty can open up when you see a 17th century Persian garden pavilion emerge from beneath the French Rococo plaster that had covered its exquisite polychrome and gold vaulting and faceted mirrored domes for 200 years. This manual outlines the basic procedure for historical, archeological and architec-

tural research, execution of a restoration, climate control in restored buildings, use of photogramming and other sneaky techniques.

The Old House Journal
188 Berkeley Place
Brooklyn, NY 11217
212/636-4514

$12/year (monthly). Subtitled "Renovation and Maintenance Ideas for the Antique House," here's the journal that will keep you up to date on how to do it. Preserving exterior woodwork, Gothic decoration in the American house, patching up your old piping, refinishing old floors, and more. There's also a yearly *Buyer's Guide* ($5.50) with sources for hard-to-find products and services. Encouraging to see that it's still possible to find handmade bricks, exterior cornices, Victorian door handles and gingerbread trim, and that people are putting loving care into preserving and enhancing the legacy given us by past generations.

Urban Homesteading: Process and Potential, 1974, $2.50 from:
> National Urban Coalition,
> 2100 M Street, N.W.
> Washington, DC 20037

Several cities are now experimenting with urban homesteading—selling abandoned houses for a buck to people committed to fixing them up. In most programs taxes and increased assessments are waived for up to ten years.

How to Rehabilitate Abandoned Buildings, Donald R. Brann, $3.50 from:
> Easi-Bild Pattern Co., Inc.
> Briarcliff Manor, NY 10510

Deals with the specific problems of owner-rehab in the city—from security to sagging floors—and gives a lot of useful how-to information for potential urban homesteaders.

A. A. Abbingdon Ceiling Co.
2149 Utica Ave.
Brooklyn, NY 11234

These folks are the only ones we know who produce the decorative stamped metal ceilings that were common in the turn-of-the-century stores. They still have advantages for certain applications—non-flammable, washable, yet decorative. More than twenty ceiling patterns available, along with 10 different cornice and trim designs. (TB)

Reader's Digest Complete Do-it-Yourself Manual, 1973, $13.95 from:
Reader's Digest
Pleasantville, NY 10570

Most home repairs aren't really difficult. The major hangup is figuring out the tricks, how to go about it, and what tools you really do or don't need to bother with. This manual covers almost every kind of situation you're likely to run into, and gives simple step by step instructions/photos/drawings explaining the essentials you need to know. If you need a little self-confidence to get into figuring things out for yourself, this is quite worth the money.

Velux Roof Windows
Velux-America Inc.
80 Cummings Park
Woburn, MA 01801

Roof windows are a good approach to pulling a lot of sun heat and light into a building, renovating and using attics in old houses for more efficient space use and not having to build complex and expensive dormers into a roof. Get the information from these folks—showing a lot of varied applications, how to flash to prevent leaks and how to deal with the new problems of sloping windows! Whether you use their products or make your own, it's a good idea. If they would come out with a sliding insulating shutter similar to their decorative one, I'd give them our four-dandelion award.

"Parking Facilities for Alternative Uses," Swedish Building Research Report R41-1975, Jan Dyfrerman and Jan-Erik Hollander. Summarized in English in *Synopses and Summaries from National Swedish Building Research* (See the next page for access.)

The future life of our buildings and equipment becomes of more concern to us as our energy/wealth decreases. It also becomes increasingly important to consider the durability of buildings, the possibilities for disassembling and reusing materials rather than demolishing, and the adaptability of buildings to new uses and conditions as the present activities of a high energy society give way to gentler ways of a more austere society. This study explores the technical and economic problems connected with conversion of parking garages to other uses. Slight modification of basic design—greater room height, clearance to eradicate floor

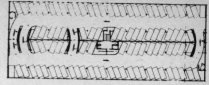
Figure 1. Parking storey in split-level structure. 96 car stalls.

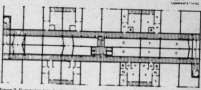
Figure 2. Conversion into dwellings. Floor layout. Symbols: V = living room, S = bedroom, K = kitchen, P = kitchenette, B = bathroom, H = hall, Kl = wardrobe, F = storeroom, D = optional use.

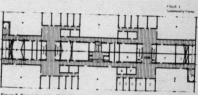
Figure 3. Conversion into offices. Floor layout. Symbols: C = cell office, S = landscape office, A = filing room, F = storeroom, K = conference room, I = installations room, KPR = cloakroom.

drainage slopes; structural capacity for such floor leveling materials; layout to provide light and ventilation for future enclosed uses are shown to be desirable. They require only about 4 percent increase in cost for the garages and make future conversion economically sound, improving the financial uncertainties of parking garage development. Layouts for use as apartments and offices are studied. Similar studies for other elements of our urban form (such as suburban land use) need to be made.

Local Materials

The July 1972 issue of *Architectural Design* published a useful bibliography on low-cost building which contains good sources—mostly British—on dry stone walling, roof slating and tiling, bamboo as a building material, grass, thatch, canework and other presently uncommon materials.

The Thatcher's Craft, Rural Industries Bureau, 1961, 42s. from:
Rural Industries Bureau
35 Camp Road
Wimbledon Common, SW 19
Wimbledon 5101 England

A unique and authoritative book containing very clear and detailed photo-documented instructions for use of long straw, combed wheat or Norfolk reed roof thatch construction. Chapters on materials, tools and costs; fire protection, roof structure construction. Explanation of beautiful traditional ridge and flashing trim details.

Ideas and Methods Exchange
Office of International Affairs
Department of Housing and Urban Development
Washington, DC 20410

This exchange is a series of free specialized publications developed for use of U.S. AID missions.

Palms—Their Use in Building A survey of of different uses of palm trees in building, including listing of species desirable or unfavorable for different applications, along with means of overcoming some of the shortcomings of palms. The vinelike stems of some rattans attain 500-600 foot lengths and are used for pedestrian bridge cables!

Mud Brick Roofs (No. 42)
An expansion of the explanation in Hassan Fathey's *Architecture for the Poor* of construction of mud brick vaults and domes without scaffolding. Photos of different construction steps.

Bamboo as a Building Material Not part of the above series, but available free from the same source, this provides an excellent introduction to the subject. Properties and uses of the many different kinds of bamboo, tool requirements, how to work the material, joints, designs, and even bamboo reinforcement of concrete. One of their better publications.

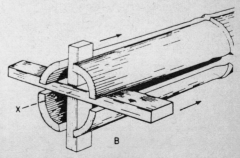

HANDS-ON BUILDING

People are beginning to share useful building skills in good ways—direct, non-institutional programs and even hands-on programs in universities. Vocational-Technical Schools and community colleges, take note: these programs have a lot to offer. Send SASE to these groups for information on programs and publications.

"Original Log House Construction School," $20 course fee, $30 per couple, for pre-registration details, contact:
Skip Ellsworth
Bar E Ranch
Redmond, WA 98052
206-885-4972, after 7 p.m.
Concentrated two-day building program with hands-on learning of tree-felling, rigging, peeling, layout, stacking, shake-splitting and other log-building processes. Use of all necessary tools, discussion session, slide lecture, potluck dinner.

Farallones Institute
15290 Coleman Valley Rd.
Occidental, CA 95465
Hands-on building program combined with design and testing of solar energy systems, compost toilets, grey-water systems, blacksmithing, etc.

The Shelter Institute
72 Front Street
Bath, ME 04530
Set up specifically to help prospective owner-builders learn to design and build their own low-cost, energy-conserving homes. Basic course gives 45 intensive hours of wood engineering, framing methods, wiring, plumbing, foundation design, insulation and heating. Further courses in refinement of the builder's design, actual carpentry and building experience are available.

The Laboratory for Maximum Potential Systems
School of Architecture
University of Texas
Austin, TX 78712
Max's Pot, the research group working with Pliney and Daria Fisk at the School of Architecture at the University of Texas, Austin, is continuing their excellent and practical experimentation with simpler and more appropriate energy sources and conversion devices at a new location. Their combination of solid technical and engineering skills and strong concern to develop things that are simple, wise, effective and home-buildable is producing excellent results. Among their current projects is an elegantly simple water-filled concrete block Trombe wall, heat

storage units using water-filled beer cans, muffin tin solar-air collectors, and a quite detailed series of charts bringing together information on appropriate building materials, bioclimatology, waste systems, and conditions affecting choice of heat source.

Ouroboros Project
School of Architecture
University of Minnesota
Minneapolis, MN 55455
Students in this program have researched, designed and built one of the earliest full-scale working experimental dwellings combining solar, wind, energy and water conservation with sensitive architectural design. They have since worked on retrofitting an old urban house for energy-efficiency and prepared plans for moving a small town towards self-reliance.

Sweat Equity
One of the best routes to low-cost housing is owner-building—using your own sweat as equity rather than going into hock to pay for someone else to build for you. The Consumer-Farmer Foundation, 101 E. 15th St., New York, NY 10003, has sponsored a number of innovative sweat-equity projects with youth gangs in NYC renovating and solar heating abandoned tenements.

Small Homes Council
Building Research Council
University of Illinois at Urbana-Champaign
One E. St. Mary's Road
Champaign, IL 61820
Numerous useful publications and periodic bulletins for people wanting to do their own home design. Kitchen design, windows, insulation, post and beam framing and many other topics in a continuing series.

Synopses and Summaries from National Swedish Building Research
The National Swedish Institute for Building Research
Box 785 S-801 29
Gävle, Sweden
English summaries of the many excellent research reports prepared for the Swedish Council for Building Research. Published nine times a year. Most reports are in Swedish, but summaries in English are excellent and some technical papers are available in English.
"The Window as an Energy Factor,"

Research

Swedish Building Research Report R43-1975, Folke Hagman. Hagman provides computer simulation of optimal patterns of use of insulating shutters on windows to prevent unwanted heat loss and gain while permitting loss and gain where desirable. Energy savings of 25 percent for houses and 20 percent for apartments is shown to be attainable through this simple process, which also provides increased security and noise protection. Economic consequences are explored.

American Institute of Architects
1735 New York Ave., N.W.
Washington, DC 20006
The AIA and the AIA Research Corp. have published a good number of useful documents over the years—most oriented to practicing architects. *Regional Climate Analyses* is their jewel (see Energy section). Write for their new publications catalog.

The Solar Home Book, by Bruce Anderson (see review in solar section). Discusses in good detail many of the "autonomous" designs, their energy systems and how to design your own.

Good research is as frequently done by obscure, obsessed individuals as by well-known organizations, and the key for access to such research is usually held by a gatekeeper—someone who has the instinct and interest to snarf out obscure gold nuggets. Ken Kern is one of the best gatekeepers for building. The references in *Owner-Built Home, Owner-Built Homestead*, and other Kern publications, are often goldmines, ferreting out the gems from the U.S.D.A. reports, Farmers' Bulletins and other government reports, as well as the fine work of independent researchers. Or contact him at Owner-Builder Publications, Box 550, Oakhurst, CA 93644.

COURSES

Total Environmental Action
  Church Hill
  Harrisville, NH 03450
Offers seminars and courses on the fundamentals of solar energy utilization—emphasizing domestic applications to heat and cool houses and provide hot water.

The Social Ecology Program
  Goddard College
  Plainfield, VT 05667
Provides a summer program focusing on building, renewable energy systems and decentralized communities. The college used to have a unique architectural program where the students designed and built the college's buildings.

The Housing Assistance Service
  4615 Bagley Avenue
  Seattle, WA 98103
Works with owner-builders of low-cost pole constructed homes and log dwellings.

The Minimum Cost Housing Group
  School of Architecture
  McGill University
  P.O. Box 6070
  Station A
  Montreal, Quebec H3C 3G1 Canada
Has been doing pioneering research for a number of years on low-cost construction, waterless toilets and use of waste products in construction.

The School of Architecture
  University of Oregon
  Eugene, OR 97403
Frequently has programs where students design, build and test innovative buildings. A passive solar heated greenhouse and sauna was recently designed and built by the students in Noti, Oregon, and a number of buildings, pavilions and remodeling projects have been built on the university campus.

Access Program
  School of Architecture
  University of Wisconsin
  Milwaukee, WI 53201
These folks have been working on rehabilitating existing urban homes, adapting them with solar energy, insulating shutters, water conservation with emphasis on economic viability.

Owner-Building Courses
Organic Gardening & Farming published in their November 1975 issue a list of schools in the U.S. that teach homebuilding. Their Reader Service (33 E. Minor St., Emmaus, PA 18049) is preparing a more extensive list of such courses across the country.

Handcarved sinks at Farallones Rural Site (use solar-heated water)

AUTONOMOUS HOUSES

A lot of fascination and energy has recently gone into design and building of "Autonomous Houses." They have been a dream of independence—of providing heat, electricity, water and food

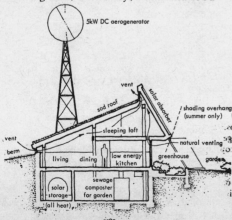

right on the homesite and passing on no sewage, trash or problems to others. This has been a dream pushed by fear of a collapsing society and omnipotent utility corporations holding homeowners for ransom. It has also been a dream pulled by a desire to live lightly in ways which don't burden us or our resources, ways which make visible and comprehensible the strands of support, interdependence and connection which reach out from our lives. Total autonomy is total freedom and total freedom is total power—neither possible nor desirable in an interactive ecosystem. The main value these experiments have given is to provide a counter-balancing dream to a hooked-up, plugged-in world and demonstrate that a range of ways to live is possible, attainable and desirable. Their message has been what we spoke of early in the Ouroboros Project—self-reliance, not self-sufficiency. This means understanding and being able to reduce our demands on others and ourselves so that the bonds that we create are knowledgeable bonds and are bonds

of choice and mutual benefit not of fear and perceived necessity.

Radical Technology, Geofrey Boyle and Peter Harper, 1975, $5.95 from:
  Pantheon Books
  201 E. 50th St.,
  New York, NY 10022
Provides an analysis and overview of a considerable number of autonomous house projects in various countries as well as a critique of the concept.

The Autonomous House, by Robert and Brenda Vale, 1974, $10 from:
  Universe Books
  381 Park Avenue South
  New York, NY 10016
Some of the most rigorous analytical engineering work on self-sufficient housing has been carried out by the Technical Research Division, Department of Architecture, University of Cambridge, 1 Scroope Terrace, Cambridge, England CB2 1PX, under Alexander Pike. Write for their publication list. This book is one of the most thorough reports out of that project.

Cheap energy dealt a paralyzing blow to the quality of our urban surroundings. It became more expensive for an architect to plant trees to stay cool than to air-condition glass buildings, and cheaper to pave outside spaces with concrete and asphalt than to hire a gardener to maintain plants.

That's all changing. The importance of trees and plants in cooling the air, shading streets and buildings, and beautifying our surroundings is being relearned, and the results are encouraging: 20° cooler air temperature on hot summer days, 60° cooler sidewalks and streets, and valuable dollar and energy savings in summer cooling of buildings.

ENERGY CONSERVING

Plants, People and Environmental Quality, G. O. Robinette, 1972, $4.35 from:
> U.S. Government Printing Office
> Washington, DC 20402

A good guide to what plants can do for you—privacy, climate control, engineering, and beauty. How to control sun, ventilation, temperature, noise and wind. Important information to know before building or planting.

"Technology of the Cooling Effects of Trees and Shrubs," by Robert Deering, *Housing and Building in Hot Climates*, Building Research Advisory Board Report No. 5, 1952, available from:
> National Academy of Sciences
> Printing and Publications Office
> 2101 Constitution Ave., N.W.
> Washington, DC 20418

Gives an excellent and detailed presentation of how and how much cooling takes place under different conditions.

"Effects of Landscape Development on the Natural Ventilation of Buildings and their Adjacent Areas," by Robert F. White, *Texas A&M Research Report No. 45* March 1954, p
Pioneering study of the effects of vegetation placement upon air flow through buildings.

Climate and Architecture, Jeffrey Aronin, 1953, Reinhold, out of print—check your library or interlibrary loan.
Of the many books on climate and building design, this one most strongly covers the use of plant materials in conjunction with buildings for shade, cooling, wind and noise control.

"Worcester MA Zoning for Climate," by C. F. Brooks, *Bulletin of American Meteorological Society*, June/July 1923, p. 83-86
A report on the pioneering achievement of one of the first cities to zone land usage based on microclimatological considerations. Up to 20°F. temperature difference can be obtained in some locales by careful microclimate choice and maintenance.

The Climate Near the Ground, Rudolf Geiger, 1960, $18 from:
> Harvard University Press
> 79 Garden Street
> Cambridge, MA 02138

Gives all sorts of detailed information about microclimates and how they develop from topography, sun, vegetation and wind. Good information to determine where you want what kind of landscaping to shade you, block winds, drain cold air, or just make you feel good.

"Natural Air Flow Around Buildings," Benjamin Evans, *Texas A&M Research Report No. 59*, March 1957
Basic study of aerodynamics of buildings and their effect upon surrounding regions.

A Strategy for Energy Conservation, 1974, $5 from:
> Living Systems
> Route 1, Box 170
> Winters, CA 95694

Proposed energy conservation and solar utilization ordinances for the city of Davis, California, that have since been implemented. Of particular interest are sections on "sun rights" or shading limits and on requirements for narrow streets and planting of large trees to shade pavement and reduce summer temperatures.

Plant Form Studies—The Design Characteristics of Plant Materials, Gary O. Robinette, 1967, $12 from:
> American Printing & Publishing Co.
> 2909 Syene Road
> Madison, WI 53713

One-eighth inch scale drawings of both summer and winter silhouettes of a wide range of landscape materials. Useful for determining shading patterns and size and rough estimation of summer and winter shade factors.

Plant a Tree, Michael Weiner, 1975, $6.95 from:
> MacMillan Publishing Co.
> 866 Third Avenue
> New York, NY 10022

An excellent manual for planting and maintenance of trees. Describes many city street planting programs, urban tree maintenance, planting for rural conditions, and a photographic survey of American, European and Oriental trees.

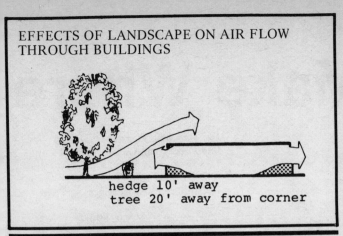

EFFECTS OF LANDSCAPE ON AIR FLOW
THROUGH BUILDINGS

hedge 10' away
tree 20' away from corner

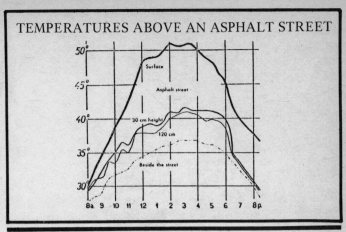

TEMPERATURES ABOVE AN ASPHALT STREET

LANDSCAPING

Sunset Western Garden Book, 1973,
$5.95 from:
  Lane Publishing Co.
  Willow & Middlefield Roads
  Menlo Park, CA 94025
Outstanding basic resource for any landscaping for the western U.S. Climate
zones, plant selection guide for a wide
variety of special situations and a western plant encyclopedia covering more
than 5000 plants. Highly useful, and
should be emulated for other regions.
Another Sunset book, *Low Maintenance
Gardening*, 1974, $2.45, covers selection
of low maintenance plants and their
care for many climates and situations.

*Philadelphia Area Green Pages: A Hand-
book of Tools, Information and Resources for the Greening of Philadelphia.*
1975, 70 pages, $3.50 from:
  Pennsylvania Horticultural Society
  325 Walnut Street
  Philadelphia, PA 19106
For the local resident it's a dandy reference to regional growing conditions,
finding garden plots, useful stores,
agencies, arboreta, trade organizations
and local lore. For everyone else it provides useful information on national
plant organizations, horticulture correspondence courses and techniques. It's
also a fine model for similar publication
efforts elsewhere.

Water Conserving Gardening
  Marin Municipal Water District
  Water Conservation Education
    Program
  220 Nellen Ave.
  Corte Madera, CA 94925
Useful guide to choosing native regional
plants that don't require massive irrigation and care. Worth replicating for
other areas.

There are a number of county water districts in California involved in setting up
low water and low energy using gardens
and landscapes for people to see. Examples are Santa Clara County Water
District (*A Landscaping Guide to Native
and Naturalized Plants of Santa Clara
County*, Win Stiles); Marin Municipal
Water District; East Bay Municipal
Utilities District. It's useful to contact
your water district for tips on energy
conserving landscaping, or contact the
State Department of Water Resources,
1416 Ninth St., Sacramento, CA 95814.

The Community Development Department of the Planning Division, 226 F
Street, Davis, CA 95616, also has available a booklet, "Drought-Tolerant Ornamental Plants for Davis, CA," and the
October 1976 *Sunset* Magazine contained a useful article, "For Summer
Dry California, Water-Saving Planting
Ideas."

Where to Get
  Pacific Bamboo Gardens, 4754 Vista
Lane, San Diego, California 92116
  Forestation Notes. Frank TerBush,
editor. U.S. Forest Service, Division of
State & Private Forestray, Box 3623,
Portland 97208. One issue has listings
of nurseries which supply bare-root
seedlings for forestry plantings.
  USDA's Agricultural Stabilization &
Conservation Service has reforestation
and other land-building programs. They
will pay 75% of cost of reforestation at
the rates of $85/M seedlings planted,
$35/acre for site preparation.
  F.W. Schumacher, Sandwich, Mass.
Excellent seed company—grow your
own woodlot of useful trees (See Eric
Sloane, *A Reverence for Wood*, et al.,
and Rutherford Platt, *The Great American Forest.*)
  Department of Forestry, State of
Oregon, 2600 State Street, Salem 97310.

*To determine light intensity in stands of trees, multiply unobstructed light intensity
by the following factors.*

Type of tree (old stand)	Without foliage	With foliage
Deciduous trees		
Red beech	.26—.66	.02—.40
Oak	.43—.69	.03—.35
Ash	.39—.80	.08—.60
Birch	—	.20—.30
Evergreen trees		
Silver fir	—	.02—.20
Spruce	—	.04—.40
Pine	—	.22—.40

After Geiger

Make Where

Floral Clock.

Little of our effort goes for our survival. Most of it in some complex way goes to satisfy or stimulate our fantasies—towards our feeling good. Yet we spend less effort making where we live beautiful and good feeling than we do traveling to other places to get away from our bad ones. Travel less—give more to making where you are paradise.

Many communities that now enjoy beautiful, cool, tree-shaded streets owe them all to a single Arbor Day—*one weekend* when the whole community got out and planted trees! Those who plant trees now will have similar streets twenty years from now, leaving a lasting legacy for our grandchildren. If we plant fruit or nut trees there will always be a food source handy—as well as blossoms in the spring.

Gardens are an important part of making any place a paradise! And as everyone knows, the Japanese are masters at feasting the eye and the soul, making the commonplace seem beautiful and turning even the tiniest of spaces into flowering gems with the merest of means. Take a look at:

The World of the Japanese Garden, Loraine Kuck, 1968, from:
Walker & Co.
720 Fifth Ave.
New York, NY 10019

A good beginning book on landscaping is:

Landscape Architecture, John Simonds, 1961, from:
McGraw Hill
1221 Avenue of the Americas
New York, NY 10036

Floral Clocks
The famous European botanist, Linneaus, had a floral clock known all over Europe, with flowers that opened at different hours of day and night arranged in the form of a clock.

Moonlight Gardens
The Moghul rulers of India were famed for their moonlight gardens—gardens designed for special beauty at night. Waterfalls with flickering lamps behind, candles floating on mirror-smooth lakes, plants selected for their evening fragrances, patterns of foliage silhouetted against marble pavillions glowing softly in the light of the moon.

"Why Not Plant for Moonlight?," Louise Riette, *Organic Gardening & Farming*, **May, 1973.**
Contains numerous suggestions for night-blooming plants: Midnight to 2:30 a.m.—night-blooming cereus; 3 a.m.—Amazon water lily is open; 4:30 a.m.—Virginia spiderwort is unfolding; 5 a.m.—Purple morning glory opens, so does wild rose, Iceland poppy and blue chicory; 5:20 a.m.—Common blue flax is "fully unscrewed."

The Dutch Mountain Nursery Catalog
The Dutch Mountain Nursery
Augusta, MI 49012
Specializes in plants which birds and wild animals eat—information on who eats what when, how many species are supported by different plants, lifezone studies, and how to encourage different species.

Bare root forest trees can be gotten for as little as 3¢/tree from forest tree nurseries in all but 5 states.

Forest Tree Nurseries in the United States, from
Chief, U.S. Forest Service
Washington, DC 20250
Lists local nurseries.

The Man Who Planted Hope and Grew Happiness, Jean Giono, 1967, 16 pp., $.75 from:
Friends of Nature
c/o Miss Ellen R. Riggs
92 Arlington St.
Winchester, MA 01890

1913 in Provence. Barren, colorless land. Most villages were abandoned, their springs gone dry. In one village, people made charcoal and it was an unhappy life: greed and rivalry among neighbors, everyone trying to escape the area. Hot, dry winds blew through the treeless landscape, which was turning to desert from lack of vegetation and water.

In the hills, through the valleys, walked a shepherd with his flock. In a bucket each day he carried 100 acorns soaked the night before in water. With an iron rod as thick as your thumb he would poke a hole in the earth, carefully plant the acorn, and walk on. 100 each day. Jean Giono came across the shepherd, Elezard Bouffier, when hiking in the Alps that year before WWI. In three years' time the 55-year-old man had planted 100,000 acorns. 20,000 had taken, and he expected to lose half of these.

"There remained 10,000 oak trees to grow where nothing had grown before."

Seven years later, Giono returned to the area and went with Bouffier for a walk amongst ten-year-old oaks," . . . beech trees as high as my shoulder, spreading out as far as the eye could reach . . ." and birches planted where there was moisture in the valleys. In 1945 Giono returned again:

Everything was changed. Even the air. Instead of the harsh dry winds that used to attack me, a gentle breeze was blowing, laden with scents. A sound like water came from the mountains; it was the wind in the forest; most amazing of all, I heard the actual sound of water falling into a pool. . . . The old streams, fed by the rains and snows that the forest conserves, are flowing again. Their waters have been channeled. On each farm, in groves of maples, fountain pools overflow onto carpets of fresh mint. Little by little the villages have been rebuilt. People from the plains, where land is costly, have settled here, bringing youth, motion, the spirit of adventure. Along the roads you meet hearty men and women, boys and girls who understand laughter and have recovered a taste for picnics. Counting the former population, unrecognizable now that they live in comfort, more than 10,000 people owe their happiness to Elezard Bouffier.

You Are a Paradise

The Fragrant Garden, Louise Wilder, 1932, $3.50 from:
    Dover Publications
    180 Varick St.
    New York, NY 10014

Daphne and cherry blossoms in Kyoto, wisteria and lilacs outside bedroom windows when we were growing up, the gentle fragrance of nicotinia in the evening, fresh mown fields of mint or alfalfa—we've traded a beautiful symphony of smells for auto exhausts and industrial effluents. This book gets into things I never dreamed of—sweet-leaved geraniums, herbs and grasses, night-scented flowers, shrubs and trees, orchards and berry patches, ferns, mushrooms, wild scents and much more.

Should Trees Have Standing: Towards Legal Rights for Natural Objects, Christopher Stone, 1973, $1.50 from:
    Avon Books
    959 Eighth Ave.
    New York, NY 10011

A brilliant case for granting legal rights to natural objects, which has already had impact on our legal system. Resource limits require protecting our resources, and Stone develops persuasive legal reasoning for allowing groups or individuals to act as guardians for trees and other living things.

Tree People
California Conservation Project
1745 Selby Ave., No. 18
Los Angeles, CA 90024

We've always gotten off on the idea of giving trees as gifts and memorials. Here are some people making that easy (and who needs it more than L.A.?) A $5 donation will sponsor the cost of purchasing, planting and maintenance "to fair state of survival of one smog-resistant seedling." They also do a lot of educational and tree-planting for groups in the L.A. area. Sponsor a tree for a friend or send a self-addressed stamped envelope for more info on their project.

Forest Farming, J. Sholto Douglas and Robert de Hart, 1976, 3.85£ from:
    Watkins Publishing
    45 Lower Belgrave St.
    London, SW1W OLT
    England

Some time ago I read J. Russel Smith's pioneering book, *Tree Crops: A Permanent Culture* (1950, Devin-Adair Co., 1 Park Ave., Old Greenwich, CT 06870, $7.95). It hit a sensitive chord—I had felt strange about farming practices in the Northwest where we irrigate field crops through our 6-month summer drought while native trees are able to suck up deeper ground water left from the 6-month winter deluge of rain. I thought it sure would be simpler if we could live on nuts and acorns, but assumed trees were much less productive than field crops.

Forest Farming goes the important next step of showing that in food productivity alone tree crops can produce 10 to 15 times as much food per acre as field crops. It also thoroughly explores other important features of forest farming—timber and firewood production, ability to use hillsides unsuitable for field crops, lower labor demands, combination of tree crops and pasturage or livestock foraging, multi-level farming, production of medicines, chemicals, oils, etc. from trees, use of trees in desert reclamation (some trees have 100-foot taproots to draw up deep groundwater), leguminous trees which improve soil fertility, and the importance of vegetation in tropical forests where nutrients are held in *vegetation* rather than in the soil where the rains would leach them away, etc.

The International Book of Trees, Hugh Johnson, 1973, $29.95 from:
    Simon & Schuster
    630 Fifth Avenue
    New York, NY 10020

This is the finest and most beautiful guide to becoming a tree lover I've ever found. It's an incredible collection. Almost 250 pages of the best color pictures I've seen of every kind of tree in different seasons—their leaves, bark, flowers and structure, along with encyclopedic information on the different kinds of trees. Combine that with beautifully illustrated explanations of how a tree grows and works, trees and weather, hardiness zones, trees and wildlife, planting and caring for trees, a useful index to trees, the meaning of botanical names, a guide to choosing trees (which resent moving, have ornamental bark, tolerate heavy shade, etc.), charts of rate of growth and ultimate size, a 12-month calendar of ornamental flowers, fruit, and foliage, and much more!

- 80 to 90% of a tree is water, drawn from the ground by its roots. Of the remaining 10 to 20%, no less than 91% is derived from the atmosphere by the leaves, which are thus the tree's main feeding organs.
- The sap of a tree carries nutrients to its roots. Removing the bark of a tree deprives the roots, not the tree above, of nourishment.
- Pears, apples and almonds are related to *roses*.
- A line of ancient gnarled beeches occur through Denmark, Champagne and Brittany, whose malformation is believed to have been caused by a radioactive meteor several centuries ago.
- The "Chinese cedar" or "toon" tree, common in Paris, would probably be extinct if Parisian gourmets realized the delicacy of its onion-flavored leaves and shoots.

AGRICULTURE

Our agriculture and food systems are an excellent example of the need for more appropriate ways of doing things and how they can be developed. They are also a clear demonstration that new attitudes, organizational patterns and careful research are equally as important as new tools themselves, and that together they can lead to better results as well as simpler, less costly and less damaging ones. Our beliefs that tilling the land is degrading and doesn't make good use of our personal capabilities could only arise in a society divorced from the land and from the rewards that close ties to it can bring. Real skills and sensitivity are necessary to successfully and sustainably coax the food we depend on from the vicissitudes of cold and heat, drought and flood, diseases, insects, and the marketplace.

Our attempts to turn that difficult process over to "someone else" have resulted in pesticide-contaminated, nutritionally poor, "rubberized" food—bred for mechanized growing, and so old by the time we eat it that we've almost forgotten the taste of good food.

More and more, people are choosing other options—food purchased direct from growers and picked the same day, U-pick food, home gardening, eating lower on the food chain and co-op buying. Those choices are resulting in money savings, energy savings, stronger communities, better food, and a lot more enjoyment in the process. People feel so good about it they often call it "Eating High and Lightly"!

Radical Agriculture, edited by Richard Merrill, 459 pp., index, $6.95 paperback from:

> Harper & Row
> 10 E. 53rd St.
> New York, NY 10022

California's New Alchemist, Rich Merrill, has put together the best introduction to the new—with the best from the old—agriculture. Contributors read like a roll call of pragmatic food futurists: Jerry Goldstein, Helga Olkowski, John Todd, Paul Relis, Bill McLarney, Michael Perelman, Murray Bookchin, Wendell Berry and Peter Barnes; covering land reform, agribusiness, energy efficiency, the green revulsion, food cooperatives, urban agriculture, organic farming, aquaculture, biological pest control.

Highly recommended for 4-H'ers, land-grant college agri-engineering courses and an important addition to all agriculture and energy libraries.

Farming, $2 from:
> **Alternative Agriculture Resources Project**
> **Dept. of Applied Behavioral Science**
> **University of California**
> **Davis, CA 95616**

Although new understandings and techniques have been emerging as rapidly in farming as elsewhere, there's no sense in us covering most of what's been going on because these folks have already covered it and done a better job than we could ever do. If you're interested in composting, seeds, soil fertility, forage, field and tree crops, biological control, beekeeping, animal husbandry, water management, machinery and farm building, urban gardening, technical assistance, certification or training programs, this is the place to go to find out the best sources available. This excellent sourcebook is to be followed by ones on food distribution, nutrition and eating, land reform, energy, networks and sharing. Keep in touch with them.

ENERGY AND AGRICULTURE

Energy, Agriculture and the Environment, Larry Geno, 1975, 70 pp, prepared for Environment Canada and available from:
> Larry Geno
> R.R. 1
> Morrisburg, Ontario
> Canada K0C 1X0

Environment Canada should be commended for having the foresight to commission studies such as this—which amounts to an environmental impact statement on our present agricultural practices and a comparative analysis of alternatives available to us. It analyzes the impact of energy inputs and outputs, economic damage, losses of agricultural land, potential climate changes, economic costs of development, and policy and process alternatives. A basic planning document for agricultural/environmental policy.

Center for Studies in Food Self-Sufficiency
> **Vermont Institute of Community Involvement**
> **90 Main Street**
> **Burlington, VT 05401**

These folks have carried out a well-organized study of Vermont's agriculture and the potentials for change towards more self-reliant patterns for food production and consumption.
▪ *Land, Bread and History* ($2.50). Explores the institutional changes in Vermont's agriculture from a time when it was largely self-sufficient to increasing impacts of outside transportation and land developments that caused a specialization in dairy, maple syrup, fruit and poultry products. It surveys the state's present food consumption and marketing patterns and develops a methodology for aligning agricultural land capability in relation to diet choices. Agricultural land is shown to be available to feed much more than the present population on present diets and change to a diary/vegetarian or largely vegetarian diet is shown to reduce agricultural land needs by up to 40%.

▪ *Energy Utilization in Vermont Agriculture*, Summary (50¢), Vol. 1—Maple and Apple Production ($1.50), Vol. 2—Egg and Dairy Production ($1.50). A full net energy accounting of various existing options for different sectors of the state's agriculture. Size offers little advantage in maple or apple production. Commercial egg operations are more efficient than homestead operations, while small dairy farms are more than large ones. Overall state agricultural efficiency is 5.5%—requiring input of 18 calories per calorie of output. Suggestions for improved efficiency are given, as well as social concerns which should be included in determining state farm policy.

Proposals for Vermont's Agriculture and Food Future, Report of the Governor's Commission on Food, January 1976, $10 (summary 50¢) from:
> **Vermont Dept. of Agriculture**
> **116 State Street**
> **Montpelier, VT 05607**

An excellent complement to the above research studies which helps round out the process for change in one specific region. Commission recommendations to the government include setting up community canneries, community composting projects, farmers' markets, grain storage and cooperatives.

Council for Agricultural Science & Technology
Agronomy Building
Iowa State University
Ames, IA 50011

Many published reports, including "Energy and Agriculture," submitted to Congress Nov. 26, 1973; also a valuable "Directory of Environmental Scientists in Agriculture," Nov. 1972 ($3). Also publish a newsletter reporting on developments in technology, science and agriculture.

Energy, Agriculture and Waste Materials, by William J. Jewell, 540 pp., $22.50 from:

> Ann Arbor Science Publishers
> P.O. Box 1425
> Ann Arbor, MI 48106

Details, from the viewpoint of the agricultural engineer, of energy consumed in food production, technology and energy costs of pollution control and potential for producing energy from agricultural wastes. Recommended by Ken Smith.

Comparative Efficiency of Energy Use in Crop Production, by G.H. Heichel, free bulletin no. 739, Nov. 73, from

> Connecticut Agricultural Experiment
> Station
> Editorial Office
> 123 Huntington St., Box 1106
> New Haven, CT 06504

Full of useful numbers, ending with suggestions for increased energy efficiency via green manure fertilizing—the manure spreader returns!—and using crop residue for fuel. Long and comprehensive bibliography. Ask for their publications list.

Energy and Food: Energy Used in Production, Processing, Delivery and Marketing of Selected Food Items, by Fritsch, Dujack & Jimerson, June '75, $4 from:

> Center for Science in the Public
> Interest
> 1776 Church St. N.W.
> Washington, DC 20036

More numbers on the energy inherent in different foods at each step in their route to our dinner tables. A basic reference in this area as well as a primer on energy-intensive agriculture and on ways to reduce energy consumption while keeping high nutrition standards.

Energy Efficiency in the Food System, An Annotated Bibliography, by Christina Peterson, 10 pp., single copies free with SASE from:

> Environmental Farm Program
> Shoreline School District
> N.E. 158th and 20th Ave., N.E.
> Seattle, WA 98155

Comprehensive, understandable, especially useful for high school, undergraduate and teacher training courses.

Enhancing Biological Nitrogen Fixation, edited by Harold Evans, single copies free from:

> Office of the Deputy Assistant
> Director for Biological and Social
> Sciences, NSF
> 1800 G St., N.W.
> Washington, DC 20550

The annual market value of nitrogen obtained from the atmosphere by agricultural legumes in the U.S. is about $3.3 billion dollars. This nonpolluting biological process utilizes neither natural gas nor petroleum as its major source of energy, but is primarily dependent upon solar energy captured by plants through photosynthesis. This report summarizes present knowledge about nitrogen fixation and suggests ways to increase the process in other species. It suggests gaps in understanding where further research would be useful.

Agriculture/Energy Project Reports
> Center for the Biology of Natural
> Systems
> Box 1126
> Washington University
> St. Louis, MO 63130

Barry Commoner's team has completed six excellent studies which are available free, analyzing the comparative energetic and economic performance of organic and conventional farms in the Corn Belt. In both the first and second year of the study organic farms outperformed others. Although yields per acre were somewhat less, costs of fertilizer and other inputs were substantially less, and return on investment greater.

CBNS-AE-1: *Effect of Recent Energy Price Increases on Field Crop Production Costs*, Dec. '74, 108 pp.
CBNS-AE-2: *Vulnerability of Crop Production to Energy Problems* (simplified version of CBNS-AE-1), Jan. '75, 34 pp.
CBNS-AE-3: *Agricultural Resources Consumed in Beef Production*, June '75, 41 pp.
CBNS-AE-4: *A Comparison of the Production, Economic Returns and Energy Intensiveness of Corn Belt Farms That Do and Do Not Use Inorganic Fertilizers and Pesticides*, July '75, 62 pp.
CBNS-AE-5: *Energy in Corn Belt Production*, July '75, 15 pp.
CBNS-AE-6: *A Comparison of Organic and Conventional Farms in the Corn Belt*, July '75, 27 pp. (simplified version of CBNS-AE-4).

"Economies and Diseconomies of Large-Scale Agriculture," Philip M. Raup, 1969, from:
> Department of Agricultural
> Economics
> University of Minnesota
> Minneapolis, MN 55455

"Farmworkers in Rural America, 1971-72," Part 3-A, B and C; January 11, 12 and 13, 1972: Land Ownership, Use and Distribution, U.S. Senate Committee on Labor and Public Welfare, Subcommittee on Migratory Labor.

"Will the Small Family Farm Survive in America?" Joint Hearings before the Select Committee on Small Business and the Committee on Interior and Insular Affairs, U.S. Senate, 94th Congress.

The above reports all document the absence of economies of scale in most agricultural situations beyond the size of a single family farm. All reports found the single family farm to have production efficiency equal to larger organizational structures and superior performance in many categories. The argument is made for removal of subsidies and tax advantages that make possible unequal competition by large farming enterprises.

Agriculture and Economic Growth, U.S. Department of Agriculture, 1963, Economic Research Service, Agricultural Report No. 28 (A93.28:28), 25¢ from:
> U.S. Government Printing Office
> Washington, DC 20402

Economics of Size in Farming, by J. Patrick Madden, Agricultural Report No. 107 (A93.28:107), 55¢ from:
> U.S. Government Printing Office
> Washington, DC 20402

U.S.D.A.'s own research findings on the relationship between farm size and efficiency of production. In case after case, economies of scale could be achieved equally well on one and two person farms.

Small Farm Project
> George D. Kemper
> Produce Development Section
> State Dept. of Agriculture
> Charleston, WV

In cooperation with the extension service of West Virginia University, the eight-acre farm is operated to research and demonstrate methods of farming on limited land resources. Total sales from the 8-acre farm last year were $1100 per acre.

American Farmers and the Rise of Agribusiness: Seeds of Struggle.
Arno Press
New York Times Co.
330 Madison Ave.
New York, N.Y. 10017

Arno is an established reprint publishing house, and this collection, which in total (46 books) costs $1,200, is obviously a library purchase. (Editions may be bought separately but not inexpensively.) For anyone doing research on the politics of agriculture in the U.S., this is an important collection. (Write for description of the books in collection.) They have also made available the Annual Agriculture Economics bibliographies which were published by the U.S. Dept. of Agriculture from 1929 to 1942.

"A Tale of Two Towns," Walter Goldschmidt, in *The People's Land*, ed. by Peter Barnes, 1975, $6.95 from:
Rodale Press
33 E. Minor
Emmaus, PA 18049

The effects of small vs. large businesses go far beyond the mere question of costs of production. They influence the whole social structure of communities and nations. Goldschmidt's pioneering study of the social effects of large vs. small scale farming on towns in California showed this so clearly that the U.S. Department of Agriculture refused to publish it.

Here's why:

"The study showed the small-farm community had twice as many business establishments and did 61% more retail business; the small farms supported 20% more people at a measurably higher standard of living; the small-farm community had more institutions for democratic decision-making and much broader citizen participation in such activities; it had far better physical facilities, such as sidewalks, paved streets, garbage and sewage disposal, schools, parks, newspapers, churches and civic organizations; and the majority of the small-farm community population were independent entrepreneurs, while 2/3 of the large-farm communities were agricultural wage laborers."

Corporate Secrecy: Agribusiness, Stock No. 5270-0178, $2.25 from:
U.S. Government Printing Office
Washington, DC 20402

Hearings before the Subcommittee on Monopoly of the Select Committee on Small Business, U.S. Senate. A 500-page report. Testimony, newspaper clippings, studies, articles.

The Agbiz Tiller, $10/year for individuals, $30/yr for institutions, from:
San Francisco Study Center
P.O. Box 5646
San Francisco, CA 94101

A monthly newsletter monitoring the activities of agribusiness from a public interest perspective. Also publishes a directory of major U.S. corporations involved in agribusiness ($3.50/$5).

Politics of Land, Robert Fellmeth, 1973, $5.95 from:
Grossman Publishers
625 Madison Ave.
New York, NY 10022

Condensation of Ralph Nader's Study Group Report on Land Use in California. Politics of land ownership, who owns what and what the effects are, corporate agriculture and the effects of vertical integration on land values.

Wheels of Fortune, 1976, from:
Center for Rural Affairs
P.O. Box 504
Walthill, NE 68067

Emergence of new patterns is always a signal to delve into what lies behind them and what implications these forces have beyond the surface events. Center-pivot irrigation in Nebraska is on the surface a shift to capital and energy-intensive farming. But underneath it represents a shift to investment schemes, tax shelters and lack of self-interest in the long-term viability of soils, farming practices and rural society. Big circles on the plains spell bad news. This is a good analysis of what's happening and why, although it doesn't continue its analysis strongly into the broad implications of such events.

AGRICULTURE AND SCALE

awareness that life divorced from the land is somehow fragmented, incomplete, lacking the sense of stability and purpose that accompanies a land-based experience.

Yet, as we begin to explore ways of reestablishing our bond with the land, we find ourselves confronted again and again with the results of our past ignorance and carelessness. People's right to land is one of the most basic principles of our national heritage; yet, increasingly, we are being denied the means of realizing those rights. Lands that were once appropriated for human settlement and the growth of communities are now being increasingly owned or controlled by large corporate industries—mining, forestry, railroads, agribusiness—and those corporations are displacing people from the land at an ever-increasing rate. The American Public Domain—once encompassing seemingly inexhaustible areas—has shrunk almost to the point of memory. Lands that were taken forcibly from our Native American forebears are now being taken from us through the various more subtle methods that our society has since developed: increasing taxation, zoning, spiraling inflation and economic "efficiency."

There are several fundamental ideas that need to be considered. The first of these has to do with the way that we regard the land. This country—and this culture—needs a new land ethic: an attitude that considers the needs and requirements of the land *first* and which then attempts to foster human relationships with the land to the extent that the land itself will allow. This kind of attitude, instinctively a part of cultures that have maintained their ties with the land, has somehow been lost in our society, and we need to devise ways of making it known once again.

The creation of such a land ethic must of necessity begin with individual response. If we are to reestablish our bond with the land, each of us must examine his/her personal land sense, and seek ways of strengthening and increasing it. We need to work more closely with and upon the land, experiencing it, *feeling* it directly. And we particularly need to look to the land as a source of wisdom and learning—to, as the poet Gary Snyder has written, "accommodate the possibility that nature has a degree of authenticity and intelligence that requires that we look at it more sensitively." If we can culture this kind of an attitude within ourselves, then we will have achieved a first and critical step toward establishing a renewed land ethic in our culture.

Only now, as we begin to face the loss of irreplaceable wilderness areas, agricultural lands and mineral resources, are there beginning to be heard those voices who maintain that the integrity of the land is a concern which demands our attention and to which we must respond. This renewed regard for the land has come partly from the blunt realization that it *is* a finite commodity and that human growth is occurring on a much more rapid basis than the land can possibly keep up with or support. But it is also coming from an increasing

LAND

by Becky Deryckx

Becky Deryckx is an articulate spokesperson for the land reform movement. And she lives it too: I've watched her putting splints on a newborn goat's weak ankles. She's involved in both the Evergreen Land Trust and Tilth (Rt. 2, Box 190-A, Arlington, WA 98223).

Land Settlement, Land Speculation, Land Tenure, Land Transfer, Land Utilization, The Encyclopedia of the Social Sciences, ed. by Seligman & Johnson, Vol. IX, The MacMillan Co., New York, pp. 53-137.

This series of in-depth articles provides an excellent introduction to the basic concepts pertaining to man's relationship with the land. Each presents historical perspectives and outlines some of the social consequences of given people-land developments, and they do an excellent job of including non-European viewpoints. Not at all outdated, they are a fine place to start; some of the statements, in fact, are as radical as

anything being heard today. Check your local library.

Land Reform

The People's Land, ed. by Peter Barnes, 1975, $6.95 from:
Rodale Press
Emmaus, PA 18049

An excellent primer, *The People's Land* presents historical, contemporary and regional perspectives on land holding patterns in the U.S. and explores in depth some of the possible alternative institutions and policies that can create

a more equitable system of land tenure in America: co-ops, farmworkers' unions, anti-corporate farm laws, land trusts and many others. Contributors range from Thomas Jefferson to Ralph Nader; individually, they are both highly readable and concise, and together they present a good overview of the land reform movement in the U.S. today.

The Lands No One Knows, T. H. Watkins and Charles S. Watson, 1975, $9.95 from:
Sierra Club Books
930 Bush St.
San Francisco, CA 94108

This is the kind of book that can take

people who are just moderately interested in the need for land reform in America and turn them into jump-up-and-down, screaming, hard-core radicals. The story of the American public domain, *The Lands No One Knows* traces the progressive loss of our common landed inheritance to the increased control of private landholders; it is a thoroughly researched account of the literal giveaway of hundreds of millions of acres to speculators and corporate interests. In the process, however, the book also portrays the tragic social patterns that have characterized the Great American Land Grab: fraud and corruption, racial exploitation and economic discrimination, and a wanton disregard for the needs of the land itself. It is a stark and devastating picture of what we as a people have already lost through mismanagement, abuse and our own confusion, but its major contribution is that, by providing such a clear picture of the effects of uneven land distribution it provides the kind of stimulation that is going to be necessary if we are to save what we have left for the generations who are to succeed us. An important—and very readable—work.

People and Land

An infrequent, but enormously worthwhile, publication, *People and Land* was originally published by the National Coalition for Land Reform in San Francisco. Intended as a means of distributing information and articles about land and people in America, *P&L* is the kind of publication that can give the American land reform movement a sense of cohesiveness. Due to a lack of financial support, the Coalition was forced to discontinue publication of *P&L*, but a new issue is currently being put together by National Land for People in Fresno, California. Write to them for more information, or contact the Coalition for information about back issues (both addresses are listed at the end of this page.)

Akwasasane Notes, suggested subscription donation $6/year, from:
    Roosevelt Town, NY 13683
The paper of the Mohawk nation, *AN* is an eloquent voice for the perspective of the Native American peoples on matters relating to the land and our cultural relationship with it. Fine articles deal with both the continuing legacy of exploitation and land deprivation which the Native Americans still suffer and—by sharp contrast—the Indian peoples' concepts of the land's sacredness and inviolate non-divisibility. Extremely helpful for those interested in banning the notion of land ownership from our cultural headspace.

A Bibliography on Land Reform in Rural America, Charles L. Smith, published by The Center for Rural Studies, now available for $1.25 from:
    Earthwork
    1499 Potrero
    San Francisco, CA 94110
Published in 1975, this bibliography is the definitive reference work for information dealing with land reform in America. Over 1,000 entries, referencing books and articles, periodicals and organizations currently on the forefront of the movement. A valuable tool—worth every cent.

❖

The following are several short but powerful papers dealing with the need for a reassessment of our current land tenure system. While their individual contents overlap somewhat, they are all very worthwhile; their collective impact is greater than the sum of the parts.

The Sharing of Land and Resources in America, by Peter Barnes, $1.00 from:
    New Republic Pamphlets
    1244 19th St., N.W.
    Washington, DC 20036
A hard-hitting little book in which Barnes outlines the growing inequities of our current land tenure system and makes a solid case for redistribution.

It should be seen around more; its price makes it more accessible than *The People's Land*, in which Barnes explores some of the same concepts to a greater depth.

Rural Land Use: Patterns and Proposals for Reform, Ronald P. Erickson, published for the First National Conference on Rural America, 1975, by:
    Rural Housing Alliance and
    Rural America, Inc.
    1346 Washington Ave., N.W.
    Washington, DC 20036
Another brief but concise paper which catalogues the uses and misuses of American land and which provides statistical documentation as additional weight in its argument for widespread

reform measures. Write to the address given above; ask for Conference Working Paper No. 3. $1.00 should do it.

Who Owns the Land?, Peter Barnes and Larry Casalino, 1972, Clear Creek, now available from:
    Earthwork
    1499 Potrero
    San Francisco, CA 94110
Probably the most familiar and widely distributed land reform document now out; proposes appropriate and specific remedies for the misuse of America by timber companies, railroads, energy companies, agribusiness and other speculators. Includes a short but dynamic statement on land economics.

"Buying Back the Land: A Proposal for California," Peter Barnes, in Working Papers for a New Society, Vol. I, No. 2, Summer 1973
Quite obviously, Peter Barnes is one of the most articulate spokespersons in the American land reform movement. In this short (7 pp.) article, he outlines a state land trust fund as a possible means of redistributing the land. Deals specifically with California, but the concept may well be relevant to other states as well. Contact Earthwork for reprint info if you can't locate *Working Papers*. See page 57 for access information.

The National Coalition for Land Reform
RR 4
Creston, IA 40801
The NCLR is an organization made up of farmers, farmworkers, environmentalists and others who believe that "ownership of the land by those who live and work on it is the key to alleviating poverty, easing urban overcrowding, reducing welfare costs and unemployment and building a stronger democracy." Both a political and educational organization, the Coalition invites support and membership.

National Land for People
4696 North Millbrook
Fresno, CA 93726
Probably the most highly political organization in the movement and certainly one of the most dynamic, NLFP has been concerned primarily

with the enforcement of the 160-acre limit on lands irrigated with federally-financed water in the Westlands Water District in California, but they are also emerging more and more as an overall clearinghouse for reform activists. As mentioned above, they are currently working on another issue of *People and Land*; they also have available for rent a couple of intensely eloquent films, *The Richest Land* and *The Dispossessed*.

Heathcote Center
Rt. 1, Box 129
Freeland, MD 21053
Heathcote Center is the home of The School of Living, which for more than 30 years has served as a voice for de-

workbook/cpf

centralism in the U.S. The Center sponsors workshops and seminars on all aspects of decentralist philosophy and application—including land reform—and is performing an important function in putting people interested in such matters into touch with each other. Home base, too, for *The Green Revolution*

Institute for Liberty and Community
Concord, VT 05824
Founded and directed by John Mc-Claughry, the Institute serves primarily as a dispensing agent for McClaughry's numerous articles on decentralism and local autonomy. Write for their publications list.

Land Trusts

As one specific solution to the need for a new way of regarding the land and a new approach to land tenure, the concept of the land trust is showing a great deal of promise. Based on the notion that, because land *is* the common resource of all people, it must be stewarded in such a way as to protect the long-term common interest, the land trust holds title to the land in perpetuity and grants use rights to the occupants only if they abide by the conditions which define that common interest. Still a rather difficult idea to grasp in a society which places so much emphasis on land ownership, the land trust has been successfully implemented on a widespread basis in India, Israel and Tanzania as a means of providing the peoples of those countries with a more equitable opportunity for land access. In this country its growth and acceptance have been much more restricted; trusts have begun to be considered as a viable alternative only within the last couple of decades, and as a result the land trust movement in America is still in a fairly embryonic state. Numerous trusts—and types of trusts—are arising, however; and increased familiarity with and support for the land trust concept should result in its more widespread application as an alternative land-holding mechanism.

The Community Land Trust: A Guide to a New Model for Land Tenure in America, Bob Swann, 1972, $3.50 from:

International Independence Institute
West Road, Box 183
Ashby, MA 01431
An excellent introduction to both the idea and its application, the *CLT Guide* examines the history of land tenure systems in other cultures, traces the beginnings of a single large land trust in the U.S. rural south, offers suggestions about setting up legal structures and provides numerous examples of existing trust documents. Now a bit outdated due to the number of trusts that have arisen since it was published four years ago, the *Guide* is nevertheless the only book that is currently available on land trusts, and it remains well worth the money. III is now in the process of preparing a sequel to the *CLT Guide*; the new book should be ready early next year and will bring developments in the movement up-to-date.

Since 1967, they have been providing people with information and consultation about land reform, land trusts, credit and financing alternatives and the creation of viable rural economies. Write for their complete publications list and sample newsletter; subscriptions $10/year.

The Maine Land Advocate, quarterly, subscriptions $5/year from:

Box 653
Bangor, ME 04401
The MLA focuses on what is going on with general land issues in the New England area, but it also includes fine in-depth articles on land trusts specifically. The MLA has been around for several years now; its staff are good folks to contact for information about the development of the land trust from idea to practical application.

The Green Revolution, 10 times a year, subscription $6 from:
The School of Living
Heathcote Center
Route 1, Box 129
Freeland, MD 21053
Long recognized as the voice of decentralism in America (the GR has been published for nearly thirty years), this fine publication has begun to place increased emphasis on land trusts and is showing signs of developing into a regular exchange medium for people who are involved with promoting their acceptance.

"A Proposal for a State Land Trust Act," John McClaughry, *The Harvard Journal on Legislation*, June 1975, Vol. 12, No. 4
An example of one way that the land trust idea could be applied on a widespread basis in the U.S. McClaughry proposes legialtion that would establish a State Land Trust in Vermont, with trustees appointed by the governor and income for the Trust to be derived from a 1% tax on real estate transfer. The State Land Trust's purpose would be to protect open space woodlands and agricultural areas from overdevelopment,

while at the same time providing farmers with relief from excessive tax burdens. Linked with the notion of transferable development rights that has been tried in several eastern states (mentioned in the section on Land Reform), McClaughry's proposal cuts through many of the problems that usually accompany that notion and enables the benefits from the legislative process to go to the grass-roots level. The idea is a complicated one, but it is an important consideration for those who are interested in seeing legislation help to implement land trusts at the local level. (See below)

COMMUNITY LAND TRUSTS

Of the several different types of land trusts that are now emerging, CLTs are in many ways the most exciting. Widely decentralized and usually arising from the personal dedication and commitment of individuals and small groups, Community Land Trusts consistently share a concern for making land available to people who, for economic or social reasons, could not otherwise obtain access to it. It is with the Community Land Trusts that the different implications of the land trust idea are being explored and tested most fully, and because they are so closely tied to the communities in which they function, the CLTs stand the best chance of enduring over the long run.

The following is a list of several trusts across the country which, because of their emphasis on community involvement, are good sources of information and how-to advice. Virtually all are subsisting on shoestring budgets, and they incur a lot of out-of-pocket expenses; small donations to cover mailing costs will be much appreciated (and will probably speed answers!).

The Sam Ely Community Land Trust
  136 Maine Street
  P.O. Box 116
  Brunswick, ME
One of the oldest CLTs in the country, Sam Ely publishes the *Maine Land Advocate* (cited above). A good group to be in touch with; they're thoughtful and responsible in their promotion of trusts.

The Evergreen Land Trust
  P.O. Box 303
  Clear Lake, WA 98235
The first land trust in the country to receive a federally non-profit, tax exempt status, Evergreen is working on developing other legal precedents for the movement. ELT is also one of the more flexible/creative trusts currently in existence, looking at ways that the

trust concept can be made applicable to a wide variety of possible situations and individual needs.

Northern California Land Trust
  330 Ellis Street, Room 504
  San Francisco, CA 94102
Organized for the specific purpose of providing farmable lands to otherwise disenfranchised people, NCLT has this year acquired its first piece of land and has placed occupants upon it. Because it has been relying entirely upon gifts of land and money to further its goals, NCLT is currently trying to reconcile a slow *actual* growth with the vast numbers of inquiries that they are receiving from people who would like to occupy trust lands. They publish a newsletter ($3.00/yr.) and offer membership ($6.00/yr.) as an added means of drawing those who are interested in their activities into closer involvement.

Abnaki Regional Land Trust
  Putney, VT 05346
One of the quieter but more successful trusts in the country, Abnaki is expanding steadily. Good ideas, good approach. It *works.*

The People's Land Trust
  1000 Harris Street
  Bellingham, WA 98225
The People's Land Trust is unique in that it is, thus far, an urban-centered trust. Holding title to about half a dozen houses and a community-use building in the town of Bellingham, People's can offer assistance in dealing with various potential problems connected with urban properties held in perpetuity.

PUBLIC LAND TRUSTS

Another effective type of land trust that has arisen in the U.S., the public trusts are attempting to free large amounts of land from the speculative market by operating on a more professional, big-money level. Both of the following organizations have been highly successful in this regard; and while neither is trying to provide people with places where they can live on the land, they have done much to set aside public-use areas such as greenbelts, parks and wildlife preserves.

The Nature Conservancy
  1800 North Kent Street
  Arlington, VA 22209
With offices in many parts of the country, the Nature Conservancy has acquired numerous areas for public access. Their emphasis is on wilderness land; they have initiated many local programs in regional inventories of unique areas. (Northwest Office: 1234 N.W. 25th, Portland, OR 97210).

The Trust for Public Land
  82 Second Street
  San Francisco, CA 94105
  415/495-4014
Similar to the Nature Conservancy but more oriented toward urban/suburban open space property. They have a highly polished approach and have managed to convince various large corporations and wealthy landowners to give land to the public through them. Currently setting up an intensive—and expensive—training program for those who are interested in promoting this particular approach to the land trust idea.

Oregon Historical Society

New Food Sources

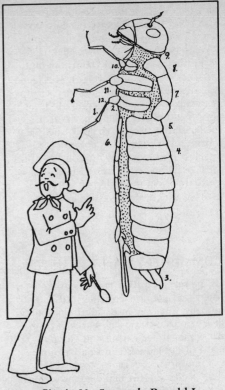

Good and Wild, International Association for Education, Development and Distribution of Lesser Known Food Plants and Trees, quarterly, $7.50/yr. from:

P.O. Box 599
Lynwood, CA 90262

A small California-based group with a strong sense of simple grassroots ways to obtain more food. Knowledgeable, direct and from the heart newsletter discusses the properties of different plants and how to grow them, acts as a network among people working in related areas. Seedbank and nurseries planned.

Underexploited Tropical Plants with Promising Economic Value, by the National Academy of Sciences, 1975, free from:

Board on Science and Technology
for Industrial Development
National Science Foundation
2101 Constitution Ave., JH 215
Washington, DC 20418

This belongs on your bookshelf next to *Forest Farming* (see page 148). Underexploited is probably a good category to be in if the other options are Extinct, Exploited and Over-Exploited, but it's definitely our loss that we have tried to feed the world's people with only about 20 plants. We have an incredible range of soils and climates, and these 20 plants form a pretty small bulwark between us and starvation. Diversity has benefits, and this study lays out some astounding potentials we've overlooked in the rest of the plant kingdom—in tropical areas alone! Cultural colonialization and balloon bread may be good for some but not for all. Try these for a sampling: a wild Australian grass that yields nutritious grain on just one deep watering; amaranthis—a Central American grain with high yields and extremely high levels and quality of protein; zostera—a grain-producing grass-like plant that grows in sea water; arracacha—a Peruvian "parsnip" often grown instead of potatoes, at half the cost; mangosteen—probably the world's best-tasting fruit; plants that grow through salt crusts on the ground; and gourds that produce more oil, protein and starch on the desert than most crops do with plentiful rainfall. This list goes on and on. An important pathfinder for future agricultural directions.

Perennial Farming

Dear Rain,

The proper agronomy will preserve the land forever, and those who live on the land. Perennials, once well-rooted, if properly chosen, will live for years, protecting the land and feeding it with their droppings, and protecting and feeding the life inhabiting the land.

Perennials provide many kinds of foods: cereals, flour, beans, greens, salads, fruits, nuts, sweetenings, spices, medicines, etc. Some produce more abundantly, some produce better flavored or more valuable products. They will grow on high or low level or steep lands. They are disease and pest resistant. They can survive flood, fire or draught. Trimmings are fuel to warm the home. The soil, interlaced with roots and covered with smaller plants, won't be carried away by wind and water. The falling leaves and twigs enrich and build up the soil. Nutrients added remain where placed and increase your crop.

Low perennials such as alliums, herbs, rhubarb, comfrey and higher plants like berries and even grapes will grow beneath the trees. An acre of trees can out-produce an acre of plow crops. Nuts, including acorns, can be used for cereal or flour or pressed for oils. Homemade machines can be used, or something can be adapted. Heavy-padded locust produces a big crop of a complete stock feed, replacing wheat and hay. Apples can be eaten fresh or dried, ground or boiled down for sweetening, squeezed for juice, cider, brandy or vinegar which will preserve your other foods, or they can be made into a spread or a jelly.

A perennial crop, once planted and growing, means no more plowing or hoeing. Perhaps perennials planted on a slope, uncultivated, unirrigated, given a minimum of attention, won't produce as much as hybridized, expensive, chemicalized, pampered plants on level (and expensive) ground, but you can always plant two, or even 20, for less cost and effort for the 20 than the one.

I have been interested in perennial farming for a long time, and while I am no expert, perhaps I can answer questions for you.

Paul Doerr
225 E. Utah
Fairfield, CA 94533

Butterflies in My Stomach, Ronald L. Taylor, 1975, $8.95 from:
Woodbridge Press Publishing Co.
P.O. Box 6189
Santa Barbara, CA 93111

One of the fantasies I've been playing with recently is termite farming and slug ranching for the Pacific Northwest—both for people and animal food. Someone once told me that all the Northwest is good for is growing conifers, so I started to figure out how to develop a food system appropriate to this region. We have taken our eating habits with us as we've moved from one region of the planet to another just as much as we have taken our living patterns—building stuffy English Tudor hotboxes to live in in the Florida Keys and eating oranges and bananas in the subarctic rainforests. Along with Douglas and Hart's *Forest Farming*, Taylor's book—on eating insects—begins to open some new options for rethinking our eating habits and developing ones that are both appropriate to our own regions and for understanding and respecting the value of other forms of life. We generally abhor insects and think of them only as harmful pests. Taylor shows that thinking to be both wrong and inconsistent—insects are essential and valuable in plant pollination (bees) and nutrient cycling. Termites and other insects are extremely high protein and high quality food sources and, like cows, can harvest and convert food sources we can't eat ourselves (grass and pinetrees). And we consider ocean "insects" to be gourmet foods—but not their land cousins. What is the difference between lobster and landcrabs, oysters and slugs? Other so-

cieties don't have the phobias we do and relate more positively to tasty and nutritious food sources like termites, ants, grasshoppers and bee larvae. If all this makes your stomach/mind do weird things, take a look at this book—it's good food for thought. Protein charts, recipes, extensive bibliography on health and nutrition studies. (TB)

SEEDS

Seeds, like people who have lived in one spot year after year, pass from generation to generation inscrutable ways to get along with the climate. As we have increased our research into agricultural productivity and expanded the range of native plants to encompass nearly anywhere where we can get water and people, seeds have become dumb superbeans.

There have been the formation of some small seed companies who have been attempting to generate seeds that may be able to find the path of right livelihood. *Organic Gardening and Farming* has been keeping track of those. Companies like:

Abundant Life Seed Company, P.O. Box 30018, Seattle, WA 98103 (50¢ for a mushroom-shaped catalogue).

Johnny's Selected Seeds, Albion, ME 04910 (50¢ for catalog).

J. L. Hudson Seeds, Box 30018, Redwood, CA 94064 (50¢ for catalog)

Wilson Seed Farms, Rt. 1, Box 7, Polk, NE 68654.

For possible companies in your area, write to: OGF Readers Service, 33 E. Minor, Emmaus, PA 18949.   (SJ)

AGRICULTURAL TOOLS

Simple tools are often difficult to find, but once we relearn how to add both sides of a picture and see that simple farming practices can be as effective as more expensive ones, simple tools are worth searching for. The following sources give helpful access to useful farming and food processing equipment.

Tools for Agriculture: A Buyer's Guide to Low-Cost Agricultural Implements, 2nd ed., John Boyd, 1976, $11.50 from:
> **Intermediate Technology Publications**
> **9 King Street**
> **London WC2E 8HN England**

A well-illustrated directory to more than 250 manufacturers and more than 600 hard-to-find implements from around the world. Hand, animal and small-engine powered equipment, with access to research organizations and manufacturers.

Water Lifting Devices for Irrigation, by Alder and Molenaar, 1956, FAO Agricultural Development Paper No. 60, from:
> **Food and Agriculture Organization**
> **United Nations**
> **Rome, Italy**

Out of print but worth getting from your library through inter-library loan if you are interested in the relative costs, construction, operation and performance of a wide variety of people, animal or mechanically-powered water pumping devices. Covers examples from all parts of the world, adaptations of pumps to special needs and calculation of horse- (or other) powered requirements and energy consumption.

International Rice Research Institute (IRRI)
> **P.O. Box 933**
> **Manila, Philippines**

IRRI has developed a series of simple, well-designed agricultural tools for low-cost/high employment applications. Available for licensing in the U.S. and other areas.

Manufacturers of Pesticide Application Equipment, by Deutsch and Poole, 1976, available in photocopy from:
> **AID Reproduction Center**
> **3853 Research Park Drive**
> **Ann Arbor, MI 48104**

A 56-page international listing of sources of equipment used for pesticide application. Not restricted just to pesticide use, equipment includes both manual and power operated granule dust and liquid applicators, special purpose applications, components and safety gear. Bilingual— English/Spanish.

CECOCO Catalogue, $11 airmail, from:
> **CECOCO**
> **P.O. Box 8**
> **Ibaraki, Osaka, Japan**

A guide to rural cottage industry and agricultural and food processing equipment produced in Japan.

Village Technology Handbook, $9 from:
> **Volunteers in Technical Assistance**
> **3706 Rhode Island Ave.**
> **Mt. Ranier, MD 20822**

A do-it-yourself manual for useful techniques and tools for farming, home-steading or village applications.

Metastasis
> **P.O. Box 128**
> **Marblemount, WA 98267**

An excellent mail order source for hard-to-find information and tools, such as FAO's *Tools for Arid and Tropical Regions* and horse and oxen farming manuals.

AGRICULTURAL ORGANIZATIONS

Rural America
1346 Connecticut Ave., N.W.
Washington, DC 20036

National, citizen-based clearinghouse for information on rural issues and advocacy on behalf of rural people. They monitor government programs to assure equitable treatment of rural people, do research and sponsor a yearly conference. There are some fine people involved here.

Maine Organic Farmers and Gardeners Association (MOFGA)
P.O. Box 187
Hallowell, ME 04347

An example of an organic group at their best—MOFGA has been working with the State Department of Agriculture to provide extension agents and assistance to organic farmers and generally on certification and distribution. $2.50/yr. ($3 outside the U.S.) for their monthly newsletter which is a wealth of information.

Center for Rural Affairs
P.O. Box 405
Walthill, Nebraska 68067

Though this 4-page newsletter has a focus on Nebraska, there's also national news affecting the small farmers of America.

IFOAM (International Federation of Organic Agriculture Movements)
c/o Research Institute of Biological Husbandry
Postfach, CH-4104
Oberwil, Switzerland

Recently reorganized at an International Conference, IFOAM coordinates and networks developments in research, agricultural techniques and education on organic farming worldwide. A quarterly newsletter in English, French or German is available for $4. Well worth it for keeping up with the organic movement as a whole.

Tilth
Rt. 2, Box 190-A
Arlington, WA 98223

Our good friends at Tilth are continuing their hard work to network produce truckers, sellers, and experimenters. They're the ones to ask about farmers, markets, community gardens, agricultural research (biological pest control, slug eating, etc.), land trusts, agri-business reports, etc., etc.

Their most recent projects include a proposal for a N.W. Trade Network and an experimental greenhouse/aquaculture project at their Pragtree Farm. See Solar Greenhouse section. Their newsletter—still $5/yr.—is the best bargain going. It's always chock full of good new information.

PUBLICATIONS

Countryside, $9/year, monthly, from:
Hwy. 19 East
Waterloo, WI 53594

Practical information with a stress on the small family farm as an energy-efficient, productive and ecologically balanced food producing operation. How-to and general articles.

Organic Gardening and Farming, $7.85/year, monthly, from:
Rodale Press
Emmaus, PA 18049

This is the much-loved basic journal of how-to organic gardening that comes fat with ideas each month. You'll learn different methods of composting (so many it will be hard to choose), how to make canned spaghetti sauce, and what to do about pests.

Acres, USA, $5.50/yr., monthly, from:
10227 East 61st St.
Raytown, MO 64133

This "Voice for Eco-Agriculture" covers a wide variety of areas including research, news, politics, alternative energy and how-to. Informative ads (organic fertilizers, wood stoves, seeds) tend to be midwest based. Recent issues have been carrying a fascinating journal from Editor Charles Walter's trip to China.

Garden Way Publishing
Charlotte, Vt. 05445

Many people know about this excellent resource, but just in case: They publish and distribute some of the best down-to-earth, how-to-do-it books. Heating with wood ($3); Veterinary Guide for Farmers ($6.95); Making Apple Cider ($1.00); Have More Plan ($2.50); Beginner's Guide to Hydroponics ($5.95). Write for a catalog—a delight in itself.

Road Apple Press
159 Annoven Rd.
Winlock, Wash. 98596

They publish delightfully "downhome" (but professional) books. One especially of interest is *The Vegetable Garden Displayed*, a reprint of a 1940s vegetable garden: how to do it, published by the Royal Horticultural Society, London. Of course, some of the information is not perfectly appropriate, but generally good stuff, and some techniques I've not seen elsewhere. 300 photos. A good book to hold. $2.50. Ask about other publications. They will also help people publish worthwhile materials/resource tools and help on occasion train people in the use of offset press techniques.

REGIONAL ORGANIC FARMING GROUPS

CALIFORNIA

California Organic Growers
D. E. Foote, Director
Box 540-H
Halcyon, CA 93420
805/489-3829

COLORADO

Colorado Growers' & Marketers'
Assn.
Jim Fowler
2555 W. 37th Ave.
Denver, CO 80211
303/477-6291

GEORGIA

Eastern Georgia Farmers Co-op
Box 35
Waynesboro, GA 30830

ILLINOIS

Organic Growers
Alexander J. Smith
R.R. 1, Box 133
Dixon, IL 61021

KANSAS

Kansas Organic Growers
Charles Gardiner
2324 W. 25th
Topeka, KS 66611
913/357-0873

KENTUCKY

Bluegrass Organic Assn.
Mrs. Jean Warriner
137 Eastover Dr.
Lexington, KY 40502
606/266-6758

LOUISIANA

Tangipaho Organic Farmers Assn.
Hurd A. Hess
P.O. Box 457
Albany, LA 70711

MAINE

Maine Organic Farmers &
Gardeners Assn.
Chaitanya York
Bump Hill Rd., RFD No. 2
Union, ME 04862
207/785-3455

MICHIGAN

Organic Growers of Michigan
P.O. Box 136
Decatur, MI 49045

MINNESOTA

Minnesota Organic Growers
& Buyers Assn.
624 Jefferson St., N.E.
Minneapolis, MN 55413

MISSOURI

Ozark Growers & Buyers
Organization
Noah & Elitta January
Earth Magic Farm
Macomb, MO 65702

**NEW HAMPSHIRE &
VERMONT**

Natural Organic Farmers Assn.
Robert Houriet
Box 247
Plainfield, VT 05667
802/426-3249

NEW MEXICO

Organic Growers Assn.
David Rowley
1312 Lobo Pl., N.E.
Albuquerque, NM 87106
505/268-5504

NEW YORK

New York Organic Farmers
Nick Veeder
R.D. 1
Jordanville, NY 13361
315/858-0729 or 823-0818

NORTH CAROLINA

Rural Advancement Fund
Jim Pierce, Exec. Dir.
1947 Lansdale Dr.
Charlotte, NC 28205
704/537-6509 or 537-1745

PENNSYLVANIA

Pennsylvania Organic Farmers-
Consumers Organization
Paul Hartz, Pres.
R.D. 1, Box 86
Morgantown, PA 19534
215/286-5268

SOUTH CAROLINA

Piedmont Organic Movement
Assn.
Charles Parrott
714 S. Line St.
Greer, SC 29651
803/877-4101

TEXAS

Organic Growers Cooperative
& Ext. Serv.
P.O. Box 'OGC'
McKinney, TX 75069

Family Farmers
Malcolm Beck
P.O. Box 1056
New Braunfels, TX 78130
512/651-6307

VIRGINIA

Southern Agricultural Assn.
of Va.
Box 734
So. Boston, VA 24592
703/476-2543

WASHINGTON

Northwest Organic Food
Producers Assn.
Pat Langan, Pres.
Rt. 2, Box 2152
Toppenish, WA 98948
509/865-5534

WISCONSIN

Wisconsin Organic Growers
Assn.
Joseph Pleski
10780 S. 92nd St.
Franklin, WI 53132
414/425-4771

NOVA SCOTIA

Organic Growers Cooperative
P.O. Box 493
Middleton, Nova Scotia
902/825-4902

ONTARIO

Organic Gardeners & Farmers
Assn.
33 Karnwood Dr.
Scarborough, Ontario M1L 2Z4

QUEBEC

Mouvement pour L'Agriculture
Biologique
Clement Boulanger
340, Willowdale, No. 2
Montreal, Quebec
514/342-9264

*Thanks to Rodale Press. Write
them for the complete Organic
Directory ($2.95)—150 pages
including health food outlets,
shippers of wholesale organic
foods.*

Oregon Historical Society

URBAN GARDENING

As people all over the country are finding out, there are plenty of places in a city for growing food—vacant lots, back yards, roof tops or window boxes. You have to be more careful in your use of space, but imagination and tender loving care are bringing home-grown fresh veggies to many a hardened urban dweller's table.

Farallones Institute— Integral Urban House
    1516 5th Street
    Berkeley, CA 94710

$25 membership. A remodeled Victorian house with greenhouses, rabbits, chickens, fish, bees, cabbages, strawberries, solar water heater, Clivus Multrum, Minuse shower, mulberry trees (for silk worms) and more on an ordinary tiny urban lot. Thanks to good publicity, they are getting an average of 150 people for their Saturday afternoon (1-5 p.m.) tours plus school and garden groups. They teach classes and workshops in gardening and small stock raising and have a master's program available through Antioch West. Regular credit is available through UC Berkeley. A 32-page "self-guided tour" of the project is available. Watch for a forthcoming book by Sierra Club.

School Gardens: Earthcare in the Dooryard Garden, Doris Cellarius, 1976, 11 pp., 15¢ from:
    Sierra Club
    530 Bush Street
    San Francisco, CA 94108
I well remember the excitement of waiting for the first little seedlings to sprout —coming into the classroom each morning to see if they were up yet. This is a good place to begin for teachers or parents who want to get kids gardening in the schools. It has been done successfully in many places. The Cleveland Schools have been doing it for years (write them for some nice materials). This booklet has an excellent bibliography as well as how-to information.

Institute for Local Self-Reliance
    1717 18th St. N.W.
    Washington, DC 20009

ILSR is involved in a program of experimentation and demonstration of the elements of an integrated neighborhood food/waste/energy system. This includes rooftop hydroponic vegetables, bio-dynamic/French Intensive gardening, commercial sprout production (they have a neat how-to on that), large-scale composting, development of community gardens, and research and organization for expansion of D.C.'s non-profit food distribution system and its diversification into food production and processing.

City People's Book of Raising Food, by Helga and Bill Olkowski, $4.95 from:
    Rodale Press
    33 East Minor
    Emmaus, PA 18049
With usual Rodale quality, a good holding hand book for city dwellers by some of the people involved with the Farallones Integral Urban House.

How to Grow More Vegetables, by John Jeavons, 1974, $4 from:
    Ecology Action of Mid-Peninsula
    2225 El Camino Real
    Palo Alto, Ca. 94306
This is a thorough, detailed study and workbook on the French intensive method of gardening. It enables you to produce four times more vegetables per acre using 1/2 the water and 1% of the energy consumed in commercial agriculture. Obviously of importance to city dwellers.

Almost half of U.S. households (47 percent, or approximately 33 million) had some kind of vegetable garden in 1974. The primary reason given for planting a vegetable garden is economic, the Gallup survey revealed. Of all new gardeners surveyed in 1974, 46 percent gave "helps budget/saves money" as the most important reason. Sixteen percent gave "for fun/joy of it" as the most important reason. In third place was "better tasting food," given by only 7 percent as the most important reason.

A Guide Through the Vegetable Garden, 32 pp., 50¢ from:
    Gardens for All
    Bay and Harbor Rds.
    P.O. Box 371
    Shelburne, VT 05482
Illustrated booklet that can be used by experienced and novice alike. It touches on all phases of gardening from starting plants indoors to winter storage.

Agriculture in the City, 1976, 74 pp., $2.75 from:
    Community Environmental Council
    109 E. De La Guerra
    Santa Barbara, CA 93101
This book is a cross between a how-to urban gardening manual and a description of the innovative El Mirasol gardening project that CEC had going until the land was sold. Both aspects are interesting and useful, although the image of all that sun in Santa Barbara makes my Oregon garden feel soggy. Now is the time to plan for community gardens if you don't already have one going and this book can give you some exciting ideas for what's possible in the middle of the city: bees, chickens, huge compost piles, classes and enough surplus veggies to generate some extra cash for the project.

"Poisoned Cities and Urban Gardens," in *The Elements*, Jan. 1976,
    1901 Q Street N.W.
    Washington, DC 20009
$5/yr ($10 institutions). Gil Friend from the Institute for Local Self-Reliance wrote this excellent article in response to one in the September *Elements* entitled "Poisoned Gardens." It puts the whole issue of lead contamination of urban (and suburban) gardens into a broader perspective. Do we stop trying to grow food in the city or do we attack the root of the problem?—replacing autos and industrial pollution with mass transit systems and neighborhood production units. The situation is a bothersome one because serious health problems are at stake. Research is currently being done on lead levels by Environmental Response of Washington University in St. Louis. Watch for their results. In the meantime, wash your lettuce!

COMMUNITY GARDENS

Community gardening is an idea whose time has certainly come. I am sure every city and most small towns in the country have at least one, if not several, vacant lots which spring magically each year into tomato and zucchini patches. They are a means of bringing community people together, greening up the city, growing fresh vegetables and generally getting one's hands in the soil. The following are some references to help you get started or bring new energy into an existing program:

Gardens for All
Bay and Harbor Roads
P.O. Box 371
Shelburne, VT 05482
These people are a sort of clearinghouse for the nationwide community garden movement. They have a series of useful publications and a continually updated listing of existing programs across the country. *Community Garden Procedural Manual* ($10) is a super step-by-step manual for organizers from finding land to harvesting. Write for a complete publications list.

Organic Gardening and Farming, $7.85/ year, monthly, from:
Rodale Press
33 East Minor
Emmaus, PA 18049
This magazine covers information on community gardening from time to time. Several of their staff people know quite a lot about it and can often steer you to people or agencies in your area who could help you. Please send a self-addressed, stamped envelope with any request.

"Community Gardens" is a free 18-page pamphlet produced by the Hunger Action Center describing Seattle's P-Patch program, sample guidelines, etc. From:
Susan Jamison
Hunger Action Center
Evergreen State College
Olympia, Wash. 98505

Recreational Community Gardening, Susan York Drake, Bureau of Outdoor Recreation, Interior Dept., 80¢ from:

U.S. Government Printing Office
Washington, DC 20402

A good bit of information here for setting up community garden programs: organizing, insurance, potential problems, budget, seed sources, how much to plant, books on gardening. Should help avoid some pitfalls if you're just getting going.

Rodale Press
33 E. Minor
Emmaus, PA 18049
215/967-5171
They've been around for quite a while and have a wide assortment of how-to books—too many to detail here, so you'd better write for a list. Mentioned elsewhere is their fine *Organic Gardening and Farming Magazine, Compost Science*, and *Environment Action Bulletin*. They also do a lot of networking and a self-addressed, stamped envelope to OGF Reader's Service will get you information about organic groups in your area, community gardens, or basic information in reprint form on biological prest control, natural fertilizers, companion planting, etc. Good folks to get to know.

Bureau of Outdoor Recreation
Box 36062
450 Golden Gate Ave.
San Francisco, CA 94102
Has available a pamphlet entitled "Profiles of California Community Garden Projects."

Radical Technology

by Woody Deryckx

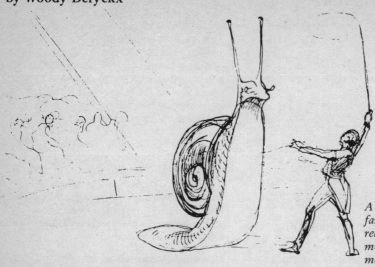

NATURAL PEST CONTROL

A growing number of farmers are moving away from chemical farming methods to more "organic" means—for very practical reasons. Chemical costs are skyrocketing and it's becoming more profitable to use less expensive natural means. What's more important, farmers are tired of dealing with chemicals—nausea when neighbors spray 2-4D, carbuncles, skin and lung poisoning are pretty high costs to pay when alternatives are available. And they are. Healthy soils, resistant seeds, appropriate crops, good plant nutrition, natural predators, companion planting, herbal sprays and careful crop rotation are a few of the many effective techniques available and becoming more widely applied.

The use of chemical poisons is giving way to natural controls in urban areas as well. Projects in Berkeley and other California cities have shown savings of up to $25,000 by converting to natural controls of predators on street trees and public open spaces.

Woody Deryckx is a farmer par excellence and truly committed to organic methods. He knows as much about it as anyone we've come across. A founding member of Tilth, he's presently teaching at Evergreen State College in Olympia, Washington.

A change is occurring both in our attitudes toward and in our practices of pest control in agriculture and forestry. Although synthetic insecticides and herbicides continue to be used at increasing rates, ecological, economic and social factors are beginning to effect a change toward a more appropriate approach to pest management. The "only good bug is a dead bug" mentality is being replaced by the realization that farms and gardens are really complex agro-ecosystems, subject to all the laws of ecology, and that the farmers, gardeners and foresters are fulfilling an important role as systems managers. Some of the members of these agro-ecosystems are potential pests, which is to say that they generally make their living at the expense of the crop species and can sometimes reach levels of population and activity that significantly compete with people for a share of the harvest. Whereas the chemical approach to pest control seeks to "eliminate the

competition" by the use of strong broad-spectrum pesticides (often without due cause), the increasing trend is toward a practice that exercises only those control measures necessary to keep pest populations below the economic injury threshold—the level at which pests threaten the value of the crop itself. The key to successful pest management seems to lie with an awareness of the ecological dynamics of the system and an ability to identify trends, anticipate problems and to employ the most effective and least disruptive control measures. Often, the most progressive thing that can be done is simply to STOP doing something that is damaging the system's ability to control itself.

Some casual definitions may be helpful when using the references listed below:

● NATURAL CONTROL: Any potential pest is to some degree regulated or controlled by naturally-occurring influences. Temperature, moisture levels, photoperiod (length of day), nutritional limitations and environmental factors act directly as natural controls. Natural enemies—predators and parasites—birds, other insects, nematodes, fungus diseases and other biological agents join with direct environmental influences in affecting potential pest populations, and to-

gether they comprise a complexity of natural control factors.

● BIOLOGICAL CONTROL generally involves the direct manipulation of the pest/natural enemy relationship system. This is done either by introducing natural enemies that are imported from other bio-geographical regions or by boosting populations of indigenous beneficial predator and parasitic insects.

● CULTURAL CONTROL: Tillage, crop rotation, crop selection, timing strategies, fertilizing, irrigation, harvesting, companion planting—most any routine cultural practice can either accentuate or hinder natural control factors. Every activity influences the whole system in ways that are often not considered.

● CHEMICAL CONTROL: There are many kinds of chemical insecticides and herbicides being used now. Essentially, they fall into the following five categories:

1) Chlorinated hydrocarbons (DDT, Aldrin, etc.), generally very toxic and persistent.

2) Organophosphates (Parathion, Malathion, etc.), varying widely in both persistence and toxicity.

3) Heavy metal compounds (lead arsenate, Paris Green, etc.), very dangerous and persistent in soils.

4) Non-persistent botanicals (Ryania, Rotenone, Derris, Garlic, etc.), generally not specific, but they break down fast. Some, like nicotine compounds, are as dangerous as many synthetics.

5) Phenoxy-herbicides (2,4-D and 2,4,5-T, etc.): These act as growth hormones to disrupt and distort plant growth. These compounds seem to be very dangerous to ecosystems in ways that are not yet clearly understood. Their use is increasing very rapidly as growers seek chemical shortcuts in cultivation and weed control.

The important thing to remember about chemical control is that even the safest, least persistent chemicals (botanicals included) are inclined to disrupt natural control mechanisms. By decimating natural enemies, chemical measures can create whole new pest problems.

● INTEGRATED CONTROL: Now that most of the ecological and economic assumptions that chemical control has traditionally been based on have been demonstrated to be false, even many very orthodox agriculturalists are embracing this new approach. Integrated control combines biological and cultural methods with a minimized use of specific insecticides whenever pest populations reach the economic injury threshold. Integrated control involves the careful and thorough use of regular field observations and life table studies.

BIOLOGICAL CONTROL

Handbook on Biological Control of Plant Pests, 1974, available from:
 Brooklyn Botanical Garden
 1000 Washington Ave.
 Brooklyn, NY 11225
An introduction most valuable for its illustrations and descriptions of many beneficial insects.

Biological Control, Robert Van Den Bosch and P. S. Messinger, 1974, $5.50 from:
 Intext Press
 Div. of Intext Publishing Group
 257 Park Ave. S.
 New York, NY 10010
Good introduction—especially to "classical biological control."

"Establishing an Integrated Pest Control Program for Street Trees," William and Helga Olkowski, in *Journal of Arboriculture*, Vol. 1, No. 9, September 1975, pp. 167-172, from:
 Intershade Tree Conference, Inc.
 Box 71
 Urbana, IL 61801

Biological Control by Natural Enemies, P. Debach, 1974, $5.95 from:
 Cambridge University Press
 32 E. 57th Street
 New York, NY 10022
The ecology of pest management; history of biological control.

Biological Control, C. B. Huffaker, 1971, $8.95 from:
 Plenum Press
 227 W. 17th Street
 New York, NY 10011
A definitive text; principles explained and illustrated with actual case studies.

"Ecosystem Management: A Framework for Urban Pest Control," W. Olkowski, in *Bio-Science*, Vol. 26, No. 6, pp. 384-389, from:
 American Institute of Bio-Science
 3900 Wisconsin Ave.
 Washington, DC 20016
It is an alarming fact that about half of the insecticides used in this country are used in cities and towns—much of it by municipal and county governments to control pests on trees, lawns and scrubs. This article and the one immediately above it deal with the biology and economics of urban pest control problems. Citizen pressure, by the way, is important in influencing public authorities to alter and improve pest control methods.

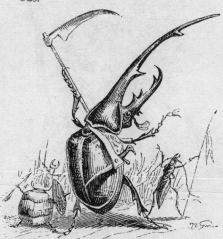

RESISTANT CROP VARIETIES

One of the most effective means of reducing pest problems is to avoid conflict by selecting crops that are less susceptible to pest damage in specific areas. Similarly, there is within crop species a wide range of relative resistance among varieties. This is a wide open and often overlooked field.

"Resistance of Plants to Insects," Beck, in *Annual Review of Entomology*, Vol. 10, pp. 207-232, yearly $15 from:
 Annual Review of Entomology
 4139 El Camino
 Palo Alto, CA

Insect Resistance in Crop Plants, 2nd Ed., R. H. Painter, 1968, $4.75 from:
 University Press of Kansas
 Lawrence, KS 66044
The most complete text treating the finding, breeding and use of resistant crop varieties.

"Breeding for Insect Resistance in Vegetables," A. Stoner, in *Horticulture-Science*, Vol. 5 (2), April 1970, quarterly $3 from:
 American Society of Horticulture
 615 Elm Street
 Joseph, MI 49085

"A Preliminary Study of Resistance in 20 Varieties of Cabbages to the Cabbage Worm Butterfly," H. Atema, in *Journal No. 2*, $6 from:
 New Alchemy Institute
 Box 432
 Woods Hole, MA
An example of how lay gardeners and farmers can make significant contributions to our understanding of plant resistance to insects with simple experimentations and careful observations.

SOURCES OF NATURAL ENEMIES

Rincon-Vitova Industries, Inc.
 P.O. Box 95
 Oak View, CA 93122
Fly parasites, lacewings, etc.

Gothard, Inc.,
 P.O. Box 370
 Canutillo, TX 79035
Trichogramma wasps.

California Green Lacewings, Inc.
 2521 Webb Ave.
 Alameda, CA 94501
Green lacewings.

Western Biological Control Labs
 P.O. Box 1045
 Tacoma, WA 98401

Natrilite Products, Inc.
 5600 Beach Blvd.
 Buena Park, CA 90620
Bacillus thuringiensis.

Abbot Laboratories
 AVPD
 North Chicago, IL 60064
Dipel (*Bacillus thuringiensis*).

For more extensive lists of insecticides and dealers of natural control agents, see *Grow It Safely: Pest Control Without Poisons*, Stephanie Harris, and *Gardening Without Poisons*, by Beatrice and Trum Hunter. Both books are referenced more completely on next page.

165

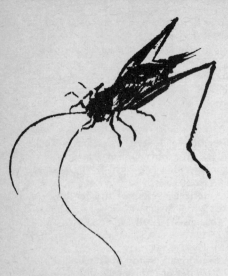

REFERENCES

UNDERSTANDING THE ECOLOGY OF INSECTS

An Introduction to the Study of Insects, D. J. Borror and D. Delong, 1971, $18.95 from:
    Holt, Rinehart and Winston
    383 Madison Ave.
    New York, NY 10017
This is a good text and reference book on insects, with a very fine keying system for identification to family.

Destructive and Useful Insects: Their Habits and Control, C. L. Metcalf, et. al., 1962, $25.00 from:
    McGraw-Hill
    1221 Avenue of the Americas
    New York, NY 10036
This is a very useful guide to insects based on the signs of damage that pests leave behind them. Good, clear information on habits and life cycles.

The Gardener's Bug Book, C. Wescott, 1973, $12.95 from:
    Doubleday and Company
    501 Franklin Ave.
    Garden City, NY 11530
Ms. Wescott's advice is generally inappropriate (she advocates heavy use of insecticides), but her descriptions and illustrations of insects make this a standard reference.

Beneficial Insects, L. Swan, 1964, $10.00 from:
    Harper & Row
    10 E. 53rd St.
    New York, NY 10022
This exciting book describes the natural history of the predators and parasites which naturally control potential pest species. Every gardener and farmer should read this comprehensive text on biological control.

WEEDS

Weeds: Guardians of the Soil, J. Cocannover, 1964, $4.95 from:
    Devin-Adair Co.
    1 Park Ave.
    Old Greenwich, CT 06870
Weeds persistently remind us that they too have a role to play in our agro-ecosystem, and this book tells us what the herbicide salesman never thought of—the beneficial soil-saving effects of certain weeds.

Weeds and What They Tell, E. Pfeiffer, 1970, $5.50, from:
    Bio-Dynamic Farming & Gardening Association, Inc.
    Stroudsburg, PA 18360
Weeds serve as indicators of the condition of our soils; this book suggests some ways to interpret and appreciate weeds.

Common Weeds of the United States, Agricultural Research Services (USDA), 1971, $7.50 from:
    Dover Publications, Inc.
    180 Varick St.
    New York, NY 10014
Identification of weed plants.

HOW-TO GUIDES

Organic Plant Protection, edited by Roger B. Yepsen, Jr., 1976, $12.95 from:
    Rodale Press, Inc.
    33 E. Minor
    Emmaus, PA 18049
The single most comprehensive reference on controlling insects and diseases in the garden, orchard and yard without using chemicals. An update of *The Organic Way to Plant Protection* (1966, Glenn F. Johns, editor), this new version has twice as many pages full of hints based on the experiences of

thousands of OGF reader-gardener-contributors across the country as well as more scientifically-based research findings. 167 pages on the various methods, such as companion planting, tillage mowing, biological control, physical traps, barriers, and weeds, are followed by 480 pages encompassing, literally, an encyclopedia of plant protection listing plants, their pests and specific remedies. Two appendices, an annotated bibliography and a detailed 33-page index end this, the best addition to your appropriate pest management library.

Common Sense Pest Control, H. Olkowski, 1971, $1.00 from:
    Consumers' Cooperative of Berkeley
    Berkeley, CA 94804

This elegant little guide to garden and household pest management serves as a clear introduction to the same principals that apply to any pest situation in any scale. Of all the books listed on this section, this one best illustrates the "whole systems" style of thinking in pest management.

Pest Control Without Poison, Lawrence D. Hill, 1964, from:
    The Henry Doubleday Research Association
    Bocking Braintree, Essex, England

How the best British gardeners exercise "pest control by cunning." Especially good sections on root insects and botanically-derived insecticides. If this booklet is out of print, HDRA has many newer publications of value—ask for their mailing list.

Grow It Safely: Pest Control Without Poisons, S. G. Harris, 1975, from:
    Public Citizens Health Research Group
    2000 "P" Street, Dept. P, Rm. 708
    Washington, DC 20036
A very good introduction to the range of possibilities—well-referenced.

Farming, $2.00 from:
    Alternative Agriculture Resources Project
    Department of Applied Behavioral Science
    University of California
    Davis, CA 95616

    Contains good resources on plant diseases, biological control of insects, farm equipment, soils and other aspects of farming.

Companion Plants and How to Use Them, by Helen Philbrick & Richard Gregg, 113 pp., $5.95 from:

> Devin-Adair Co.
> 143 Sound Beach Ave.
> Old Greenwich, CT 06870

A classic and pioneering book on one of the least understood phases of ecology, namely plant antagonisms and plant symbiosis. Why do certain species of plants grow better in the presence of others, and why do some do poorly when others are present? This publication combines the finding of many individual observant gardeners. It is the best we've got until Richard Merrill of New Alchemy Institute—West has time to write down what he's learned.

Gardening Without Poisons, B. Hunter, 1971, $6.95 from:

> Berkley Publishing Co.
> 200 Madison Ave.
> New York, NY 10016

Good introduction to biological and cultural controls. References on where to obtain biological control agents.

NOTE: Because the mainstream of commercial farming has been bound up in chemical control methods for the past 30-plus years, most of the popular literature on appropriate pest control measures has been oriented around garden rather than farm techniques. Farmers would do well to read these works anyway, then invent ways to apply the same techniques on a larger scale.

Biological Control of Plant Pathogens, by Kenneth F. Baker & R. James Cook, 1974, 433 pp., 57 illustrations, 5 tables, $12.50 from:

> W. H. Freeman
> 660 Market St.
> San Francisco, CA 94104

This is the first book devoted wholly to the microbial soil ecology. Years of research and observation has led to organization of this knowledge into a thorough treatment of principles and suggestions on practical application. The authors present bio-control as one part of an integrated disease-control program, along with cultivation practices, soil treatment, sanitation, host resistance and mild chemicals. On reading, one wonders how and to what degree the ecological principles mentioned might apply to human society. In any case, it's reassuring to have people knowledgeable about natural plant disease control right in one's own back yard . . . Prof. Cook is at Washington State University in Pullman.

SOIL BACTERIA

Dear Rain:

It is to your credit that I always learn something new about my own special field of interest, agriculture, and more especially soil biology, when your generalist paper comes around. But speaking of biology, I do have a response to your review of *Biological Control of Plant Pathogens* by Cook and Baker. Your lead statement: "This is the first book devoted wholly to the microbial soil ecology," is not quite right. Although soil micro-ecology is one of the most neglected fields of biology and agricultural science, there are a few very bright works available, a few of my favorites being: *Ecology of Soil-Borne Plant Pathogens* (prelude to biological control), edited by Bahr, K.F., and W.C. Snyder, U. of California Press, 1965. Proceedings of a symposium held in Berkeley, 1963. *The Ecology of Soil Bacteria,* edited by Gray, T.R.G. and D. Parkinson, U. of Toronto Press, 1968, 680 pp., $21.75. Also proceedings. *Soil Microorganisms and Higher Plants,* Krasiz Nikof, Nicoli Alexandrikov.

Translated by Y. Halperin. Published by NTIS (Springfield, VA 22161), No. TT-60-21126.

Plus there are Wakesman and Burgess books, listed in the *Energy Primer,* p. 120.

. . . The plant pathology people have traditionally held attitudes about control that were closer to a sensible approach than have their entomological counterparts. This is mostly because plant pathogens (i.e., fungi, irus, bacteria) are much harder to influence through toxic poisons than are insects—and usually impossible. The equivalent of spraying is soil fumigation, and, although fumigation has and will continue to be practical, it is always a gross, ecological catastrophe; it is also expensive and ineffective. The more simple the organisms are, the more difficult the control. That is why more resistance breeding is directed at disease-resistance than insect-resistance, likewise biological control.

Yours for a healthy soil community,
Woody Deryckx
Pragtree Farm
Arlington, WA

Pesticides

Citizens Against Toxic Sprays (CATS)
> Route 2, Box 190
> Tidewater, OR 97390

This group is one of the most active ones I know of anywhere, and a fine model for people wanting to stop dangerous spraying of pesticides and herbicides. They document, lobby, bring suit, put out leaflets and have an enviable ability to attract favorable publicity about the severe health hazards that are being caused by the use of toxic sprays.

Pesticide and Organic Gardening Ruling. The Langans of Toppenish sent us a clipping on the recent court ruling in their favor over a pesticides damage suit filed in June 1973. The Langans contended that pesticides sprayed near their 2-1/2 acre farm prevented their crop from receiving an organic gardening certificate. The ruling could obviously have implications elsewhere.

Food Co-ops for Small Groups

PENNY PINCHERS CO-OP

Lettuce

FOOD AND

FARMERS MARKETS

The farmers' market remains one of the central institutions of cities and villages throughout the world. In Africa, Asia, Latin America and much of Europe, public markets are a beehive of activity. The market serves as the place where small farmers and gardeners can sell their surpluses of fresh vegetables, meat, milk and eggs, providing them with enough income to keep on the land. And it is also where consumers can get to know the farmers and find the best prices on wholesome, locally-produced foods.

Farmers' markets serve as important cultural centers as well, providing consumers with an intimate connection to the foods they eat and farmers with the opportunity to meet and share knowledge and skills. Such trading centers were a common part of our experience too, until a generation ago. Farmers' markets reached their peak in this country during the Great Depression when in towns and cities across the land hundreds of farmers would queue up at daybreak in preparation for another marketing day. No sooner than the crates were unloaded, early morning shoppers would begin crowding around to haggle over prices, seek out the best buys and purchase the day's groceries. Then business would slack off until late afternoon when the crowds would return for last-minute bargains as farmers would begin packing up for the return home.

With the end of the Depression and the return of "good times" once again,

the number of farmers' markets dwindled rapidly in this country; a trend which paralleled the rise of giant supermarket chains such as Safeway and A&P. This shift didn't occur in isolation, of course, but rather was promoted by such factors as cheap energy, long-distance transportation and new technological developments such as improved refrigeration. However, a reverse trend may now be emerging, with one of the key indicators being the tremendous revival of farmers' markets around the country.

There are many reasons for this new interest in farmers' markets. In purely economic terms they offer the promise of providing the consumer with lower grocery prices by purchasing directly from the producer, thus eliminating the "middle man." The growers, in turn, can get better than wholesale prices for the crops they bring in, helping to make it possible for them to stay in business. But economics is only one of many reasons why farmers' markets are sprouting up all over.

The new markets are serving to make small farmers visible once again. People are once again able to get to know the people who grew the food they are buying and learn about where and how it was grown. In the process, urban people are discovering that an abundance of food can be produced in their own local areas and they are becoming a part of a growing constituency concerned with the preservation of small-scale agriculture close to urban areas. Thus farmers' markets have cultural and poli-

tical as well as economic functions, and they have a key role to play in the new agrarian movement.

Organizing Farmers' Markets, **Natural Organic Farmers' Association, 1975, $2.00 from:**
> **NOFA**
> **RFD 1, Box 247**
> **Plainfield, VT 05667**

There are many areas of the country that have been by-passed by the rush toward bigness and agri-business, and it is here that farmers' markets find their most natural home. One such area is Vermont, and this pamphlet, while written from the experience of forming markets in New England, can be a helpful guide for any region of the country.

Farmers' Market Organizer's Handbook, **Deborah Bowler, 1976, $1.00 from:**
> **Hunger Action Center**
> **Evergreen College**
> **Olympia, WA 98505**

The Northwest corner of the country is also experiencing a re-birth of farmers' markets, and this handbook grew out of a day-long workshop which brought representatives of many of these markets together for the first time. The handbook recognizes that, nowadays, a city person is very likely to be the organizer of a new market, representing the needs and interests of both consumers and producers. Several organizational models are presented as well as details on market management (equipment, location, rules and regulations and food stamps), plus sample budgets, a listing

As the food we eat is our body's vital link with the soil and the biological processes of the Earth, so these bonds are extended through the complex food distribution and marketing systems that link producer and consumer, countryside and city. These intimate bonds have been severed in recent years by the industrialization of agriculture and the centralization of marketing by vast corporate empires. The majority of consumers have no control over the source or the quality of the food they eat, while small farmers are increasingly squeezed out of local markets.

One of the key elements in the movement to regain control over our own lives is the emergence of new food distribution and marketing systems which are laying the foundation for a revival of small-scale agriculture, decentralization and regional self-reliance. In this section we will cover Farmers' Markets, Co-ops, and the growth of Regional Networks which are emerging as elements of the new food chain.

DISTRIBUTION MARKETING

by Mark Musick

of resources, and a directory of markets in Washington state.

Farmers' Market Packet, 1976, large SASE from:

Evanston Chamber of Commerce
807 Davis St.
Evanston, IL 60201

A group of consumers in Evanston decided they wanted the opportunity to purchase directly from farmers and then convinced the City Council to close off a downtown street for a weekly public market. They will be happy to send you a packet of information on their experience in exchange for a stamped, self-addressed, business-sized envelope.

Greenmarket
24 W. 40th St.
New York, NY 10018

Yes, and even in New York City. Write these people for info on their organizing success story.

Reader Service
Organic Gardening & Farming
Emmaus, PA 18049

Farmers' markets, with their potential for increasing the viability of small-scale agriculture, are an important part of the organic movement. OGF is a leader in this movement. It's an activist magazine, eager to help people out, and their Reader Service has basic "how to" information available on starting farmers' markets (plus a wide variety of other topics) and can assist in putting you in touch with other resources in your local areas. Please enclose a self-addressed, stamped envelope with any information request. (SASE)

FOOD CO-OPS

People form food co-ops for many reasons. For some it's simply a way of getting cheaper food—for others it's a way of getting foods that are unavailable through commercial supermarkets—foods that are organically grown, preferably from local sources, and without extensive processing or packaging.

There are now an estimated 5,000 food co-ops of various types in the country, serving over half a million people, with nearly $100 million in annual retail sales. Food co-ops are becoming a major economic force, and many people feel that they have the potential of laying the foundation for a new economic system based on cooperation rather than profit and exploitation.

Food Co-ops for Small Groups, Tony Villela, 1975, $2.95 from:
Workman Publishing Company
231 E. 51st St.
New York, NY 10022

This is a very useful, step-by-step introduction to organizing a food co-op, with systems for distributing food and handling money clearly drawn out in diagram form. It includes lots of practical information on such things as how to buy produce and how to understand food industry jargon, as well as providing basic financial information. It is a good primer for getting a co-op buying club or store off the ground, but once it's started, you'll need more detailed information such as is in *The Food Co-op Handbook*.

The Food Co-op Handbook, The Handbook Collective, 1975, $4.95 from:
Houghton-Mifflin Co.
1 Beacon St.
Boston, MA 02107

This is the most in-depth book available on the food co-op movement. It provides an analysis of the "whys" of food co-ops and shows how they can provide a true alternative to agribusiness as usual. It also includes a brief history of co-ops, from their beginning in 1844 to the wide variety that exists today.

The *Handbook* is a valuable tool both for people starting buying clubs or more complex storefront operations, including chapters on finances and inventory control. The book also includes extensive bibliographies and a 40-page national food co-op directory. Written by people involved in the movement, the *Handbook* draws on the experiences of co-ops throughout the country and provides national perspective on the various styles and directions taken by food co-ops in different regions.

The Food Co-op Handbook is also available at bulk rates ($3.35 each) from The Book Distribution Collective, 45 Mason Terrace, No. 5, Brookline, MA 02146.

"Who Shops Co-op, and Why," by Philip Kreitner in *The New Harbinger*, Vol. 3, No. 2, $8/yr. for 4 issues, $2 single copy from:

The New Harbinger
North American Student Co-Op Org.
Box 1301
Ann Arbor, MI 48106

Excellent doctoral dissertation which

should be required reading for all food co-op staffs, one of many fine articles in an issue focused on food cooperatives.

Food Co-Op Nooz, $3.00 per year from:
 Food Co-op Project
 64 East Lake St.
 Chicago, IL 60601

The food co-op movement in this country is in a period of tremendous, turbulent growth. New co-ops and buying clubs are being formed every day. Warehouses and trucking routes are being established to support and coordinate the rapidly increasing flow of food through the system. Other supportive enterprises, such as bakeries and publication collectives, are springing up, as well as the establishment of collective farms. Yet, with all of this growth, there are also serious problems confronting the new co-op movement, including political dissension and the hard realities of economics.

The *Nooz* is a bi-monthly newspaper for the national food cooperative movement. Published for people actively involved in co-ops, it offers an insider's view of what's going on throughout the country, with background reports on various communities, news of recent events and analysis of critical problems within the movement. The annual subscription includes a comprehensive Food Cooperative Directory, a listing of nearly 2,000 food stores, warehouses, bakeries and resource organizations in the United States and Canada.

cpf

Turnover, Newsletter of the People's Food System, $3.00/year from:
 Newsletter Collective
 3030 20th Street
 San Francisco, CA 94110

The People's Food System of the San Francisco Bay Area is comprised of ten co-op and collective stores and fourteen support collectives, including staple and produce warehouses, a bakery, herb, cheese and yogurt collectives, and an egg farm called "Left Wing Poultry." They are consciously setting out to create a model of a worker and consumer controlled economy. The Food System is seen as an important experiment in collective economics, and *Turnover* reports on its development and its role within the community.

In addition, the newsletter carries incisive articles on the politics of food, reports on the farmworkers' struggles, information on the foods available through the cooperative system and information on nutrition. The newsletter is very well done and provides an excellent view of one of the centers of the movement.

California Strawberries

On the Market
 c/o Citizen Action Press
 443 Russel Blvd.
 Davis, CA 95616

A monthly newsletter to provide a medium of communication for farmers, truckers, warehouses and food cooperatives in Northern California. *Loading Dock* is a similar newsletter just begun for Oregon and Washington. Write c/o Starflower, 385 Lawrence, Eugene, OR 97401.

Scoop, Cooperation in the North Country, $6.00/year from:
 2519 1st Ave. South
 Minneapolis, MN 55404

Another center of co-op activity is in the "North Country"—Minnesota, the Dakotas, Michigan and Wisconsin. It has also been a center of intense controversy in the past couple of years, especially in the Twin Cities of Minneapolis and St. Paul. An intense political struggle erupted there in the spring of 1975 over control and direction of the movement, testing the community's cooperative principles to their utmost. The past two years have been extremely difficult ones in the Twin Cities, and the conflicts there have had a major impact on the cooperative movement around the country. The *Scoop* is an independent newspaper that provides lively and critical accounts of events in the food system of the North Country.

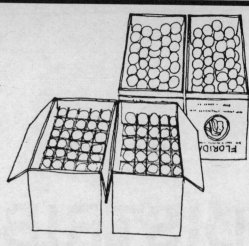

REGIONAL NETWORKS

As the alternative food system has evolved over the past few years, there has grown a higher level of integration between elements of the movement, first within urban areas and then extending out to incorporate major regions of the country. San Francisco, Austin, Minneapolis-St. Paul, Boston, Madison and Washington, D.C., all have extensive "networks" of co-ops and buying clubs supported by warehouses and numerous producer collectives. Much more extensive regional networks have also grown to inter-connect cooperating communities around the nation, with the warehouses having become important centers for the trucking and distribution of ever-increasing amounts of food.

Beyond Isolation, Las Truckaderos, 2nd ed., 1976, $1.00 from:
 Free Spirit Press
 Main P.O. Box 24112
 Oakland, CA 94623

This pamphlet is one of the first major theoretical pieces on the development of a regional network within the alternative food system. Truckers have become the main couriers in the food system carrying the latest news and information from warehouse to warehouse and from co-op to co-op around the country. *Beyond Isolation* was based on the experience of Las Truckaderos, an alternative trucking collective, as they visited collective warehouses up and down the West Coast in 1975. It includes brief descriptions of several collective warehouses in the region, noting their isolation from each other, and then goes on to critique several of the "contradictions" within the movement. This second edition of the pamphlet is especially valuable because it includes a seven-page supplement with reprints from several sources of feedback on the ideas presented, especially on the question of co-ops versus collectives. It's a mighty good introduction to the internal politics of the new food system. A new publication is also in process.

Common Ground, #3,
April, 1976, 50¢ from:

> **Free Spirit Press**
> **P.O. Box 24112**
> **Oakland, CA 94623**

The warehouses are the elements of the food system leading the push toward regional integration. Generally staffed by full-time collectives, and inter-connected with suppliers and other warehouses around the country, they serve as information centers for the rapidly expanding alternative food networks. The warehouses on the West Coast have been holding quarterly conferences for over a year now, bringing together representatives from Tucson, Arizona, to Vancouver, British Columbia, to build regional cooperation.

The West Coast warehouses are perhaps the most outspokenly political in the country. There is a strongly-held view that the collectives are in the vanguard of the food system and that the expansion of the alternative food system is a part of a revolutionary movement. There is an on-going debate on the West Coast (and elsewhere around the country) over such issues as cooperative versus collective structures, whether or not to sell to profit makers and whether or not to support small, organic farmers. *Common Ground* has been the vehicle for debating these and other issues, as well as providing information of large group buys, trucking reports and conferences. This issue gives a good sense of the dynamics of the movement towards establishing a network of collective warehouses on the West Coast.

Northwest Trade Directory, $3.25
from:

> **118 N. Bowdoin Place**
> **Seattle, WA 98103**

One of the efforts currently under way to facilitate the development of regional networks is the creation of new information systems. The *Trade Directory* is an example of such a system created for the alternative agriculture movement of the Pacific Northwest.

Like New England, the Northwest is an area where there is a great deal of interest in the concept of regional self-reliance. The directory was published by a number of individuals and groups as a model for a decentralized food system. Over 160 well-indexed pages long, the directory is intended as a vehicle for putting local growers in touch with local consumers. It includes listings for the co-ops of over 100 organic and transition farmers, plus the most comprehensive directory of alternative markets (over 300 co-ops, warehouses, etc.) ever published for the region, as well as information on trucking, storage and processing facilities. The goal of the *Trade Directory* is to decentralize the food system as much as possible, with the hope that future directories will be published for other regions and on smaller scales (for example, communities within each valley or river basin beginning to take on responsibility for providing most of their own food needs).

Farms of Puget Sound, 25¢ plus SASE
from:

> **King Co. Conservation District**
> **35 South Grady Way**
> **Renton, WA 98055**

One of the finest models of direct marketing information, *Farms of Puget Sound* is a map that directs consumers to small farmers throughout the Seattle-Tacoma area. The location of each farm is indicated and there is an index describing the kinds of crops available, whether they're U-pick or not, and other details. The first printing of 35,000 copies disappeared within two months, and now the idea is being picked up by communities all across the state (and elsewhere, too). The map is one further step toward local self-reliance. It was published as part of a larger effort to save the remaining agricultural lands near the urban centers of Puget Sound by putting small farmers "on the map." The intention was to graphically show consumers that a significant amount of food is still being grown on small farms in and near the urban areas and that these farms must be preserved.

The Cultivator, $3/year from:
> **Federation of Cooperatives**
> **Box 107**
> **Hallowell, ME 04347**

The New England area has one of the strongest networks of co-ops in the country, and, although many co-op federations publish newsletters, *The Cultivator* is among the best. It provides insights into events within individual co-ops and reports on the growth of the Federation as a whole in a way that really gives you a sense of the movement in Maine. New England is one of the areas where there is a strong drive toward regional self-reliance, and the food system there is viewed very much as a part of that effort.

Alternative Market News, $5 per year
from:

> **Earth Cyclers**
> **Rt. 1**
> **Edwall, WA 99008**

An exchange of information between farmers and co-ops, the *Alternative Market News* is part of the movement toward regional self-reliance in the Pacific Northwest. It is serving as the source for up-dates for the *Northwest Trade Directory*.

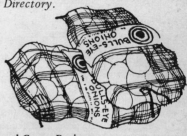

The Food Co-op Project
64 East Lake St.
Chicago, IL 60601

As mentioned before, these are the folks who have the broadest view of what's happening within the alternative food system and the growth of regional networks around the country. To keep abreast of what's going on, subscribe to their *Food Co-op Nooz*.

Mark Musick is our very dear friend from Tilth who is one of the key networkers in the Northwest. He and Tilth ($5/year for a fine agricultural networking newsletter) can be reached at Pragtree Farm, Rt. 2, Box 190-A, Arlington, WA 98223.

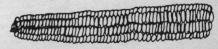

HOMESTEADING

Northwind
 Mapleville Organic Farm
 Cross Creek
 New Brunswick, EOH IEO
 Canada

$4/yr., 4 issues. Make checks payable to Judy Hinds. A mimeographed, newsy letter by Hal and Judy Hinds—organic gardening, books reviewed, an account of Judy's experiments with making rennet and tidbits about their life on the farm. For those who want to know them better and get a feel for their way of life, they're inviting 25 people to an Earthskills Workshop, August 21-28, $75. Organic gardening, beekeeping, natural crafts, cheese making and wild edibles. Sounds delightful.

Oz-Com
 P.O. Box 1126
 Branson, MO 65616

The Ozarks Communicator and Carey Carpenter have taken over the homesteading networking newsletter that Joel and Sherri Davidson put out for several years as *Living in the Ozarks*. It's typeset now, but the down-home exchange of useful information feels about the same.

The Smallholder
 Argenta, BC
 Canada

$3/12 issues. A kind of rural resources and information two-way newsletter, back to land, mother earth, especially for B.C. area. Looks like good information, friendly network of people.

Old Fashioned Recipe Book, Carla Emry, $17.45 from:
 Box 1
 Kendrick, ID 83537

This wondrous book has been revised several times and is now a huge 600-plus pages of valuable, well-indexed information. As well as good recipes, there's information about root cellars, drying, home remedies, dictionary of antique cookbooks words, butchering, crackers, soapmaking, blankets, even biography and pictures of Carla and her family. Mimeographed and 3-hole punched—ready for a notebook.

Payne Hollow, Harlan Hubbard, 1974, $5.95 from:
 The Eakins Press
 155 East 42nd
 New York, NY 10017

Shantyboat, same author, Dodd, 1953. In the late '40s, Harlan and Anna Hubbard lived on a shantyboat floating down the Ohio and Mississippi Rivers in the winter and tied up for the summer months in coves and bayous along the way. At the end of their journey they went back to one of the coves called Payne Hollow and built themselves a house along the river bank. And they live there today—"on the fringe of society"—raising almost all their own food, playing violin and cello duets and painting. They are as close to being self-sufficient as one can be. Really delightful books. The first (which I fear is out of print—I found it in the Salem library) is full of the joys and adventures of wandering, the second is peaceful and settled. Both are warmly illustrated with nice pen and ink sketches.

Country Women: A Handbook for the New Farmer, by Jeanne Tetrault and Sherry Thomas, 1976, 381 pp., $6.95 from:
 Anchor Press/Doubleday
 245 Park Ave.
 New York, NY 10017

Oooie! This is a beautiful book. It is a good, solid collection of how-to material for homesteading—finding land, building, fencing, planting, harvesting, preserving, raising animals. The photographs leave little doubt that women can do even the heaviest labor when they want to. Yet the book is warm with their experiences and graced with gentle drawings that give the heartening sense of women *nurturing* the land rather than the heroics that others go through to conquer it. It is put together by some of the same women who do a very fine magazine by the same name: *Country Women*, Box 51, Albina, CA 95410. Send a self-addressed, stamped envelope to inquire about price.

Living the Good Life, 1954, $2.25, and *The Maple Sugar Book*, 1950, $2.75, by Helen and Scott Nearing from:
 Schocken Books
 67 Park Ave.
 New York, NY 10016

The Nearings have been at it a long time. He's in his 90s—they dropped out in the 1930s to homestead first in Vermont and now in Maine. They do most things for themselves.

Glen and Kathleen Simmons
Dear Haven Farm
Star Route, Box 1370
Glenwood, OR 97120

Glen and Kathleen challenge the definition of an institution. They live at about the 1200' level on a 30-acre farm 35 miles west of Portland.

In the past several years, mostly through the courses they teach at Portland Community College on homesteading and innumerable other workshops, all in one fashion or another on homesteading, they have entertained several thousand people at their place. (Last Christmas 90 students showed up for supper). It is part of the Simmons' philosophy that in order to teach one must also show: one 98 percent self-sufficient homestead is worth 10-20 lectures (or more).

While maintaining the farm and earning about $250 a month teaching, they have managed to videotape a half-dozen shows on homesteading

And they've done a book: *From the Ground Up*, 1976, 600 pp., $9 from the address above. It's a bit hard to use (needs an index) but it's full of gems on how to do it yourself.

A couple of drying hints from the Simmons:
• Instead of slicing vegetables, like cabbage, carrots, beets, celery and green peppers, shred them. These dry readily, are easily reconstituted and can be ground into vegetable flours for baking. Mrs. Simmons says the sliced vegetables just won't go through the grinder properly after they are dried.
• Whole fruits, such as prunes, cherries and grapes, should be dipped in blanch water for about eight seconds, drained, dipped in cold water and drained before drying. This causes the fruit to dry quicker because the skin breaks.
• Fruit leathers are highly concentrated, chewy, nutritious snacks. They are made by putting fresh or canned fruit or any combination of fruits in a blender and liquefying (add small amount of water or canned fruit juice if fruit is too dry). Add sugar or honey to taste and pour the mixture about 1/4" thick on plastic wrap molded inside a cookie sheet.

Put this in the dryer until the upper side is no longer soft. Turn it out onto a cloth, peel off the plastic and let the other side dry in the dryer until no moisture is apparent. It should be dry enough to roll up, but not brittle.

Roll it between sheets of plastic wrap and seal in jars. To eat, just tear a piece off. Mrs. Simmons recommends using pectin for berries to help them set up. Their fruit leathers include grape, strawberry, apricot, apple, cherry and cinnamon-apple.

Most other foods can be blanched with steam for two or three minutes before dipping in cold water and draining. This method preserves more of the natural vitamins and usually helps food hold its color.
• Baking temperatures should be lowered when using recipes with dried foods. For instance, dried corn can be ground into corn meal to make corn bread or muffins. Use less sugar when making the bread and bake at a lower temperature so it won't burn.
• Mrs. Simmons puts most food on dish cloths or nylon netting before placing it on the dryer shelves. Things like corn that could lose moisture on a cloth or glazed fruits that would stick are dried on plastic wrap.

The Guide to Self-Sufficiency, John Seymour, 1976, $11.95 from:
Popular Mechanics Books
224 W. 57th Street
New York, NY 10019

Distillations from Seymour's lifetime of managing an 18,000-acre sheep ranch, living on a 5-acre self-sufficient smallholding, being a veterinary livestock officer in Africa, working in a copper mine, surveying and game hunting, living on a fishing boat, writing and broadcasting. This is one of the best of this genre—comprehensively illustrated and covering in detail a range of skills not usually covered in such books— working stone and splitting slate, basketry, charcoal making, barrelmaking, thatching and much more. A refreshingly broader, more experienced and more detailed presentation than most American counter-culture based books.

Cloudburst (1973, $3.95) and *Cloudburst 2* (1976, $4.95), edited by Vic Marks, available from:
Cloudburst Press
1716 North 45th Street
Seattle, WA 98103
Handbooks of rural skills and technology. Useful a.t. for homesteading in the country.

Foxfire Book (1972, $3.95), *Foxfire Two* (1973, $4.50), *Foxfire Three* (1975, $4.95), edited by Elliot Wigginton, available from:
Doubleday
245 Park Ave.
New York, NY 10017
You mean the old geezers have something to teach? You betcha. Wigginton got high school students to go find out and these classics tell you about how it all used to be done in Appalachia. A very important resource of practical information and folklore. Fine reading.

Eating High and Lightly

Vegetarian Epicure

I think the reason I like to cook is that it brings me closer to other people—whether food *with* or *for* others, there is a certain camaraderie and cooperative spirit involved that is very special. Some of my favorite memories center on fixing food with friends. The ice was quickly broken at my sister's wedding where neither of the families had met before. We all pitched in for two days and cut and chopped and mixed the food for the wedding supper as well as the meals we ate during that time—suddenly it became everybody's party! Many people at Farallones Institute this summer said that the best learning experience of all came from working in the kitchen—5 or 6 people (rotated daily) planning and preparing the mountains of zucchini hot dish, French onion soup and cream puffs, or grilled cheese sandwiches that were eaten out on the hillside. At the Community Design Center in Minnesota a couple of years ago we had homemade soup every day for lunch. It was a time for staff and visitors (often as many as 20 folks) to sit together around the big table without any other agenda than enjoying each other and the creations of our chef. I'm convinced that the ritual provided a large part of the warmth of the place.

Consideration of food—preparation and eating—is definitely a part of living lightly. In a general sense, it doesn't really matter whether one eats no meat at all, enjoys only organically grown foods, or simply stays away from the sinful yummies like sugar, bacon and white flour. I never have been much of a purist and find I can't draw any strict lines around my diet—it wouldn't be Christmas without my great-grandmother's sand tarts, and I can't resist a little nitrate-loaded bacon now and then. It's all part of the weaning process—starting easy, little by little, figuring out what you can do without or do for yourself. Getting the breadmaking down and then beginning to grind your own flour. Making choices—white flour only on special occasions or fried chicken as a treat. (Like the two friends who met each other in a Kentucky Fried Chicken—both agreed they were still vegetarian in principle!)

The main point is to be aware of what you eat—what it is doing to you, the land and our natural resources.

The folks at the Center for Science in the Public Interest in Washington, D.C. are doing some of the best work on the hidden costs and problems of food. They sponsored Food Day last year to make the public aware of problems such as nitrate in bacon, sugar in baby food and preservatives and coloring in general. Their book, *Energy and Food*, gives figures for energy costs—ice cream and frozen orange juice head the list of "gas guzzlers."

Energy & Food, Fritsch, Dujack & Jimerson, 1975, $4 from:
Center for Science in the Public Interest
1779 Church St., N.W.
Washington, D.C. 20036

Diet for a Small Planet, Frances Moore Lappé, Ballantine, 1971, $1.25.

Regional Cooking of China, Margaret Gin and Alfred Castle, 101 Reproductions, San Francisco, 1975, $4.95.

The Complete Yogurt Cookbook, Karen Cross White, Ballantine Books, 1970, $1.25.

The Vegetarian Epicure, Anna Thomas, Vintage Books, 1972, $3.95.

The Tassajara Breadbook, Edward Espe Brown, Shambala Books, 1970, $2.95.

Tassajara Cooking, Edward Espe Brown, Shambala, 1973, $3.95.

Diet for a Small Planet is the classic that lays out the case against a meat-centered diet for environmental reasons. Frances Moore Lappé talks about all the energy and valuable protein consumed by beef. More importantly, she provides alternatives for combining vegetable proteins into as good, if not more usable protein. There are fairly simple charts, as well as recipes and menu suggestions that make it all clear. I've never found the recipes themselves that great, but they do give a clear idea of what different foods work together to give you what you need. Once you get the idea there are several books that can give you more exciting ideas for cooking.

The Tassajara books are a good place to start. Ed Brown is the Zen monk who made the Tassajara retreat center in California famous for its fine vegetarian fare. Both the *Breadbook* and *Tassajara Cooking* give clear basic directions with lots of possible variations. They're really good for freeing up the fledgling cook by noting such things as "you can skimp on the eggs or double the milk" and indicating what the probable results will be. A good friend of mine says that the challenge of cooking lies in making a good soup out of a seemingly empty refrigerator. In a very nice zen way these books make the case for using every scrap possible and making feasts with what you've got on hand . . . "If you don't have lentils, try black beans" or "Zucchini would be just as good as broccoli in this soup."

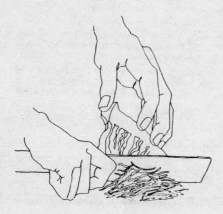

The Vegetarian Epicure is one of my favorites—it's really a gourmet cookbook with everything from crêpes with white wine sauce to onions monégasque. It includes French, Greek, Italian, Indian and German foods (there's an outstanding linzertorte) and lots of good ideas for spices and sauces. Some recipes are fairly complicated, using lots of pans (the opposite of the zen books which emphasize one-pot meals); others, like the curries, are quite simple. The author talks about serving meals to people who say they can't stand vegetarian meals and then gustily consume what she puts in front of them. The point is, very few people dislike good food . . . and if you give them just that, chances are they won't even notice they haven't consumed their usual portion of meat."

Speaking of curries, Indian food is a natural for good vegetarian cooking. I found out from one cookbook that there is no such word as "curry" in the Indian languages, so it must have been thought up by the English to describe a certain kind of spicy food. In truth, there are many combinations of spices that make up what we think of as curry—including coriander, cumin, cayenne, turmeric, saffron, mustard, cinnamon and ginger. I got a hint of the possibilities in the *Vegetarian Epicure* but am still looking for a good, simple book with lots of ideas and not too many exotic ingredients.

Food definitely doesn't have to be vegetarian to be appropriate to living lightly! Chinese cooking is a perfect example of energy-conserving food. Vegetables and meat are cut into small pieces and cooked quickly over a high flame—generally in a wok, which makes it easy to toss food from the red hot bottom to the cooler sides. Meat is thus used almost as a flavoring, and a little can go a long way—I spent $1.49 last night on 1/2 lb. of pork tenderloin which fed five—including Lee. *The Regional Cooking of China* is my latest find (actually it was given to me for Christmas). It's really excellent: easy-to-follow recipes with easy-to-find ingredients. They are basically stir-frys and thus common Chinese food as opposed to the fancy exotica in most books. I've long been looking for a book that gives an understanding of the sauces and flavoring that you get in a good Chinese restaurant. I've only tried two recipes so far, but I think this is it—all I need is a little practice in timing.

The Complete Yogurt Cookbook is a good book for getting out of any ruts you might be in. My copy is spattered with sauces, which is the mark of a well-loved source of good food. The recipes in this book include dressings and sauces, soups, vegetables, meat dishes and desserts. They range from Roast Lamb with Macedonia Sauce to Spinach Soup Tanya. Central to many dishes from Balkan countries and the Middle East, yogurt is definitely good for you. I find that it can often be substituted for sour cream for a lighter (less fattening) dish.

There are several good kinds of yogurt—my favorite is Continental, but it's expensive, so I usually use Nancy's, which comes out of the Kesey Creamery in Springfield.

CAROL COSTELLO'S FOOLPROOF YOGURT *adapted from Chris Herron's recipe*

Equipment: clean mayonnaise quart jar, or the container your last store yoghurt came in—Nancy's quart is good, an 88¢ styrofoam cooler, or 5-gallon crock. Fill with old towels or other insulating material.

Bring pint of water to full boil. Pour 1 can evaporated milk into jar. Refill can with boiling water (13 oz.?) and pour into jar. (This both measures amount and rinses any extra milk out.) Stir in several heaping teaspoons of powdered milk and several of your starter. Place in insulated vessel, cover warmly and return in 4 hours to warm, creamy yoghurt. The keys to correct temperature are efficient insulation and bringing water to full boil. I read in the WEC that some butterfat content is

necessary for little microbes to grow. I find regular evaporated milk better than lowfat. Old husband's tale—stuff should not be jiggled while growing. Old myth—yoghurt discovered by Bulgars riding around on horseback. Costello truth—made batch every day driving down bumpy Baja roads. Only used one jar, leaving last two spoons for starter each morning . . . kept the dire rear away. The best starter I ever had came from S.F.—a Russian variety in stores. I sure like not having to use a thermometer. Chris test for appropriate temperature is to hold the glass jar (doesn't work on plastic) for the space of three heartbeats. If the heat doesn't sting the hand, it's lukewarm—cool enough to add the starter. I also like using a minimum of utensils as this does.

TOFU AND MISO

Sometimes all the pieces of a puzzle come together in a very fine way, delighting our minds' search for wholistic patterns. It happened the other day when Bill Shurtleff and Akiko Aoyagi walked into the RAIN House bearing copies of their *Book of Tofu* and *Book of Miso* and a vision that links together world food utilization, good eating, cottage industry, local self-reliance and a Zen way of thinking. They are a fine example of what a couple of people can do with a strong purpose and lots of well-directed energy and generosity.

An initial love of tofu and curiosity about its making led to research in Japan, the writing of two very fine and thorough books on tofu and miso (see below), and to a resulting mushrooming of interest in these protein-rich food products. Bill and Akiko have set up the New-Age Foods Study Center to help carry out their work and now divide their time between networking here to help development of tofu and miso-making and studying and writing in Japan about food processing techniques.

Bill is learning the new art of sea farming—the cultivation of a wealth of vegetables common to the Japanese diet—nori, wakame, kombu, agar, kelp and more. They have also discovered that kuzu, a valuable delicacy in Japan, grows wild all over the Southern part of the USA, where it is presently considered an uncontrollable pest. They are planning a book on the full story of using kuzu in cookery and natural medicine, as well as employing the plant for fodder, fertilizer and erosion control.

Publications by Shurtleff & Aoyagi available from:

New Age Foods Study Center
790 Los Palos Manor
Lafayette, CA 94549

The Book of Tofu: 500 recipes, 300 illustrations, 336 pages, 8-1/2 by 11-inch large format. Contains instructions for preparing each of the seven basic types of tofu as well as soymilk, tempeh, yuba and other soy products. (Autumn Press, $6.95).

The Book of Miso: 400 recipes, 300 illustrations, 256 pages, 8-1/2 by 11-inch large format. Contains instructions for preparing many types of miso. (Autumn Press, $6.95).

The Book of Tofu, Vol. II: A technical manual for starting a commercial tofu shop. 122 pages, typewritten, unedited, 8-1/2 by 11-inch large format, staple-bound, basic chapters only. Offset printed; $12.95 each.

The Book of Miso, Vol. II: A technical manual for starting a commercial miso shop. 45 pages, typewritten, unedited, offset printed, legal size, staple-bound. $3.50 each.

Pamphlets: Ten pages, accordion-folded, packed with information, illustrations and favorite Western-style recipes. Special prices for quantity orders. *What is Tofu? What is Miso? What is Shoyu?* (coming soon), 15¢ each.

Tempeh: A 1-page brochure taken from *The Book of Tofu* describing how to prepare this savory fermented bean food. 25¢ each, 10 for $1.50

Tapes: Recorded live at lecture-demonstrations in America. Audio cassettes, 120 min., Tofu, Miso, $5 each. Color Video, 30 min., Tofu, Food for Mankind, $10 rental plus $30 deposit.

Pear Syrup

Ummm, WOW! Another really good thing is getting going—pear syrup! Ummm! Pear syrup is a beautiful alternative to white sugar or honey as a sweetener. It has a much subtler flavor than honey, doesn't crystallize, and only costs about two-thirds what honey does. Made by evaporating water out of mashed apples or pears, it is made of fruit sugars—45% fructose, 45% glucose and 10% sucrose. Can be used for baking, canning, or as a syrup or sweetener.

It should be possible to scale the production fairly small and likely will be a boon to orchard areas and tree farming in general because it gives another useful product for blemished fruit besides dried fruit and cider. Bees and honey in the spring, nectar in the fall—double crop!

Access information on pear syrup is still vague. Watch RAIN for more information.

Wild Foods Cookbook and Field Guide, Billy Joe Tatum, 1976, $4.95 from:
Workman Publishing Co.
231 East 51st
New York, NY 10022

Lots of good ideas here on how to find and how to eat such free goodies as purslane, dandelions, lamb's quarters, fern fronds and sorrel. Its dessert section was a disappointment as I was looking for some alternative sweeteners and virtually all call for sugar (not even honey). But I think I'll add this to my cookbook shelf.

Cooking in woks the Chinese way and using the traditional cooking methods of other nations greatly decreases energy use—chopped food at higher temperatures for a short time. In Japan,

hot wok joints

give you a wide variety of excellent meals in 30 seconds! Better than MacDonald's by far.

Nutrition Action
Center for Science in the Public Interest
1779 Church St.
Washington, D.C. 20036

Seems that Food Day was an idea whose time had come. We've heard directly and indirectly about numerous projects that got their initial push through the Food Day activities.

The Center is going to keep people in touch via *Nutrition Action* newsletter at $10/yr.

A couple of years ago CSPI published *Nutrition Scoreboard*, your guide to better eating. $2.50. A very interesting analysis/scoring of foods we eat, along with introductory material on vitamins, minerals, additives, etc.

Nutrition Information Center
Phoenix Reid
235 S.E. 13th
Portland, OR 97214

Especially involved with the ethics of food. Giving workshops on the use of complimentary plant proteins and unrefined, unprocessed foods. Has specific information geared to senior citizens, institutional needs, mini gardens, food dehydration, backpacking recipes.

Composition of Foods, Agriculture Handbook No. 8, $2 from:
Superintendent of Documents
U.S. Government Printing Office
Washington, DC 20402

A basic sourcebook on the nutritive quality of foods. Filled with tables covering the contents of more than 2500 raw, processed and prepared foods. Covers about everything but complementary proteins, for which you'll have to turn to *Diet for a Small Planet*.

SOUP TIME is the full-flavored 10 second soup. Ingredients: corn starch, hydrogenated vegetable oil, lactose, salt, natural flavors, dry chicken meat, chicken fat, monosodium glutamate (flavor enhancer), sodium caseinate, dehydrated onion, sugar, potassium phosphate, mono and diglycerides (stabilizers), silicon dioxide (flow conditioner), corn syrup solids, soy flour, sodium silcoaluminate (flow conditioner), dehydrated parsley, dehydrated garlic, turmeric, tricalcium phosphate, spices, thiamine hydrochloride, lecithin, polysorbate 60 (stabilizer), disodium inosinate and disodium guanylate (flavor enhancers), turmeric extract, lactic acid, artificial color. Net wt. 0.6 oz.

San Francisco Food Directory, from:
Northern California Food Network
944 Market Street, 4th Floor
San Francisco, CA 94102

This is an excellent listing of food services available in a city. Includes emergency meals, community gardens, nutrition information, senior citizen programs, co-ops, groups, publications and a speakers' bureau. Fine model for other communities.

Earthwork
1499 Potrero Ave.
San Francisco, CA 94110

Good people who are networking and organizing around food as it relates to the community, agribusiness, urban gardening, land reform and nutrition. Write for their list of available publications.

The Food Dryer's Drying Booklet, by John Magee and Connie Dexter, 1975, $2

and

How to Build Food Drying Equipment, by John Magee, 1975, $2 from:
California Wood Plans
P.O. Box 541
San Luis Obispo, CA 93406

It feels good when someone just lays out the options for you and gives you what you need to do things yourself instead of pushing a single answer. This good set of booklets lays out how, what and where to dry—in the sun, in the oven, over a heat register, with solar heating or electricity. Pros and cons of each and how to prepare foods for drying. Companion book has simple, easy-to-follow directions and drawings for making several kinds of food drying cabinets.

Eat Your Heart Out, by Jim Hightower, 1975, $1.95 from:
Vintage Books
Random House
201 E. 50th St.
New York, NY 10022

A heavily-documented account of the effects of concentrated ownership of the food growing, processing and retailing industries. Why the consumer, small farmer, and taxpayers are squeezed and who profits. Seeing what the problem is means seeing what the answer is. (TB)

Food for People, Not for Profit, by Catherine Lerza and Michael Jacobson, 1975, $1.95 from:
Ballantine Books
201 E. 50th St.
New York, NY 10022

A sourcebook prepared for Food Day, 1975, which provides a good overview of the whole range of our food problems. More importantly, it provides a series of brief case studies that support the assertions that alternatives exist and can be viable. World food problems, nutrition and disease, poverty and food, government-industry operations, costs of food and food production.

The Hunger Action Center
Evergreen State College
Olympia, WA 98505

They have given away over $50,000 in mini-grants to innovative projects dealing with hunger and world food problems. Six garden projects, six co-ops or buying clubs, five farmers' markets, two protein projects, two food-energy relationship, and two nutrition education projects, two information services, one apprenticeship program, one food organizing project, and two canning programs. Whew!

Modern Nutrition in Health and Disease, by Robert Goodhart and Maurice Shils, 5th edition, 1973, $35 from:
Lea and Febiger
Washington Square
Philadelphia, PA 19106

Voluminous (1100) pages and expensive (dig it out of a library), but the basic reference source to go to if you're seriously interested in the relation between nutrition and health. Covers the foundations of safety and adequacy of food supply, metabolism and malnutrition during emotional stress, nutrition in the prevention and treatment of disease, and an extensive appendix filled with all sorts of useful charts and tables. Oriented to the medical professions, but useful to others willing to wade through occasionally opaque terminology. (Suggested by Mim Orleans)

Steven Buetow

HEALTH

Health is an elusive goal in a society that spends more than any other on medical care and finds itself well down the list of countries on standard measures of health. We've sought the impossible—a magic repairman who can right any wrong we ingeniously inflict upon ourselves through self-indulgent ways of life and a magic shield that can keep us aloof from co-existence with other life forms with whom we share the planet. The chemical violence we inflict upon other forms of life in the name of medicine only causes the more rapid evolution of ever more lethal and resistant forms of "disease" and a temporary postponement of reckoning with the underlying problems.

We have no incentive or ethic to stay healthy, expecting a cure for anything. We've developed no self-care/paraprofessional systems to deal with minor problems and assist in more serious ones. Our medicine focuses on exotic rather than basic problems—ones that earn glamour or prestige. Our health care system is based on an elite, hierarchical, authoritarian framework centered in urban research hospitals rather than neighborhood and rural clinics. In spite of the acknowledged success of acupuncture and other processes based on foreign medical traditions, we've made no attempt to develop a broader and more inclusive life and health philosophy. Instead, we continue to focus on chemical and surgical responses to relieve symptoms rather than preventing problems. And

our whole system has no incentive to be economical or cost-effective.

Yet, much of the basis for change exists. Almost all our expensive pharmaceuticals were first isolated as active ingredients in herbal medicines, so the detailed chemical analysis of the world's natural and inexpensive pharmacopia exists and needs only to be integrated with the folklore-based herbal medicine manuals to provide the basis for effective and vastly cheaper pharmaceuticals. Detailed volumes on preventative medicine, nutrition and health, and other topics, fill the shelves of medical libraries but need to be translated so they are useful to people.

We are starting to take responsibility individually and as communities for our health. Manuals and guidebooks to support that responsibility are also appearing, though rarely yet with the necessary and difficult combination of vision, love and technical accuracy. Priorities on the spending of public monies on health (and a sense of where to stop) have seen little attention. New kinds of professionals and paraprofessionals are only beginning to be trained and the existing and highly subsidized profession only beginning to be dealt with. The roots of the change are present and visibly taking shape, much as changes in sewage, public utilities and energy were about five years ago. Watch and help.

NEW PATHS

Man Adapting, Rene Dubos, 1965, $4.95 from:

> Yale University Press
> 92A Yale Station
> New Haven, CT 06520

If I were to point to the best single book I know to give an understanding of what health means and how fundamentally to change our attitudes and health-related practices to regain health, this would be it. It doesn't spell out a structure for medical schools or how to do first aid, but once you've read Dubos, those things will fall into place when you get to them. It isn't as easy reading as some of his other books, but has the most meat in it . . . between the lines as well as in them. Call it ecology or call it health, or don't bother to call it—it's merely being aware of how things relate.

Away With All Pests, J.S. Horn, 1969, $3.75 from:

> Monthly Review Press
> 67 West 14th
> New York, NY 10011

This is a down-to-earth account of many of the social and medical programs that China has been tackling successfully, written by an English physician who emigrated to China with his family in the mid-fifties. The barefoot doctor program, the efforts to get professionals and bureaucrats to spend more time in rural areas, the incredibly successful drives to eliminate VD and schisto-somiasis (a debilitating worm disease), and the struggle to appropriately blend traditional and modern medical practices are all covered. It is the best book I've seen for giving a feeling for Maoist thought in action. Horn deals honestly with many of the fears and skepticisms he has had as he learned bit by bit to shed old values and prejudices and to truly work "for the people." And since he is writing from a Western perspective, many of the feelings he describes are

ones we can all relate to. There are a lot of good, practical examples of people working together to combat the social stigma of VD, for instance, or the exclusive tendencies of the medical profession. There is a lot we can all learn from their experiences.

Behold Man, by Lennart Nilsson, 1973, $25 from:

> Little, Brown and Company
> 34 Beacon Street
> Boston, MA 02106

If this beautiful treasure were put in every doctor's waiting room, it would probably bring about a whole new attitude towards ourselves and our health. 350 exquisite photographs of the human body taken by the Swedish photographer whose sensational photos of fetus development appeared in *Life* in the 1960s. Not your normal pictures these, but photographs of clouds in the sky as seen from inside the eye, the path taken by smoke being sucked into the lungs, synapses in the brain, fallopian tubes and mystically haunting photos of fetuses. They make clear the incredible beauty of our bodies. You won't feel the same about yourself once you've seen this.

Photographic Anatomy of the Human Body, by C. Yokochi, 1971, $14.50 from:

> University Park Press
> Chamber of Commerce Bldg.
> Baltimore, MD 21202

If you're curious and not too queasy, this will provide fascinating enlightenment about how everything goes together inside us. Photos of cutaway sections through complete torsos, a body from which the skin is removed showing how all the muscles go together. Every major organ and system in the body is shown in both exterior and interior detail.

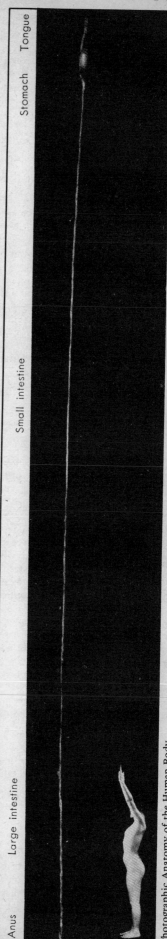

Photographic Anatomy of the Human Body

PROFESSIONAL CARE

We found this in **Self-Help and Health: A Report** from Social Policy

... I was in the courtyard of a place called McCord's Zulu Hospital, an institution of about 200 beds in Durban, South Africa. The wards and balconies opened onto a courtyard filled with flowering trees and warm subtropical air. Suddenly a single soprano voice soared from one of the wards, wavered, was joined and sustained by a chorus of women's voices and rose again. After a moment, a great deep harmonic swelled: the men's wards had joined in. And for the next ten minutes, the whole hospital sang. Someone translated for me. The Zulu song was about the pain of being ill, the loneliness and fear of being in the hospital, and the goodness of being with the people—other patients—for sharing and support. Every day at twilight, I learned, the whole hospital sang—all the patients and some of the staff. It was a profoundly moving experience. At intervals since, I have tried to imagine patients so sustaining themselves in a hospital in Boston. I cannot.

From "The Causes of Dehumanization in Health Care and Prospects for Humanization," J. Geiger in *Humanizing Health Care* by J. Howard and A. Strauss, eds., 1975, from Wiley-Interscience Press.

Preventative Medicine, Duncan Clark and Brian MacMahon, 1967, $12.50 from:

> Little, Brown and Company
> 34 Beacon Street
> Boston, MA 02106

Another one of those comprehensive, overpriced medical texts that cover everything but bury you with words. Needs translating into a more useful form, but it provides you with a resource on what's known about preventative medicine.

Nutrition and Health
Thorough and overwhelming like *Preventative Medicine*, but an equally valuable resource in an important area. See review in Agriculture and Food Section.

The End of Medicine, Rick J. Carlson, Wiley-Interscience Series, 1975, $12.95 from:

> John Wiley and Sons
> 605 Third Avenue
> New York, NY 10016

Carlson comes a lot closer to succeeding at what Ivan Illich tried to do with *Medical Nemesis*—cover the inherent limitations in our concepts and institutions of health and explore the options available to develop more positive approaches to health. *Medical Nemesis* is hard to read, polemical, and fails to substantiate assertions made—not up to Illich's earlier works such as *Tools for Conviviality*. *The End of Medicine* is readable and covers the ground well. The price is high—ask your library to order it, or maybe wait for a paperback version.

Prognosis Negative: Crisis in the Health Care System, David Kotelchuck, ed., 1976, $2.95 from:

> Vintage Books
> Random House
> 201 East 50th
> New York, NY 10022

This new Health/PAC (Health Policy Advisory Center) updates *American Health Empire* (1970) for a detailed view of the ills of our American health care system. It is a hefty collection of essays documenting the wheelings and dealings of large hospital systems, Blue Cross, nursing homes, drug companies

and government assistance (Medicare, Medicaid, grants and national insurance). It's very depressing reading but useful ammunition. Health/PAC has been doing substantial work in this area for some time and publishes an excellent bi-monthly *Bulletin*. Write for price information: Health/PAC, 17 Murray St., New York, NY 10007).

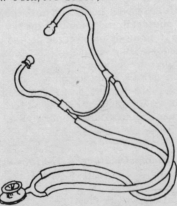

Pediatric Priorities in a Developing World, David Morley, $3 ($6 airmail) from:

> Intermediate Technology Publications
> 9 King Street
> London, England

Sensible and experienced counsel on developing the most effective possible health care programs on very limited budgets. Principles of allocation of resources, evaluation of priorities and operation of child care programs under simple conditions.

Alternative Approaches to Meeting Basic Health Needs in Developing Countries, V. Djukanovic and E.P. Mach, 1975, 24 Swiss francs from:

> Q Corporation
> 49 Sheridan Avenue
> Albany, NY 12210

A study of 10 successful or promising innovative health care programs in various parts of the world that replaced unsuccessful Western centralized health systems. Programs from China, Cuba, Tanzania, Venezuela, Bangladesh, India, Niger and Yugoslavia are examined and factors responsible for success analyzed.

Health, Manpower and Medical Auxiliaries, Intermediate Technology Development Group, $3.50 from:

> IT Publications
> 9 King Street
> London, England

An excellent overview and introduction to appropriate health care programs. Contains essays on intermediate technology in medicine, health care technology, a very useful section on ideals and examples for use of paraprofessionals, and a well-annotated bibliography on health planning, economics and manpower.

Hawaii Health Net
  Moiliili Community Center
  2535 South King Street
  Honolulu, HI 96814
Nancy and Walter Strode have been co-ordinating this pioneering networking organization for several years. People interested in innovative health care (doctors, mental health workers, lay healers) meet together once a year at a conference and at various other intervals in smaller groups to share information, skills and vibes. From all accounts, it's an exciting way to keep in touch.

On Death and Dying, E. Kubler-Ross, 1969, $1.95 from:
  Macmillan
  866 Third Ave.
  New York, NY 10022
A moving and sensitive account of experiences with dying people. Breaking into one of our society's most feared and taboo topics, Kubler-Ross has been instrumental in beginning changes in our medical practices and social beliefs to permit dignified death and acceptance of death as an integral and meaningful aspect of life.

A Manual of Simple Burial, Ernest Morgan, $1.50 from:
  Celo Press
  Burnsville, NC 28714
An extremely helpful, practical booklet for assisting people in obtaining simple, dignified and economical funeral arrangements. Information on anatomical gifts such as eyebanks, cremation, attitudes on death, funeral practices, what to do when death occurs, financial resources, simple burial practices and dealing with legal impediments.

Washington Consumers' *Checkbook*, quarterly, from:
  Washington Center for the Study of Services
  1910 K St., N.W., Suite 303
  Washington, DC 20006
$9.50/yr. An excellent new service that should serve as a model for every community—a comparative cost and service guide to various services and products available in a specific community. The first issue focused on health—the cost and service of various hospital emergency rooms, cost of drugs from every drug store and pharmacy in DC, cost of dental services, nursing homes, health insurance, abortion clinics and doctors. Future issues will explore little-known local bargain stores, finance companies, auto repair shops and other services.

Master of Science in Biomedical Communications
  College of Medicine
  University of Cincinnati
  231 Bethesda Ave.
  Cincinnati, OH 45267

A new program begun in fall of 1976 training communications specialists in health care education and delivery systems to assist in the interaction between health professionals and patients. Study areas include: health care environment and delivery systems, media, learning theory and instructional methods, applied behavioral science and communications and behavioral measurement, statistics and research design.

Madness Network News Reader, ed. by Shirley Hirsch, Joe Kennedy Adams, et al., 1975, $5.95 from:
  Glide Publications
  330 Ellis St.
  San Francisco, CA 94102
An intense collection of poems, essays and letters by former inmates, doctors and others on the politics of being crazy. Highly political and full of righteous anger, yet warm with a healthy sense of humor. It is directed at mental health care institutions, yet provides a model for the examination of all inappropriate institutions from schools to hospitals. They also publish an excellent newsletter subtitled "All the Fits That's News to Print," $4/year for 6 issues from:
  Madness Network News
  2150 Market Street
  San Francisco, CA 94114

Dear Lane,
  Our preference for a blurb about MNN would include the idea that we are people who are fighting back against psychiatric oppression (electro-shock, forced drugging, lobotomy, lack of legal rights for psychiatric inmates, etc.). We are opposed to involuntary commitment for people who have not committed any criminal act. We feel that psychiatry is a method of social control, not of healing. "We'd rather be mad with the truth than sane with lies!"
  We have a new booklet on Psychiatric Drugs by Dr. Caligari that sells for $1. You might also want to alert your readers to the documentary film "Hurry Tomorrow" that was made inside a locked men's ward in the Metropolitan State Hospital in LA. For more information about the film, write: Halfway House Films, 71 Delmar St., San Francisco, CA 94117.
  In struggle,
  Jenny Collins

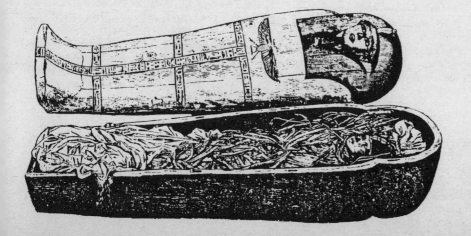

SELF CARE

Medical Self-Care: Access to Medical Tools, quarterly from:

> P.O. Box 718
> Inverness, CA 94937

$7/yr. At last! Someone is doing an access journal for self-help care. It's the area of a.t. we've been wanting to get into but lack the know-how to do in depth. Editor Tom Ferguson recently finished at Yale Medical School and just moved to the Bay Area to do community medicine. The scope of the magazine looks wide and exciting: how to take care of ourselves and our neighbors and family; first aid and long-term health needs; books, drugs, networking and how-to. Only one issue so far, but if the quality stays the same, it's a winner.

Take Care of Yourself: A Consumer's Guide to Medical Care, by Donald M. Vickery, MD, and James F. Fuies, MD, 269 pp., 1976, $5.95 from:

> Addison-Wesley
> Reading, MA 01867

A highly useful home medical guide which includes flow charts for figuring out what to do about the 68 most common complaints that bring people to a doctor's office—sprains, colds, sore throats, vaginal discharge, headache, back pain, etc. Asks key questions and allows you to follow a branching logic tree which tells you whether you need to (1) see a doctor NOW, (2) see a doctor today, (3) make appointment with doctor, (4) apply home remedies. Also tells you which home remedies to use. Lots of people go to doctors when they shouldn't and don't when they should. This book should help you use your doctor more effectively. (Tom Ferguson)

Keeping Healthy in a Polluted World
Harold Taub, 1975, $2.95 from:

> Penguin Books
> 72 Fifth Ave.
> New York, NY 10021

I have mixed feelings about this book by the former editor of *Prevention* magazine. Is there *anything* I can eat or breathe safely? Lots of good information here about health problems, from allergies to cancer caused by pollution, food additives and other chemicals in our environment, along with lots of preventive ideas. Vitamin C seems to be an incredible cure-all (and the fact that our bodies can't produce it like virtually all other animals may be a genetic mutation). Much of his advice jibes with my own knowledge and instincts, though he tends to recommend pill supplements rather than natural sources and makes a couple of inexcusably sexist comments. It's all so complicated.

Barefoot Doctor's Manual, $6.95 from:

> Cloudburst Press
> Mayne Island, VON 2JO
> BC, Canada

This translation of the 1970 Chinese Barefoot Doctor's Manual is an excellent accomplishment to which any U.S. programs to develop local self-reliant health assistance and self-care will be compared.

It contains 960 pages of solid, useful information: understanding the human body, hygiene, diagnosis, therapy, birth control, acupuncture, first aid, treatment of common diseases, and 410 pages on Chinese medicinal herbs. Techniques cover a wide range of traditional Chinese medical practices as well as usual Western medicine.

An herbal contraceptive: Decoction prepared from tender sprouts of *Pinus massoniana*, 9 stalks (each about 5 inches (ts'un) long) and roots of white stipa (1 liang) to be taken once after conclusion of menstrual period, for 5 months in succession. Effective for 3 years.

How to Practice Prospective Medicine, by Lewis Robbins and Jack Hall, 1974, $12 from:

> Health Hazards Appraisal
> c/o Methodist Hospital of Indiana
> 1604 N. Capitol
> Indianapolis, IN 46202

I've never been much of a bug on statistics, but this seems like a very valuable use. Lays out simply and directly your probability of dying from various causes based on your age, sex and habits. Then shows the impact on your expected lifespan from changing various habits—stopping smoking, losing weight, changing diet, drinking less, using seatbelts, etc. Tells you the odds; you choose how you want to live and die. Good approach and fundamental to the development of self-care responsibility. (Suggested by Mim Orleans)

A Bibliography of Chinese Sources on Medicine and Public Health in the People's Republic of China: 1960-1970, U.S. Dept. of Health, Education and Welfare Publication No. 73-439 (NIH), $5.55 from:

> U.S. Government Printing Office
> Washington, DC 20402

This has been hiding on our shelves since I don't know when. Seems to be the companion to the *Barefoot Doctor's Manual*. Would be easy to get buried in it (485 pages, some 14,550 entries), but so is a phone book, and I have a hunch it might be really useful to some people prowling around in the interesting developments in Chinese medicine. Take a look if you have interests there—contains ALL English translated or abstracted stuff from China about medicine between 1960 and 1970. Whew!

Well-Being, $5/year from:
 Box 7455
 San Diego, CA 92107

A monthly down-home healing magazine to keep you in touch with natural cures for the flu, eye exercises for better vision, herbs, acupuncture and basic naturopathic medicine. Even homemade cat food recipes.

The Medicine Show, by the editors of *Consumer Reports*, 1974, 384 pp., $3.50 from:
 Pantheon Books
 Random House
 201 E. 50th
 New York, NY 10022

This book is a good solid look at medicines in the best *Consumer Reports* tradition: how and when to take certain things and the pros and cons of different brand names. The cheapest aspirin is the same as the well-known brands. Using Alka-Seltzer as a digestive aid means taking an unnecessary dose of aspirin (no need for a painkiller for an upset stomach) which could even be harmful if the cause of the problem is ulcers. Most of us have been charmed by the ads and packaging to buy what the notoriously self-serving drug industry wants us to buy. This book is both an eyeopener and a useful tool for breaking some of our bad habits.

Alternatives to Chemical Medicines, Mildred Jackson N.D. and Terri Teague, 1975, $4.95 from:
 P.O. Box 656
 Oakland, CA 94604

There are a lot of books out now with herbal remedies—many of which are conflicting. I know in my bones that this is the way to go, but it's hard to pick up on this almost lost art. This is the most helpful resource I've found so far—straightforward with amounts given (it's easy to overdo on sometimes powerful herbs) and favorites starred. Put together by two who've been working with healing for a long time rather than faddists. It's a good beginning

The New Handbook of Prescription Drugs, Richard Burack and Fred Fox, $1.95, from:
 Ballantine Books
 Random House
 201 East 50th
 New York, NY 10022

A 1975 version of the original 1967 guidebook for finding out where and how to get the best value for your prescription dollar; what drugs to avoid and how to evaluate different generic and name brand drugs and which to choose.

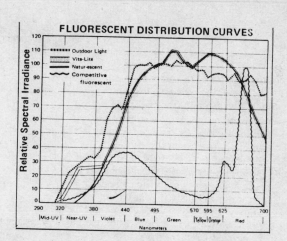

Health and Light, John N. Ott, 1973, $7.50 from:
 Devin-Adair Co.
 Old Greenwich, CT 06870

We just got another letter yesterday from a person wondering if we knew why they commonly got a headache and had trouble concentrating after a short period of time in fluorescent-lit buildings. We keep meeting more people who have that experience—as we have. Half way through a supermarket we're half asleep and have trouble remembering what we're doing. John Ott's book opens up some of the reasons why. Like anything breaking new ground, it has caused a rage of controversy. He's what "scientists" are supposed to be—people with their eyes and minds open enough to look into the reasons why things go wrong when they're not supposed to. While pioneering time-lapse photography of plants he found strange things happening when he had to grow the plants in glass greenhouses or under artificial lights. A long series of experiments by him and others revealed important effects on biological systems of spectral ranges missing from artificial light or blocked by window glass. He also pioneered research showing dangerous effects of radiation from TV sets that brought development of new safety standards—he found that some TV tubes tested had X-ray emissions up to 1.6 million times the acceptable safety level established by the National Committee on Radiological Protection! *Health and Light* is a fascinating and important study of the effects of natural and artificial lights on people and other living things.

WOMEN AND HEALTH

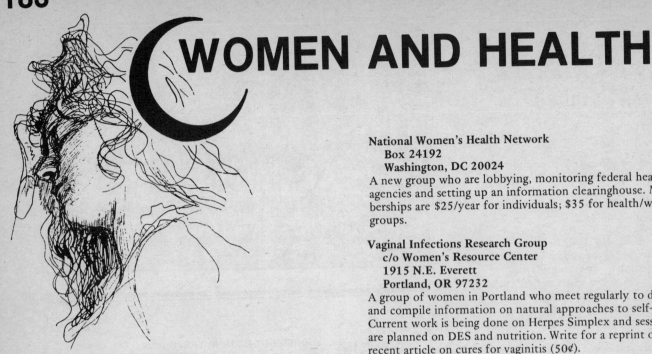

One of the most exciting aspects of the grass roots movement towards self-help care has been the women's movement. All over the country women have been taking charge of their own health needs—learning to ask questions of professionals, learning to examine themselves, and learning to use paraprofessionals—particularly other women—for such non-illness health needs as birth control and birthing.

I don't know where the movement towards self-help care for women began—in fact, I suspect it's another one of those magical urges that began simultaneously in many nooks and crannies all over the country. But in any case, one of the earliest groups was the Boston Women's Health Book Collective, a group of women who gathered to share in the consciousness-raising process and decided to present a course on women's bodies and ended up writing:

Our Bodies, Ourselves, **Boston Women's Health Book Collective, 1971, $4.95 from:**
   Simon and Schuster
   630 Fifth Ave.
   New York, NY 10020

It is a book that keeps growing—I know people who have every version, from the rough newsprint to the newest, fat Simon and Schuster. It has been enormously successful because it is so good. Sections on Anatomy, Relationships, Lesbianism, Nutrition, Rape and Self-Defense, Venereal Disease, Birth Control, Abortion, Childbearing, Menopause and Health Care. The new Sexuality section is the finest thing I've seen on the subject anywhere—good for women or men. They have a special deal for clinics or groups doing health counseling services: 70% discount (88.5¢/copy) on orders of 12 or more accompanied by an official document verifying health care status. Nice move, as it should be required for all people everywhere. A Spanish edition is also available: $2 or free if you need it from the BWHBC (see address below).

And good news, the Collective is now putting out a monthly collection of Xerox reprints on women's health from all over. It's often depressing and/or angering to read about the unproven dangerous things drug companies have fed us and the condescending, often brutal treatment of women by MDs, but it is good to have this information out. For the *Women's Health News Briefs*, send $6/year to: Boston Women's Health Book Collective, Box 192, West Somerville, MA 02144

National Women's Health Network
   Box 24192
   Washington, DC 20024
A new group who are lobbying, monitoring federal health agencies and setting up an information clearinghouse. Memberships are $25/year for individuals; $35 for health/women's groups.

Vaginal Infections Research Group
   c/o Women's Resource Center
   1915 N.E. Everett
   Portland, OR 97232
A group of women in Portland who meet regularly to discuss and compile information on natural approaches to self-care. Current work is being done on Herpes Simplex and sessions are planned on DES and nutrition. Write for a reprint of their recent article on cures for vaginitis (50¢).

Women and Health, **$12.50/year from:**
   SUNY/College at Old Westbury
   Old Westbury, NY 11568
A bi-monthly academic journal that I haven't seen yet, but it sounds good. Designed to have research and ideas on policy, structure and issues relating to women's health care delivery.

The Birth Control section of *Our Bodies, Ourselves* is thorough, but it doesn't take any sides. Many of us who are trying to wean ourselves from drugs and chemicals have become increasingly disenchanted with The Pill and the IUD ("What does my body really feel like without its daily dose of synthetic hormone?"). A milestone for me—and, as I later learned, for at least five other women I know—was the "Lunaception" article by Louise Lacey which first appeared in the Winter Solstice issue of *Co-Evolution Quarterly*. Soon thereafter it was published as a book:

Lunaception, **Louise Lacey, 1975,**
$1.75 from:
   Warner Paperback Library
   75 Rockefeller Plaza
   New York, NY 10020
                    Lunaception involves charting your temperature and watching for its mid-cycle change (ovulation) and then inducing that peak by sleeping with a light on those middle three days (no light at all the rest of the month—i.e., heavy curtains if you live in the city). Lacey found that she eventually got into cycle with the moon, ovulating when it was full!

Other books talk about other cycles—cosmic ones based on the phase of the moon when you were born and an extra cosmic fertility period at that point. For more information, read:

Natural Birth Control **(formerly Astrological Birth Control Control), Sheila Ostrander and Lynn Schroeder, 1972, $1.25 from:**
   Bantam Books
   666 Fifth Ave.
   New York, NY 10019

and
The Natural Birth Control Book, Art Rosenblum and Leah Jackson, Revised Edition, 1976, $3 from:
> Aquarian Research Foundation
> 5620 Morton St.
> Philadelphia, PA 19144

The latter book includes a chart for figuring out your own cosmic cycles and combines this method with a finger mucous test (the mucous of your cervix changes consistency at different times of your monthly cycle).

All of these methods may sound too far out and in some cases seem to contradict each other, but I feel strongly that they're more in the right direction, and I know of many women who swear by one or the other of them. Their rising popularity is indicated by the increasing number of ads I see in women's mags and elsewhere for charting of cosmic cycles. The Aquarian Research Foundation (address above) is interested in success and failure stories—and so am I. It's certainly a possibility worth exploring.

Now, if you are already happily pregnant, things are opening up in this area as well. Namely, the rising number of home deliveries and family-centered birthing.

Safe Alternatives in Childbirth, Lee and David Stewart, ed., 1976, $5 from:
> National Association of Parents and Professionals for
> Safe Alternatives in Childbirth (NAPSAC)
> P.O. Box 1307
> Chapel Hill, NC 27514

If you are at all interested in the pros and cons of different birthing practices, read this book. It is a collection of papers given at the 1st NAPSAC Conference by doctors, midwives and parents. It contains hair-raising documentation of the generally unmentioned hazards to mother and infant of routine use of drugs, forceps and IVs, as well as the high chances of contracting serious infections in the hospital. Statistics from studies in California and elsewhere show the increased health and general lack of problems in home deliveries as long as mothers with potential problems are screened out before-

hand. There are case studies of several midwives' and doctors' home delivery practices as well as descriptions of several birthing clinics—a step in between that could be a good solution for many families. The results, success stories are encouraging: hopefully we're getting back to a time where birthing can be family-centered and treated as a healthy, natural function wherever it happens.

NAPSAC is a network of parents and professionals dedicated to this cause. Contact them for information on how to find helpful professionals in your area or where to learn midwife skills.

Two groups pioneering in the development of birthing clinics and the training of midwives are on Stephen Gaskin's Farm and in Santa Cruz, California. Both groups have published books that are a joy to read—full of amazing pictures and heart-warming tales (scary ones are included as well).

And we can't forget Dr. Leboyer, the Frenchman who has made so many people aware of gentler, softer birthing.

Birth Book, 1972, $6 from:
> Genesis Press
> P.O. Box 14457
> Palo Alto, CA 94306

Spiritual Midwifery, Ina May and the Farm Midwives, 1975, $5.96 from:
> The Book Publishing Company
> The Farm
> Summertown, TN 38483

Birth Without Violence, Frederick Leboyer, 1975, $7.95 from:
> Alfred A. Knopf
> 201 E. 50th St.
> New York, NY 10022

Some other good books:

Women and Madness, Phyllis Chesler, 1972, $1.95 from:
> Avon
> 959 Eighth Ave.
> New York, NY 10019

Vaginal Politics, Ellen Frankfurt, 1973, $1.95 from:
> Bantam Books
> 666 Fifth Ave.
> New York, NY 10019

Complaints and Disorders: The Sexual Politics of Sickness, Barbara Ehrenreich and Deirdre English, 1973, 90 pp., $1.50 from:
> The Feminist Press
> Box 334
> Old Westbury, NY 11568

Getting Clear: Body Work for Women, Anne Kent Rush, 1973, $5.95 from:
> Random House Bookworks
> 201 E. 50th
> New York, NY 10022

The Joy of Birth Control, Stephanie Mills, Emory University Family Planning Program, 41 pp., $1 ea. (11-49 copies 75¢ ea., over 50 50¢ ea. plus 15% for mailing) from:
> Family Planning Program
> P.O. Box 26069
> 80 Butler St., S.E.
> Atlanta, GA 30303

High School Sexuality: A Teaching Guide, Women's Educational Project, 81 pp., $1 from:
> Amazon Reality Collective
> P.O. Box 95
> Eugene, OR 97401

VD Handbook and *Birth Control Handbook* (in English or French), 35¢ each (bulk rates available) from:
> Montreal Health Press
> C.P. 1000, Succursale G
> Montreal, Quebec H2W 2N1
> Canada

For your local library:
The Women and Health/Mental Health Collection of the former Women's History Library, 14 reels on microfilm ($32/reel) from:
> Barbara Baisley
> Northeast Micrographics
> 27 Palmer Woods Circle
> Branford, CT 06405

WASTE RECYCLING

Until recently very few people have been interested in understanding or dealing with the results of our bodily, personal or societal activity and have left the problems to be dealt with by engineers. The results have been overwhelming: left with no conscience to reduce or use wastes, we have allowed our waste stream to grow exponentially. The dollar costs of dealing with the problems have become insurmountable as more and more mechanized processes are attempted to deal with the growing deluge. Those processes frequently don't work, pass on health problems in other forms, and are becoming boxed in by other constraints of space and costs for disposal.

Citizen Science has again come to the rescue and demon-

strated its essential role in developing solutions to problems that correspond to the realities of cost, effectiveness and common sense rather than profit. Citizen groups have exposed the costs, malfunctions and health problems of present systems, have shown that source reduction and legislation such as bottle bills do work and have developed workable alternatives from compost toilets to the Ore Plan that had been shrugged off as unrealistic by lethargic and self-interested authorities. Their studies have routinely been more eye-opening and ground-breaking than official studies in spite of their lack of funding.

RECYCLING

Recycle?, 1972, $.75 from:
> League of Women Voters,
> 1730 M Street, N.W.
> Washington, DC 20036

The most comprehensive, concise and accurate study we've seen on the reasons for recycling; obstacles to recycling such as price biases, taxes, shipping rates and other laws favoring use of virgin materials; the present state of the art; and ways to encourage recycling. Solidly documented and unarguable logic.

Reduce: Targets, Means & Impacts of Source Reduction, by Diana Wahl, Publ. No. 576, $1 from:
> League of Women Voters of U.S.
> 1730 M St., N.W.
> Washington, DC 20036

Explains the difference between and relative benefits of source reduction (reducing the total amount of waste with measures such as the Oregon Bottle Bill or with methods such as the ORE PLAN for home separation and pickup of garbage) and resource recovery (trying to re-separate mixed garbage using energy-gulping air classifiers, magnetic separators and water separation systems). Unfortunately, this was written before the ORE Plan was nationally known.

Garbage in America: Approaches to Recycling, by Neil Seldman, 30 pp., 1975, $2 from:
> Institute for Local Self-Reliance
> 1717 18th St. N.W.
> Washington, DC 20009

Good overviews of the different methods of community recycling—comparing costly large-scale automated sorting facilities with more appropriate neighborhood-based separated-collection systems. These people are doing basic studies of localized waste-management systems, and this paper gives a sense of the advantages and disadvantages of different approaches across the country.

System Energy and Recycling: A Study of the Beverage Industry, by Bruce Hannon, Center for Advanced Computation, 1972, $3.75, from:
> National Technical Information Service
> U.S. Dept. of Commerce
> Springfield, VA 12151
> Doc. #PB 233-183/3G1

Demonstrates the energy, economic and employment potentials of reuse and recycling of products and materials. Among other things, the report shows that the soft drink throwaway container system is about twice as expensive as the returnable system.

"Resource Conservation Through Citizen Involvement in Waste Management" by David Beaton, 1975—summarized in "The Role of the Ore Plan in Developing a Nationwide Recycling Network," by Rich Duncan in *Compost Science*, May-June 1976.

A net energy analysis of nine different approaches to recycling indicates that "user-delivery" of waste (drop-off centers) is one of the most energy-consuming ways to go, while the ORE Plan gets the best marks for energy savings.

Oregon's Bottle Bill Two Years Later, by Don Waggoner, 1975, $2.50 from:
> Oregon Environmental Council
> 2637 S.W. Water
> Portland, OR 97201

Despite the claims of the bottling industry, the Bottle Bill works, and works well. Detailed analysis of the Oregon experience shows total litter down 39 percent by piece count and 47 percent by volume, while beverage container litter was reduced by 83 percent. Energy savings amounts to 130 million kw hours a year (enough to heat 50,000 homes) and 365 new jobs were created. Vermont, South Dakota and Maine are following suit.

All's Well on the Oregon Trail, single copies free from:
> Environmental Action Foundation
> The Dupont Circle Building
> Suite 724
> Washington, DC 20036

A short and sweet refutation of an Alcoa pamphlet that misused data to try to show that the Bottle Bill wasn't working. Bulk prices are available: 100 for $5, 500 for $20, 1000 for $35.

For details on Vermont's experience with bottle recycling, see: *Beverage Containers: The Vermont Experience*, 16 pp., free from:
> Solid Waste Information Materials Control Section
> U.S. Environmental Protection Agency
> Cincinnati, OH 45268

"China Recycles Her Wastes by Using Them on the Land," Roger Blobaum, *Compost Science*, Fall 1975, single copies $1 from:
> Rodale Press
> 33 East Minor
> Emmaus, PA 18049

With their usual resourcefulness, necessitated by scarce resources, the Chinese have come closer than anyone to eliminating waste. They follow the dictum of "highest and best use"—don't crush glass bottles for recycled glass, *reuse* them. Don't compost garbage if it can be fed to animals. In fact, almost all food processing plants are next door to hog farms—waste from one is food for another, and the manure goes right back on the gardens as fertilizer. Watch for Blobaum's forthcoming book, to be published by Rodale Press.

Recycling—Gearing Up for a Conservation Economy

$1, from:
> Community Environmental Council
> 109 E. De La Guerra
> Santa Barbara, CA 93101

Good description of the council's experiences in helping the city of Santa Barbara's recycling program.

Berkeley Solid Waste Commission
> 2105 Grove Street
> Berkeley, CA 94704

An active organization with a community compost project where people exchange their garbage and compostables to get compost in return. Proposed solid waste plan includes source separation for commercial and residential areas, a new transfer station and a pilot pick-up study for compostables.

Recycling in Maine, edited by William Ginn, 16 pp., single copies free from:
> Division of Solid Waste Management
> Dept. of Environmental Protection
> State of Maine
> Augusta, ME 04333

Very well done; useful as a model for how to get the recycling message across clearly and completely. Includes access info to recycling equipment manufacturers, materials markets, relevant organizations and publications. Excellent graphics.

1974 Annual Report, free from:
> Connecticut Resources Recovery
> Authority
> 60 Washington St.
> Hartford, CT 06106

One of the first integrated statewide solid waste management plans organized for reuse of resources as industrial materials and as an energy source.

Markets for Recyclables (1976) and The Paper Paper (1975), free from:
> Dept. of Environmental Quality
> 1234 S.W. Morrison
> Portland, OR 97205

The National Buyer's Guide to Recycled Paper, $9.95 from:
> Data Courier, Inc.
> 620 South Fifth St.
> Louisville, KY 40402

Recycling: Alabama Style, 52 pp., $2 from:
> Alabama Environmental Quality
> Association
> Box 1100
> Montgomery, AL 36111

These lists, for various materials and regions, provide extremely useful information for anyone getting involved in recycling. Firms who buy recycled materials, companies producing recycled paper, location of existing recycling centers and markets, etc. Useful information to put together for any area that doesn't have it available.

The Wastebin
> Box 14012
> Portland, OR 97214

This mimeographed newsletter is probably one of the best sources of continuing information on neighborhood recycling. It is put together by many of the people making the ORE Plan work in Portland, but it covers projects nationwide. Send them an address label and 26¢ in stamps for an issue. (They come out on an irregular basis.)

Decision-Makers Guide to Solid Waste Management (SW-500), 1976, from:
> Office of Solid Waste Management
> Programs
> U.S. Environmental Protection
> Agency
> 401 M Street, S.W.
> Washington, DC 20460

A solid survey of options and processes of solid waste management. Contains good coverage of special wastes—waste lubricating oil, tires, sewage sludge, hospital wastes and hazardous wastes, but contains only three short pages on reducing waste generation and does not cover inexpensive low energy systems such as the ORE Plan.

Resource Recovery and Recycling Handbook of Industrial Wastes, Marshall Sittig, 1975, 425 pp., $36 from:
> Noyes Data Corporation
> Mill Road at Grand Ave.
> Park Ridge, NJ 07656

Technical details of different recovery processes, laying out how to recover useful and valuable products from over 130 industrial wastes in categories ranging from metals to food to heat. Contains sources for various patented processes available as well as general discussion of various recovery process options, product options and uses, etc. This expensive resource is not for the browser but is a must for the serious recycler and of particular value to communities for demonstrating the viability of alternatives to pollution by industrial waste products.

Industrial Waste Recycling

National Resource Recycling Exchange
286 Congress St.
Boston, MA 02210

Iowa Industrial Waste Information
Exchange
Center for Industrial Research and
Service
Building E
Iowa State University
Ames, IA 50011

These are at least two working examples of a new and valuable service: a clearing house between manufacturers who generate "waste" but don't have the time to find uses or markets for them, and those potential users who'd love to give those "wastes" a new and productive home if only they knew they were available. A good way to make a living and a better world at the same time.

Solid Waste Recycling Projects: A National Directory, Penelope Hansen, 1973, U.S.EPA SW-45, $2.15 from:
U.S. Government Printing Office
Washington, DC 20402

Lists mostly volunteer recycling projects from around the country but also gives access to municipal and industrial materials recycling centers. Needs to be updated to include new self-supporting recycling services but provides a good beginning to find out what's going on where.

Recycle, 60 pp., $1.30 from:
Children's Museum
The Jamaica Way
Boston, MA 02130

Full of funny, simple sketches, this book helps teachers create games, toys and learning projects out of junk and easy findables. The resource center (also called Recycle) supports itself by selling barrels of industrial throwaways and industrial rejects to teachers who need raw material.

Garbage Guide, free from:
Environmental Action Foundation
The Dupont Circle Building
Suite 724
Washington, DC 20036

$6/yr. This four-pager, funded by EPA, gives a good overview of a specific topic each issue—plastic bottles, source reduction, hazardous wastes and the like. Always has bibliographic material and contact people. A good way to stay informed.

Both Oregon and Washington have good systems where people can call to find out where to take newspapers, misprinted envelopes, old tennis rackets, whatever, to be recycled. It is also possible to leave information on things one would be willing to take.

Recycling Switchboard
Dept. of Environmental Quality
1234 S.W. Morrison
Portland, OR 97205
503/292-5555

Recycling Information Service
Dept. of Ecology
Northwest Regional Office
4350 150th Ave., N.E.
Redmond, WA 98052
1-800-RECYCLE (toll-free in Wa.)
206/885-3300 (outside Wa.)

Solid Waste Informational Materials
Control Section
U.S. Environmental Protection
Agency
Cincinnati, OH 45268
This agency is doing a good job of making general information available to the public on solid waste and recycling problems and projects. Write them for their publications list—many of their things are free. They also have names of solid waste officials at the local level. For general questions about research and projects, contact:

The Office of Solid Waste Management
Programs
U.S. Environmental Protection
Agency
1835 K St., N.W.
Washington, DC 20460

National Referral Center
Science and Technology Division
Library of Congress
Washington, DC 20540
Write them for a good bibliography: *Selected Information Resources on Solid Wastes*. Contains access information on paper, plastic, metal and other recycling industry associations which can give detailed information in their specific areas.

National Association of Recycling
Industries, Inc.
330 Madison Ave.
New York, NY 10017

The Association sponsors research and provides information and consulting services on the reuse of solid waste materials. Questions which cannot be answered are referred to cooperating members for reply.

by Rich Duncan

Recycling

Almost no one believed it when Portland recyclers claimed it would be possible and economical to get householders to keep their trash separated, to pick it up with pushcarts and small vehicles and recycle it directly—thus eliminating the need for mammoth and expensive mechanical sorting systems, saving money and energy, and providing more jobs in the process. A big order! Yet it works, and works well enough that more than 30 ORE Plans are now starting around the country. Many cities, and even the EPA, are beginning to look seriously at this ridiculously simple mini-system that outperforms the biggest and best technology around.

Rich Duncan

Rich Duncan

The following is an excerpt from Prof. Richard Duncan's *Compost Science* paper on the ORE Plan. See the Jan.-Feb. 1976 issue of *C.S.* ($6/yr. from Rodale Press, 33 E. Minor, Emmaus, PA 18049, single copies $1 postpaid). His earlier ORE Plan article can be found in the Jan.-Feb. 1975 *C.S.* (Vol. 16, No. 1, pp. 24-32).

Portland State University's Prof. Duncan has been shepherding these neighborhood recycling organizations through the city-county-state-federal political thickets, providing the researched, academic analysis and conceptual background that is needed to keep a working "small is beautiful" technology in front of waste-management decision-makers.

The ORE Plan started in 1974 when Sunflower Recycling, Inc., extended their operations by using a small hand-pushed cart to pick up grouped recyclable wastes from homes in the community. Wastes collected included paper, bottles and cans, which were later sold to secondary materials markets. Later, a separate experiment added organic wastes, which were composted and used as a soil conditioner in local gardens. More than 50% of the households in the community participated in this 10-month experiment. In March 1975 Sunflower began using an Alsport UT-10 vehicle with a trailer for home collection, as shown in Figure 1. The positive results of this project led to the design of an alternative garbage collection system where the main financial base would come from collection fees.

The ORE Plan is now a full-line garbage collection service where recyclable materials are kept separated by householders and small-sized vehicles are used to pick up both recyclable wastes and mixed garbage at one visit. ORE Plan organizations are designed to be financially self-sufficient and pay fair wages to all workers. Collection fees, averaging 20 to 40 percent below fees for standard service, provide the main economic base and are supplemented by income from the sale of secondary materials.

In May 1975, Cloudburst Recycling, Inc. became the first new ORE Plan based business. Recycling collection fees averaged about $3 per home per month, compared to about $5 for standard collection service. Their strategy for obtaining an initial set of customers was to canvass households already known to be doing recycling. Over 80 percent of the first seventy households contacted signed up for the service. The community serviced by Cloudburst is a relatively flat area about 1-1/2 miles long by 1 mile wide, containing about 5,000 single-family residences. Cloudburst is now serving about 100 families in this area, representing a collection density of 1.5 percent.

Waste materials are collected by two people using a small pick-up truck with trailer as shown in Figure 2. The truck acts as a "satellite vehicle" to a large van truck parked in the neighborhood where materials are temporarily stored, reducing collection costs by lowering gasoline consumption. A recent "net energy" analysis by David Beaton, former director of the Oregon Energy Study, indicated that the ORE Plan was first among the nine systems studied in terms of overall energy-efficiency.

Basic collection fees range from $1.50 to $4 per month in January 1976, with over 50 percent of the subscribers preferring weekly collection of all their wastes. Collection times to serve about 80 customers have ranged from 3 to 5-1/2 hours. These hourly figures include backyard pick-up of wastes, breaking bottles into containers and personal attention to customers and potential customers, but exclude lunch and rest stops. Cloudburst estimates that two workers, using a pick-up truck and trailer, could collect from 150 households in 8 hours, including the time needed to transport wastes to markets or disposal sites. An estimated 2,800 pounds of wastes were collected from 80 households, of which more than 50 percent by weight were recycled. Income derived from the sale of recyclables is currently between $0.55 and $0.75 per household per month. The potential gross monthly income from a Cloudburst-type recycling operation is estimated at about $2,700 per month.

Oregon Style

Several crucial factors influence successful implementation of ORE Plan type systems: 1) rodent control in organic wastes, 2) flow control legislation and 3) franchising fees.

Both Sunflower and Cloudburst were composting organic wastes near their shared recycling center in an industrial-zoned area. The expense of physical facilities necessary to resolve rodent control problems caused them to cease composting operations in summer 1975, and all organic wastes have been landfilled since that date. Experience to date indicates a substantial demand exists for compost as a fertilizer and soil conditioner. Composting could be successfully done within city areas with 1) recognition by decision-makers that composting is a cost-effective method of both waste utilization and disposal, with 2) cooperation from elected official and government agencies, and through 3) policies making grants or small business loans available for construction of proper facilities and purchase of equipment.

A second problem facing recycling collection services is proposed "flow control" legislation that would guarantee all wastes collected in a municipal area would be destined for processing by big machine "resource recovery" systems. Biased legislation of this type could eliminate recycling collection services and force householders to deliver mixed wastes to expensive "authorized" services, as excerpts from one "flow control" ordinance show:

> "All solid wastes collected by a solid waste collection service within the Metropolitan Service District (MSD) boundaries must be disposed of in transfer stations or solid waste disposal sites designated by the MSD and in accordance with the ordinances and regulations of the MSD."

> "No person engaged in business as a solid waste collection service may deposit solid wastes at any facility owned, operated or regulated by the MSD if he has culled, separated or removed from the refuse at the facility and sold, recycled or otherwise reused."

ORE Plan kinds of home collection of recyclable wastes would significantly reduce the purchase and operating cost of large-scale, mixed-waste sorting systems. Any problems of exclusion and big machine monopoly could be avoided by explicitly stating in a "flow control" ordinance that "home grouped wastes" (i.e. also called "source-separated wastes") are not "solid waste" as used in the above excerpt.

Collection of garbage is now done by non-franchised private companies in Portland. Presently these companies serve overlapping areas and result in as many as three or more different collectors serving some streets. With good reason, efforts are underway to franchise routes to reduce expenses. Franchising in Portland could either help or harm existing home collection and recycling services. The main benefits of a fair franchise ordinance are obvious: increased collection efficiency and reduced costs. The dangers of a poorly designed ordinance are three in number:

1. Sector assignment. The city might be divided into sectors and assigned to collectors in proportion to their present cash flow. Since a standard garbage collection business has about 1000 households compared to the current figure of 100 for Cloudburst, this would end their operations even though they are the most rapidly growing collection service in the city due to lower prices.

2. Customer assignment. Cloudburst and Sunflower now serve only customers who have voluntarily chosen their recycling services. Thus, they are dealing with a specific clientele who cannot be arbitrarily assigned.

3. Standard franchise fee. A third way that a poorly designed franchise ordinance might eliminate existing recycling collection services is by requiring a standard fee, say $1,000, from all businesses. Clearly this would end small ORE Plan type business because most of their capital flow is needed for reinvestment during an initial period of rapid growth.

Most home collection recyclers and citizens alike would welcome a properly worded, non-discriminatory franchise ordinance which would continue to allow customers to choose among competing services according to price and services rendered.

Implementation of the ORE Plan in Portland, Oregon, indicates it is an economically viable garbage collection and recycling system. It is an energy-saving method for recycling household solid waste that has reduced garbage bills 20 to 40 percent, compared to fees for standard collection service. More rapid spread of this approach should be possible now that that operating data exists for cities and private garbage collectors to explore the relative economic and social advantages of offering an ORE Plan type service.

Simple Separating

Suellen McDonough of Durham, New Hampshire, has invented a simple aid for keeping separate the glass, metal and paper household wastes that remain even when we reduce the waste we generate. Her "Recycl-it," a three-section plastic wastebasket, is specifically designed to hold three supermarket bags, allowing easy handling of recyclable materials. "Recycl-it" is currently available at East Coast department stores, such as Jordan Marsh and from Solid Waste Recovery Co. (16 Meserve Rd., Durham, NH 03824).

Bob McDonough

DRYING UP THE TOILETS

Our sewage problems are a good reminder that it's usually easier to avoid problems than to correct them. Why do we dump our sewage into our drinking water to begin with—and then have to figure out how to repurify the water at great effort and expense? Diluting our sewage 100 times with pure drinking water overloads our septic and leach systems. Central sewers compound the problem, bringing the sewage together with even more water from storm sewers and resulting in such vast volumes of water that expensive mechanical and chemical treatment is required. Yet that frequently doesn't work and much water remains wasted and polluted. Nutrients are not returned to the fields where they came from.

No amount of adding band-aids to a bad system can make it good. Particularly when a whole range of options has been developed. Compost toilets, vacuum-flush systems, holding tanks, and low-flush toilets that avoid the mixing of sewage with water are elements of new approaches to sewage, while often saving money in the process. Our sewage is a valuable resource—not "waste" to be disposed of—and that realization is bringing fundamental changes to our sewage management process.

"The Sewerless Society," by Harold Leich, *Bulletin of Atomic Scientists*, Nov. 1975, $15/yr., 10 issues, from:
>   1020-24 E. 58th Street
>   Chicago, IL 60637

Examines where our present trends in sewage treatment are taking us and some better alternatives to those somewhat frightening prospects. Health hazards, water demands and economic costs of centralized sewage systems, need for agricultural applications of nutrients, and examination of available technologies for simpler and more direct sewage treatment.

"Goodbye to the Flush Toilet," *RAIN Magazine*, April 1976, $1 from:
>   2270 N.W. Irving
>   Portland, OR 97210

Surveys problems of water-borne sewage systems and presents a range of options—manufacturers and how-to plans for various waterless toilet systems.

Sewage Treatment Technology and Our Urban Communities, Nesbitt and Seldman, 1976, $2 from:
>   Institute for Local Self-Reliance
>   1717 18th Street, N.W.
>   Washington, DC 20009

Comprehensive comparison of financial and environmental aspects of Washington DC's present high-technology sewage plant and currently available in-house systems, plus methodology for analysis of other municipal systems.

Clean and Decent, Lawrence Wright, 1960, $2.95, from:
>   University of Toronto Press
>   33 E. Tupper St.
>   Buffalo, NY 14203

A fascinating history of the bathroom and the water closet, through which flow 75% of our home water use. Our phobias, fantasies and dalliances make interesting reading once we're free enough from them to view them with humor. They provide useful insights for rethinking good and enjoyable ways to accommodate our various bodily needs and desires. Lots of interesting and peculiar data here: Roman hot water heaters, Queen Elizabeth I's valve water closet, Louis XIV's cushions in his bath, washbasins in pianos and baths concealed in sofas, and the sex life of sponges. But also absorbing insights into how different our sense of what is clean, decent and enjoyable has been at different times. Our attitudes towards toilets and sewers and bathing are going through some big changes—and hopefully some satisfying and resourceful new patterns are emerging.

> RODALE PRESS
> conducted a modest experiment. For one month, toilet paper rolls used in the main building of Rodale Press were trimmed by 1/2 inch in the print shop. Unsuspecting employees went through just about the same number of rolls as before, using 11% less paper without even knowing it. Trivial? The savings translates into over 2-1/2 million trees.

"Life in a Compost Pile," Paper presented at 1976 Rodale Waste Recycling Conference by
>   **Daniel Dindal**
>   **State Univ. of New York**
>   **College of Environmental Science**
>   **& Forestry**
>   **Syracuse, NY 13210**

Sometimes the obvious is hardest to see. Nature takes care of health problems of sewage, given space and time. Dindal shows the whole host of hungry creatures that love to eat up pathogens if given the opportunity. Almost all of our sewage problems come from our belief that centralized large-scale sewage plants would be better, and the complex, expensive, and ineffective processes necessary because of the ensuing volumes of waste requiring rapid treatment.

Composting, by Harold Gotaas, 1956, World Health Organization Monograph Series No. 31, $12.80 from:
>   Q Corp.
>   49 Sheridan Avenue
>   Albany, NY 12210

The basic sourcebook for composting—the processes next in line behind natural soil processes for treating sewage. Detailed references to exhaustive pathogen studies, chapter on anaerobic methane production, and a variety of composting processes. Composting provides more speed, with sanitation and production of fertilizer—and methane if anaerobic composting is used.

What's Safe?

Chlorination and Ozone Depletion
Not Man Apart Letter, Sept. 1975
Herbert Schwartz, Ph.D.
Vineland, NJ

Dear Editor: Although aerosol propellants are being blamed for damage to the ozone layer, I feel that greater blame should be placed on chloroform. Chloroform is produced by the haloform reaction in waste and drinking water by chlorination according to the following equations:

$$Cl_2 + H_2O \rightleftarrows HCL + HOCl$$
$$3HOCl + CH_3COR \rightarrow RCOOH + 2H_2O + HCCl_3$$

The volatile chloroform thus produced enters the atmosphere and reaches the ozone layer where it could react in the following manner:

$$HCCl_3 \rightarrow uv\ HCCl_2\bullet$$
$$Cl\bullet + O_3 \rightarrow \grave{o}_2 \rightarrow Cl\bullet$$

When one realizes the amount of chlorine used for water treatment, the amount of freon-type aerosol propellants used to date becomes almost insignificant by comparison.

Chlorination of municipal drinking water was also the primary cause of the crippling epidemics of polio in the '40s and '50s. The vast sums spent on the development of polio vaccines were spent purely because chlorination of drinking water prevented people from contracting a very mild form of polio previously universal in early childhood, which provided their bodies with antibodies that prevented their being stricken later by the dangerous form of polio.

Chlorination of water—like all our violent, and in the long run ineffective and dangerous means of dealing with other endemic life forms—also has proven to be merely a means of speeding the evolution of more resistant and dangerous varieties of the disease vectors they attempt to control. To a point you can play ping-pong with larger and larger doses of drugs and chemicals against more and more resistant bugs, but such games forget that our bodies are innocent bystanders that don't evolve that fast and are the recipients of ever more violent and dangerous diseases and drugs. In the not-too-long run the odds are also that the winner of the ping-pong game will be the bugs, as the resources we can devote to such games—like all our games—are becoming more and more limited, and we are reaching the levels of toxicity that our bodies can stand.

There's really no lazy-man's shortcut to doing things properly. All we really have to do is keep our water sources clean and stop dumping our sewage into them (which we ought not do anyhow)!

Preliminary Assessment of Suspected Carcinogens in Drinking Water, Report to Congress, December 1975, from:
Office of Toxic Substances
U.S. EPA
Washington, DC 20460

If you think that waterless toilets are ridiculous or that our present practices of mixing our sewage with our drinking water have no health problems, this report (or "Viruses in Water: the problem, some solutions" by Gerba, Wallis and Melnick in *Environment, Science and Technology*, Dec. 1975) will cause some serious rethinking. Many viruses from our sewage are not affected by present water disinfection processes. Those same processes—particularly chlorination—are pretty clearly linked with cancer and heart disease. There are simpler and better ways—these studies give reason to seek them.

Taking Pipe

What happens when a town decides to go onto a sewer system? Is it cheaper and more efficient? Who profits?

The people already living in a town presumably have installed and are using septic or other on-site sewage treatment systems (at a cost of about $1,500 per household). Installation of the sewer system costs another $4,000 per household. Because it is often "Federally Funded," most people forget it still costs the same or more but just comes out of our tax pocket instead of our sewer bill pocket. Add another $250 for a hookup and maybe $300 to install sewer lines from the street to the house. Then pay $7 per month forever and lose your nutrients and contaminate your drinking water. The sewer project ends up with expenditure of at least four times the original cost of providing satisfactory sewage systems and duplicates those already working systems.

How about the costs for people building a home once the sewer is installed. We're told it will only cost a couple of hundred dollars to connect instead of $1,500 for a septic system. However, because a lot with a sewer doesn't require the expense of a septic system it is equal in value to a lot with a septic system, and the developers have probably paid $200 for a sewer tap and marked the price of the lot up by $1,500, making a windfall profit of $1,300. The homebuyer ends up paying the cost of the septic system without receiving a septic system in return! So the costs for serving a new home add up: $4,000 in taxes to build the system, $1,500 hidden in increased land cost because the septic system is unneeded, $300-$500 for lateral and hookup, and $7 per month forever—a total of $5,800-$6,000 immediately or $7,500 over 20 years. Or five times the cost of a septic system or as much as 25 times as much as an owner-built compost toilet system. Studies by the Institute for Local Self-Reliance of the Washington, D.C., sewage system show similar figures for larger cities.

Why do it? The main beneficiaries are the developers who can now market land that wouldn't qualify for septic systems and who can gain windfall profits from the public expenditure on the sewage system. Any community taking seriously its charge to provide needed services at minimum cost to the residents should take a hard second look and consider such things as septic system management districts for all except the highest density locations.

Waterless Toilets

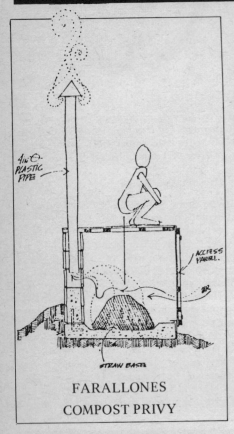

FARALLONES
COMPOST PRIVY

Squat design
flush toilet

problems with waterless toilets gives a good, detailed review of operating problems found with various designs, efforts to correct them, and a comparative evaluation of different products. Flies, brick-like solidification of wastes, ventilation, heating problems, energy costs of house air evacuated through the units, and the effects of bathroom exhaust fans sucking air from the units into the bathrooms—all the nightmares you could dream of. In sum, it looks like things will shake down okay with the whole composting toilet picture.

Residential Water Conservation, Murray Milne, 1976, $7.50 from:
California Water Resources Center
University of California
Davis, CA 95616

"Goodbye to the Flush Toilet," *RAIN Magazine*, April 1976, $1 from:
2270 N.W. Irving
Portland, OR 97210

Stop the 5-Gallon Flush, $2 Canadian from:
Minimum Cost Housing Group
School of Architecture
McGill University
P.O. Box 6070
Montreal H3C 3G1 Canada
These three sources all contain detailed information on various means of adapting or replacing present toilet systems, along with access information for manufacturers of the various equipment.

United Stand Privy Booklet, $2.50 from:
United Stand
P.O. Box 191
Potter Valley, CA 95469
Construction drawings and explanation of several models of homemade composting privys for rural applications.

Technical Bulletin No. 1—Composting Privy, $2 from:
Farallones Institute
15290 Coleman Valley Road
Occidental, CA 95465
Detailed explanation of principles, operation and construction of the Farallones composting privy. Construction drawings.

Examination of the Operating Characteristics of a Composting Installation for Organic Household Wastes, Carl R. Lindstrom, 1969, available from:
Clivus Multrum USA
14A Eliot Street
Cambridge, MA 02138
Performance evaluation of aerobic home compost toilet systems using normal low-temperature soil bacteria to destroy pathogens rather than higher-temperature processes which depend upon thermal destruction of pathogens. Further U.S. evaluations are being carried out by the Center for the Biology of Natural Systems, Washington University, St. Louis, MO 63130.

WATERLESS TOILET PERFORMANCE

Dry toilets have now been installed and used in enough far-flung places that the bugs in different processes are showing up and attempts made to correct them. We've seen two recent reports on testing in cold climate conditions:

"Waterless Toilets," *Maine Times*, Nov. 19, 1976, 30¢/issue, $12/year from:
41 Main Street
Topsham, ME 04086
This fine paper keeps coming up with excellent reports . . . it's really worth subscribing to. This six-page report on

Experiences with the Clivus-Multrum and Mull-Toa Toilets in Northern Manitoba, by J. M. McKernan and D. S. Morgan, 1976; inquire for price and availability from:
Sym/bios
16-74 Carlton Street
Winnipeg, Manitoba R3C 1N9
Canada
An interim report on testing in extremely cold conditions where normal sewage systems have been found prohibitively expensive or impossible. Installation and operating problems and costs are described (including one case where the basement flooded and the Clivus almost floated away . . . use your toilet for a lifeboat!). The small, electrically-assisted Mull-Toa was found to be of little practical value in the extreme Manitoba conditions—being particularly sensitive to overloading from beer parties. The Clivus was felt to have a great deal of promise in such northern areas in spite of the lack of kitchen vegetable wastes inhibiting rapid composting action.

'Pedestal Lion' Closet

Septic Tank Practices, Peter Warshall, 1976, $2.50 from:

P.O. Box 42,
Elm Road
Bolinas, CA 94924

Careful description of the benefits of staying with small-scale on-site sewage treatment rather than going to collection systems. Explains design, construction, care and maintenance of on-site systems. Demonstrates that on-site systems can be designed for almost *any* site if system is designed for site conditions rather than allowable site conditions being determined by design of standard manufactured systems. Excellent bibliography to more technical or detailed studies.

Manual of Grey Water Treatment Practice, John H. Timothy Winneberger, 1974, $10 from:

Ann Arbor Science Publishers, Inc.
P.O. Box 1425
Ann Arbor, MI 48106

Design data for on-site treatment of household wastewater remaining when sewerless toilets are used. Pollution content of grey water from various sources, grey water drainage fixture unit values, and sizing information for grey water treatment and subsurface disposal. Lacks information on inexpensive, home-built systems (see *Village Technology Handbook*, VITA, 3706 Rhode Island Ave., Mt. Rainier, MD 20822, $9), but provides solid engineering data for typical household application.

Use of Wind Energy for the Aeration of Waste Waters: A Case Study, by N. Galanis, S. Narasiah, C.C. Dang, 1975, 3 pgs. Send self-addressed envelope to:

Nicolas Galanis
Mechanical Engineering Dept.
University of Sherbrooke
Sherbrooke, Quebec, J1K 2RI
Canada

Aeration, a phase in solid waste and waste water treatment, provides oxygen, which promotes bacterial growth and consequent bio-degradation of organic waste. Aeration, which is done by surface aerators, mechanical mixers or by bubbling compressed air through diffusers at the bottom of aeration tanks, could, as shown in this paper, be powered by the wind. Many sewage treatment plants are located in windy areas near seacoasts.

Most Japanese cities use holding tanks and truck collection of sewage rather than wasteful central sewers

Tom Bender

CAN-PEE
AND
OTHER DELIGHTS

Helga Olkowski, one of the developers of biological pest control programs for several California cities, constantly shocks male audiences when she talks about fertilizing the amazing gardens at the Farallones Urban House in Berkeley. She merely placed a 5-gallon can with a funnel sticking into it in the bathroom for men to use. Diluting the urine 5 to 1 with water prevented it from burning out the plants, and it was used directly as a high-nitrogen fertilizer. Composting would normally lose much of the nitrogen, and keeping the urine separate from the compost made composting easier!

Other simple you-can-do toiletry changes include the legendary brick-in-the-tank idea. It saves 34 million gallons of water per year in Cherry Hill, N.J., where free bricks were passed out to every home to reduce the water used with every toilet flushing. Bending the float arm will do the same, and save bricks. Or you can remember to flush the toilet when it needs it, not every time you use it.

The following are some of the organizations active in continuing development and implementation of more sensible human waste recycling techniques:

Institute for Local Self-Reliance
1717 18th Street, N.W.
Washington, DC 20009
Self-Reliance Newsletter, $6/year, 6 issues.

Farallones Institute
15290 Coleman Valley Road
Occidental CA 95465
Newsletter, $1/issue.

United Stand
P.O. Box 191
Potter Valley, CA 95469
Occasonal newsletter. Inquire for publications.

Rodale Press
33 E. Minor
Emmaus, PA 18049
Organic Gardening and Farming Magazine, $6.85/year, monthly. *Compost Science*, $6/year, bimonthly

The states of Maine, Vermont and California have large-scale testing programs underway on various sewage treatment alternatives.

"China Recycles Her Wastes by Using Them on the Land," Roger Blobaum, *Compost Science*, Autumn, 1975, single copies $1 from:
Rodale Press
Emmaus, PA 18049
We had to review this just to show you this picture—vines planted to provide a crop of grapes and summer shade to cool poultry and pigs. They are planted where they can utilize manure washed out of the pens during a rain.

Perceptive observations on China's frugal wisdom of reusing her wastes as well and as completely as possible.

LAND APPLICATION OF SEWAGE

Clean Water, Leonard A. Stevens, 1974, $10 from:
E. P. Dutton & Co.
201 Park Ave., So.
New York, NY 10003

A history and survey of numerous interesting programs of applying sewage to farm and forest land. Covers projects designed for water recovery, agricultural production, sewage disposal and economics. Explores effectiveness and safety of various processes, but doesn't deal with the problems of heavy metals in sewage of cities that haven't yet instituted recovery systems to keep such valuable and dangerous materials out of the sewage. An appendix gives location of land treatment systems worth visiting.

Biological Control of Water Pollution, Tourbier and Pierson, 1976, $20 from:
University of Pennsylvania Press
3933 Walnut Street
Philadelphia, PA 19174

The use of natural systems for sewage treatment requires unique design for different situations. Although prohibitively priced, this collection of concise papers provides an extremely useful survey of international projects employing diverse biological treatments—reeds, tidal marshes, aquaculture, algae and forests to effectively treat sewage.

Biological Sewage Treatment

Natural systems are almost always cheaper and more effective than our mechanical ones. NASA has discovered the value of common plants and has reached the unsurprising conclusion that common plants can process sewage much more economically than our mechanized sewage treatment facilities.

The town of Bay St. Louis, with a population of 8,000, is using water hyacinth plants for its sewage filtration system. After the sewage flows through 4 acres of hyacinth, the water meets all EPA and state standards. The city is able to harvest the plants and use them for fertilizer and cattle feed. Eventually the 4 acres of plants may be able to supply the town with all the natural gas it needs. (*C.B.S. Morning News*, 8/29/75)

Waste Water Renovation and Conservation, Richard Parazek, Pennsylvania State University, 1967.
Contains a summary of the pioneering work at Penn State on using cropland and forests for sewage treatment, aquifer recharge, and nutrient recycling for plant growth. Ask for list of reprints covering stripmine spoils revegetation, soils as nutrient filters, and use of sewage sludge and liquids for fertilizer.

Land Application of Sewage Effluents and Sludges: selected abstracts, EPA 660/2-74-042 ($2.50); and *Study of Current and Proposed Practices in Animal Waste Management*, EPA 430/9-74-003 ($4.70).
Both from:
Supt. of Documents
U.S. Gov. Printing Office
Washington, D.C. 20402

As well as use by methane production, the use of "sewage" in application as "fertilizer" is important method of recycling. Saves a step, doesn't it?

Conservation of the Land and the Use of Waste Materials for Man's Benefit, Committee on Agriculture and Forestry, U.S. Senate, March 25, 1975.
A pretty well-known summary of the present and prolonged effects of mono crop agriculture in the midwest and lack of or failure of adequate windbreak systems. The second half of the report is most interesting, outlining the use of sewage sludge and animal manures as fertilizers.

"Of the 7 million tons of dry sewage sludge equivalent now produced annually in the United States, it is estimated that 40% goes into landfills, 20% is applied on land, 25% is incinerated and 15% is discharged into the ocean. Because land use is the only direct beneficial use of this material, we have opportunities for a five-fold increase in such use.

Changing our sewage patterns can have a big effect on our water use and water quality. Avoiding the need for sanitary sewers removes some of the temptation to build stormwater sewers instead of on-site and surface management, opening the way for lower costs for water supply and purification, sewage and stormwater control.

WATER

Residential Water Conservation, by Murray Milne, 1976, $7.50 from:

> California Water Resources Center
> University of California
> Davis, CA 95616

Best available source on water conserving hardware for the home—diagrams of equipment available, description of operation and economic analysis of savings and costs involved. Directory of manufacturers for toilets, bathing, drinking, washing, outdoor uses. Dry and low flush toilets, code changes and hot water use reduction are not covered well, but it is comprehensive and extremely useful in other areas.

Water Conservation in California, Bulletin 198, May 1976, free from:

> State of California
> Dept. of Water Resources
> P.O. Box 388
> Sacramento, CA 95802

Water may seem too plentiful to be concerned about, but it is getting scarce in many places as population density, industrial and irrigation demands increase. Massive shortages may be seen in the near future in some areas. It also costs a lot of money to drain, purify and distribute and to process again as sewage. We often feel hesitant to implement residential water use reduction because some people feel it just makes more available for wasteful industrial or agricultural practices. California has had an early taste of these conditions in the last few years and this report has some hard figures on how water is used, what savings can be obtained and what measures were possible to obtain them. 85% of all state water use is agricultural, 0.1% is for power plant cooling, 2% for fish and wildlife and 13% urban. 68% of the urban use is residential, 14% commercial and governmental and 18% industrial. 44% of the residential use is for landscaping and 55% for interior use, of which 42% is used by the toilet and 32% by the bath. The report projects 50% water savings in new construction, 38% in existing buildings, 5-10% in agriculture. Case studies of water conservation in industry are presented but no projections of statewide effects.

Water Conservation and Wasteflow Reduction in the Home, by William Sharpe, Special Circular No. 184, available from:

> Pennsylvania St. University
> College of Agriculture
> Extension Service
> University Park, PA 16802

A less technical introduction to water use reduction than the NTIS document, this report gives one an excellent feel for what is easily possible to do in this area. Contains photos, cost analysis of flow reduction options and a bibliography.

Practices in Detention of Urban Stormwater Runoff, Special Report No. 43, 1974, $12.50 from:

> American Public Works Association
> 1313 E. 60th Street
> Chicago, IL 60637

Because it's cheaper than having separate sewers, most urban sewage systems combine storm water with human sewage, causing overflows and pollution with every major storm. The same sewers contribute to floods by letting storm waters drain together all at one time. One alternative is not to have any sewers at all—using compost toilets or home septic tanks for sewage and using on-site absorption and surface management of storm water. This report surveys techniques, costs and problems of surface stormwater management, finding that such systems can frequently be cheaper and more effective than conventional sewers. Both simple things and unusual ideas are surveyed—detention ponds, soil infiltration, detention of water on building roofs and in parking lots, underground storage for special uses, and use of porous pavement. Of value to planners or citizen groups evaluating costs and procedures for alternatives to expensive sewage systems.

Small leaks

Small leaks add up to big losses. The surest way to prevent the loss of water or other liquid commodity is to stop leaks.

As figures here show, the cumulative effect of even small leaks can add up to large volumes:

one drop per second	in an hour =	6 ounces
	in a day =	1 gal. & 1 pint
	in a week =	8 gallons
	in a month =	34 gallons
drop breaking to a stream	in an hour =	1 gallon
	in a day =	24 gallons
	in a week =	147 gallons
	in a month =	588 gallons
1/8" stream	in an hour =	11 gallons
	in a day =	260 gallons
	in a week =	1,512 gallons
	in a month =	6,636 gallons

Demonstration of Waste Flow Reduction from Households, PB-236 904, Sept. 1974, $5.25 print copy, $2.25 microfiche from:

> National Technical Information Service
> U.S. Dept. of Commerce
> Springfield, VA 22151

A 2-year demonstration program was conducted to evaluate water savings, costs performance and acceptability of various water-savings devices. Reduced flow toilets and flow limiting showers were installed in 8 single-family dwellings. In 3 of the homes bath and laundry water were filtered, disinfected and reused for toilet flushing and/or lawn sprinkling. Toilet water savings were 25%, with reuse of water for lawns resulting in an additional 16-18% water savings. For single-family homes recycle system could give cost savings in high water and sewer use rate areas and in areas of poor septic system drainage.

Meadow Marsh Systems as Sewage Treatment Plants, Maxwell M. Small, Nov. '75, pub. no. BNL-20757, $4.00 from:

> NTIS
> 5285 Port Royal Rd.
> Springfield, VA 22151

The exciting, common-sense and plain money-saving possibility (where useful natural filter systems haven't yet been paved over or tract-housed) is that "both systems produce water suitable for ground water recharge or other reuse without public health hazard. On the basis of investigations to date, both systems can be recommended as sewage treatment plants and water producers for human populations between 100 and 10,000."

Groundwater Newsletter, twice monthly, $60 per year, and **Water Newsletter**, $36 per year, twice monthly, from

> Water Information Center
> 14 Vanderventer Ave.
> Port Washington, L.I., NY 11050

Water Information Center, Inc. (WIC) is a private publishing firm specializing in water matters. They issue the oldest commercial newsletter on the subject (*Water Newsletter*), the only professional newsletter covering ground water (*Ground Water Newsletter*) and a list of rather unique professional, reference and text books on the subject.

Ancil Nance

ENERGY

It often sounds today like energy is the most important thing on earth. It isn't. It has *been a central element in the growth culture we've developed, and our present paranoia about it is closer to an addict's fears while stumbling around trying to get another fix than any real measure of its importance. The changes in the energy picture are causing important changes in our society. We're going to have to cut way back. We'll survive. Things are going to be different—but perhaps better.*

Safe, affordable nuclear power is out of the question. Conservation is the cheapest and best energy source next to the sun. Our star provides us enough energy for our needs. It's our responsibility now to keep our demands and numbers within what is available and what we can afford. The outlines are clear. Much work remains, but it's time to start thinking about where we go from here.

Limits
to Growth

Our own paths veered sharply into these big woods of change when Howard T. Odum's Energy, Ecology and Economics burst on the scene in late 1973, and we suddenly realized that we were already into the transition to "steady-state" caused by limits to growth. More importantly, though, we realized that the values, ways of living and working, and general life-quality that we had been seeking, exploring and trying to sustain within the pressures of a gargantuan society were either necessary or at least compatible and possible in the kind of society that must evolve through our transition to living within limits.

We discovered that a growth-limited future is likely to be BETTER rather than worse to live in!

While the energy crisis and all it pertained to was still apprehensively feared by those aware of its approach, it meant to us that unavoidable pressures were going to force us toward choices that could well improve our quality of life, and that fundamental changes which we would normally consider impossible to achieve would suddenly become desirable and likely, if not inevitable. Those changes are already well in process in energy, as is related in the following pages, and are diffusing into the other dimensions of society—the beginnings of which the previous parts of this book relate.

Energy Basis for Man and Nature, by Howard and Elisabeth Odum, 1976, 297 pp., $7.95 from:
   McGraw-Hill Book Co.
   1221 Avenue of the Americas
   New York, NY 10020
The clearest exposition of Odum's energetic theory, net energy calculations and the relationships between energy

and money and growth, this primer is full of interesting illustrations, diagrams and cartoons which drive home the point that no system can live beyond its energy means and hope to survive. An important, basic book to be read along with Transition and Odum's short paper, Energy, Ecology and Economics.

Environment, Power and Society, H.T. Odum, 1971, $6.50 from:
   Wiley-Interscience
   605 Third Avenue
   New York, NY 10016
After you've read Odum's Energy, Ecology and Economics paper (p. 34), you'll be ready and able to tackle this classic, which presents the energetics of ecosystems as they apply to the complex systems of nature and people. Important basics for how steady-state systems differ from growth systems, how to make a transition, and what this all means for economics, religion and politics.

Emerging Energy Policy Principles, Tom Bender, and **Cosmic Economics**, Joel Schatz and Tom Bender, 1974, $1 each from:
   RAIN
   2270 N.W. Irving
   Portland, OR 97210
These papers, prepared during the turbulent days of Oregon Governor McCall's Office of Energy Research and Planning, still stand as perhaps the most succinct and far-looking energy policy statements to be prepared in any governmental agency in the U.S. Principles to be carefully remembered in wending our way through this transition, and outlines for the simplest and most effective economic mechanism we've seen for guiding that transition.

The Limits to Growth, 2nd ed., Donella H. Meadows, et al., 1974, $2.95 from:
   Potomac Associates
   1707 "L" Street, N.W.
   Washington, DC 20036
You don't really need to read this unless having something substantiated by computer modeling offers you a needed credibility. But a lot of people seem to need that, so it's considered a "basic book." Repeats what others have long said—there are limits and diminishing returns. Those global limits are now upon us and not to be shrugged off.

Toward a Steady State Economy, Herman Daly, 1973
See review on page 34—basic source on transition of economics to resource limited operation.

The Entropy Law and the Economic Process, Nicholas Georgescu-Roegen, 1974, 457 pp., $5.95 from:
   Harvard University Press
   79 Garden St.
   Cambridge, MA 02138
If one wants to understand the economic hows and whys of limits to growth, this work is an excellent point of departure. Written to explain the entropy law of biology and physics to his more mechanistically- and mathematically-oriented fellow economists, the book proceeds slowly enough and abounds in enough humorous, yet instructve, gems so that the interested layman can read with relish. Still, it is best as a follow-on to Odum, Commoner or Lovins.

Net Energy Clearinghouse. Contact:
   D. Johnson
   Industrial Economics Div.
   University of Denver Research Inst.
   Denver. CO 80210
Heads a team of researchers assembling a clearinghouse to disseminate information on analyses of "net energy" methods used and studies made throughout the nation.

toast, $180 (inquire about rental) from:
   Earth Chronicles
   1714 N.W. Overton
   Portland, OR 97209
An excellent 11-minute film tracing oil from the well to a piece of burnt toast, again available. Made by the Office of Energy Research & Planning.

THE SECOND LAW OF THERMODYNAMICS SAYS CUTTING BUTTER WITH A NUCLEAR-ELECTRIC CHAINSAW DOESN'T MAKE SENSE AND HAS GOT TO STOP

Step by step, Amory Lovins has put together in a simple, understandable way the path we need to follow in dealing with our energy problems. He's laid out a solid overview of our energy situation and options, the technical problems with nuclear power, the reasons electrification is economically unaffordable, and now, in detail, the patterns possible for different countries to develop a fully renewable energy supply and the hazards of not making that choice (see book list following these excerpts). His suggestions deserve careful thought.

We keep telling you that Amory Lovins is someone all of you out there ought to begin paying attention to. I first perked up my ears to him and got deep into his work at the '75 "Limits to Growth" conference in Houston, Texas. There we were, in the heart of the fossil-fueled dinosaur, the deep-carpeted (petroleum-based), plush-seated, Woodlands resort and meeting center . . . and Amory was listening intently to Harry Bovay, board chairman of Bovay Engineers, engineer emeritus and fellow panelist, as Harry condescendingly explained why nuclear electricity was the only way to go. But the match was a bit unfair, for Harry was unwittingly supplying Amory with all the facts and figures he needed to produce a withering return volley. Quick as a flash, Amory drew his pocket calculator, took aim at the dinosaur, and shot it with his own data. A standing-room-only crowd watched Harry's head roll, figuratively, and turn beet-red, literally, and burst into cheers. For it was a modern David versus Goliath, and we enjoyed it immensely.

We've selected excerpts from the Oak Ridge paper that might be considered Amory's responses to the Bonneville Power Administration's latest "non-policy trial balloon." BPA may contract in advance to buy power from private utilities who are unable to get loans and sell stock as cheaply or easily as before. With such secure, federally-backed contracts in hand, private power companies can easily get low interest loans for continuing construction of large-scale electrical power plants. This is what Lovins calls the "hard path" of high energy, primary-supply-oriented, high technology, centralized, increasingly electrified, and reliant chiefly on depletable coal and uranium resources.

The following excerpts are from "Scale, Centralization and Electrification in Energy Systems," delivered at a conference on *Future Strategies for Energy Development* held at Oak Ridge, Tennessee, and to be part of his forthcoming *Soft Energy Paths: Towards a Durable Peace.*

If existing centralized systems do not now make economic and engineering sense, why were they built? There are at least four rational explanations. First, because objective conditions have changed drastically, and an industry not noted for quick and imaginative responses has been slow to adapt. Second, because centralized energy systems have been built by institutions in no position to ask whether those systems are the best way to perform particular end-use functions—an omission reinforced by our failure to price fuels at long-run marginal cost. Third, at times we have seen powerful institutions deliberately seeking to reinforce their power by constricting consumer choice, as in the classic monopoly tactics of the early electric utilities or the fight against public power and (abroad) private wind machines. Fourth, the long economic shadow cast by large sunk costs has often led us to seek to reinforce past mistakes through subsidies, bailouts, $100-billion slush funds, etc., thus further restricting consumer choice, rather than writing off (or gradually retiring through attrition) ill-conceived infrastructure. Energy decisions are always implemented gradually and incrementally; major shifts take decades. A chief element of strategy, inherent in the soft path, is thus to avoid incremental commitments of resources to major infrastructure that locks us into particular supply patterns for more decades thereafter. We are already stuck with gigantic infrastructure that constrains our choices, and nobody is suggesting we wipe the slate clean. The question is rather what we do at the margin. What made sense on the up-side of the Hubbert blip, when real costs of electricity (both average and marginal) were steadily falling, may need to be reversed on the down-side of the blip and when real costs are rapidly rising with no end in sight.

The illogic of the ERDA position is this: if we are running out of oil and gas but do not like coal, it is said, we need nuclear power; but if we are not going to have nuclear power, we need other systems that would do what nuclear stations would have done—namely, deliver GW blocks of electricity. But we should instead be seeking systems that will do what we would have done with the oil and gas if we had had them in the first place. It is the function that interests us, not substituting for reactors. By not structuring the problem in this way, ERDA has so far failed to grasp the immense short- and medium-term opportunities for deploying available technologies for end-use efficiency, cogeneration, fluidized-bed boiler backfits, organic conversion, and extensive solar space heating. The longer this delay, the worse will be our shortages of clean heat and fluid fuels. I hope that the discussion arising from this Symposium will increase ERDA's awareness of the existence of coherent non-electrified views of our energy future.

In a soft energy path, the technological measure to be achieved can be readily separated from the policy instrument used to encourage it. The former—cogeneration, bioconversion, insulation—is neutral, the latter politically charged. It is the latter only that is likely to irritate us if ill-conceived. But I believe the policy tool can be chosen, according to practical and ideological convenience, from such an enormous armamentarium that the choice can fully respect pluralism and voluntarism.

I do not see how the same pluralism can possibly extend to a hard, coarse-grained energy path. The scale and the technical difficulty of its enterprises are so vast that corresponding concentrations of social resources must be efficiently mobilized without substantive regard to diverse opinions and circumstances. Only large corporations, encouraged by large government agencies, using large sums of private and public money to employ large numbers of workers on large areas of land, can possibly get the job done. It is not a task for householders, small businesses, block associations or town meetings.

Soft technologies are thus inherently, structurally less coercive and more participatory than hard technologies. In a nuclear society, nobody can opt out of nuclear risk. In an electrified society, everyone's lifestyle is shaped by the economic imperatives of the energy system, and, from the viewpoint of the consumer, diversity becomes a vanishing luxury. Like purchasers of model T Fords, the consumer can have anything he wants so long as it's electrified. But in a soft path, each person can choose his own risk-benefit balance and his own energy systems to match his own degree of caution and involvement. People who do not care to partake of the advantages of district heating will be free to reject them—and, if the system if thoughtfully designed, to change their minds later. People who want to drive big cars or inhabit uninsulated houses will be free to do so—and to pay the social costs. People can choose to live in city centers, remote countryside, or in between, without being told their lifestyle is uneconomic. People can choose to minimize their "consumer humiliation"—their forced dependence on systems they cannot understand, control, diagnose, repair, or modify—or can continue to depend on traditional utilities, for large grids are already with us and in some degree will persist for a long time. In a soft path, then, dissent and diversity are not just a futile gesture but a basis for political action and a spur to private enterprise. But the monolithic nature, gargantuan scale, exacting requirements, and homogenizing infrastructure of hard technologies does not offer such pluralism. Only our largest conglomerations of resources, shielded by the poweres of the state from the vagaries of the economic and political marketplace, can perform such demanding tasks.

Centralized energy systems are also inequitable in principle because they separate the energy output from its side-effects, allocating them to different people at opposite ends of the transmission lines, pipelines, or rail lines. The export of these side-effects from Los Angeles and New York to Navajo country, Appalachia, Wyoming, and the Brooks Range (not to mention Venezuela, the Caribbean, Kuwait, and British Columbia) makes the former more habitable and the latter more resentful. That resentment is finding political expression. As the weakest groups in society, such as the native peoples, come to appear to stronger groups as miners' canaries whose fate foretells their own, sympathy for the recipients of the exported side-effects grows.

Throughout the world, central government is trying to promote expansionist energy policies by preempting regulatory authority, and in the process is eliciting a strong State (or Provincial) and local response. Washington, Ottawa, Bonn, Paris, and Auckland are coming to be viewed locally as the common enemy. Unholy alliances form. Perhaps Montana might mutter to Massachusetts, "We won't oil your beaches if you won't strip our coal." As Congress—made of State people with no Federal constituency—increasingly molds interregional conflict into a common States'-rights front, decisions gravitate by default to the lower political levels at which consensus is still possible. At those levels, further insults to local autonomy by remote utilities, oil companies, banks, and Federal agencies are intolerable. Thus people in Washington sit drawing reactors and coalplexes on maps, but the exercise has increasingly an air of unreality because it is overtaken by political events at the grassroots. The greater the Federal preemption (as in offshore oil leasing), the greater the homeostatic State response. The more the Federal authorities treat centrifugal politics as a public-relations problem, the more likely it becomes that they will not only fail to get their facilities sited, but will also in the process destroy their own legitimacy. To some extent this has already occurred, and I have no doubt that States will soon gain a veto power, at least, over nuclear facilities in their jurisdiction (as current Federal legislation proposes). On this issue, as in other spheres, the traditional linear right-left political spectrum seems to become cyclic as differently grounded distastes for big government merge across gaps of rhetoric. The resurgency of individual, decentralized citizen effort in politics, as in private life and career, seems to me an important political universal in most industrial nations today.

Big Brother does not like losing his grip. Only last year, for example, some Federal officials were speculating that they might have to seek central regulation of domestic solar technologies, lest mass defections from utility grids damage utility cash-flows and the State and municipal budgets dependent on utility tax revenues. Since utilities are perceived as having too much power and utility regulators too little sensitivity already, a surer recipe for grassroots revolt would be hard to imagine. I think perceptions of the value of dependence on utilities are shifting rapidly as the enterprise reaches such a size that it starts to intrude on life in many traditionally "safe" areas, as in Ontario, or as its vulnerability becomes painfully manifest, as in England, or as general political consciousness rises in step with utility bills. The disillusionment and resentment I see in many industrial countries is akin, perhaps, to that of a citizen of a poor country who is realizing that an energy technology predicted to bring him self-reliance, pride, and the development of his village has actually brought him dependence, a cargo-cult mentality, and the enrichment of urban elites. I believe the recent shift of institutional and individual investment away from utilities reflects not only concern with debt structure and interest coverage but also, more fundamentally, with gradual withdrawal of legitimacy by a fickle public that has already done the same to oil majors. I believe further that the grounds of this shift among a previously tolerant, even supportive public are structural, arise essentially from suspicion of centrism, and would not be reversed by nationalization or rechartering that ignored scale.

It is perhaps encouraging, then, that the concept of a soft energy path brings a broad convergence which, even as it coincides with many pre-existing strands of social change, cuts across traditional lines of political conflict. It offers a potential argument for every constituency: civil rights for liberals, States' rights for conservatives, availability of capital for businesspeople, environmental protection for conservationists, old values for the old, new values for the young, exciting technologies for the secular, spiritual rebirth for the religious. As we realize that when we have come to the edge of an abyss, the only progressive move we can make is to step backwards, we begin to see that we can instead turn around and then step forwards, and that the turning around—the transition to a future unlike anything we have ever known—will be supremely interesting, an unprecedented central project for our species.

Faust, having made a bad bargain by not reading the fine print and so brought disaster on the innocent bystanders (Gretchen's family), was eventually redeemed and accepted in heaven because he changed his career, redevoting his talents to bringing soft technologies to the rural villagers. That choice of "the road less travelled by" made all the difference to him; and so it can to us. For underlying the structural differences between the soft and hard paths is a difference of perceptions about mankind and his works. Some people, impressed and fascinated by the glittering achievements of technology, say that if we will only have faith in human ingenuity (theirs) we shall witness the Second Coming of Prometheus (if we have yet recovered from the First), bringing us undreamed-of tyrannies and perils; and that even if we had a clean and unlimited energy source, we would lack the discipline to use it wisely. Such people are really saying, firstly, that energy is not enough to solve the ancient problems of the human spirit, and secondly, that the technologists who claim they can satisfy the condition that "No acts of God can be permitted" are guilty of *hubris*, the human sin of divine arrogance. In choosing our energy path we have today an opportunity—perhaps our last—to foster in our society a greater humility, one that springs from an appreciation of the essential frailty of the human design.

Amory says it so well. Another one of his major arguments, seconded by Barry Commoner in his *The Poverty of Power* (Knopf, 1976), is that we must now begin to match the thermodynamic quality of end-use energy needed with the renewable energy sources that most readily supply that level of energy quality. Lovins, Commoner and many more Americans daily are realizing that trying to heat one's home, office or industrial plant to 68°F. with electricity generated by burning uranium at 10,000°F. in a nuclear fission reactor is the thermodynamic equivalent of trying to cut butter with a chainsaw.

If we, the people, through BPA, supply cheap money to power companies with our government's (i.e. the public's) credit rating, the power plants should belong to us, the public. Despite their thermodynamic silliness, we ought to at least *own* the chainsaws we'll now be paying for on both ends!

The following books by Amory Lovins are available from Friends of the Earth, 529 Commercial Street, San Francisco, CA 94111:

World Energy Strategies: Facts, Issues and Options, 1973, $4.95
This provides one of the best introductions to the whole energy picture—at once readable, clearly explained, yet technically precise. Carefully pulls out a lot of the issues where people get confused or deliberately try to sidestep the issues—what timescale people are talking about, how much of existing resources are recoverable, the rate and magnitude problems of altering a huge and expensive industry and capital constraints on energy growth. One of few overviews that get into real energy issues—*who* gets it, at what risk, *whose* risk, ethical problems of relegating our radioactive wastes to our children, and military and political issues.

Non-Nuclear Futures, with John H. Price, 1975, $5.95
Carefully lays out a detailed picture of the technical reasons for concern about nuclear power—walking the incredibly thin line of being understandable to the layperson yet technically convincing to the expert. Lists such things as more than a dozen successful sabotage or military actions against nuclear facilities, major reactor accidents, and covers reactor safety, the absurd methods used to calculate "safety," fuel transport problems, waste management, plutonium toxicity, and net energy questions. The second part of the book is John Price's excellent dynamic energy analysis of nuclear power programs which shows that rapid programs of implementing nuclear power may cause a net energy drain during most of their lifetime. *The* overview of nuclear power.

You Can't Switch Horsepower in the Middle of the Stream

The importance of the choices we must now make about our future energy sources has come clearly into focus in two recent reports by Amory Lovins, author of *Non-Nuclear Futures* and *World Energy Strategies*. Lovins has completed studies for a number of countries, including Japan, England, Sweden, Canada and the United States, outlining their individual potentials for conservation, wind and solar power, organic liquid fuels and other nondepleting energy sources. In each case he has demonstrated, as Bent Sørensen did earlier for Denmark (*Science*, July 25, 1975), that by tailoring the mix of energy sources to the specific situation, each country can develop a future that is totally free of fossil fuel and nuclear energy. Lovins points out that only about 5% of energy uses in industrialized countries requires expensive electricity. Other needs can be met with low temperature solar, liqwood (organic liquid fuels), wind and hydro. Such presently available techniques of proven safety

are shown to cost significantly less than fossil or nuclear futures.

Most importantly, Lovins' studies demonstrate that such viable soft technology options and nuclear are mutually exclusive—once we commit ourselves to one it becomes virtually impossible to make a transition to the other if our initial choice proves wrong. Lovins' analyses are essential readings for the debate on our energy futures:

"Exploring Energy-Efficient Futures for Canada," *Conserver Society Notes*, May-June, 1976, free from:
    Science Council of Canada
    150 Kent Street, 7th Floor
    Ottawa, Canada K1P 5P4

"Energy Strategy: The Road Not Taken", *Foreign Affairs*, October 1975, $10/yr. from:
    Council on Foreign Relations, Inc.
    58 East 68th St.
    New York, NY 10021

Soft Energy Paths: Towards a Durable Peace, 1977
This third volume of Lovin's energy trilogy will contain the full version of the paper excerpted above along with information on the studies Lovins has performed for various countries (see box) demonstrating how they can make a smooth transition to full operation on renewable energies at lower cost and less risk than with nuclear power. A map into the future that should be carefully read by everyone interested in energy or economics.

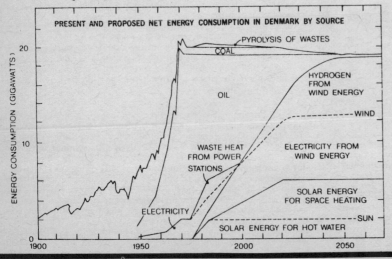

PRESENT AND PROPOSED NET ENERGY CONSUMPTION IN DENMARK BY SOURCE

Energy Overview

Energy for Survival, Wilson Clark, 1974, $4.95 from:

> Doubleday & Co.
> 245 Park Avenue
> New York, NY 10017

A comprehensive and highly useful overview of the development and operation of our high-energy society, future energy resources, and the history and potential of renewable energy development. Encyclopedic, and filled with fascinating detail.

The Energy Primer, Richard Merrill et al., 1975, $4.50 from:

> Portola Institute
> 540 Santa Cruz Avenue
> Menlo Park, CA 94025

The focus is on small-scale systems which can be applied to the needs of the individual, small group or community. (More than 1/4 of the book is devoted to reviews of books and hardware sources. Hundreds of illustrations and a dozen original articles are used to describe the workings of solar water heaters, space heaters and dryers, waterwheels, windmills, wind generators, wood burning heaters, alcohol stills and methane digesters.) The introduction and the final section of the book focuses on the need for energy conservation and some of the problems and potentials of integrated energy systems. An expanded edition, published by Dell Books, will be out in 1977.

The Best Present of All, Oliver Houck, 15¢ each from:

> National Wildlife Federation
> 1412 16th St., N.W.
> Washington, DC 20036

The best elementary school level story of the best present—Energy—from various sources, such as: Mr. Gas and Mr. Oil, Mr. Coal, Mr. Atom, General Water, Mr. Geothermal, and Ms. Sun. One of many "Ranger Rick" nature magazine reprints, this one is colorfully illustrated with lively writing to explain energy resource facts and explore their meaning in ways that maintain one's interest. Well-balanced presentations of advantages/disadvantages of each energy source are presented.

"Coming: the Real Energy Crisis" by Dr. Lewis R. Conta, Dean, College of Engineering, Univ. of Rhode Island, Kingston, RI, and member of ASME (Amer. Soc. of Mech. Engineers), in *Mechanical Engineering*, Aug. 1975, p. 18-24.

"If we don't get off the exponential growth curve, the year 2000 could unfold on a U.S. landscape dotted with 3000 1000-MW fossil and nuclear power plants. A grievous price will have been paid: capital cost—$2 trillion; water for condenser cooling—more than 2/3 the total runoff of our major rivers; and the ecological impact—a possible disastrous climatological effecting resulting from the massive heat flux. A far more vigorous conservation effort is needed until solar energy, sea thermal, or another self-renewing system—virtually pollution-free of heat, gaseous and particulate matter—becomes commercially feasible."

The Poverty of Power, Barry Commoner, 1976, 314 pp., $10.00 from:

> Alfred A. Knopf
> 201 E. 50th
> New York, NY 10022

One of the important perspectives on America's presently energy-wasteful and environmentally-polluted modes of production and consumption, how they got that way, and how we must not be afraid to borrow useful socialist solutions in order to survive. After the clearest explication of the 2nd Law of Thermodynamics now extant, examples are given of how our profit system has failed to direct national resources toward the obvious, best solutions in energy transportation, housing and other areas.

Energy-Entropy-Economics-Environment: The Basics
Commoner, Odum, Georgescu-Roegen and Lovins should all be read for a sound basis in what's going on in energy-environment-economics relationships in the mid-70s.

Energy Essays, by Malcolm Wells, 70 pp., illus., $5.95 from:

> Edmund Scientific
> 150 Edscorp Bldg.
> Barrington, NJ 08007

If you liked Steve Baer's *Sunspots*, you'll love these "hey, what'd he say" perspectives on such 3rd planet from Sol topics as: air, water, food, waste management, solar energy, miracles and energy-smugness. And you'll be glad Gutenburg did it. Dave Deppen says his favorites start on p. 9, 11, 27, 43, 47, 63 and 65. Malcolm is the architect who may know the most in the world about underground energy-conserving houses and who brought us the "Wilderness Graph," suggesting man's works ought to at least do as well as a forest.

Energy and Power, 1971, $3.50 from:

> W.H. Freeman
> 660 Market Street
> San Francisco, CA 94104

Reprint of the very fine September, 1971, issue of *Scientific American* on energy. A fine graphic introduction to energy resources, energy flows in agricultural and industrial societies, energy and information, and resource depletion.

Comparison of Energy Consumption between West Germany and the United States, by Stanford Research Institute (SRI) for FEA, NTIS number PB 245-652-AS, $5.25 for full report from:

> National Technical Information
> Service
> Springfield, VA 22151

or, a limited number of free summaries are available from:

> FEA
> Room 6438
> Washington, DC 20461

West Germans use only 2/3 as much energy as Americans: 1/4 the fuel in transportation, 1/2 the energy in home heating, 1/4 for other residential uses such as appliances and hot water heating. The U.S. uses 40% more energy per unit of production than Germany. According to the FEA, "the large disparity in energy uses between these economically similar countries suggests it is possible for the U.S. to substantially reduce the ratio of energy use to national income, without cutting living standards or economic growth."

ENERGY POLICY

A Time to Choose, Ford Foundation, 1974, $4.95 from:

> Ballinger Publishing Co.
> 17 Dunster St.
> Cambridge, MA 02138

Historical growth, technical mix and zero energy growh scenarios, reforming electric utility regulations, energy employment and economic growth. A two-year, $4 million inquiry.

Energy: The Power of the States, 237 pp., write:

> Jan L. Mills, Director
> Center for Governmental Responsibility
> Holland Law Center, U. of Florida
> Gainesville, FL 32601

Prepared for the Fla. Energy Committee, deals with federal and state authority in the energy area, various phases of energy control: exploration, leasing, production of energy, and processing and conversion of natural resources. This plus publications by the Council of State Governments would be useful to the energy-aware legislator.

Turning Toward the Sun, Vol. I, Abstracts of State Legislative Enactments of 1974 and 1975 Regarding Solar Energy, Patrick Binns, editor, published by National Conference of State Legislatures under National Science Foundation Grant, publication no. PB 253-836, $4.00 from:

> NTIS
> 5285 Port Royal Rd.
> Springfield, VA 22161

Excellent overview by a recognized energy legislation expert and recent consultant to state governments such as Montana on energy codes, ordinances and executive orders. See also:
A Survey of State Legislation Related to Solar Energy, National Bureau of Standards, publication no. PB 258-235, $6.75 from:

> NTIS
> 5285 Port Royal Rd.
> Springfield, VA 22161

Electricity Consumption and Investment Finance in California, W. R. Z. Willey, May 1976, from:

> Environmental Defense Fund
> 2728 Durant Avenue
> Berkeley, CA 94704

Willey explores the investment impacts of alternative means of matching California's future electrical needs and supplies and shows that current projections are economically irrational and environmentally destructive. Improved end-use efficiency would reduce by one-third the investment needed for supply electricity, and a scenario where investment is shifted from the supply to the demand side of the electricity market explores the social and economic impacts of such actions. Energy conservation in end use of electricity is shown to be a lucrative opportunity to the energy investor when compared to the investment opportunities in generation (better show this to your P.U.C. and your local bank) to provide increased employment and a redistributive economic effect.

Transition, Oregon Office of Energy Research and Planning, 1975, $6.95 ($9.95 to libraries) from:

> Prometheus Unbound, Specialty Books
> P.O. Box 42261
> Portland, OR 97242

An excellent antidote for people who

cpf

Dirty-Handed A.T.

One of the most enjoyable ways of sharing a.t. techniques quickly is in the on-site, hands-on, weekend workshop. Many towns not served by an energy center such as TEA, AERO, Max's Pot or RAIN can still easily be reached by outreach efforts which teach local residents. A small but growing number of a.t. practitioners are available to co-ordinate such training sessions in a variety of fields and a few have produced do-it-yourself manuals as well. They can be reached at the following addresses:

Jack Park
Helion, Inc.
Box 445
Brownsville, CA 95919
(wind-turbine construction workshop using 3-blade, 1200 watt, Kedco)

Lee Johnson/Ken Smith
RAIN-Ecotope Group
2270 N.W. Irving St.
Portland, OR 97210
(solar water heater construction workshop; manual available from RAIN for $3.00)

Bill Yanda
Solar Sustenance Project
Rt. 1, Box 107AA
Santa Fe, NM 87501
(dwelling-attached greenhouse construction workshop; manual available, see solar greenhouses, p. 226)

Kye Cochran
New Western Energy Show
AERO
417 Stapleton Bldg.
Billings, MT 59101
(Ms. Cochran is available for consulting on how to set up energy show tours in other states)

Jim Parker
Center for Social and Environmental Concern
710 11th St.
Helena, MT 59601
(has been sponsoring an excellent series of practical workshops in the above areas for the Community Action Agencies in the Upper Northwest).

look at only one piece of the puzzle at a time. A summary of U.S. resource situation and how the state's fuel supplies, population, electrical grids, manufacturing and consumer patterns interface with the U.S. ones.

Center for Advanced Computation
University of Illinois at Urbana-
Champaign
Urbana, IL 61801
These studies are some of the best total energy input/output studies available. Computations of energy use options as related to the economic employment picture in America. A must for planners, government agencies, environmentalists, and opens up many possibilities for educators—on how to relate personal consumption options to the environmental/ energy system at large.

Write for publications list.
Especially recommended:
1) The Dollar, Energy and Employment Impacts of Air, Rail and Automobile Passenger Transportation, CAC #96. $3.
2) Transferring from Urban Cars to Buses: the Energy and Employment Impacts, CAC #98. $5.
3) The Dollar, Energy and Employment Impacts of Certain Consumer Options, CAC #97. $3.
4) Energy and the Regional Planner, CAC #116. $3.

Citizens Energy Platform
National Consumers Congress
1346 Connecticut Ave., N.W.
Washington, D.C. 20036
A coalition of leading environmental groups has prepared a statement of purpose (with background and bibliographic information) on strategies for energy legislation. ($1.00 donation)

Energy Costs of Using Columbia River Water for Irrigation, by David F. Schuy, Jan. 1975 (E.M. 3891), available from:
Cooperative Extension Service
Washington State University
Pullman, WA 99163
This study describes an old shell game on a grand scale. Large corporations in eastern Washington and Oregon request use of Columbia River water to irrigate the desert—"We need food, you know." Removal of the water from the river would decrease hydro-electric generation, requiring new and expensive nuclear power plants to make up the deficit. The irrigation would also require a lot of electricity itself to pump and distribute the water. And who pays the costs? Not those who benefit, but the electrical users of Washington, Idaho, Oregon, Montana and California—to the tune of $88 million per year. The game is called passing the buck. "The Columbia River as a Resource" by Hastay, Millard, et. al. (State of Washington Water Research Center Report No. 5A, Washington State University, Pullman, WA 99163, June 1971) discusses similar proposals for eastern Oregon. If we wouldn't pave our good fields, we wouldn't have to farm the desert.

"Energy and Resources" in *Science*, 25 July 1975, Vol. 189, No. 4199, pp. 255-260, by Bent Sørenson, Niels Bohr Institute, U. of Copenhagen.
A plan is outlined according to which solar and wind energy would supply Denmark's needs by the year 2050. These are the first steps to be taken in developing a regional renewable energy system. Biomass and ocean thermal gradient surveys added to this and then overlaying all the data on maps à la McHarg would probably give planners and industrial park developers some idea about where to put what, depending on the type of energy needed (fuel, heat, electricity) and the availability of a renewable supply/storage.

A Planner's Handbook on Energy, Robert Pozzo and James Clark, 1976, from:
State Energy Office
Dept. of Administration
108 Collins Bldg.
Tallahassee, FL 32304
Good coverage of information useful for planners in evaluating future energy policy options and low energy housing for hot humid climates. Useful outside of these areas for people to see how specific regional energy uses, problems and solutions are. When we see passive systems for New Mexico's high daily temperature fluctuations, shading for Florida, snow reflective systems for Minnesota, or wood heat for Vermont, we tend to think their problems must be easier to solve than our own. They aren't—they're just different.

Other organizations which do not now conduct mobile workshops but have the capability of doing so within their regions, if requested, include:

Total Environmental Action, (TEA)
12 Church Hill
Harrisville, NH 03450

Domestic Technology Institute
Box 2043
Evergreen, CO 80439

Office of Appropriate Technology
State of California
P.O. Box 1677
Sacramento, CA 95808

Farallones Urban Center
1516 5th Ave.
Berkeley, CA 94710

The Shelter Institute
72 Front St.
Bath, ME 04530

(See also Hands-on Building, pp. 143-144)

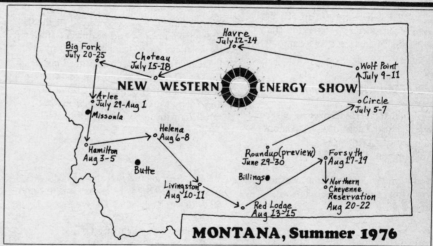

Other topics which could use this approach include: log cabin construction, compost toilets, community gardening, home insulation retrofitting, plumbing, accounting, small business operation, etc. RAIN would like to hear about other construction workshops which go to the people.

INFORMATION RESOURCES

National Energy Information Center
Federal Energy Administration
4508 New Post Office Bldg.
12th and Pennsylvania Ave., N.W.
Washington, DC 20461

Statistics, bibliographic materials, abstracts, studies, *Petroleum Situation Report* (weekly), *Energy Indicators* (monthly); *Petroleum Import Weekly*.

Development of an Energy Information Retrieval System, by Donald Mazziotti and Ilene Wright, Nov. 1975
Single copies $5.00 from:
　Portland Planning Bureau Library
　424 S.W. Main
　Portland, OR 97204

A good, useful attempt at using simple and inexpensive methods—optical coincidence retrieval (OCR)—to keep track of energy-related publications in such a way that small towns and cities can afford and manage (i.e., non-computerized). This first product of the Portland Energy Conservation Project is an excellent example of appropriate technology which bows to human nature as represented by the ubiquitous KISS rule . . . "Keep it simple, stupid!" Yet it is one level more sophisticated than your usual key-sort card system.

Selected Information Resources on Energy
　National Referral Center
　Science and Technology Division
　Library of Congress
　Washington, D.C. 20540

A handy guide to agencies and other information-gathering associations. Order #sl 73-7.

Directory of Current Energy Research
　Oak Ridge National Laboratory
　P.O. Box X
　Oak Ridge, TN 37830

Maintaining a computerized inventory of energy related research in the U.S. 4400 entries to date.

Decentralized Energy Systems Bibliography, available for $1 plus a self-addressed, 24¢ stamped, 11x14 envelope from:
　Critical Mass
　Dept. W
　Box 1538
　Washington, DC 20013

LC Science Tracer Bullets and Computer Printouts of Topic Area Resource People, free from:
　Reference Section
　Science & Technology Div.
　Library of Congress
　10 First St., S.E.
　Washington, DC 20540

A tracer bullet is a bibliography including places to query for additional info; they can also produce computer lists of schools, companies and individuals working on a specific subject, such as energy conservation in industry, wind-power, wave energy, etc.

Environmental Action Reprint Service (EARS) Catalog　　50¢ from:
　2239 East Colfax
　Denver, CO 80206

Want a handy way to get hold of most alternative energy and major AT materials we mention? Order them from EARS. Their newest annotated collection is 20 pages packed full of familiar goodies, including papers, books, plans and films. Once on their mailing list, you'll continue to receive their useful catalogues.

ERDA Research Abstracts (ERA), $119 per year, $148.75 overseas (Index only $30.50 per year, $38.15 overseas), from:
　Ass't. Public Printer
　Government Printing Office
　Washington, DC 20402
ERDA's monthly abstract journal, published since March '75 but available only to ERDA, its contractors and grantees, is now available to the public. ERA abstracts and indexes reports, patents, journal articles, conference papers, theses, books and monographs sponsored by ERDA.

The Alternative Energy Resources Organization
　435 Stapleton Building
　Billings, MT 59101
Our good friend Kye Cochran and her friends at AERO are an excellent example of what a non-profit citizens educational group can do—also what any state or local energy office *could* do to let people know what's possible and happening with renewable energy sources. They sponsor hands-on and informational workshops, did a traveling energy show that visited towns around the state with interesting and effective exhibits, publish *Sun-Times*, and act as resource people. They've had a huge impact by making people aware of alternatives that the power companies and media were avoiding mention of.

State Energy Organizations: A Catalog
　National Energy Information Center
　Federal Energy Administration
　Federal Building
　Washington, D.C. 20461
Free. Activities, publications, personnel in all 50 states.

ERDA Speakers Bureau, contact:
　Office of Public Affairs
　ERDA
　20 Massachusetts Ave., N.W.
　Washington, DC 20545

ERDA can provide qualified speakers for a variety of forums on subjects ranging from wind energy and fuels from biomass to nuclear fusion, energy conservation and solar thermal-electric power. Slides, films and publications can supplement presentations.

Who's Got the Power?, $1.50 from:
　Center for Science in the Public
　　Interest
　1757 "S" St., N.W.
　Washington, DC 20009
Conference listings for the February, 1975, Conference on Energy. One of the best leads into energy research centers, state agencies, industrial projects.

NEWSLETTERS and MAGAZINES

Information from ERDA: Weekly Announcements, available free from:
> U.S. Energy Research & Development Administration
> Washington, D.C. 20545

Covers everything done in any connection with ERDA: reports, conferences, RFPs (requests for proposals), contract awards in energy conservation, energy generation, conversion, transmission and use; in solar, wind, nuclear, coal, oil, transportation, storage, geothermal fusion.

Energy Reporter (monthly). Free from:
> Energy Reporter Registration
> Federal Energy Administration
> Old Post Office Bldg., Rm 307B
> Washington, D.C. 20461

Also ask to receive notices of new FEA publications.

FPC News, weekly, $56.50/year (free to media), from:
> Federal Power Commission
> Washington, DC 20426

Useful to energy activists. Contains: press releases; rate changes proposed by independent gas producers and interstate pipeline companies; quality statements filed by independent producers; and listings of formal documents issued by the FPC.

People and Energy, monthly, $10/year from:
> Center for Science in the Public Interest
> 1757 "S" Street, N.W.
> Washington, DC 20009

An excellent source for current developments in energy policy, legislation, citizen action, nuclear and utility initiatives. Focuses on energy resources for energy activists, nuclear and utility intervenors, and those wanting public control of "public" utilities.

The Energy Index, free monthly from:
> Energy Index
> Sen. Mike Gravel
> 3317 Dirksen Bldg.
> Washington, DC 20510

As news stories, debates, votes and transcripts are entered in the *Congressional Record*, Sen. Gravel and his staff will compile an index to nuclear and alternative energy information. Citizens can subscribe to the *Record* ($45 per year) or read their public library's copy. Sen. Gravel asks for citizens to send him any important energy items they see so that others across the U.S. can learn about them quickly. Hopefully, we'll see much more on energy conservation.

Alternative Sources of Energy
> Route 2, Box 90A
> Milaca, MN 56353

$5/yr., quarterly. Long the only source of grass roots development in use of renewable energy, ASE is more and more solid and useful. Now produced quarterly, typeset and with more practical information. Latest issue had good articles on "Icy-Ball" refrigerators, ambient air food coolers, and excellent nuts and bolts column on wind power by Martin Jopp and a supplement to their earlier *Spectrum* catalogue of ASE hardware (See A.T. section)

Energy Perspectives, monthly, free from:
> Battelle Energy Program
> 505 King Ave.
> Columbus, OH 43201

4-page primers on the current state-of-the-art in various energy fields and a calendar of energy conferences.

Natural Energy, ed. by Robin Clarke, quarterly, subscriptions via:
> Conservation Tools & Technology (CTT) Association
> 143 Maple Road
> Surbiton, Surrey KT6 4BH
> England

This second issue of *Alternative Energy Sources*, fortunately renamed so as not to be confused with *Alternative Sources of Energy* in Milaca, MN, USA, features articles by the Vale duo on the autonomous house, on BRAD's do-it-yourself solar collector, on solar collector testing, and windmill costs-benefits. Perceptive book reviews, news items and letters to the editor round out this handy publication.

Energy Today, 8-pg. bi-monthly, $90/yr. from:
> Trends Publishing, Inc.
> National Press Bldg.
> Washington, D.C. 20004

If you've the money, this is the energy newsletter to get. Covers all areas, nuclear, fossil, solar, legislation, projects, research, international, domestic, relevant new publications and energy trends (who's doing what where, conferences). Highly recommended for public libraries, corporate libraries.

Government R&D Report, 12 pp., twice monthly, $80 per year from:
> William G. Margetts, Publisher
> Gov't R&D Report
> MIT Station, P.O. Box 284
> Cambridge, MA 02139

March 15, 1976 (vol. 5, no. 6) issue contained comprehensive and perceptive articles on 1) support and opposition to continued breeder reactor R&D funding, 2) debate between Congress and the White House on conservation, solar, wind, geothermal development, which the citizens' representatives favor, vs. more nuclear reactors, deregulation of oil and gas, which the Administration favors, and 3) politics of SERI, the Solar Energy Research Institute. Single sample copies available free.

Synerjy: A Directory of Energy Alternatives. $10 per year, twice yearly from:
> P.O. Box 4790
> Grand Central Station
> New York, N.Y. 10017

A real gold mine. Finally, a directory-bibliography-index to publications, products and organizations dealing only with alternatives to conventional fossil fuel and atomic power; for those who have gotten past solar, wind and bioconversion basics and need help keeping up with the latest developments. Also covers geothermal, steam power, heat pipes, heat pumps, hydrogen, electric vehicles, fuel cells, direct energy conversion, waterpower, tidal power, energy storage. Better, more concise services. (How about a monthly or quarterly, Jeff?)

Hawaii Energy Newsletter, free from:
> Dept. of Planning & Econ. Dev.
> P.O. Box 2359
> Honolulu, HI 96804

Part of an energy awareness drive, which also includes a pamphlet, a report on alternative energy sources for Hawaii, the newsletter is a special issue on energy.

"Clean, limitless energy so cheap you won't even have to meter it."—that was the dream we were promised in our guilt from Hiroshima. There were a lot of things we didn't know about then that we do now—safety problems of large, complex and radioactive systems, incredible health hazards of plutonium, apparently unsolvable problems of storing wastes for 250,000 years, the unfavorable economics and energetics of nuclear power, and the political and military hazards of its use. Despite massive obstruction and opposition by the powers that were, the facts are together, the alternatives laid out, and the implications of our choices known. We can't afford to choose nuclear power. We have better and safer options.

A Faustian Bargain

Probably the best perspective and overview on nuclear power is Amory Lovin's trilogy reviewed earlier in this section. For more detailed information, see the following:

The Electric War: The Fight Over Nuclear Power, by Sheldon Novick, 1976, 376 pp., $12.50 from:
   Sierra Club Books
   530 Bush Street
   San Francisco, CA 94108
This book is so outrageous in the story it tells and the comprehensiveness of its telling that Lane has still not gotten to read it, though she ordered it. I could not put it down. Novick provides us with the observations of a passive eye, not the exaggerations or hyperbole of a pro- or an anti-, or of the news muckraker. We see Thomas Edison, the electrical wizard of Menlo Park, and Sam Insull, his private secretary, as Edison fails and Insull finally wins in the attempt to create the electric-power monopolies we have today. We learn how the Cold War provided the breeding ground for civilian nuclear power's multi-billion-dollar industry. We hear how Creative Initiative formed Project Survival to back nuclear safeguards legislation in Oregon, California and other states. We learn a lot, yet are not told how to decide . . . but come to understand that we must soon do so. For, as Jefferson and Samuel Johnson both have said, when we see experts and concerned citizens on both sides, we know the decision will ultimately be up to all the people. Novick's work is an excellent primer for that decision.

Nuclear Power: The Fifth Horseman, Denis Hayes, 1976, 68 pp., $2 from:
   Worldwatch Institute
   1776 Massachusetts Ave., N.W.
   Washington, DC 20036

This paper evaluates the future of nuclear power, subjecting it to several tests—those of economics, safety, adequacy of fuel supplies, environmental impact, and both national and international security. If the world is to "go nuclear," adopting nuclear power as the principal source of energy, each of these criteria should be satisfied. In fact, as explained within, none may be.

"Dynamic Energy Analysis and Nuclear Power," by John H. Price, December 1974. Contained in *Non-nuclear Futures: The Case for an Ethical Energy Strategy*, available from:
   Friends of the Earth
   529 Commercial Street
   San Francisco, CA 94111

$5.95 paperback ($4.94 for members). The Price study documents the energy consumed and produced by exponential growth of energy conversion facilities; the energy inputs and outputs of nuclear reactors, both singly and in such programs; and demonstrates that under many conditions (including many current national energy development programs) such exponential growth programs consume more energy than they produce during the life of the program.

The Rasmussen Report, the study of nuclear reactor safety by the Atomic Energy Commission, has come under criticism in a recent Environmental Protection Agency Report. Especially critical of the AEC's definition of "acceptable risks."
   EPA
   Waterside Mall Bldg.
   4th & M Streets
   Washington, D.C. 20002

The Accident Hazards of Nuclear Power Plants, Richard E. Webb, 1976, 228 pp., $6.95 from:
   University of Massachusetts Press
   Amherst, MA 01002
Amazing. Now I know that WPA means "worst possible accident," none of which AEC-ERDA have included in their list of DBA's ("design basis accidents") used in planning reactor safety, that "power excursion accident" probabilities have never been verified in a large core, and that there have been 14 accidents and near-accidents in the world's nuclear reactors. An excellent primer to what starts nuclear accidents, keeps 'em going and stops them; the gaps in the Rasmussen Report; and an intro to the jargon of LOCA, SCRAM and PCMA.

Curve of Binding Energy, John McPhee, 1975, $1.50 from:
   Ballantine Books
   201 E. 50th Street
   New York, NY 10022
McPhee's interviews with nuclear bomb designer Theodore Taylor, which were excerpted in the *New Yorker*. Taylor

lays out in frightening detail the ease
with which even schoolchildren can fabricate effective nuclear bombs, the ease
of stealing plutonium from the nuclear
waste processing cycle, and the ability
to hold a city for ransom without even
needing to fabricate a bomb. Sobering
view of the Faustian bargain nuclear
power offers us.

Prometheus Crisis, by Thomas N. Scortia and Frank Robinson, Doubleday,
1975, $8.95. *We Almost Lost Detroit*,
by John G. Fuller, Readers Digest
Press, 1975, $8.95.
Two amazing books
on nuclear accidents—one truth, one
fiction. Both scary. The *Prometheus
Crisis*, written by the authors of *Tow-
ering Inferno*, is soon to be made into a
major film.

Not Man Apart, twice monthly, $10/
year from:
    Friends of the Earth
    529 Commercial Street
    San Francisco, CA 94111
This whole newsletter, and its *Nuclear
Blowdown* section in particular, has
been probably the finest resource with
which to keep up to date on what's
happening on the nuclear power scene.

"Nuclear Power Facilities in the U.S.
1977," a map; "Safety-Related Inci-
dents at U.S. Nuclear Facilities," a
diagram, and "World Nuclear Prolifera-
tion and Opposition," a map, are available as a set for $10 postpaid from:
    Special Nuclear Materials
    Eco Graphix
    13 Center St.
    Rutland, VT 05701
All are 17" x 24" reference charts
chock-full of useful details. Ask about
their bulk rates for organizations.

The Directory of Nuclear Activists and
mailing lists, $7 and $5, respectively
($25 and $10 if profit-making business,
utility, government and persons associated with the nuclear industry), from:
    Environmental Action of Colorado
    1100 14th St.
    Denver, CO 80202

*Energy Conservation Alternatives to
Nuclear Power: A Case Study*, Robert
F. Mueller, July, 1973.
    Planetology Branch
    Goddard Space Flight Center
    Greenbelt, Maryland 20771
Mueller shows that construction of a
2,200 megawatt nuclear power plant
could be avoided through cutting back
on resistance heating & excessive lighting.
A classic paper, the first on conservation
versus nuclear power, and a classic situation, like that of the civilian who lost
his job in Air Force cost control when
he blew the whistle on the C5A cost
overruns to Congress, since Mr. Mueller
was told that NASA employees don't
do such things, In any case, you should
hassle NASA and, if necessary, remind
them of the Freedom of Information
Act via your congressperson until you
get a copy.

*See also the large-scale wind electricity
page for economic and immediately
implementable alternatives to nuclear
power.

*Fast Breeder Reactor: Analysis of
Limits and Limits of Analysis*, by Mark
Sharefkin, single copies free from:
    Chairman
    Joint Economic Committee
    U.S. Congress
    Washington, DC 20510
This new Congressional study, prepared
for the JEC, is calling for a delay in the
multi-million dollar breeder reactor
program. The report disputes the two
primary arguments supporting rapid
development of the LMFBR: (1) diminishing uranium supplies and (2)
sharply rising demands for energy.
Rather than energy growth rates of 7%
per year projected by government
studies. Sharefkin foresees electricity
growth rates beyond 1980 being closer
to 2%. He also notes that uranium reserves may have been greatly under-
estimated.

*The Liquid Metal Fast Breeder Reactor:
An Economic Analysis* by Brian G.
Chow, 76 pp., $3 from:
    American Enterprise Institute
        for Public Policy Research
    1150 17th St., N.W.
    Washington, DC 20036
The book disputes government assertions that the breeder reactor can provide an overall saving in electric generating costs. An incisive study of the cost-
benefit analyses that have previously
supported the development of the
LMFBR program, the report concludes
that future energy demand is overstated,
uranium resources are under-estimated,
and program costs for the LFMBR are
too low.

Fast Breeder Reactor Report. Available
for $1 from:
    **U.S. General Accounting Office
    Distribution Office
    Box 1020
    Washington, D.C. 20013**
Copies of the July 30, 1975 GAO report
on the fast breeder reactor. Check or
money orders only. Cost overruns, etc.

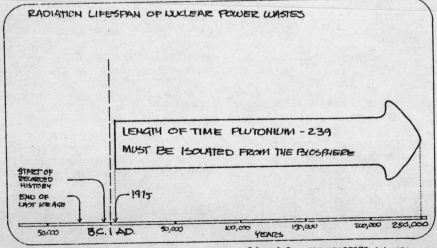

RADIATION LIFESPAN OF NUCLEAR POWER WASTES

LENGTH OF TIME PLUTONIUM - 239
MUST BE ISOLATED FROM THE BIOSPHERE

START OF
RECORDED
HISTORY

END OF
LAST ICE AGE

-1975

50,000   BC. I AD.   50,000   100,000   150,000   200,000   250,000
YEARS

NUCLEAR HAZARDS

Adapted from NOT MAN APART, July, 1974

Utilities

Here's a good example of what happens when something gets too big and powerful without good mechanisms of control. The efforts by citizen groups to regain control of the powers that are supposed to serve them are important to look at—if only because you might need to do the same soon yourself.

Taking Charge—A New Look at Public Power, 1976, $2.50 from:
> Environmental Action Foundation
> 724 Dupont Circle Building
> Washington, DC 20036

Examines the country's 3000 public power systems, describes their benefits, and analyzes the tactics and strategies public power advocates have successfully used to take over the facilities of their private power companies. A useful resource.

Power Over People, by Louise B. Young, 1973, $7.50 from:
> Oxford University Press
> 200 Madison Ave.
> New York, NY 10016

A community in Ohio decided to give fight to the power company's plans to build high tension lines through their farms and a state park. Lots of information about the "powers that be" over the rights and desires of small town folks. Also data on environmental effects of the big wires. Much of the info on electrical energy is dated, but the book is another example of the importance of standing up for what one believes.

An Organizer's Notebook on Public Utilities and Energy for New York State, 300 pgs., $15 from:
> Human Affairs Program
> Cornell University
> 410 College Ave.
> Ithaca, NY 14853

Excellent looseleaf guide to "citizen action" against a utility or oil company. Specific examples in NY state but recommended for any consumer or public interest group, or to any individual wondering what to do about high-handed practices or high energy bills.

The Power Line, monthly, $15/year from:
> Environmental Action Foundation
> 724 Dupont Circle Building
> Washington, DC 20036

Excellent access newsletter for what is going on in the area of utilities. Whose money pays for utility lobbying on nuclear referendums, what states now have lifeline rates or bans on utility practices of charging consumers for promotional advertising, what's happening with municipal takeover of utilities, and resources for citizen action against utilities.

How to Challenge Your Local Electrical Utility, Richard Morgan, Sandra Jerabek, $1.50 from:
> Environmental Action Foundation
> 724 Dupont Circle Bldg.
> Washington, DC 20036

Utility regulation, energy conservation, tax loopholes, rate-making formulas, challenging a rate increase, additional information referral.

Regional Electric Maps, Cat. No. FPC M-104, 60¢ per region from:
> Assistant Public Printer
> U.S. Government Printing Office
> Washington, DC 20402

The 1975 edition of the Federal Power Commission's regional "Principal Electric Facilities" maps, reflecting data as of June 30, 1974, are excellent for school and state energy office use.

Electric Utility Expansion Plans for 1975-1984, Federal Power Commission Staff Summary, issued June 30, 1975, reported in the July 4, 1975, *FPC News*, available from:

> Office of Public Information
> Federal Power Commission
> Washington, D.C. 20426

States that projected national energy requirements for the next 10 years will increase at an average annual rate of 6.73% rather than the 7.43% projected in the 1974 report. This is the first such report including mention of new power generation by solar energy, fuel cells and magnetohydrodynamics (MHD).

Local Energy Action Program, for information write:
> LEAP
> Center for Science in the Public Interest
> 1757 "S" St., N.W.
> Washington, DC 20009

Aimed at filling the information gap that has precluded interested communities and individuals from effectively using federal assistance programs and undertaking local energy efforts, LEAP includes 1) the publication of a comprehensive study of all currently existing renewable energy and energy conservation applications that could serve as models for other communities; 2) the publication of a Citizens Energy Directory and Resource Guide of tapable expertise; 3) a series of "how-to" manuals on the steps local governments must follow to initiate energy programs.

*See review of *Phantom Taxes in Your Electric Bill* on page 33 for another dimension of the utility problem.

Fossil Fuels

"The Energy Resources of the Earth," M. King Hubbert, *Scientific American*, September 1971
This and other of Hubbert's publications (see *Resources and Man*, National Academy of Sciences, 1969) are among the most respected analyses of our proven and estimated remaining energy and mineral resources. Pretty sobering. With a given quantity, how long we have such resources is inversely related to how fast we use them.

U.S. oil fields are replenishing their supplies through natural processes at the rate of 10 barrels a day. The U.S. uses more than 17 million barrels per day. This is to say that we are currently using as much oil in 3 hours as oil deposits have produced in 5 centuries. (From the *Minneapolis Tribune* via *Alternative Sources of Energy*)

The fuel reserve estimates continue to drop: the U.S. Geological Survey now says that there is 80% *less* oil available than previously estimated off the Atlantic Coast. Meanwhile, in California, a bill has passed the legislature and been signed by Governor Brown that effectively delays leasing oil lands for drilling off the California coast for a few more years by banning construction of new oil pipelines across state-owned tidelands till 1978. (Source: *Not Man Apart*, mid-September, 1975)

The nation's supply of natural gas, which provides about 50% of industry's energy needs, is running short. U.S. production has peaked and the country is beginning to live partly off its reserves. (And Canada has curtailed exports of gas to the U.S.) (*Time Magazine*)

Oilweek
    Observer Publishing Co.
    2420 Wilson Blvd.
    Arlington, Va. 22201
$60/yr. A reporting service (Observer Co. has several) published weekly. Trends in the oil industry, national and international. Research and legislation affecting the oil industry.

Mineral Resources and the Environment
    National Research Council
    National Academy of the Sciences
    2101 Constitution Ave.
    Washington, D.C. 20418
This 348-page report comes up with some estimates of America's energy resources that undercut estimates made previously by the Dept. of the Interior. Including the estimate that the U.S. would run out of oil and natural gas (assuming the consumption remains the same) in 25 years and not the 40 to 60 years forecast by the government.

A new U.S. energy source has been discovered recently by Entropy Evasion League researchers who have mapped a large network of surface deposits of petroleum-bearing strata criss-crossing the country. The strata are relics of an age of highly mobile petroleum-eating dinosaurs whose pathways covered a vast portion of our land area by the late 1970s before the deep earth petroleum deposits that fed their metabolism ran out. These surface deposits, once known as an "Interstate Highway System," are now highly valued for the energy content of their asphaltic compounds. Miners are said to be paying exorbitant prices for old maps locating the deposits. (Courtesy *Ecotopian News Register*)

Fort Union Coal Field Symposium, sponsored by Montana Academy of Sciences, Eastern Montana College. $8.75, order from:
    Eastern Montana College Bookstore
    Billings, MT 59101
This five-volume work is an important technical compilation on the development and use of coal resources, especially in Montana, though applicable in general. An impressive range of considerations, including one volume on social impact. A six-month turnaround between conference and published proceedings, too!

Coalition Against Strip Mining
    324 C St., S.E.
    Washington, D.C. 20003

Surface Mining in Alabama: the Environmental Impact examines in layman's terms such topics as current land reclamation in Alabama, principles of good land reclamation, the need for public awareness of surface mining's environmental impact, and options for the future. Copies are $1.00 each.
    I would appreciate your publicizing these materials in an upcoming issue of *RAIN*.
    Thank you for your interest.
        Nancy Callahan
        Alabama Environmental Quality Assn.
        P.O. Box 11000
        Montgomery,
        AL 36111

Toward A Steady State Economy, Energy and Power, and *Transition* all contain easily accessible information on fossil fuel and other natural resource reserves.

It's almost embarrassing to realize how far we can tighten our belts without it hurting—and to discover it may even feel better! Five years ago people were certain we couldn't stand any reduction in energy use, and considered it outrageous when we asserted that we could live well on one-tenth the energy we then used. The figures for conservation potential *listed in energy studies has gotten bigger even faster than our fuel bills. Already people are talking commonly about 50% reductions. Conservation is so much cheaper than any energy source that no community should consider any new generating facilities until after a stringent and broad conservation program has been put into effect.*

WASTE NOT, WATT NOT

Long Island, New York—A study recently completed by the well-known energy engineering firm of Dubin-Mindell-Bloome for Suffolk County, NY, concluded that planned new electrical generating plants on Long Island would not be needed over the next 20 years if conservation measures were implemented. They further concluded that Long Island was well adapted for solar and wind energy use and that more than 400 million gallons of oil could be saved per year—in addition to fuel saved at electrical generating plants through conservation—by adapting existing buildings for simultaneous energy and heat generation (total energy systems) and conversion to solar energy use. Conservation measures would be paid back in ten years and solar and wind energy systems costs could be repaid within 20 years—all at significantly lower cost than new generating facilities. Contact Dubin-Mindell-Bloome Associates P.C., 42 W. 39th Street, New York, NY 10018.

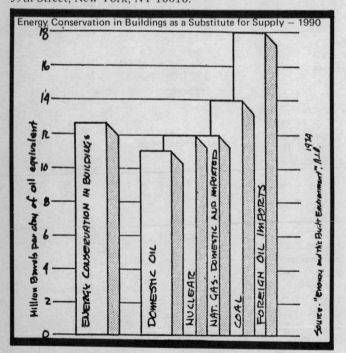

Seattle, Washington—The Seattle City Council has denied Seattle City Light, the municipal-owned utility, permission to participate in the construction of new nuclear power generating facilities on the basis of a report which indicated that the city could give away insulation to all homeowners in the service area cheaper than they could supply new electrical power. The council voted to set up an energy conservation office in place of generating facilities. See *Public White Papers*, Seattle Community Information Project, on page 98.

Vermont—Depending on our own resources can be good for us. Skyrocketing petroleum prices caused Vermont to look into using waste wood for home heating and electrical generation. Not surprisingly, they found that wood could be economically competitive in both areas and could provide at least 25% of Vermont's energy needs. But, more interestingly, they realized that using their own renewable fuel resources instead of imported fuel could be expected to provide direct employment for 3,500 Vermonters, plus additional secondary employment, and produce $63 million in gross income within the state per year by 1985. See *Vermont Governor's Task Force on Wood as a Source of Energy* (free) from E. Bradford Walker, Director of Forests, Agency of Environmental Conservation, Montpelier, VT 05602.

Japan—A 1974 study by Amory Lovins, author of *World Energy Strategies* and *Non-Nuclear Futures*, indicated that careful examination of countries even as dependent upon imported oil as highly-industrialized Japan would show conservation and income energy options to be significantly cheaper and easier to develop than new fossil fuel or nuclear power generating capacity. Conservation, wind, solar heat, use of agricultural wastes, and co-generation of industrial heat and electricity were shown to be a practical and desirable policy direction. "Energy Strategies and Nuclear Power: An International Perspective," presented to the Centre Party Symposium on Energy, Development and the Future, Stockholm, 25 Sweden, 6 Nov. 1974, by Amory Lovins, Friends of the Earth, Ltd., 9 Poland Street, London W1, England.

Denmark—A plan has been outlined for conversion of Denmark's energy supply to wind and solar energy sources by the year 2050, indicating their technical and economical feasibility. "Energy and Resources," by Bent Sørenson, *Science*, 25 July 1975, pp. 255-260.

Sweden—In a recent article in the *Christian Science Monitor*, 31 December 1975, p. 19, Ruth Link reports on the decision of Sweden to cancel plans for building any further nuclear power plants and to limit its growth in energy use through conservation, use of total energy systems, and increased use of solar and wind energy. The new policy resulted from extensive debate in the country on the costs, safety and political implications of various energy policy options.

Norway—seems prepared to move even further away from wasteful, high-energy lifestyles. Norway has had the third highest standard of living in the world and faces even greater wealth through the export of newly-developed oil reserves. Both the government and the people seem alarmed at the prospect of what that wealth would do to the country and are taking measures to limit the release of the oil profits within the country. A recent Gallup poll revealed that an overwhelming majority of Norwegians—between 81 and 88 percent—believe that more wealth will not bring happiness but rather more problems, such as increased materialism and pollution. Seventy-six percent felt their standard of living was already too high, and 35 percent of those in the lowest tax bracket felt that more money would not improve their lives. "Poll Shows Norwegians Yearn for Simple Life," *The Montreal Star*, Oct. 27, 1975, p. C-2 (From *Conserver Society Notes*, Dec. 1975).

United States—A report prepared under a grant from the Federal Energy Administration by Denis Hayes, former Illinois Energy Chief, calculates that conservation efforts alone could meet all new energy needs in the U.S. for the next quarter-century without lowering the nation's standard of living. Prime targets for more efficient energy use include auto gasoline mileage, building insulation and use of waste heat, elimination of inefficiency in food production, and changes in how electric power is produced. Hayes says that Americans waste more than half the energy they consume, rapidly depleting energy resources with little regard for energy needs of future generations. Contact Denis Hayes, Worldwatch Institute, 1776 Massachusetts Ave., Washington, DC 20036.

California—Two recently-released ERDA-supported studies by David Goldstein and Arthur Rosenfeld of the Physics Department and Lawrence Berkeley Laboratory at the University of California, Berkeley, CA 94720, conclude that it is almost always cheaper to save a kW of peak power than to invest $1000 for new capacity. They claim that with an affirmative energy management program, planned hydro and geothermal plants will satisfy California energy demand for the next 20 years, and that such conservation scenarios would result in cost savings to consumers, lower electric rates, greater employment, and no sacrifice in well-being. "Conservation and Peak Power: Cost and Demand," LBL 4438. Reprinted in the February 1976 *Not Man Apart* ($10/year from Friends of the Earth, 529 Commercial Street, San Francisco, CA 94111). Also, "Projecting an Energy-Efficient California," Goldstein and Rosenfeld, LBL 3274.

IN THE BANK OR UP THE CHIMNEY?

The Seattle Trust and Savings Bank this summer became one of the first in the country to offer lower loan interest rates as an incentive to energy conservation. The bank is offering home purchase, remodeling, car and boat loans at 1/2 to 3/4 percent below its normal rates if certain energy conservation or efficiency standards are met (it pays to get a sailboat rather than a motorboat). The program, developed with the assistance of Wilson Clark, reflects the bank's concern for the impact of energy costs upon the monetary value of real and personal property. The bank's officers state that a natural relationship exists between resource conservation and sound economic practices—that the desirable social and economic impact of rehabilitation and maintenance of the community's older housing stock is directly connected with the ability of people to live in the most efficient and economical manner. Wilson Clark states that the conservation program could reduce fuel needs by 40-60% yearly and provide economic savings which would be paid back in four years or less. The program complements the decision made by the City Council to develop energy conservation programs in lieu of developing new generating capacity.

For more information, contact: Mr. J. C. Baillargeon, Seattle Trust and Savings Bank, 804 Second Avenue, Seattle, WA 98104.

Ecotopia—A report sponsored by the Bonneville Power Administration concludes that 1) electrical energy needs forecasted for 1995 could be reduced 33% by conservation, 2) the energy made available by investments in conservation is six times less expensive than energy delivered by investments in new thermal plants, 3) more jobs would be created by these conservation programs than would be by building new thermal plants, 4) these conservation measures are in limited use today, and their broad application would have no significant effect on comfort or customary life style, and 6) environmental quality would be improved. See "The Bonneville Power Administration Energy Conservation Study" by Skidmore, Owings & Merrill, in the *BPA Role Environmental Impact Statement*, Document No. 256766/AS, $10.00 from: National Technical Information Service, U.S. Dept. of Commerce, 5285 Port Royal Road, Springfield, VA 22161. An excellent, 4-page pamphlet detailing the conclusions is available free from: Forelaws on Board, Senator Building, Portland, OR 97204.

Living Lightly

Living lightly is what can happen when the cumulative burden placed on us by our possessions and lifestyles suddenly dawns on us and we begin to get rid of those things that cause the burden. It happened to me in 1970 when my stereo, car and refrigerator all broke down at the same time and I saw how much of my time and energy went into paying for, maintaining, hauling around, or just supporting the way I was living. I had a big sale and got rid of almost everything I owned. What relief. I traveled for a year, living in a van—happily and lightly.

Cleaning things out is something we have to do again and again, because "stuff" piles up around us gradually and quietly. But the sense of release, relief and happiness of living by what we need or truly desire rather than what we can manage to afford—of realizing the effects of our lifestyles on ourselves and others—is a touchstone that stays with us, constantly reminding us that too much can be too much.

Living Lightly, Tom Bender, 1973, $2 from:

> RAIN
> 2270 N.W. Irving
> Portland, OR 97210

I put this together several years ago for an architecture class I was teaching—as a report on the thinking behind the Ouroboros project we had begun the previous year and to outline what we could do in our own homes and lives to live more simply. Discusses avoiding problems rather than solving them, energy flows through the home, the Ouroboros experimental house, broadening our measures of economy, why live lightly, and how all this opens options in how we live. A lot of still valuable thinking.

99 Ways to a Simple Lifestyle, David Taylor, editor, 1976, $5.50 ($11 institutions), from:

> Center for Science in the Public Interest
> 1757 S St., N.W.
> Washington, DC 20009

Here's the book I always meant to write. Lots and lots of things to do— each section is followed by a good bibliography. Nothing fancy and not much new here, but it's nice to see it all in one place.

And—hot off the CSPI press—the revised *Lifestyle Index 76*, by Anne Pierotti and Albert J. Fritsch, $2.

This little booklet will help you tally up your energy score—what you use in your life, from hairdryers to your share of the national defense budget. We've found it extremely useful in "living lightly" workshops. It helps to see where it all goes. And you might also want to use its companion, the *Simple Lifestyle Calendar 1977* (single copy $2.25). Each day has another idea.

Less Is More, quarterly newsletter, $5 per year from:

> Alex Wade
> Box 43
> Barrytown, NY 12507

Covers cheaper housing, transportation and food and includes feedback from owner-builders. This is neat stuff. The Fall '76 *L.I.M.* contained consumer evaluations of small cars: Honda Civic, Renault R5, VW Rabbit, Chevette and Subaru; low-cost heating systems; building codes and the energy-efficient houses and other very interesting hints on how to live lightly.

Simple Living, quarterly newsletter of the

> Simple Living Program
> American Friends Service Committee
> 514 Bryant Street
> Palo Alto, CA 94302

$3 contribution requested. More efficient schools, agriculture or transportation won't break the holds those institutions have on our imagination. We consciously have to go other directions to discover how we can live lives of quality and happiness without massive demands on resources. This newsletter and the project behind it is exploring some of these new directions.

Our Corner of the Earth
(A New Mexican's Guide for Environmental Living)
New Mexico Citizens for Clean Air & Water
P.O. Box 4524
Albuquerque, N. M. 87106

This is a well-conceived/executed booklet (150 plus pages), giving an overall view of environmental problems, with both individual and group responsibilities and possible actions—though mostly individual. A good how to keep your house clean (environmental Hints from Heloise) section. Might serve well as a model for the kind of project other local groups could work on.

Becoming an Environmentalist, Barbara Clark, 1976, 60 pp., $1.95 from:

> Cottonwood Publishing Co.
> P.O. Box 1644
> Walla Walla, WA 99362

Subtitle: "Or How I Learned to Stop Worrying and Love the Energy Crisis." If you are just beginning the long, slow and joyful process of weaning you and your family from the consumer-oriented /energy-full lifestyle that has become the American Dream, this little book will give you courage and a few ideas. Here's how Barbara Clark and her family did it . . . room by room and bit by bit. Enjoy.

The Garbage Book, Canadian Office of Energy Conservation, June 1976, free from:

> Box 3516, Station C
> Ottawa, Ontario, K1Y 4G1
> Canada

"How to Save Energy and Money by Throwing Out Less"—a good companion to your other living lightly booklets. It's always nice to add new ideas.

Family Energy Watch Calendar, $1.50 from:

> Dept. of Energy
> 528 Cottage St., N.W.
> Salem, OR 97310

The most informative, dense calendar I think I've ever seen; yet laid out in such a way as to still be useful as a calendar. The information included is of near book proportions. Many, many good energy use charts, facts, quotations. Designed to help people keep a watch over their energy intake.

Changing Habits or Changing Technology?

Some people still claim that insulation programs won't work or won't be effective, or that people won't change their habits of energy use. Not only have both proven effective, but it seems that social innovation, or changing our habits, may be more effective than technical innovation such as more efficient heaters or insulation!

In a recent West Virginia experiment, people participating in a rebate program reduced their use of electricity by an average of 29% per household. People were given a cash refund for lowering their home energy use by changing their energy use habits. For more information, contact J.D. Cone, Department of Psychology, West Virginia University, Ogleby Hall, Downtown Campus, Morgantown, WV 26506.

In a Pennsylvania winterization program, 762 homeowners have experienced an average 23% reduction in fuel costs. Insulation costs will be paid back by fuel savings in 5 years or less. Contact Department of Community Affairs, Bureau of Housing and Development, Rm. 503, South Office Building, Harrisburg, PA 17120.

Under a Puerto Rican law which went into effect in July 1974, the government pays for fuel cost increases for anyone using less than 425 kwh of electricity per month. 74% (736,000) of residential customers are keeping their use of electricity low enough to meet the subsidy standards at a cost of $48 million to the government. Much of the success of the program is attributed to the island's energy conservation campaign, which includes teaching people to read their meters to be sure they are staying within the limits. For more information contact Nydia Verge, Head, Consumer Relations Office, Puerto Rico Water Resources Authority, GPO Box 4267, San Juan PR 00936.

Source: Alternative Sources of Energy

ENERGY CONSERVATION POLICY

The Energy Conservation Project
Environmental Law Institute
1346 Connecticut Avenue N.W.
Suite 620
Washington, DC 20036
These folks are preparing a series of handbooks on energy conservation policy in transportation, land use, industry and other areas. See review in Transportation section. Good complement to the Ford Foundation's *A Time to Choose* and their publications on energy conservation in industry and other areas.

Energy Conservation and Economic Growth—Are They Incompatible?
$1 from:
The Conference Board Record
Box 908, FDR Station
New York, NY 10022
The Board, a non-profit business research organization, concludes that a substantial degree of energy conservation is an attainable U.S. goal without ill economic effects.

Energy Conservation Task Force Report to Governor Straub, Nov. 24, 1975, available from:
Oregon Dept. of Energy
528 Cottage St., N.E.
Salem, OR 97310
Excellent suggestions by a 21-member citizen task force on the establishment of a state energy conservation plan for the various sectors: residential, commercial-industrial, transportation, com-

munications and agriculture. Full of good ideas and implementable, practical methods.

Energy Conservation: It's Nature, Hidden Benefits, and Hidden Barriers,
UCID-3725, 92 pp., $5 from:
NTIS
U.S. Dept. of Commerce
Springfield, VA 22161
Discusses "hidden benefits"—such as higher total employment, less pollution, lower demand for capital and hence lower interest rates—and "hidden barriers"—such as ignorance of energy's role in economic processes, lack of detailed information about individual energy systems or options, inelasticity of demand by users.

UCAN Manual of Conservation Measures
(Conservation Paper No. 35)
Office of Utilities Programs
Federal Energy Administration
Washington, DC 20461
Or maybe your local FEA office. Free. This manual was prepared for the "Utilities Conservation Action Now" workshops of FEA. Unsurpassed as a guide from the utilities' point of view of what can be done to save power. Some measures are silly, others excellent, but the whole way through you can watch how their minds tick.

The Potential for Energy Savings Through Reductions in Hot Water Consumption, by John George Muller, April 1975, 43 pp., FEA/D-75/453, contact:
Federal Energy Administration
Publications Distribution Office
Office of Communications & Public Affairs
Washington, DC 20461

An excellent report! Contains an outline and summary which estimate that the U.S. uses 1.1 million barrels per day of oil equivalent but that we could save 560,000 BPD without adverse effect on comfort, health or life style. Excellent and comprehensive references specific to dishwashing, laundering and details on all calculations. Mr. Muller, formerly at the FEA Energy Conservation Office and the *Energy Reporter*, has moved to emergency energy planning. Does he know something we don't?

HOME INSULATION

It feels good to know that by putting insulation into our attics or weather stripping on our windows, any of us can be more effective energy producers than nuclear engineers and billion-dollar power plants! Reducing our need for energy avoids the need for building new power generating facilities, conserves energy resources, and is far cheaper and longer lasting besides. Here are the details:

Retrofitting Existing Housing for Energy Conservation: An Economic Analysis, National Bureau of Standards Building Science Series 64, $1.35 from
  U.S. Government Printing Office
  Washington, DC 20402

An excellent technical analysis comparing the economic desirability of different combinations of adding additional insulation, storm windows, and weatherstripping to existing houses. The first study available which analyzes for a wide range of energy costs as well as climatic conditions. It also contains a model that can be used to calculate what combinations will give homeowners the greatest savings in investing different amounts of money in energy conservation measures for their homes.

Making the Most of Your Energy Dollars
  National Bureau of Standards
  Consumer Information Series 8
  U.S. Government Printing Office
  70¢

The homeowner's guide to selecting energy conservation measures for the home based on the technical report, *Retrofitting Existing Housing for Energy Conservation: An Economic Analysis.* Both the technical report and the homeowner's guide are still the "best of the bunch" of all the insulation guides we've seen. Insulation values are keyed to climate and energy costs—you pick what you think energy will cost through the life of your home! They also give economics for storm windows, weather stripping, floor insulation and other conservation measures.

"Thermography Helps Save Energy," *Engineering News-Record*, 27 March 1975, p. 11.

Short summary of a project by a midwest utility that used aerial infra-red photography to measure heat escaping from buildings in order to notify the owners of their potential insulation savings. Also reports on close-up analysis of buildings by these thermography techniques to determine insulation savings.

"Infra Red Scanners," *Popular Science*, Sept. 1975, p. 86, contains dramatic thermograms and survey of developments in the field, and *Thermography of Buildings*, by Paljak and Pattersson, 1972, available from Svensk Byggtjanst, Box 1403, S-111 84, Stockholm, Sweden (40 Swedish Kroner) is the basic reference manual for thermography, describing theory and techniques and containing a catalog of black and white and color thermograms for common wall design conditions.

The Arkansas Story, 1975, free from:
  Owens-Corning Fiberglass Corp.
  Fiberglass Tower
  Toledo, OH 43659

Despite governmental claims to the contrary, energy conservation is demonstrating its superior cost-effectiveness and is being implemented rapidly. Energy-conserving house designs, reducing heating demands by 50-60%, are now being rapidly adopted even by speculative builders because of their demonstrated savings. Financing institutions are endorsing such designs, saying that non-conserving homes are going to be a drag on the market. Owens-Corning's brochure explains one widely-adopted design.

Have a Wrap Session with Your Electric Water Heater, 4 pp., free from:
  Water Heater Wrap
  Conservation Dept.
  Portland General Electric Co.
  121 S.W. Salmon
  Portland, OR 97204

If yours is an *electric* hot water heater located in an *unheated* space, you can save $15 maximum, $8-$10 average, per year on your electric bill. Takes 45 minutes of your time, 1 roll of R-11 (3-1/2") kraft-backed insulation, 15" wide, a 15-yd. roll of duct tape, scissors, marking pen, a measuring tape and gloves. An excellent idea being ably promoted by Pacific Power & Light's full-page "how-to-wrap-it" newspaper ads and by PGE's nifty little red booklet. Easiest $20/hour we've seen.

Project Retro-Tech: Instructor's Kit for Home Weatherization Course, Conservation Paper No. 28A, available from:
  Director
  Office of Weatherization for Low
    Income
  Federal Energy Administration
  Washington, DC 20461

A beautifully done series of lesson plans designed to help supervisors of work crews engaged in home insulation, storm window installation and weatherstripping. Also, vocational-technical schools will find these four manuals very useful in training the large cadre of skilled technicians specializing in weatherizing homes who will be needed as homeowners turn to retrofit measures for relief from higher energy costs.

Insulation Reporter, quarterly newsletter free from:
  National Mineral Wool Insulation
    Assoc.
  382 Springfield Ave.
  Summit, NJ 07901

Contains info on developments in home insulation and use, gas and electric-utility energy-conservation programs; gov't studies, energy legislation and conservation effort.

Keeping Warm for Half the Cost, Phil Townsend and John Colesby, 1975, available for $3 U.S. from:
Conservation Tools & Technology
143 Maple Road, Surbiton
Surrey KT6 4BH ENGLAND

This is by far the best homeowner's guide for reducing energy use in the home that we've seen since Eugene Eccli's *Save Energy, Save Money*. Belts are tighter in England, and they have a stock of houses several hundred years old that require thoughtful techniques for insulating, so the British have a lot of experience we can learn from. The book's best new information seemed to be a section on clear how-to information for making insulating window shutters and storm windows, and ideas for commercial products available in England that could be usefully produced here: sheetrock laminated to styrene insulation for direct application to existing walls; rigid foam insulating tiles to apply to ceilings where access to rafter space is difficult; foam panels covered with masonite for insulating existing concrete floors; kits for glass storm windows. Good detailed instructions, clear illustrations and lots of practical know-how for dealing with difficult or unusual situations. Insulation levels suggested should be at least doubled for the U.S. (and probably for England), but otherwise pretty directly applicable here.

Save Energy: Save Money! by Sandra & Eugene Eccli, Dec. 1974, 40 pp., free from:
The National Center for Community
Action
Network Services: Energy
1711 Connecticut Ave., N.W.
Washington, DC 20009

Well-illustrated, straightforward "how-to-do-it" home energy conservation booklet by the co-editors of *Alternative Sources of Energy* magazine. More tips on how to save energy than most manuals supplied by utility companies: sealing the house against heat loss, getting heat where you need it when you want it, using the sun, furnaces-stoves-fireplaces, appliance savings, do-it-yourself projects, what to do in emergencies. Includes a list of CSA Regional Offices who can help you winterize your home, get heating fuel and gasoline.
Oriented to sensible actions that poor people can take in rented houses as well as economical homeowner projects.

In the Bank or Up the Chimney, U.S. Dept. of Housing and Urban Development, 1976, $1.95 from:
Chilton Book Company
Radnor, PA 19089
Well-illustrated, useful how-to manual both for calculating what insulation measures are economic for you and for actually doing them. Insulating basements, how-to and how not to insulate existing walls, etc. All with a comparative list of the options available.

The Window Book, Fred Schmidt, 1976, free from:
Season-All Industries Inc.
Indiana, PA 15701
Written to promote the company's storm and replacement window products but contains a lot of sensible information on heat loss and gain through windows and doors, how they are constructed, how to fix, improve, or replace them, and when it benefits to do so.

"Insulating Shutters," *Alternative Sources of Energy*, Nos. 18 and 20, $1.50 and $1.75, respectively, from:
ASE
Route 2, Box 90A
Milaca, MN 56353
Two articles on design and construction of insulating shutters to reduce night heat loss through windows. *RAIN Magazine* is assembling a collection of designs and how-to information that should be available early spring 1977.

Storm Windows:
Vinyl storm windows are a good temporary substitute for permanent glass storm windows, yet most vinyls have a lot of visual distortion. A good exception is Sear's Super-clear Vinyl—about 12¢ per square foot—available from any Sears store or catalog.

Cellulose Fiber Insulation Manufacturers:
Not widely known yet, cellulose fiber insulation, made from treated recycled paper, is inexpensive and effective. *Low-Cost, Energy-Efficient Shelter*, by Eugene Eccli,($10.95 from Rodale Press, Emmaus, PA 18049), provides a list of manufacturers on page 208. Some questions remain as to the permanence of its fire retardant and possible absorption of moisture—but it's worth checking out.

Mortite, $1.95 for 90 ft., from
Mortell Company
Kankakee, IL 60901
or from your hardware store

Modeling-clay-like caulking that comes like a long grey earthworm wound into a coil. You just unroll it and squish it into the cracks around your windows. Doesn't give the dead air space storm windows are supposed to, but it really takes care of infiltration—which is the biggest heat loss in a house. In the spring, just roll it up again for next year. Good stuff. May be produced by other manufacturers, but this is the only kind we've found available.

Insulation Values of Materials and Construction can be found in several reference sources if you are figuring the insulation value of a particular design or construction. *Handbook of Fundamentals* of the American Society of Heating, Refrigerating and Air Conditioning Engineers contains detailed insulation values for a broad range of conventional and uncommon building materials and common building designs. *Architectural Graphic Standards* by Ramsey and Sleeper also contains drawings of different kinds of construction with related insulation values. Both are expensive reference books best found in a library or architect or engineer's office.

"Best" insulation depends on your needs. Foam insulations give most insulation for the same thickness but cost most. Fiberglass has given the most insulation per dollar, while new cellulose fiber insulations promise to be cheaper if settling, moisture and fire performance is equal.

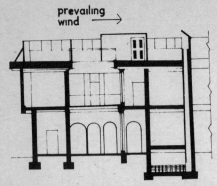

prevailing wind →

Ventilation Shaft in Pakistan House

ENERGY CONSERVATION IN BUILDINGS

A Nation of Energy Efficient Buildings by 1990. Free from:
 The American Institute of Architects
 1735 New York Ave., N.W.
 Washington, D.C. 20006

In their earlier report, *Energy and the Built Environment: A Gap in Current Strategies,* the AIA concluded, "We are now investing vast quantities of increasingly scarce capital resources in strategies which have less potential, less certainty and longer-delayed payoffs than an alternative strategy emphasizing a national program for energy efficient buildings." This new report shows how such a program can be economically, financially and administratively feasible, and presents recommendations for immediate action. Shows the national significance of energy conservation in buildings.

Energy Conservation Guidelines for Existing Buildings, FEA, 1975, from:
 Federal Energy Administration
 Washington, DC 20461

A two-volume set of guidelines equally applicable to new or old buildings. ECM-1, the first volume, covers savings through improved operating procedures. ECM-1 contains an excellent series of curves and charts that allow quantification of savings for each conservation measure.

Energy Conservation Design Guidelines for New Office Buildings, 2nd Edition, $2 from:
 Regional GSA Business Serv. Centers
 or
 Business Service Center (3F1)
 General Services Administration
 7th & D St., S.W.
 Washington, DC 20407

This latest edition features new sections on computer software programs useful for energy design and analysis, and the state-of-the-art in solar energy.

Energy Conservation in Building Design, 1974, $5 from:
 The American Institute of Architects
 1735 New York Avenue N.W.
 Washington, DC 20006

A good beginning primer for architects to give a sense of what contributes to the energy use of buildings and where potentials for conservation exist. Doesn't cover any of the reams of detailed, technical and how-to stuff now available, but is still a good place to start for anyone needing an overview not buried in numbers and tables and charts.

Energy, Environment and Building, by Philip Steadman. $5.95 ppbk from:
 Cambridge University Press
 32 E. 57th St.
 New York, N.Y. 10022

Energy conservation in buildings, solar energy for water and space heating, directory and maps of solar heated buildings in the U.S., windpower, small scale water power, composting waste treatment and methane gas, water conservation and local water collection covered in a clear and easy way. This and the *Energy Primer* will bring you up to date quickly.

Earth Covered Building for Energy Conservation Conference Proceedings. Write:
 Frank L. Moreland, Director
 Center for Energy Policy Studies
 Inst. of Urban Affairs
 Univ. of Texas at Arlington
 Arlington, TX 76019

Covers life-cycle costs, finance and insurance implications, social and behavioral aspects, energy and material consumption patterns, aesthetics, interfaces with city networks, political and legal considerations, technical considerations, environmental impact, implementation strategies.

Energy Conservation Program Guide for Commercial Buildings, by Louis A. de Latour, P.E., Oct. 1975, NRE-PE-75-2, single copies free from:
 Project Engineering Section
 Dept. of Conservation
 State Land & Natural Res. Bldg.
 P.O. Box 44156
 Baton Rouge, LA 70804

One of the nice things about this item is a comprehensive, annotated bibliography on energy conservation publications and computer programs focused on commercial buildings; another is the almost layman level of explanation which pervades, increasing its utility and, finally, separation of conservation measures into those needing little or no capital outlay and those which mean a major expenditure.

New Energy Technologies for Buildings, by Schoen, Hirshberg & Weingart; edited by Jane Stein, $5.95 from:
 Ballinger Publishing
 17 Dunster St.
 Cambridge, MA 02138

Another excellent Ford Foundation Energy Policy Project report, this time on the institutional barriers to energy conservation and solar technologies and methods to remove them: Trade unions, building codes, sun rights, the housing construction industry. An excellent overview.

SECA (Service for Energy Conservation in Architecture)
 c/o Boston Architectural Center
 320 Newbury St.
 Boston, MA 02115

24-hour a day clearinghouse phone line for energy conservation information relating to the industry that supports it. Acts as a referral service drawing on professional expertise.

"Energy Conservation Legislation Dealing with Buildings." from:
 Federal Energy Office
 Washington, D.C. 20461

Community Conservation

Planning for Energy Conservation, $7.50
from:
> Living Systems
> Route 1, Box 170
> Winters, CA 95694

Living Systems has been doing some of the finest innovative work in energy conservation we've seen. They've recently completed the design of a passive solar heated and cooled office building for the state of California that should reduce energy use in the building by 90%. They've built a number of homes with insulating shutters, water walls and other simple techniques that cause energy use to plummet. *Planning for Energy Conservation* contains a series of city ordinances they've prepared for energy conservation, many of which have already been adopted in Davis, CA. Their new building code reduces energy needed to heat and cool dwellings by 50%. Tree planting ordinances are expected to reduce summer temperatures in the city by 10°F. Ordinances establishing solar zoning, reducing setbacks of buildings (allowing more effective use of land), reducing street widths, setting up bikeways to open lower energy transportation options, allowing work at home, restricting fossil fuel pool heaters and permitting clotheslines (!)

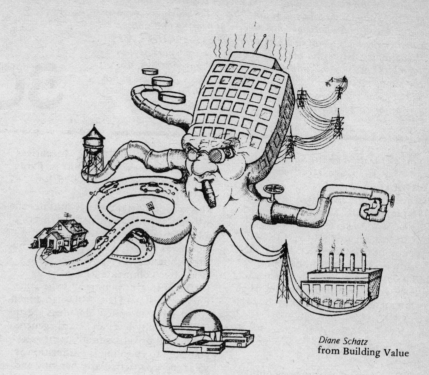

Diane Schatz
from Building Value

TYPICAL SUBDIVISION BLOCK SHOWING WASTED SPACE

■ UNUSEABLE PARKING SPACE
▦ UNUSED FRONT YARD SPACE
□ UNUSED SIDE YARD SPACE

Using Energy Wisely, free from:
> Mayor's Energy Office
> 124 W. Ashley St.
> Jacksonville, FL 32202

A fine information packet on energy that can serve as a good model for other communities. Outlines energy use in the city, how to read your meters, how to save $600/year using their shuttle bus service, vacationing near to home, a "where-to-call" guide to community services, calculation sheets for home energy use, and flexible working hours the city has instigated to lessen rush hour problems.

"Energy" issue of *The New Harbinger*, Vol. 2, No. 6, Sept. 1975, quarterly, $2.00, single copy postpaid, $6/yr. subscription from:
> *The New Harbinger*
> Box 1301
> Ann Arbor, MI 48106

Food co-ops, utility co-ops, farmers' co-ops, auto repair co-ops even! This time the *Journal of the Cooperative Movement*, published by the North American Student Cooperative Organization, examines "co-ops in energy" with emphasis on existing oil co-ops which supply over 30% of U.S. and Canadian farmers' petroleum needs. Includes the story of the world's first co-op refinery, on co-ops banding together to find and produce their own oil, on credit union gasoline. Instructive to those who say "we can't do it alone" . . . they don't have to.

District Heating Development Work in Sweden, Peter Margen, 1975, Report AE-VS-159 from:
> Studsvik AB Atomenergi, Sweden
> S-611-01 Nykoping 1
> Sweden

Two-thirds of the energy in our fossil fuels that are used to generate electricity ends up as wasted heat energy. At least *we* waste it. Sweden has for years been using that "waste" heat for space heating in the districts surrounding the electrical generating plants, resulting in beneficial use of 70-80% of the energy in the fuel rather than the 20-30% that we get. Makes sense. This report is outdated in that it refers to use with nuclear as well as fossil fuel thermal plants and was produced before Sweden's recent decision to abandon nuclear power in favor of energy conservation, but it contains reports on recent studies on district heating.

*See Waste Recycling, Transportation and other sections for other community energy conservation ideas.

Wise use of the sun should be as obvious as day and night, yet it's been a long time coming. Even ERDA has finally had to give in to the inevitable and report that solar heating is already economically competitive with electrical heating and will be cheaper than gas or oil in a few years. The even better news is that simpler, wiser and more direct ways to use solar heat are even less costly. And unlike wind and methane systems, use of the sun is most favorable on an individual basis. The last major use of solar energy—solar industrial process heat—is finally beginning to be developed. Long live our star!

SOLAR

I've Got a Question about Solar Energy, 16 pp., May 1976, available free from:
ERDA
Office of Public Affairs
Washington, DC 20545
Everyone who has ever written RAIN about solar energy ought to write ERDA for a copy of this pamphlet. In a RAIN-style info access format, the 11 most-asked solar questions are answered and addresses given for further queries. Highly recommended. (Suggested by Bill Rice, ERDA)

Toll-free Solar Info, call:
800/523-2929 or
800/462-4983 (Pennsylvania only)
Open since Oct. 1976, the National Solar Heating and Cooling Information Center has available a list of financial incentives reports from government and private industry, and a general reading list covering periodicals, directories, technical solar textbooks, architectural publications, catalogs and non-technical books. Or write: P.O. Box 1607, Rockville, MD 20850.

Free solar, wind and other energy films, write:
Film Library
Technical Information Center
Box 62
Oak Ridge, TN 37830

The *Solar Home Book* by Bruce Anderson is probably the most informative general introduction to the use of solar energy in housing—see review on page 221.

A Citizen's Handbook on Solar Energy, 56 pp., $1.50 for individuals, $8 for institutions and businesses from:
Public Interest Research Group
2000 P St., N.W., Suite 711
Washington, DC 20036
Introduction to the economic and technical feasibility of solar energy. Acquaints the reader with current areas of solar research. Lists solar experts and information sources.

"Technological Utilization: Incentives and Solar Energy" by Arthur A. Ezra in *Science*, February 28, 1975, Vol. 187, pp. 707-713.
This very important article outlines the difficulties which hinder the delivery of solar technology, and where and how incentives can be best applied to stimulate public use of solar energy. Ezra's perceptive comments were used by ERDA in the formulation of the Solar Energy National Plan. Although aimed at federal level policy, the ideas are applicable at any level and local agencies, public and private, should use it as a guideline to speeding the transition to solar energy, particularly banking and lending institutions.

A Floridian's Guide to Solar Energy, Robert J. Pozzo, 1976, $1.50 from:
Florida Solar Energy Center
300 State Road 401
Cape Canaveral, FL 32920
A useful consumer's guide to solar energy—explains graphically the basic concepts of solar radiation, collection, storage, water and space heating and air conditioning. Gives detailed information on safety, costs, how to find a reputable manufacturer, and current status of solar systems and equipment. Particularly this latter half of the book provides a good model for other states to help people know the specific potentials and problems in their area.

Sunspots: Collected Facts and Solar Fiction, by Steve Baer, $3.00 postpaid from:
Zomeworks Press
P.O. Box 712
Albuquerque, NM 87103

Absolutely great! Solar humor, workable fantasies open up your brain cells, hard science is applied with a friendly Mr. Wizard "watch this now, my friends" touch. Subtly educational passages by an inventor-philosopher who has listened to the questions and his own head are interspersed with smile-provoking "old-timer" witticisms aimed at our expensive energy establishment. A gas to read, bound to be a word-of-mouth best seller.

Tilly's Catch-A-Sunbeam Coloring Book: The Story of Solar Heat Even Grownups Can Understand, by Tilly Spetgang, illus. by Malcolm Wells, arch., $1.50 each (80¢ each for 50 or more) from:
Solar Service Corp.
306 Cranford Rd.
Cherry Hill, NJ 08003
A funny, yet highly educational book on solar energy for children 4 to 14. Lovely. Now all we need is one each on energy conservation, wind power, gardening, recycling and ? and we'll all make it into the next century safely. What did you put in the blank? Maybe we can find it and tell you about it next issue of RAIN.

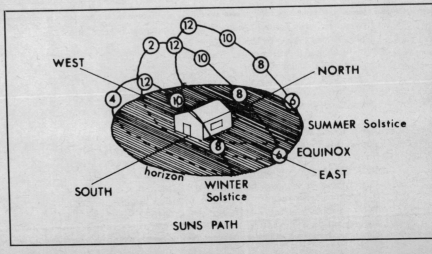

Building Value: Energy Design Guidelines for State Buildings, Tom Bender and Lane deMoll, 1976, $3.25 from:

> **Office of the State Architect**
> **P.O. Box 1079**
> **Sacramento, CA 95805**

Policy guidelines prepared for the California State Architect, containing a guide to design resources for energy-wise design, energy conserving landscaping, dry toilets, and economic evaluation. Outlines valuation of buildings to include lifecycle costs, externalized costs, and institutional performance in addition to regular fiscal economics. The State Architect's guidelines for state buildings include low-flush toilets, solar heating, accounting of unused solar energy as lost income to a building, source-stream energy analysis, and landscaping for summer shading of streets and sidewalks.

'76 ISES-SESCI Conference Proceedings, including 350 papers from August 15-20, 1976, Winnipeg, Canada, joint meeting of the International Solar Energy Society and the Solar Energy Society of Canada, Inc., $7.25 per volume (members), $8.25/vol. (non-members), full 10-volume set for $57.50 (members), $67.50 (non-members) from:

> **'76 Conference Proceedings**
> **American Section—ISES**
> **300 State Rd. 401**
> **Cape Canaveral, FL 32920**

Volumes are: (1) international and U.S. programs, solar flux; (2) solar collectors; (3) solar heating and cooling; (4) solar systems, simulation, design; (5) solar thermal and ocean thermal energy conversion; (6) photovoltaics and materials; (7) agriculture, biomass, wind, new developments; (8) storage, water heaters, data communication education; (9) socio-economics and cultural; and (10) business, commercial, poster section, miscellaneous. If you're serious about solar energy, ask for info on how to become an ISES member.

Solar Energy for Space Heating and Hot Water, document SE-101, single copies free from:

> **ERDA Technical Information Center**
> **Box 62**
> **Oak Ridge, TN 37830**

Provides some of the cost and savings figures that consumers and builders need to decide whether or not to use solar space heating and water heating equipment. Charts, graphs and drawings help the reader decide if solar equipment would be economical for a home or building in his particular climate zone. Excellent handout for state energy offices, environmental groups and solar conferences. *Solar Energy and Conservation for Home Heating and*

Cooling (EDM-817) is a useful companion piece which is also available. It explains how solar and conservation technologies can be combined to help homeowners save money. Ask for their publications list.

There are two government publications which should be on the shelves of every solar engineer and architect in America. They are:

Development of Proposed Standards for Testing Solar Collectors and Thermal Storage Devices, by NBS (National Bureau of Standards), February 1976, 265 pp., available from:

> **Superintendent of Documents**
> **U.S. Government Printing Office**
> **Washington, DC 20402**
> **SD Cat. No. C13.46:899**

and

Solar Heating and Cooling of Buildings: Methods of Economic Evaluation, by NBS, May 1975, 47 pp., $3.75 from
> **NTIS**
> **Nat'l Technical Information Service**
> **Springfield, VA 22151**

The first reviews different techniques that are or could be used for testing collectors/storage and then outlines a recommended test method, including apparatus and instrumentation, for both components. This document is very useful to anyone, even a layman, working on his own "new" collector design because the theoretical equations, backed by an outstanding 163 reference bibliography, will aid in refining a design toward that goal of less $ cost/BTU output.

The second item explains and illustrates with simple, but realistic examples the use of life-cycle cost analysis and benefit cost analysis to evaluate and compare the economic efficiency of solar and conventional energy systems. Since the equations are difficult for anyone without experience in the field of engineering economics (although programmable on a pocket calculator), their recommendation that a consumer-oriented handbook be produced is an excellent idea.

Proceedings of Pre-Submission Conference on Program Opportunity Announcement, DSE-75-1, and *Program Opportunity Notice*, DSE-75-2, Oct. 1975, free from:

> **Solar POA/PON Conference**
> **Transcript**
> **Division of Solar Energy**
> **US-ERDA**
> **Washington, DC 20545**

This unedited question and answer session will be very useful to any architect, engineer, city planner or solar-oriented individual who is trying to figure out how all this solar energy

demonstration-project money at ERDA and HUD will be spent. Financing cost-sharing, government procurement of solar equipment, ownership, retrofitting . . . most of the questions are asked, and the answers are clearly stated. Vital for the solar library; also useful for its list of small and large solar firm/consultant attendees at the back.

Description of the Solar Energy R&D Programs in Many Nations, edited by F. deWinter and J.W. deWinter, 294 pp., $7.60 (print), $2.25 (microfiche) from:
> **NTIS**
> **U.S. Dept. of Commerce**
> **5285 Port Royal Rd.**
> **Springfield, VA 22161**

Prepared for ERDA, report covers 32 countries, Organization of American States, UNESCO, and several private organizations. Descriptions were supplied by representatives of each country; many were taken from presentations given at the Aug. 1975 International Solar Energy Society Conference held in Los Angeles, California.

Solar Thermal Energy Utilization
> **Energy Information Center**
> **Technology Application Center**
> **University of New Mexico**
> **Albuquerque, N. Mexico 87131**

Bibliography of 2,100 references with abstracts. Space heating & cooling, power generation, water distillation, solar furnace operation, crop drying, cooking. A subscription with update to bibliography $50/yr. Bib. alone $37.50.

ERDA Solar Bibliography, TID-3351-RIP1, $13.75 (print), $2.25 (microfiche) from:
> **NTIS**
> **U.S. Dept. of Commerce**
> **5285 Port Royal Rd.**
> **Springfield, VA 22161**

This updated version supercedes ERDA's 1975 bibliography. A 2-volume source list, it goes as far back as could be obtained, is complete through 1975, and is divided into broad subject areas such as solar energy conversion, photovoltaic power plants, solar radiation use, and others.

MOVABLE INSULATION

from Solar Oriented Architecture

THERMAL MASS

INSULATION

DIRECT SOLAR

Higher energy prices make heavily-insulated houses an economic necessity. Insulation, in turn, reduces energy use so much (50-60%) that direct (passive) systems of solar heating become more practical than mechanical systems to provide the remaining heat needed for single family homes. Mechanical systems require the same pumps, thermostats and controls *no matter what the size of the system, so small systems cost more for the heat delivered. The sun's heat can be used at a much lower cost by south facing windows with insulation over them at night to keep the heat gained in the daytime from being lost again. Water beds, concrete floors and adobe walls that soak up the heat in the daytime and release it into the rooms at night are other simple, yet effective, techniques.*

"Solar Era," Harold Hay, *Mechanical Engineering*, Oct., 1972.

Demonstrates the necessity for insight into the elegance of simple ways of doing things in addition to careful engineering. Making ice in the desert, why black is cooler than white, and elegant houses that heat, cool, make ice and hot water in their roofs.

The Solar Home Book, by Bruce Anderson, 304 pp., $7.50 from:
  Cheshire Books
  Church Hill
  Harrisville, NH 03450
Buy this book, the best amid a now overwhelming flood of often jargony or plain redundant solar texts, if (1) you're an architect-engineer who has begun to rediscover the "more BTU per buck" potential of designing with the climate and using direct (i.e. passive) solar techniques and you need more info; (2) you're about to build or have an architect design your solar home, as it will enable you to understand what you should include to "build-it-yourself and to talk knowledgeably with your architect; or (3) you're simply interested in solar energy and want enjoyably to find out more.

Design with Climate: A Bio-Climatic Approach to Architectural Regionalism, by Victor Olgyay, 1963, 190 pp., $25 from Princeton University Press
  41 William Street
  Princeton, NJ 08540
Best basic guide to climate sensitive siting and design of buildings. Quantitative info and techniques for measuring and calculating needed information are usually given.

Passive Solar Heating & Cooling Conference Proceedings, Univ. of New Mexico, Albuquerque, NM, May 18-19, 1976, for availability and price write:
  Solar Energy Lab (Mail Stop 571)
  Los Alamos Scientific Lab
  P.O. Box 1663
  Los Alamos, CA 87543

If you can only afford one publication on this list, this is the one to get. The 40 main speakers included most of the direct-solar experts in the U.S., covering all aspects in the field.

Climatic Data Reference List, free with stamped, large self-addressed business envelope from:
  Technology Applications Center
   (TAC)
  University of New Mexico
  Albuquerque, NM 87131
Excellent, 4-page annotated sourcelist

to the weather data needed for direct-solar design, compiled for the Albuquerque conference above. Ask for their publications list.

"Why Not Just Build the House Right in the First Place?" by Raymond W. Bliss, in *Bulletin of the Atomic Scientists*, March 1976, pp. 32-40
A simple yet powerful conventional analysis of the individual and national energy- and dollar-savings possible via direct solar plus energy conservation home design, using Boston, Mass. climate examples.

Regional Climate Analyses, published by the American Institute of Architects and *House Beautiful* in the AIA Bulletin from 1949 to 1952. Now $28 paperback, $5 microfilm from:
  Xerox University Microfilms
  300 N. Zeeb Rd.
  Ann Arbor, MI 48106
Graphically displays all climate characteristics of 15 typical cities and regions of the U.S. Fortunately, you can Xerox all 200 pages yourself for $10, or the section on your region for 60¢. Since it only costs 85¢ a copy to print a document this size, you might write the AIA (1735 New York Ave., N.W., Washington, DC 20006) and request they reprint it at a reasonable price.

SUN NUMBERS

LOF Sun Angle Calculator, $5 from:
    Attn: Corporate Affairs—MDSE
    Libbey-Owens-Ford Co.
    811 Madison Ave.
    Toledo, OH 43695

First issued in 1951 to help architects design natural daylighting, solar shade overhangs and "giant south-facing picture window with night curtain" solar homes, this re-issue includes the classic plastic bubble, a completely revised and updated instruction book and an added daylight availability overlay. Get one quick before the price goes up and thank them for a simple, straightforward solar energy tool.

Solar Guide & Calculator, by Edward Mazria and David Winitzky, 1976, 11 pp., $3 from:
    Center for Environmental Research
    School of Architecture
    University of Oregon
    Eugene, OR 97403

Graphically explains where and how the sun works in relation to a building and site, and provides the user with a simplified method of calculating sun angles and the available heat energy from the sun on vertical and horizontal surfaces. Ask to be notified when the complete direct-solar workbook is available.

Solar and Terrestrial Radiation: Methods and Measurement, by Kinsell Coulson, 336 pp., 1975, $27 from:
    Academic Press
    111 Fifth Ave.
    New York, NY 10003

Detailed professional study of the theory and measurement techniques and instrumentation. Everything you always wanted to know about. . . . Excellent for college libraries.

U.S. Solar Radiation Data. Write:
    Grady McKay, Chief
    ADP Services Division
    Environmental Data Service—NOAA
    National Climatic Center
    Federal Building
    Asheville, NC 28801

Data from 60 stations across the nation is available on either an hourly or daily format on magnetic tape, punched cards or listing from the tape. Write above for free reference manuals on hourly (CD-280) or daily (CD-480) data and information on ordering. The manuals contain maps, suitable for framing, locating each station.

Direct Solar Radiation on Various Slopes for 30 to 60 degrees north latitude, John Buffo, Leo J. Fritschien, James L. Murphy, from:
    Pacific NW Forest & Range Exper. Station
    809 N.E. 6th
    Portland, OR 97232

Tables of daily values of direct solar radiation for selected slopes, in 15 degree gradients, and isograms of hourly values of direct solar radiation in 10 degree gradients. (no price)

Solar Radiation Reception, Probabilities, and Areal Distribution in the North Central Region, North Central Regional Research Publication 225—Technical Bulletin 300-1975, 54 pp., limited copies available, write:
    Agricultural Experiment Station
    Univ. of Minnesota
    St. Paul, MN

Very useful to anyone needing solar radiation data for North Dakota, South Dakota, Nebraska, Kansas, Missouri, Iowa, Minnesota, Wisconsin, Illinois, Indiana, Michigan and Ohio. Extremely comprehensive and accurate presentation.

Diane Schatz

from Building Value

MODELS

Solar-Heated Buildings: A Brief Survey, by William A. Shurcliff, $12 if check enclosed; $13 otherwise (add $2 for first class shipment), from:

William A. Shurcliff
19 Appleton St.
Cambridge, MA 02138

Now in its 13th edition, updated about every 6 months, this comprehensive survey of indirect and direct solar applications includes descriptions of 17 such direct-solar buildings as St. George's School (England), the Odeillo Houses (France), Pointe Bleue (Canada), Lawrance (Australia), Kruschke (U.S.), Terry (U.S.), Wright (U.S.), Mudd (U.S.), Dasburg (U.S.), Baer (U.S.), Kelbaugh (U.S.), Tyrrell (U.S.), Croft (U.S.), Saunders (U.S.), Lasar (U.S.), Aspen (U.S.), Hay (U.S.) and Cleveland (U.S.).

A Naturally Air-Conditioned Building, by Harold Hay, $1.00 plus stamped, large self-addressed envelope from:

Skytherm Processes & Engineering
2424 Wilshire Blvd.,
Los Angeles, CA 90057.

Introduction to the "water-bed roof for thermal mass" concept, which heats and cools the Hay-designed Atascadero, California, home.

A Strategy for Energy Conservation, by Jon Hammond, $5 from:

Living Systems
Rt. 1, Box 170
Winters, CA 95694

Excellent Davis, Calif., area analysis of direct-solar in chapter 6, pp. 39-46, showing Steve Baer's guiding hand.

TECHNICAL EVALUATION

Simulation Analysis of Passive Solar-Heated Buildings, LA-UR-76-89, by Douglas Balcomb and Jim Hedstrom, free with stamped, large self-addressed envelope from:

Los Alamos Scientific Lab
Solar Energy Lab (Mail Stop 571)
Los Alamos, NM 87544

Reprinted in *Sunpaper*, Winter 1976 (see page 230 for access), the results of this comparison between direct- and indirect-solar systems illustrate that direct solar can provide a major fraction of the heat energy required to operate a building. What to pay attention to in order to achieve such results is explained.

Preliminary Design and Performance Analysis for New State Office Building Site No. 1, 1976, from:

Office of the State Architect
P.O. Box 1079
Sacramento, CA 95805

Design, energy and economic analysis of the new $12 million state office building in Sacramento being designed by the State Architect's Office. The building is expected to reduce energy use by 90% and be almost totally heated, cooled and lit by passive renewable energy systems. Detailed analysis of solar heating, night cooling, lighting and solar hot water systems performance.

Skylight Energy Performance and *Systems Analysis for Skylight Energy Performance*, by Donald A. Moore, 1975, from:

Center for Industrial and Institutional Development
McConnell Hall
University of New Hampshire
Durham, NH 03824

Skylights and roof windows are excellent ways to get daylighting and solar heating far inside of buildings. They save electricity for lighting, fuel for heating and make rooms feel good. Combined with insulating shutters, or Zomeworks' "Skylid," and letting the sun shine on water-filled containers, they make a simple and effective direct solar heating system. These two papers evaluate the savings and extra costs from use of skylights over a year's time and show that if properly designed they will save energy in almost every climate. The second report is a guide to both manual and computer calculations to enable engineers, code officials or people to analyze overall performance of skylights—including data necessary.

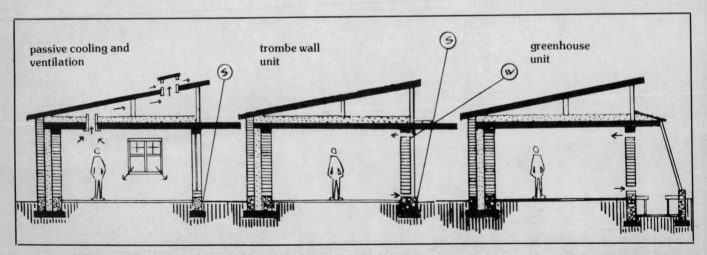

passive cooling and ventilation

trombe wall unit

greenhouse unit

"Roof-, Ceiling- and Thermal-Ponds," by Harold Hay, pp. 335-36; "Thermal Evaluation of a House Using a Movable-Insulation Heating and Cooling System," by Phillip Niles, pp. 338-39; and "Some Performance Characteristics of the CNRS (Odeillo) Solar Houses" by F. Trombe, pp. 366-67, in *Solar Use Now—A Resource for the People*, Extended Abstracts, ISES Conference, Los Angeles, July 28-August 1, 1975, from:

> ERDA Technical Information Center
> P.O. Box 62
> Oak Ridge, TN 37830

Theory and practical evaluation of two direct solar-thermal mass applications: "Skytherm" and "French Trombe Wall."

"Beadwall" by David Harrison in *Solar Energy*, vol. 17, no. 5, Nov. 1975. Description of normal and possible system configurations, BTU energy and dollar cost savings relative to single- and double-glazing and overall economics of blowing bean-bag polystyrene beads between two sheets of glass to insulate at night. A Zomeworks product.

Thermal Environmental Engineering, by James L. Threlkeld, 1970, 495 pp., $16.15 from:

> Prentice-Hall
> Englewood Cliffs, NJ 07632

This comprehensive text, which covers the basic principles of psychometrics, moist air thermodynamics, solar radiation calculations for buildings, heating and cooling via mechanical systems, also includes information on how to figure thermal lag in heat flows through walls and roofs. The best general treatment available until someone writes a book focusing on direct-solar.

HOW TO / ACCESS

"Designing the Solar-Tempered Home," by Eugene Eccli, in *Low-Cost Energy Efficient Shelter*, pp. 257-287, 1976, $10.95 from:

> Rodale Press
> Emmaus, PA 18049

Includes designs for adjustable solar shade overhangs, solar window construction, moving carpeting, interior masonry walls for thermal mass, including modifications to existing homes.

Solar Heating Papers (Guide, $.50; Basics, $4; Supplement, $4; Builders Set, $4; Index, $1), from:

> Norman B. Saunders, P.E.
> 15 Ellis Rd.
> Weston, MA 02193

A phased self-teaching course that begins at the layperson high school level, proceeds through construction to a high professional level. Questions are answered clearly and comprehensively. Emphasizes use of passive methods and energy conservation before application of more expensive, active solar heating systems. Covers cost tradeoffs and economics of life cycle. Excellent and highly recommended.

—Solar altitude and azimuth for selected days of the year at 40 degrees north latitude.

Passive Solar Water Heater, by Horace McCracken, 18 pp., May 1976, $6 postpaid from:

> Horace McCracken
> Rt. 1, Box 417
> Alpine, CA 92000

Similar to Steve Baer's (ZOMEWORKS) "Breadbox" solar water heater, except that the insulated box has much larger tanks and the sides do not open at sunrise and close at sunset.

Drum Wall Plans, by Steve Baer, $5 from:

> Zomeworks
> P.O. Box 712
> Albuquerque, NM 87103

How to install and operate a water-mass south wall. Includes materials list and instructions. Ask for product-publication price list.

Bread Box Water Heater Plans, $2.50 from:

> Zomeworks
> Box 712
> Albuquerque, NM 87103

A simple and effective design, one of which heats shower water at the Farallones Institute Rural Site in Occidental, California. One or more ordinary 30-gal. hot water tanks (recycled) are stripped of insulation, painted flat black and placed in a glass-covered insulated box with insulated reflecting doors. The sun shines through the glass onto the tank and also bounces off the reflecting doors onto the tank. The doors are open during the day to receive the sun and closed at night to conserve heat. Zomeworks strikes again!

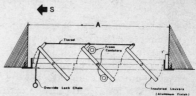

Skylid Insulating Shutters

"Nightwall" by Steve Baer, 1975
Zomeworks Corp.
P.O. Box 712
Albuquerque, N.M. 87103
$6.00 for a minimum order of 20 magnetic window glass clips with which to create your own styrofoam beadboard panels to insulate your large picture windows at night (get ready for next winter) and save money on fuel bills. Represents the kind of simple excellence and common sense for which Steve is justly famous and which government grants never seem to elicit. Superior to drapes, storm windows or double glazing for energy conservation. Do-it-yourself with clips and plans (buy bead board locally) or have Z-Works fabricate them for you. Free brochure on request.

SOLAR GREENHOUSES

"In mastering the science of origins (excuse me, the science of Godward solutions), Ziller carried the quest to its most personal extreme. Clear-eyed and confident, he returned—literally—to energy, dissolving in the pure essence that spawned all life.

Even as I type these words, John Paul Ziller, the baboon with the firebug buttocks, and Jesus the Christ of Nazareth are melting together into sunlight."—*Another Roadside Attraction*, by Tom Robbins

It is not enough to see solar greenhouses as a way of beating the high cost of petroleum. They embody a rediscovered awareness of our wholistic relationship to sun and biosphere. The economic, cultural and energetic factors that indicate the continuing metamorphosis are beginning to be articulated. For instance, John Todd of the New Alchemists writes:

"If modern industrial agriculture were replaced with a diversity of alternatives that included small, biologically-gardened or -farmed regions during the normal growing season and terrestrial capsules such as Arks for year-round production of foods, then a good deal beyond agriculture would be affected."

"The replacement of fossil fuel agriculture might alleviate some of the impact of the seemingly inevitable economic crash or famine. It would encourage agriculture to be less corporate and to re-establish it as a local and regional pursuit, involving as it eventually must, a much larger proportion of the society. . . . Thus decentralization might in turn lead to a repopulation of the countryside and perhaps even to a re-birth of a diversity of cultures and customs which are bio-regional in their content."

Yes, bio-regionalism. The humble solar greenhouse reflects, to a greater degree than even the passive solar home, this rekindled human attention to what Peter Berg, ace watershed analyst of the Pacific Rim, calls "living-in-place" and "reinhabitation." For, to the already myriad climatological parameters of passive design for dwellings (insulation, temperature, humidity, windspeed and direction, soil type, site landscaping and topography), we must now add the long-evolved limits of various living organisms, both plant and animal. And we must design life-provoking niches for them.

Green plants are exercise enough for most experimenters. In fact, there is no ERDA-USDA funded solar aquaculture-greenhouse now being monitored. Yet it is the tri-fold combination of sun, plant and animal that pushes us to the limits of our knowledge about such a greenhouse's site bio-region and of our design and construction skills. We have commercial greenhouses, rabbit ranches and aquaculture farms, yet few models of any potential food production systems for an energy-short future which mix them all together: the New Alchemist's Cape Cod and Prince Edward Island Arks (vegetables, fish), Jim DeKorne's Survival Greenhouse (vegetables, rabbits) and the Reichmuth-Barnes passive parabolic reflector solar greenhouse near Seattle, Washington (vegetables, fish).

Even on this delicate and scientific frontier of food and energy, individual resourcefulness and private initiative have already established a clear lead over the ivory-tower specialists in the "more for less" sweepstakes. While the USDA's Agricultural Research Service funds no university greenhouse researcher for less than $50,000, they still have all completely missed what the pathfinders mentioned above have not only already intuited, but accomplished as finished, working systems. It is doubtful our nation can afford much longer the stupidity of well-funded, certified-by-peer-review, greenhouse academics unaware of integrated bio-solar systems. In this field, innovative and informed inter-disciplinary talents are required. You'll find little of it in the government documents listed; rather, as Steve Baer's example reminds us, pay attention to the writings of those who watched "Mr. Wizard" as kids. Unless you have $250,000 in taxpayers' money to waste, of course, like the U.S. Dept. of Agriculture—Agricultural Research Service.

A bit unhappy? Send your queries, suggestions and complaints to the men responsible for the program, for writing the RFPs (request for proposals), etc.:

Mr. T. E. Bond
Rural Housing Research Unit
USDA-ARS
P.O. Box 792
Clemson, SC 29631

and

Bill Cherry
ERDA
Div. of Solar Energy
20 Massachusetts Ave., N.W.
Washington, DC 20545

● TECHNICAL EVALUATION

Climatic Data Reference List, compiled for Passive Solar Heating & Cooling Conference & Workshop, May 18-20, 1976, Albuquerque, NM. Free with self-addressed, stamped large envelope, from:

Technology Applications Center (TAC)
University of New Mexico
Albuquerque, NM 87131

Basic sources for data and methods in the analysis of any micro-climate for a specific solar greenhouse or passive solar building site.

Climate Under Glass, Technical Note No. 131, WMO No. 373, by Dr. J. Seeman, 40 pp., 1974, available from:

World Meteorological Organization (WMO)
Geneva, Switzerland

Highly recommended technical treatment of general greehouse climatology covering: radiation and heat balance, heat transformation, temperature conditions, air-soil-plant temperature, air humidity, evaporation and consumption of water, carbon dioxide, climate control basics, regulation of light, temperature, shading, ventilation, water-atomizing installations and short-period spraying. Excellent bibliography on each topic, clear drawings and graphs complete this excellent survey. We need it updated with plant and animal data for integrated bio-solar greenhouses.

"The Development and Testing of an Environmentally-Designed Greenhouse for Colder Regions," by Tom A. Lawand, et al., in *Solar Energy*, Vol. 17, No. 5, 1975, or send $1.25 to:
> Brace Research Institute
> MacDonald College—McGill Univ.
> Ste. Anne de Bellevue 800
> Quebec, Canada H9X 3MI

This is the best starting point for a technical understanding of reflective, interior north wall solar greenhouses. Ask for their extensive and excellent a.t. publications list.

Simulation Analysis of Passive Solar Heated Buildings, by J. Douglas Balcomb and James C.Hedstrom,LA-UR-76-89, available from:
> Los Alamos Scientific Lab
> Solar Energy Lab
> Mail Stop 571
> Los Alamos, NM 87544

This important paper, while not strictly about greenhouses, explains in understandable text and straightforward equations the physical basis for passive design which can be then applied to solar greenhouse design.

●MODELS

Two Solar Aquaculture-Greenhouse Systems for Western Washington: A Preliminary Report, by Woody Deryckx, Becky Deryckx and Howard Reichmuth, December 1976 (Hunger Action Center, Community Services Administration Grant No. 00071-T-75/01), 51 pp., $10 from:
> Ecotope Group
> 747 16th Ave. East
> Seattle, WA 98112

Two solar-heated greenhouse-aquaculture facilities have been constructed at Pragtree Farm, near Arlington, Washington, as a joint venture by Tilth and Ecotope Group. These structures, the small rhombicube octahedron and the parabolic north wall greenhouse, represent an attempt to determine the feasibility of integrating warm-water aquaculture systems into solar-heated greenhouses designed for the specific climatic conditions of Western Washington and to develop optimally efficient food-raising facilities for use by low-income families and individuals.

Evaluation of a Solar Heated, Waterwall Greenhouse, by Patricia Moodie, Ken Smith, Howard Reichmuth, $3.00 from:
> Ecotope Group
> 747 16th Ave. East
> Seattle, WA 98112

Design drawing, structural description and technical analysis of heat-gain and -loss balances for a passive design with a 4' high wall of clear plastic water-filled bags stacked behind the south vertical windows. Graphs, tables and equations included.

The Journal of the New Alchemists, Vol. 2, $6 single copy from:
> Nancy Todd, editor
> New Alchemy Institute
> P.O. Box 432
> Woods Hole, MA 02543

Explains your basic ARK I à la Cape Cod. A descriptive and artistic poster of Ark II (Prince Edward Island) is available, and future *Journal*s will contain updates of their work.

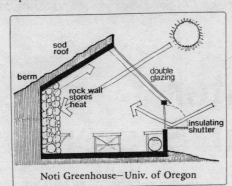

Noti Greenhouse—Univ. of Oregon

An Attached Solar Greenhouse, by Bill Yanda, $1.75 from:
> The Lightning Tree
> P.O. Box 1837
> Santa Fe, NM 87501

Step-by-step illustrated instructions, in English and Spanish, for locating and building low-cost extensions to existing dwellings which grow food and provide supplement home heat. Based on the Solar Sustenance Project construction of many such units at high, isolated, rural New Mexico homesteads. Excellent example of a.t. instruction which can be applied in hands-on weekend workshops.

The Survival Greenhouse, by James B. DeKorne, $7.50 from:
> The Walden Foundation
> P.O. Box 5
> El Rito, NM 87530

Construction and operation details of a pit greenhouse. Tells how keeping four rabbits inside one can increase vegetable 15 to 70% and provide 400 lbs. of protein annually; how to build a food-producing aquarium from a 55-gallon drum. 150 pp., 30 drawings and charts, 20 photos.

● ACCESS

The Food- and Heat-Producing Solar Greenhouse: Design, Construction, Operation, by Bill Yanda and Rick Fisher, $5.50 from:
> John Muir Publications
> P.O. Box 613
> Santa Fe, NM 87501

Best survey available on the types of solar greenhouses now being built in various U.S. bio-regions, covering the work of 30 innovators in the field.

Energy in U.S. Agriculture: Compendium of Energy Research Reports, Conservation Paper No. 37A, by Jim Rathwell and Gwendolyn Gales, 176 pp., 1976, $7.50 from:
> Superintendent of Documents
> U.S. Government Printing Office
> Washington, DC 20402

21 out of the 1291 entries in this document list ongoing or recently-completed research projects and articles related to greenhouses. Projects include direct and indirect (i.e. solar panels—storage) solar heating, waste heat utilization, off-peak power for heating and lighting, and conservation of water, heat and fertilizer. Lists the grant award of each university greenhouse research team which presented papers at the "Fuel & Food" Conference. Find a local library which is a U.S. government document depository.

Solar Energy—Fuel and Food Workshop Proceedings, April 5-6, 1976, Tucson, Arizona, edited by Merle Jensen, 258 pp., $5 per copy (checks payable to Univ. of Arizona) from:
> Environmental Research Lab
> Tucson International Airport
> Tucson, AZ 85706

Includes 17 reports from U.S. Dept. of Agriculture—Agricultural Research Service, corporate and university researchers with emphasis on retro-fitting large commercial greenhouses for energy conservation and solar heating via a variety of methods. Only one of the reports, starting on page 129, considers the possibility, for new greenhouses, of a direct (i.e. passive) solar design in which the greenhouse is the collector-storage system à la Brace Research Institute, New Alchemy Institute, Reichmuth-Barnes and others listed in the "Models" section. However, forewarned of this shortcoming, home and commercial greenhouse builders will still glean some useful hints. Best of all, the name and address list of participants at the back will aid you in contacting nearby resource people for answers to specific questions. (Courtesy Bill Rice, ERDA)

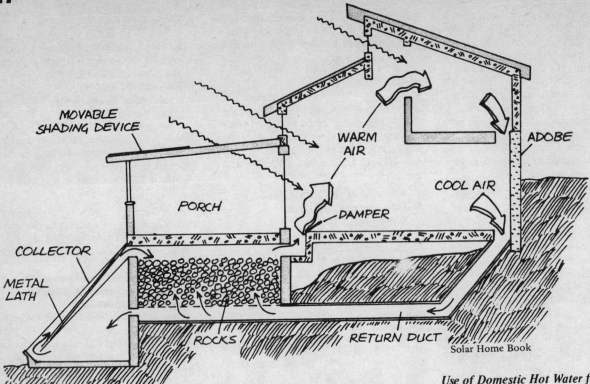

MOVABLE SHADING DEVICE

WARM AIR

ADOBE

COOL AIR

PORCH

DAMPER

COLLECTOR

METAL LATH

ROCKS

RETURN DUCT

Solar Home Book

Air and Water Solar Systems

Solar Energy and the Flat Plate Collector, by Francis de Winter, June 1974, 29 pgs., free from:

    Copper Development Association
    405 Lexington Avenue
    New York, N.Y. 10017

An extremely useful annotated bibliography which clues one in to solar collector invention and development history, generally accepted (i.e., experimentally proven) design principles for different types of collectors which grew out of such experimentation; economic factors, relation of solar panel to solar radiation available. A lot in a few pages.

Illustrated Solar Energy Guide of Flat-Plate Collectors for Home Application, $3.00 from:

    EI&I Associates
    P.O. Box 37
    Newbury Park, CA 91320

One of the least expensive, yet practically useful, laymen-oriented introductions to the basic theory and installation of solar hot water heaters. It includes clear system diagrams as the various installation options are explained as well as concisely defining and describing the advantages and disadvantages of direct use vs. heat exchange and natural thermosiphon vs. forced circulation by pumping.

Solar Heating of Buildings and Domestic Hot Water, by E. J. Beck and R. L. Field, Technical Report R-835, 80 pp., April 1976, free from:

    Civil Engineering Laboratory,
    Code L80
    Naval Construction Battalion Center
    Port Hueneme, CA 93043

Much valuable material on a great variety of approaches to solar heating is clearly presented in brief yet effective descriptions and 15 pages of excellent drawings and sketches. Much attention is given to cost and energy savings calculations, and the authors include many charts and worksheets.

Solar Water Heating, by S. Paige, 30 pp. paperback, $4 from:

    Edmund Scientific Co.
    555 Edscorp Bldg.
    Barrington, NJ 08007

A complete guide to solar water heating including how a basic heater works, effects of climate on your solar heater and how to compute your solar water heating needs. Full of large charts & diagrams on building solar water heating systems. An excellent, practical introduction.

Use of Domestic Hot Water for Space Heating. $10 ($5 to members) from:

    Circulation Sales Department
    ASHRAE
    United Engineering Center
    345 E. 47th St.,
    New York, N.Y. 10017

How to put all that conserved, solar-heated water to use. Ask for their "Symposium Bulletin" publication list.

Solar Collector Manufacturing Activity, compiled by the Office of Data, FEA, every 6 months, free from:

    National Energy Information Center
    Federal Energy Administration
    Washington, DC 20461

Contains number of manufacturers, their addresses, phones; sq. footage of solar panels produced from Jan.-June and July-Dec. of each year; analysis of number of bbls. of oil/day displaced by use of solar collectors in the U.S.

Enhanced Solar Energy Collection Using Reflector-Thermal Collector Combinations by D.K. McDaniels, D.H. Lowndes, 20 pgs., $.75 postpaid from:

    Solar Energy Center
    University of Oregon
    Eugene, OR 97403

Theoretical derivation of the help available from reflective surfaces to solar collectors, based on Henry Mathew's use of an aluminum foil horizontal rooftop reflector and a nearly vertical collector at his Coos Bay, Oregon, home. Summary: Reflector increases solar radiation available to collector by 1.2 to 1.7 times, averaging 1.5 times what would be collectable by solar panel alone.

Solar Energy Heat Pump Systems for Heating and Cooling Buildings, Workshop Proceedings, June 12-14, 1975, Pennsylvania State Univ., edited by Stanley F. Gilman, ERDA Document No. C00-2560-1, available from:

ERDA Technical Information Center
P.O. Box 62
Oak Ridge, TN

The reports in these proceedings cover everything you ever wanted to know about heat pumps of all kinds and how they relate to solar energy, utility load factors and energy conservation. An excellent refresher for architects and engineers, it has introductory material on what a heat pump is and does for the beginner as well. (Courtesy Dr. Fred Morse, ERDA Solar Heating & Cooling Branch Chief).

MITRE Air Solar Heating & Cooling Systems Report, inquire as to availability and price to:

MITRE Corp.
Westgate Research Park
McLean, VA 22101

A research study done for the Sheet Metal Workers International Association finds Solar HVAC systems using air rather than water have lower initial cost, lower maintenance costs, lighter weight, no freezing, leakage or corrosion problems, and greater simplicity and ruggedness. (From Sept. 1975 *Advanced Solar Energy Technology Newsletter*.

Solar Water Heating in South Florida: 1923-1974, and *Lending Institution Attitudes Toward Solar Heating and Cooling of Residences*, NSF-RA-N-74-190, by Scott, Melicher and Sciglimpaglia, 169 pgs., $2.45 from:

Superintendent of Documents
U.S. Government Printing Office
Washington, D.C. 20402

Much-needed history, clearly graphed explanations of economic payoff (time relative to different levels of initial investment (installation cost) versus rising fuel costs, why owners-nonowners, contractors and bankers like and dislike solar systems.

Solar Water Heating in South Africa, CSIR Research Report 248, available from:

Will Cawood, Director
Solar Water Heating Program
National Building Research Institute
Pretoria, South Africa

Reports on efforts to find a collector able to withstand the deteriorating effects of South Africa's intense and ultraviolet-rich sunshine. Part of a national campaign to install solar water heaters in residences.

"The Sun Can Heat Our Homes—Even in the North," by Richard A. Mirth, in Vol. 6, No. 3, pp. 3-10, of
The Northern Engineer
Univ. of Alaska
Institute of Arctic Environmental Engineering
College, Alaska 99701

Problems and potential of solar energy in Alaska by a registered professional civil engineer; contains Seattle, Spokane solar heating analysis for comparison with Alaskan communities.

*For up-to-date information on rapid developments in both air and water solar systems, see the following pages on solar access, and check the Solar Industries Index.

THERE'LL BE A HEAT PIPE IN YOUR FUTURE

Line the inside of a metal tube with a wick from a kerosene lamp, saturate the wick with water, evacuate the tube, seal both ends, and you have a heat pipe. Dip one end in a pot of boiling water and within a few seconds the other end will be too hot to handle.

Basically, a heat pipe is a super thermal conductor that transmits heat by the evaporation and condensation of a working fluid. It can transfer about 1000 times more heat energy than copper, one of the best known conductors and do it with a temperature drop of less than 3°F. per ft. Heat pipes have no moving parts, require no external energy (other than the heat they transmit), are reversible in operation, and completely silent. And, like any piece of tubing or pipe, they are rugged and can stand lots of abuse.

Already in use in medicine, nuclear reactors, space flight and as heat sinks in electronic equipment, the energy crisis and the increasing demand for more efficient use of fuels is prompting renewed interest in heat pipes for waste heat recovery and solar energy collection. Since you'll soon be seeing and hearing more about heat pipes, we've selected a few articles that will introduce you to their theory and applications and listed manufacturers who supply them:

"Heat Pipes: Breakthrough in Thermal Economy?" by Charles Behrens, in *Appliance Manufacturer*, Nov. 1973, pp. 72-75.

"How Heat Pipes Work" by Don Noren, in *Chemical Engineering*, August 19, 1975, pp. 89-91.

"The Heat Pipe," by G. Yale Eastman, in *Scientific American*, May 1968, pp. 39-46.

MANUFACTURERS:

Noren Products, Inc.
3511 Haven Ave.
Menlo Park, CA 94025
415/365-0632

Isothermics, Inc.
Dept. PM, Box 86
Augusta, NJ 07822
201/383-3500

E. B. Kaiser Co.
2114 Chestnut
Glenview, IL
312/724-4500

Acme Manufacturing
7500 State Rd.
Philadelphia, PA
215/338-2850

Bry-Air, Inc.
Rt. 37W
Sunbury, OH 43074
614/965-2974

Solar News & Views, monthly
International Solar Energy Society
   News (ISES), quarterly
Solar Energy Journal, quarterly
$30 per year for all three from:
   ISES, American Section
   300 State Road 401
   Cape Canaveral, FL 32920

$30 yearly membership dues in ISES brings the American section newsletter, with 8 pages on U.S. local chapter activities, conferences, educational seminars, expositions, book reviews; the 8-page *ISES News* with international coverage, solar energy history; and the *Journal* with in-depth technical and academic studies by solar scientists, engineers, architects, inventors and economists the world around. A very good deal but please be patient. Membership has recently gone through the top of the charts. These are the people who can tell you how to organize a local chapter in your town. The American section is now compiling a directory listing members and their solar energy interests.

Sunworld, quarterly, $12/year, $3.50 single copy to non-members of the International Solar Energy Society from:
   SUNWORLD-ISES
   320 Vassar Ave.
   Berkeley, CA 94708

First July '76 issue contained Harold "Skytherm" Hay's article on ancient and modern direct solar technology. Watch for increasing coverage of direct solar design and engineering. Free to ISES members.

Informal Directory of the Organizations and People Involved in the Solar Heating of Buildings, by William A. Shurcliff, $5 if check enclosed with order; $7 otherwise; add $1 for shipment by 1st class mail. Make checks to:
   New England Solar Energy Assoc.
   P.O. Box 121
   Townshend, VT 05353

Covers institutions (gov't agencies, commercial concerns, universities, professional societies, foundations), individuals (solar engineers, architects, inventors, house owners, planners, writers), 26 countries (U.S. emphasis, much material on Canada, Great Britain, France, Australia) and activities (all aspects of solar heating of buildings: invention, research, development, design, manufacture, marketing, operation, use, government).

Solar Utilization News—SUN, monthly, $8 per year to individuals, $15 to libraries or industry, from:
   Alternate Energy Institute
   P.O. Box 3100
   Estes Park, CO 80517

Rachel Snyder, former editor of *Solar Energy Washington Letter* and *Solar Energy Industry Report*, has gotten off to a fine start as *SUN*'s editor. It's inexpensive and well-done, with names and addresses for further information where appropriate. Ask for a free sample copy and send the names of a few friends who are also interested in solar energy. (Suggested by Ken Smith, Ecotope Group)

Solar Engineering Magazine, free to qualifying solar professionals, $10/yr. for 12 issues to all others, from:
   Solar Engineering Magazine
   8435 N. Stemmons Freeway,
   Suite 880
   Dallas, TX 75247

Although indirect (active) solar systems are presently emphasized, this is the best place to look for the few direct solar components now on the market, since it is the only solar mag with reader service cards for easy access to product information.

Solar Age, monthly, $20/year, 12 issues, from:
   Solar Age
   Rt. 515, Box 288
   Vernon, NJ 07462

Edited by Sandra Oddo and Bruce Anderson of TEA (Total Environmental Action), after 3 issues *S.A.* seems to have what a solar magazine should: the understanding that wind and bioconversion are "solar" as they are solar-derived, an excellent editorial advisory board of familiar names (Dubin, Farber, Kreider, Kreith, Meyer, Rittelmann, Wright), understandable Capitol Hill legislative coverage, attention to energy conservation and storage since these help all renewable energy sources, and a refreshing optimism that we can not only make the necessary transition to a new solar-based society and lifestyle . . . but that it will be a gas.

Solar Access

Sunpaper: Newsletter & Journal of the N.M. Solar Energy Assoc., $10/year
    P.O. Box 2004
    Santa Fe, NM 87501

Sunpaper comes with membership in NMSEA and covers more advanced direct-solar work than any other state solar newsletter. Most of America's passive system pioneers live and work in New Mexico.

New England Solar Energy Association Newsletter. $5 per year, from:
    John T. Schnebly, Jr., Acting Coord.
    NESEA
    P.O. Box 121
    Townshend, Vt. 05353

Usually filled with useful regional info, edited by John Schnebly.

Colorado Solar Energy Association News, free to dues-paying members of:
    Colorado Solar Energy Assoc.
    University of Colorado at Denver
    1100 14th St.
    Denver, CO 80202

CSEA is just now completing its formation as a regional chapter of the American Section of the International Solar Energy Society. Their Sept. 1976 *News* contains much information of regional interest and a membership questionnaire. This is a good spot to watch for Colorado's solar developments.

Solarscope, free to dues-paying members, $1 single-copy, from:
    So. Calif. Solar Energy Assoc.
    202 "C" St.—11B
    San Diego, CA 92101

This regional chapter of the ISES American Section puts out an excellent 16-page newsletter full of useful solar info, with a Southern California focus. Their *Western Regional Solar Directory* covers manufacturers, engineers, architects, contractors, distributors and consultants in California, Arizona, Nevada and Hawaii with over 500 listings. It's $2.35 postpaid ($1.35 to members) from SCSEA.

Solar Energy Intelligence Report. $75 per year, twice monthly, from:
    Business Publishers
    P.O. Box 1067
    Silver Spring, Md. 20910

Covers significant developments and issues involving solar energy of all types . . . heating and cooling, wind energy, bioconversion to fuels, solar thermal-electric, photovoltaic, and ocean thermal conversion. Includes information on federal, state and local legislation, new technologies, publications, contracts and grants, marketing opportunities. Averages 8 pages. Excellent conference calendar. Name, address and phone contacts for further information. Ask about *Energy Resources Report*.

Solar Energy Index, inquire for price and availability from:
    Solar Energy Industries Association
    1001 Connecticut Avenue, N.W.
    Washington, DC 20036

In preparation by the above group, this index will replace the *Catalog of Solar Energy Heating and Cooling Products* (ERDA-75) presently put out by ERDA. The present volume contains company names, addresses, phones, contact persons, product description and product information on 251 solar manufacturers. For continuing update on new solar products, see magazines, such as *Solar Engineering Magazine*, that cover technical and economic developments and keep track of manufacturers and their products.

Advanced Solar Energy Technology Newsletter. $60 per year, monthly, from:
    Carl M. Langdon, editor-publisher
    A.S.E.T. Newsletter
    1609 W. Windrose
    Phoenix, Az. 85029

Emphasis on hi-tech developments in solar flat-plate collectors, solar thermal electric power plants, solar test facilities, storage, NSF-NASA level of applied technology. Covers important legislation, conferences. Succinct, very readable.

Solar Energy Digest, by William B. Edmondson. $27.50 per year, monthly, from:
    Lillian B. Edmondson, Circulation Manager
    S.E.D.
    P.O. Box 17776
    San Diego, Ca. 92117

The first and most widely read, started by the Edmondsons before the sun looked better as a result of energy crisis rising prices. Emphasis on all solar techniques, including wind and biomass conversion; covers only the most important legislation on all levels. Attention devoted to hand tools and reference books for the backyard "do-it-yourselfer" is unique and extremely useful. Especially recommended for high school libraries, vocational and community colleges. Ask for flyer on patented SOLARSAN collector invented by Mr. Edmondson.

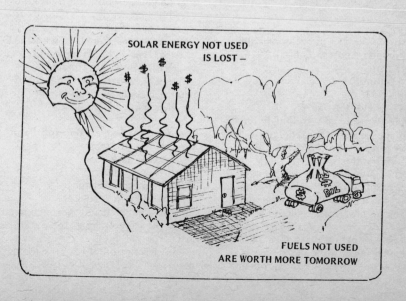

SOLAR ENERGY NOT USED IS LOST—

FUELS NOT USED ARE WORTH MORE TOMORROW

> *Yes, wood is stored solar energy. And yes, you can heat your house with it, and cook with it, and use it to stretch out your heating budget. And yes, there is a lot of wood around—if we manage our forests and our appetites.*

WOOD ENERGY

Wood as a Source of Energy
For current availability, contact:

E. Bradford Walker
Director of Forests
Agency of Environmental
Conservation
Montpelier, VT 05602

A task force led by R. Sam Lloyd (D-Vermont) has released findings that there is enough annual growth of cull or unmarketable wood in Vermont to supply all the state's fuel requirements. On a practical basis, wood burning would only supply 25% of the state's energy needs. It would be an economical move to use wood as a fuel, as it would use 4.7 million tons of cull wood that otherwise rots.

The Physical Energy Potential of Wood,
by Helmuth Resch, 5 pp., 1974, free
from:
Forest Research Lab
Oregon State University
Corvallis, OR 97331

A good companion to Vermont's "Wood as a Source of Energy," this also discusses the use of wood as a fuel. The amounts and types of residue available and the BTU/ton and per cu. ft. heating characteristics of various woods are explained.

Additional studies have been made of the potential of wood as a major energy source in Minnesota, New Hampshire and Maine, and the Mitre Corporation and Georgia Pacific have received a half-million dollar grant to evaluate wood energy potential on a national scale.

The Woodburner's Encyclopedia, Jay Shelton and Andrew Shapiro, 1976, $6.95 from:
Vermont Crossroads Press
Box 333
Waitsfield, VT 05673

A long-awaited and refreshingly candid comparative analysis of energy efficiency of different kinds of wood heaters. Should fuel the fire of efficiency studies for quite a while. Stoves studied ranged from Franklin fireplaces to oil barrel stoves to air-tight heaters and Scandinavian imports. Efficiencies of stoves tested ranged from 40 to 65 percent. Almost all stoves tested appeared similar in efficiency, with all displaying a wide range of performance depending on how they were operated. A number

of factors significant in performance are discussed, including size of pieces of wood burned, heat transfer from stovepipes, low vs. high burning rates, ease of operation and fuel capacity. A number of useful pointers for choosing wood heaters are given.

Bill Day's Consumer Guide to Wood Stoves, 1976, $1 from:
RAIN
2270 N.W. Irving
Portland, OR 97210

Bill Day is a second generation wood stove repairperson from Oregon. His advice on wood stove selection, installation and repair is based on long-term performance and durability rather than what a salesperson can tell you about a new stove in a showroom. These two pages are exerpted from the *Guide.*

"Getting Fire—A Field Guide to the Stoves" in *Maine Times,* October 22, 1976, 30¢ from:
Maine Times
Topsham, ME 04086

A good guide to how different kinds of wood heaters work and feedback from users on specific problems/features of different stoves. Compiled with the help of Albie Barden of Maine Wood Heat Co., RFD 1, Box 38, Norridgewock, ME 04957, who is preparing a more extensive guide to wood-burning stoves and heaters.

Woodburning Stoves, Bob and Carol Ross, 1977, $10 from:
The Overlook Press
c/o Viking Press
625 Madison Avenue
New York, NY 10022

The most detailed and thorough manual we've yet seen on design, operation and installation of wood stoves. Gives a model description of features and design of a very wide range of heaters, using a fireplace for heating, and converting

fireplaces to wood heaters. Complements Shelton's work on efficiencies and Bill Day and Albie Barden's guides to actual use performance of various units. Appendices with houses designed for wood heat, details of Ken Kern's barrel stove, chimney installation, manufacturers, tables comparing wood and other fuel costs with various heater efficiencies.

The SEVCA Stove
Southeastern Vermont Community
Action
9 Westminster Street
Bellows Falls, VT 05101

This is the stove that got top rating in Jay Shelton's wood stove energy efficiency tests. It's not a slick commercial model but produced by a local anti-poverty agency for low-income clients. It sells for $105 to people meeting OEO poverty guidelines (that's most of us!) or $235 to anyone else. Made out of discarded propane tanks. Hmmm! . . . if everyone who uses bottled gas cut up their tanks... . . A good example of top quality work being done by small local groups.

Wood 'N Energy, $5/yr. (at least 4 issues) from:
Society for the Protection of New
Hampshire Forests
5 South State Street
Concord, NH 03301

Keep your eye on New England in energy matters—they've raced ahead of the rest of the country in energy conservation and conversion to renewable energy sources, pushed by skyrocketing energy costs and restricted fuel imports. *Wood 'N Energy* covers the real cutting edge of developments in use of wood energy—from the long range prospects for wood as an energy source in New England to the immediate "how-to" details of stoves and cordwood.

Wood Burning Quarterly, $4.95/yr. from:
8009 34th Avenue So.
Minneapolis, MN 55420

Similar in format to *Organic Gardening and Farming* but oriented to people who heat with wood. Short consumer articles on topics such as energy-efficient fireplaces and avoiding chimney fires and an extensive product access for wood stoves, heaters and accessories.

STRETCH YOUR ENERGY and COVER YOUR BETS

Depending on solar energy for hot water heating is a lot easier when small wood, gas or electric demand heaters are available to raise the water the final step to desired temperatures when there isn't enough sunshine available. Similarly, more people are converting to burning wood since combination wood/oil or wood/gas units are available—the oil can be used to ignite the wood and to heat the house when people are away or too tired to deal with wood. Some of the units that are available:

Spring Mountain Hot Tubs, Inc.
  2617 San Pablo Ave.
  Berkeley, CA 94702
Produces copper coil convection heaters for hot tubs, operating on propane, natural gas or electricity to supplement solar heating. Larger convection heaters available also for use without solar panels, as well as redwood hot tubs. Brochure and price list available.

Blazing Showers
  P.O. Box 327
  Point Arena, CA 95468
Produces stovepipe water heaters for wood stoves and firebox waterheaters for efficient wood-stoves (that don't send so much heat up the stovepipe). Soon will have available a solar water heating system to use in conjunction with the wood heat—a natural combination as in many areas there is usually need for the woodstove anyhow when there's not enough sunshine to heat the water. All these units can be made yourself pretty easily. Someone (you? us?) should put together some simple how-to guides. Blazing Showers has one for their stovepipe heaters.

Wood and wood/oil furnaces are becoming available again in the U.S. Some claim high efficiency, but beware —the efficiency of wood burning isn't the same as the efficiency of the whole system. Few people put furnaces in their living rooms, which means that heat radiated from the furnace and distribu-tion systems frequently ends up heating a basement, crawlspace, unused rooms or the sky instead of you. Some of the wood/oil, wood/gas furnaces available in the U.S. are:

The Yukon
  Wilson Industries, Inc.
  2296 Wycliff
  St. Paul, MN 55114
This furnace is being specified now on many Indian reservations in Minnesota, North Dakota and Alaska. Wood, wood/oil or wood/gas units. Forced-air space heating.

HS Tarm
  Tekton Design Corp.
  Conway, MA 01341
Made in Denmark. Hot water space heating and water heating from wood, coal, gas, electricity or oil, with auto-matic switching between fuels.

Len-Jay Furnace Co.
  Underwood, MN 56586
A wood-burning furnace designed to add on next to an existing oil or gas furnace, sharing blower, ducts and chimney.

Riteway
  Marco Industries, Inc.
  P.O. Box 6
  Harrisonburg, VA 22801

Modern-Aire Wood or Wood-Oil Furnace
  Modern Machine and Welding
  2307 Hwy. 2 West
  Grand Rapids, MN 55744

Richard Hill
  Department of Industry
    Cooperation
  Boardman Hall
  University of Maine
  Orono, ME 04473
Designed experimental high-efficiency wood furnace installed in conjunction with a solar heating system in the new Maine Audubon Society Headquarters. The furnace is designed to transfer so much of its heat to the solar storage unit that a small fan is necessary to pull the flue air out of the chimney. Water in the wood that is converted to steam in burning is recondensed in the heat-exchanger, recovering significant amounts amounts of energy.

Across our northern border can be found more wood furnace manufac-turers. Three Canadian companies, Newmac, Duomatic and Lunenburg Foundries, manufacture combination wood-oil furnaces. Regular wood fur-naces are manufactured by Valley Comfort, Fawcett and Lunenburg Foundries. Add-on wood stoves that attach to existing oil furnaces and util-ize their fans are made by Hallmack Heating Ltd. Contact:
  Bruce McCallum
  Conserver Society News
  512 Blvd. Wilfred Lavigne
  Aylmer, Quebec
  J9H 3W3 Canada
for more information.

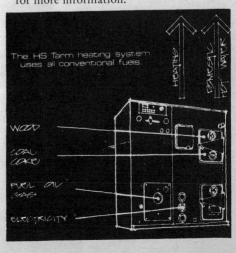

The HS Tarm heating system uses all conventional fuels.

Michael Shakespear on his
pedaled lawnmower.

*Energy? You won't hear ERDA talking
about it, but we really need to keep in
mind that we are our own best resource
—physically as well as intellectually and
spiritually. We are each born with two
hands and a strong back, and are capable
of providing for our own needs. Other
energy sources are a free bonus.*

PEOPLE

● The contrast between the bicycle and the motor car is a very good illustration of technology of human scale. The bicycle is a supreme example of ergonomics—the optimum adaptation of a machine to the human body, so that it uses this power efficiently. Hence the worldwide success of the bicycle and its derivations in meeting the real needs of people in both rich and poor countries, with a minimum demand for energy and raw materials or ill effect on the environment. The motor car, on the other hand, is a machine of inhuman scale as regards size, its weight, its power (from 100 to 1,000 times that of the driver himself) or its speed. It is for these reasons that not only is it a great consumer of fuel and raw materials, but it is a great polluter of the environment—by fumes, noise and also visually. The social costs are immense, though largely overlooked, not least the fact that vastly increased mobility has scattered families to such an extent that rarely are the three generations close enough for mutual support.

● In general, pedal drive can be expected to give a continuous power output of 75 watts or 1/10th H.P. per man, but up to 10 times this amount for short bursts. In consequence it can be considered as an alternative to any fractional horsepower motor drive for a machine or tool, e.g. spin drier, washing machine, lathe, bandsaw, fans (forge blower), small compressor or hydraulic pump.

Pedal power is of course only one manifestation of muscle power; it seems that muscle power, the most fundamental and indefinitely sustainable source of power—of essentially human scale—is unduly neglected in the present discussion of energy sources. Other animals—horses, donkeys, etc.—are also possible sources of power, as well as the more frequently-canvassed wind power and water power. All of these deserve widespread attention, particularly in the way of prototype design, production, testing and development. Not until the practical problems are faced and overcome can any proposal be taken seriously, but unfortunately suitable facilities for such work—people, facilities and money—tend to be in short supply.

Chinese bicycle transport using vintage equipment still provides adequate transportation service.

Energy-Cycle, developed by the research wing of Rodale Press, is adaptable for a variety of uses.

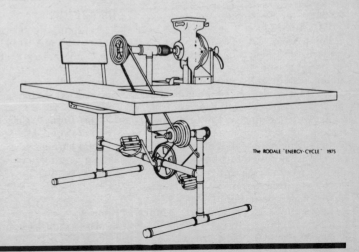

The RODALE "ENERGY-CYCLE" 1975

POWER

by S. S. Wilson, M.A., M.I.Mech.E.
Department of Engineering Science, Oxford University
Oxford, ENGLAND

Energy Efficiency of Different Means of Transport

● Apart from the ubiquitous bicycle, still a growing field, pedal power can be applied to goods transport and to a variety of stationary power uses, most of which are applicable in the U.K. as well as in less developed countries. The OXTRIKE, below, is a basic tricycle chassis to take a variety of bodies for transport of goods or people. Prototype construction has been funded by OXFAM, and it is designed to be built from kits in any small workshop, e.g. school/community workshops. The innovations include sheet steel construction, three-speed gears, powerful foot brakes and a simple form of differential drive. Such a vehicle fitted with box van, hopper or flat truck body would be useful for OXFAM shops or for use with the OXFAM Wastesaver project, as an alternative to a 35 cwt van—the OXTRIKE payload is 3 cwt, which is more than the average load in the majority of city delivery vans.

● Other uses of pedal power actually demonstrated are for corn milling and for water pumping, in which pedalling can improve the output by a factor of three over manual effort. One use for the pedal pump is as a standby for a windpump during periods of insufficient wind.

Among the plans awaiting the building of prototypes is a design for a two-man pedal-driven winch. One major use for such a winch is for cable ploughing and cultivation on the lines of the 'Snail,' as described in an earlier paper. For many purposes, including small plots and allotments, the pedal winch may be as effective as a motor-driven winch.

These excerpts are from "Technology of Human Scale" by S. S. Wilson. Wilson has been instrumental in recent development of improved people-powered vehicles. His more extensive essays in Lectures on Socially Appropriate Technology *(see A.T. section)* and Scientific American, *March 1973, explore both the social and technological aspects of improved bicycle transport.*

OXTRIKE chassis, designed for transport of goods or people.

Pedal-powered diaphragm water pump, developed by IRRI for irrigation use.

Handle bar
Discharge tube
Outlet valve
Foot rest
Water
Inlet valve

A lot of research and experimentation on the production of methane gas from fermentation of human, animal and plant wastes has fairly well defined the potentials and problems involved. Production of methane from a single household is rarely worth the cost and effort for the amount of energy produced. The productivity of methane plants in colder climates is greatly reduced because of the energy that must go back

by Ken Smith and Evan Brown

BIOCONVERSION: Methane Production

Monroe, Washington, Methane Plant, now completed and operating. Shown while under construction in summer 1975.

OVERVIEW

Capturing the Sun Through Bioconversion, the Conference Proceedings, 865 pp., March 10-12, 1976, Washington, DC, are $18.00 from:

> The Washington Center
> 1717 Massachusetts Ave., N.W.
> Washington, DC 20036

Methane is part of a larger field of activity called Bioconversion. The energy available and waste utilization possibilities are covered in numerous "state-of-the-art" reports on: (1) urban, industry, agricultural and forestry waste biomass sources; (2) land, fresh-water and ocean farming of energy crops, such as wood and kelp; (3) processes producing gaseous, liquid and solid fuels and their further products, such as fertilizer, feed and feedstocks; (4) technology assessment; (5) economic and social impacts and (6) environmental impacts. Displays the scope of bioconversion better than any other single source. Ask your library to buy it.

Methane Digesters for Fuel Gas and Fertilizer, by L. John Fry and Richard Merrill, Newsletter No. 3, 1973, $3 from:

> New Alchemy Institute-West
> Box 376
> Pescadero, CA 94060

This is the most comprehensive and available introductory publication on the subject of methane. The background information is presented in understandable laymen's language and while some of the calculations are off, it clearly describes methane generation and presents some small scale ideas and designs that can be built to explore the process.

Energy, Agriculture and Waste Management: Proceedings of the 1975 Cornell Agricultural Waste Management Conference, William Jewell, ed., 540 pp., $22.50 from:

> Ann Arbor Science
> Box 1425
> Ann Arbor, MI 48106

Jewell has collected some of the best and most up-to-date articles on waste management and its effects on energy use in agriculture. Techniques, economics, alternatives and limitations are presented.

EPA Methane Digester State-of-the-Art Report

> Tom Abeles
> OASIS 2000
> Box 1, Admin. Bldg.
> University Drive
> Rice Lake, WI 54868

Conducting a $100,000 study of digester state-of-the-art, including: design for safety, standardizing digester operations, effluent use for fertilizer/greenhouses/refeeding, electrical output, methane gas utilization, use of other rural wastes as digester input.

TECHNICAL EVALUATION

"Alternative Animal Waste Anaerobic Fermentation Designs and Their Costs," by Morris, Jewell and Casler, in *Energy, Agriculture and Waste Management* (see above)

This short article in Jewell's book goes through the economics of available options for anaerobic digestion. The economics of these alternative anaerobic systems are compared with current energy costs and current manure handling systems costs, showing that a 1000-cow operation methane generator has the potential for competing with present energy sources.

"Anaerobic Waste Treatment Fundamentals," Perry McCarty, in *Public Works*, Vol. 95, Nos. 9-12, 1964 (check your library).

This four-part article discusses: (1) the advantages and disadvantages, conventional practices, and the current understanding of the chemistry and microbiology; (2) environmental requirements and control methods; (3) control of toxic materials; (4) process design. Well done by an expert in this field.

Process Feasibility Study: The Anaerobic Digestion of Dairy Cow Manure at the State Reformatory Honor Farm, Monroe, Washington, 1975, $8 from:

> Ecotope Group
> 747-16th Ave. E.
> Seattle, WA 98112

The specific application to an existing manure maintenance system is thoroughly investigated. A review of popular and state-of-the-art literature indicated the benefits of: (1) high rate mixing through gas recirculation; (2) heat conservation through insulation and influent/effluent heat exchanger; and (3) use of easily available and relatively inexpensive manure storage tanks which are sealed to form digesters. The economics of fertilizer enhancement are evaluated.

"An Economic Analysis of Fuel Gas Production from Solid Waste," by R. G. Kispert, S. E. Sawdek and D. L. Wise, in *Resource Recovery and Conservation*, Vol. 1, No. 1, pp. 95-109, 1975.

Summary of a study done for NSF-RANN on an anaerobic system for converting 1000 tons/day of urban solid waste to methane gas. The concept, *into keeping the plant warm enough to operate. However, as a growing number of plants testify, practical amounts of methane can be produced with a homestead, neighborhood or larger operation. Amory Lovins has calculated that liquid fuels for transportation in this country could be produced by a fermentation industry only seven times as large as our present beer brewing industry.*

similar to the older L.A. plant (see p. 237), is being demonstrated by ERDA at a $2 million plant now under construction in Pompano Beach, Florida. Contact Don Walters, ERDA Fuels from Biomass Program, Washington, DC for progress reports.

Also:

"An Evaluation of Methane Production from Solid Waste," by the same authors, in the same journal as above, vol. 3, no. 3, pp. 245-255, 1976.
A technology assessment of where methane conversion of solid waste would be most economically attractive in the U.S. A map suggesting 18 specific sites, mostly in the northeastern U.S., is included.
Resource Recovery is $43.40/year. For subscription, reprint and single-copy price, write:

> Dr. Harvey Alter, editor
> Resource Recovery and Conservation
> National Center for Resource
> Recovery, Inc.
> 1211 Connecticut Ave., N.W.
> Washington, D.C. 20036

MODELS

Bio-Gas Plant: Generating Methane from Organic Waste, 70 pp., 1973, $5 plus overseas postage from:
> Gobar Gas Research Station
> Ajitmal
> Etawah (U.P.)
> INDIA

Ram Bux Singh and his associates document plans for above- and below-ground, heated and unheated, single- and dual-stage digesters. Performance data on these options is not presented.

"Production and Use of Methane from Animal Wastes in Taiwan," by Chung Po, in *International Biomass Energy Proceedings* (see ACCESS section), or write:
> Dept. of Animal Science
> National Taiwan University
> Taipei, Taiwan

Chung Po has helped build over 7500 digesters in Taiwan with 3000 gal. capacity and 3 digestion chambers with floating covers, each costing about $150. Growing algae on the effluent is also explained.

"Energy and Nutrient Conservation in Swine Waste Management," by C. L. Barth and D. T. Hill, June 1975, presented at the 1975 American Society of Agricultural Engineers Annual Meeting. Send $1.50 for Paper No. 75-4040 to:
> American Society of Agricultural
> Engineers
> 2950 Niles Road
> St. Joseph, MI 49085

Report on 1000-gallon digester built in summer 1974 by Clemson University agricultural engineers. Gives $127.90 per year as value of energy produced from one 1300 lb. cow. Cross-section drawings include Savonious wind-rotor for stirring and solar collector for heating.

Monroe State Prison Honor Farm Methane Plant, built by:
> Ecotope Group
> 747 16th Ave. East
> Seattle, WA 98112

100,000 gal. capacity with 2 digesters at Monroe, Washington. Work to resume soon on completion of system for digestion of manure from 350 dairy cows. (See Technical Evaluation section for feasibility study of this plant.)

Montfort Feed Lot Methane Plant, for info write:
> Hamilton-Standard Labs
> Windsor Locks, CT 06096

A digestion system capable of accepting large amounts of cattle manure is being developed. Methane will be upgraded to pipeline quality (CO_2 and H_2S removed) and sold as "natural gas." A 1500-gallon pilot plant is now operating there under an ERDA contract.

Bio-Conversion of Agricultural Waste for Energy Conservation and Pollution Control, by William J. Jewell, 1976, available from:
> ERDA Technical Info Center
> P.O. Box 62
> Oak Ridge, TN 37830

A new design for the small, 20-40 cow, digester. A trench above the water table lined with clay or a membrane, a reinforced "Hypalon" rubber cover and gravity feed produce a low-cost system. Initial results of this "plug flow" design indicate high efficiency at only 25 days retention time.

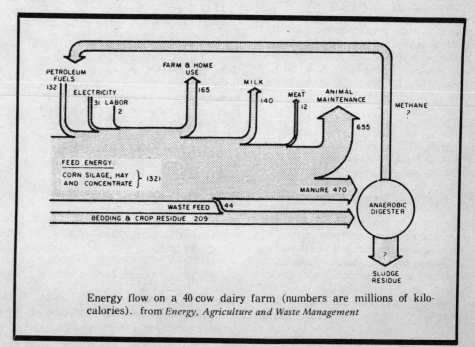

Energy flow on a 40-cow dairy farm (numbers are millions of kilocalories). from *Energy, Agriculture and Waste Management*

Los Angeles Sewage Treatment Plant,
for info write:
> Hyperion Treatment Plant (Playa
> del Rey)
> 12000 Vista del Mar
> Playa Del Rey, CA 90291

Built in 1942, 18 digesters each 100' in diameter produce a total of 5 million cu. ft. of methane gas daily. 2.5 Mcf runs the plant, the other 2.5 Mcf runs gas turbines which produce electricity at the public utility located next to it. Its fertilizer plant, at which dried digester sludge was bagged and sold to nearby farms, is no longer operational although all equipment is intact. A free pamphlet is available.

Palos Verdes Landfill Methane Recovery,
for info write:
> Fred Rice
> Reserve Synthetic Fuels
> 1602 Monrovia Avenue
> Newport Beach, CA 92663

The collection of methane from urban landfills is commercially feasible. Although it is almost impossible to recover any nutrients from a landfill, the earth cover acts as a digester lid which can be pierced to remove methane.

HOW-TO

"Turnkey" Methane Systems
> Gene Dale, President
> Agriculture Energy Corp.
> 704 W. Ludington Ave.
> Ludington, MI 49431

This company has completed two farm methane systems, a 250-cow feedlot plant near Ludington and a 150-dairy cow plant near Rice Lake, Wisconsin. Both are totally automatic, with hydraulically operated pumps and motors to end the spark danger of electrically powered equipment. They offer complete "turnkey" systems as well as design and engineering consulting.

Methane R&D and Digester Tanks
> John H. Brinker, President
> A. O. Smith—Harvestore Products,
> Inc.
> 550 W. Algonquin Rd.
> Arlington, Heights, IL 60006

Ecotope Group used two *"25-15"* (25 ft. diameter by 15 ft. high) sections of this company's *"Slurrystore"* tanks with silo roofs as digesters at Monroe, Washington, and got on-site help from a Harvestore construction supervisor and a field engineer. Harvestore has done 4 years of methane research and development. Mr. Brinker will personally route your query to appropriate people in marketing or R&D

Water Quality Engineering for Practicing Engineers, W. Wesley Eckenfelder, 1970, $7.95 paperback, from:
> Cahners
> 89 Franklin St.
> Boston, MA 02110

This is one of the standard texts in the field of waste treatment for municipal sewage treatment systems and includes municipal methane plants.

Practical Building of Methane Power Plants, L. John Fry, 96 pp., $12 from:
> L. John Fry
> 1223 North Nopal St.
> Santa Barbara, CA 93103

This is a documentation of how Mr. Fry built a farm-scale displacement (plug flow) digester in South Africa. The manure from 1000 hogs generated enough methane to run a small diesel engine and generator. Fry's book comes the closest to a "how-to-" cookbook, but it doesn't really tell you everything you need to know (i.e. drip traps, pressure relief safety valves, flame arresters, etc.).

ACCESS

Conference on Solar Energy: Biological Conversion Systems, CONF-750694, 33 pp., $4 from:
> NTIS
> U.S. Dept. of Commerce
> Springfield, VA 22161

Proceedings of the June 1975 meeting sponsored by the British Photobiology Society and the U.K. section of the International Solar Energy Society.

International Biomass Energy Conference Proceedings, $12 from:
> The Biomass Energy Institute
> Box 129
> Postal Station "C"
> Winnipeg, Canada R3M 357

The proceedings cover many aspects of bioconversion, including: production of single cell protein; mass cultivation of algae; the effects of biomass by-products on the environment, and dissociation of biomass by plasma generators. A wealth of information from an interesting source.

Compost Science: Journal of Waste Recycling, bi-monthly, $6/year from:
> Rodale Press, Inc.
> 33 East Minor Street
> Emmaus, PA 18049

An excellent source of articles on methane and other resource recovery techniques.

"Fuel Gas Production from Solid Waste," by D. L. Wise, et. al., in *Bio-Technology and Bio-Engineering Journal,* Symposium No. 5, pp. 285-301, 1975, $75/yr. from:
> Elmer L. Gadden, Jr., Editor
> Biotechnology and Bioengineering
> Interscience Publishers
> Div. of John Wiley & Sons
> 605 3rd Ave.
> New York, NY 10016

A survey of who is doing what, where with solid methane-to-methane on the municipal level, in another journal which covers the bioconversion field.

Study of Current and Proposed Practices in Animal Waste Management, by Whetstone, Parker and Wells, Environmental Protection Agency Report No. 430/9-74-003, January 1974 from:
> Environmental Protection Agency
> Washington, DC 20460

1162 publications are abstracted which deal with all aspects of animal waste utilization and/or disposal. About 30 deal directly with methane. Other subjects include algae culturing, composting, conventional sewage treatment, fish culture, lagoons, pathogens and refeeding of manure.

:

Biomass Energy Institute Newsletter
$5 per year, quarterly, from:
 Biomass Energy Inst.
 304-870 Cambridge St.
 Winnipeg, Manitoba
 Canada R3M 3H5

Annual dues includes 4-page newsletter emphasizing biomass (bioconversion) energy conversion to fuel, anaerobic decomposition of organic wastes to methane gas and fertilizer.

Bioconversion Conference Mailing List, for March 10-12, Washington, DC, inquire as to availability and price from:
 Peter Schauffler, Coordinator
 Bioconversion Conference
 Washington Center for Metropolitan
 Affairs
 1717 Massachusetts Ave., N.W.
 Washington, DC 20036

Lists over 150 speakers, panelists, reporters and chairmen and 400 participants by name, title, address and organization. Extremely useful to anyone looking for people who can answer their questions on all phases of bioconversion.

The Anaerobic Digestion of Livestock Wastes to Produce Methane, 1946-June 1975: A Bibliography with Abstracts, Gregg Shadduck and James A. Moore, 1975, $2 from:
 J. A. Moore
 Ag. Engineering Dept.
 University of Minnesota
 St. Paul, MN 55108

Most of the current interest in methane is focused on manure as a prime resource. This is the best annotated bibliography on the subject, tracing the history of the process from its beginning, through many foreign experiences (Germany, India, France), laboratory results, and current projects. Smaller sections focus on digestion of farm-generated cellulosic materials (straw, cornstalks, etc.) and the fertilizing qualities of digester effluent.

LC Science Tracer Bullet: Organic Fuels (TB 74-6), free from:
 National Referral Center
 Science & Technology Division
 Library of Congress
 Washington, DC 20540

A guide to the literature on the technology and economic feasibility of converting organic materials such as garbage, animal wastes, sewage sludge and waste paper to oil, gas and other fuels. The NRC can also supply, if asked, a computer printout of information resources relative to bioconversion for methane gas production.

BIO-GAS ECONOMICS

	Western Technology (Large-scale coal-based fertilizer plant)	Alternative Technology (Village-scale 5000 cft/day bio-gas-fertilizer plant)
Number of plants	1	26,150 (@ 8.8 tonnes per year per plant)
Capital cost	Rs.1200 million	Rs.1070 million (@ Rs.41,000 per plant)
Foreign Exchange	Rs.600 million	nil
Capital/sales ratio @ Rs.4350 per tonne nitrogen	1.20	1.07
Employment	1000	130,750 (@ 5 per plant)
Energy	about 0.1 million MWH per year *consumption*	6.35 million MWH per year *generation*

Table 1. The Production of 230,000 Tonnes of Nitrogen per Year by Western and Alternative Technologies

Village-sized bio-gas plants have proven a very effective source of both energy and nitrogen fertilizer in India without disruption of local lifestyles. Adoption of this technology throughout the country rather than Western coal-based fertilizer production will result in the dispersal of production to 26,150 villages rather than concentrating it in one center; save Rs600 millions of foreign exchange; conserve Rs130 millions of precious capital in a capital-poor country; yield a much higher rate of return on investment; generate 130 times more employment; generate energy instead of consuming it; and provide employment to the rural poor rather than the urban elite. Bio-gas plants have been adapted in India more rapidly than in the U.S. because of India's more equatorial location and lesser heating requirements which allow a greater net production of energy from the wastes than in the U.S. (*Undercurrents* 14)

> Wind has been well used as a source of mechanical energy for thousands of years—for sailing ships, grain mills, water pumping, even sails on wheelbarrows. It has been used effectively to produce electrical energy for situations where fossil fuels are difficult to supply or costs of electrical transmission are high. Wind electricity is fairly expensive, though no more so than nuclear energy, and is technically much simpler.
>
> The real problem for any society depending upon electricity for a large percentage of its energy supply is the unaffordably high cost of electrifying a whole economy. Conducting materials are in limited supply and increasingly costly. Distribution costs are high. It is doubtful if any countries outside the Persian Gulf can afford such luxury when we only need electricity for about 5% of our use. Revived interest in wind-generated mechanical power, wind-powered transportation, refined wind-electrical generators, and inverters to minimize the need for electrical storage systems by tying wind-electrical systems into the existing grid all promise to widen the effective applications of wind energy over the next few years.

Wind Energy

**ERDA-NASA 100 kW
WIND TURBINE GENERATOR**

Catch the Wind: A Book of Windmills and Windpower, by Landt Dennis, 114 pp., 1976, $7.95 from:
  Four Wind Press
  Scholastic Magazines, Inc.
  50 W. 44th St.
  New York, NY 10036

An excellent intro to wind energy for both adults and children, covering how the wind gets all that kinetic energy, the early history of windmills, windpower in the U.S., the rest of the world and prospects for its adoption as a major power source. Footnotes, appendix of research, manufacturing and marketing companies' addresses, bibliography and index. For elementary, high school libraries or gift-giving.

A Tale of Two Energies, by David R. Inglis, 1976, 10pp., 50¢ from:
  Committee for Nuclear
    Responsibility
  P.O. Box 332
  Yachats, OR 97498

An historical comparison of nuclear and wind power, their proponents, the famous experiments, and a critique of the slowness of present ERDA wind energy programs. An enlightening presentation by a professor emeritus of physics. U. of Massachusetts, Amherst, MA.

Wind Machines (NSF-RA-N-75-051), by Frank R. Eldridge, 1975, MITRE Corp., McLean, VA, 77 pp., Stock No. 938-000-00272-4, $2.25 from:
  Government Printing Office
  Washington, DC 20402

Although little attention is given to small wind generators, the focus being on the past, present and future of large wind-turbines, much information valuable for small-scale applications is presented in a concise, informative, visually superb treatment with excellent photos, graphics and layout. Up-to-date manufacturer-distributor list.

The Generation of Electricity by Wind Power, by E. W. Golding, 1976, $19.95 (hardbound) from:
  Halsted Press
  John Wiley & Sons, Inc.
  605 Third Ave.
  New York, NY 10016
or $9 paperback (surface mail) from:
  Conservation Tools & Technology
  143 Maple Rd.
  Surbiton, Surrey, England KT6 4BH

Among the best references on windpower, with extensive treatment of the history and range of wind machine designs, wind characteristics, wind distribution and large-scale installations.

Windworks Poster, $3 from:
  Windworks
  Box 329, Rt. 3
  Mukwonago, WI 53149

Beautiful four-color poster with a historical-technical survey of 17 wind machines on the front and an introduction to small-scale wind energy on the back, with expert commentary, references on commercial and do-it-yourself windpower.

Wind Power Climatology of the United States (SAND74-0348), by J. W. Reed, 1975, $7 from:
  NTIS
  Department of Commerce
  Springfield, VA 22151

A wind survey of the entire country which can give you an idea about winds in your area. All suitable data in the National Climatic Center archives for 758 stations have been analyzed for monthly, seasonal and annual average windpower.

"Generation of Power from the Wind," by E. Wendell Hewson, in *American Meteorological Society Bulletin*, vol. 56, no. 7, July 1975, pp. 660-675, single copies free from:
  Dept. of Atmospheric Sciences
  Oregon State Univ.
  Corvallis, OR 97331

Excellent introduction to windpower done by Prof. Hewson for the Oregon State Senate Subcommittee on Environment and Energy. Covers history, the atmosphere, large wind turbines, wind site surveys, power duration curves, aerogenerator design, windmill farms, novel designs, environmental impacts, cost estimates, time schedule for implementation, and general conclusions. Includes an excellent bibliography.

"Advanced & Innovative Wind Energy Concepts" RFP, organizations desiring to produce a study, write:

US-ERDA
Headquarters Procurement Operations Office
2400 M St., N.W.
Washington, DC 20545

Aimed at stimulating the investigation of wind energy concepts which might provide a significant improvement in performance per unit cost (or other factors) over more conventional wind energy systems. Multiple awards are planned.

SMALL SYSTEMS

Wind Power for Farms, Homes and Small Industry, by Jack Park and Dick Schwind, for ERDA (Contract No. E 04-3-1270), 1977. For price, write:

Wind Energy Conversion Branch
ERDA
Washington, DC 20545

"Everything you wanted to know about windmills. . . ." is covered in this excellent primer on the selection and siting of small windmachines. Written for the layman, it proceeds through history, aerodynamic theory, wind behavior-site selection, power and energy requirements, wind system components, owning a windmill, windmill economics and legal hurdles. Examples with illustrations and graphs are provided throughout. A glossary and wind power data for 750 U.S. and southern Canada stations end the compendium. Kudos to ERDA's Lou Divone (Wind Energy Branch Manager), the authors, their consultants and reviewers for this modern classic, a vital addition to the library of all who are contemplating small wind systems.

Windpower Calculator, by Robert G. Flower, free with self-addressed, stamped envelope from:

Life Size Aero Design
P.O. Box 246
Albartus, PA 18011

A nomograph for the easy "at-a-glance" figuring wind-plant power output of small- and medium-scale wind machines (i.e. under 40' blade diameter).

The Selection and Characteristics of Wind-Power Sites, C/T108, by Golding and Stodhart, 1952, $24 (U.S. nonmember), $12 (U.S. member) from:

Electrical Research Association
Cleeve Rd.
Leatherhead, Surrey, KT22 7SA, England

Explains how to develop the various stages of a wind survey. Expensive, so try a large library or inter-library loan.

Applied Aerodynamics of Wind Power Machines, NTIS PB 238594, $5.25 from:

National Technical Information Service
Dept. of Commerce
Springfield, VA 22151

Covers the operation and characteristics of any wind machine.

Wind and Solar Thermal Combinations for Space Heating, by McGowan, Heronemus and Darkazalli, single copies free with business-sized SASE from:

Wind Power Group
University of Massachusetts
Amherst, MA 01002

Results of an analytical study to determine the feasibility of a residential heating system for the northeastern U.S. designed to be powered or augmented by a wind generator system, with and without thermal energy storage, and combining these systems with a solar flat-plate collector. Also includes a description of an experimental system, "The Wind Furnace Project" built at U. Mass.

Simplified Windpower Systems for Experimenters. 1975, by Jack Park. $6.00 from:

Helion, Inc.
Box 445
Brownsville, CA 95919

From basics to exotica gently yet completely in workbook format with example problems next to clear drawings and graphs. Angle of attack; relative wind, blade layout, aspect ratio . . . all that will be clear enough to you when you're done reading that you'll be able to critique the plans you bought or design-it-yourself.

Wind and Wind Spinners, by Hackleman and House, $7.50 from:

Earthmind, Josel
Saugus, CA 91350

Wind generator design and construction with an emphasis on Savonious rotors and solid-state electronic controls, for which schematics and parts lists are included.

Wind Measurement Equipment:
1. Dwyer Instruments, Inc.
   P.O. Box 373
   Michigan City, IN 46360
2. Helion, Inc.
   Box 445
   Brownsville, CA 95919
3. Natural Power, Inc.
   Box 167-B4
   New Boxton, NH 03070
4. Sencenbaugh Wind Electric
   P.O. Box 11174
   Palo Alto, CA 94306

The above offer the necessary wind-monitoring equipment at low cost.

Do-It-Yourself Plans:
1. Helion — 12' and 16' (2-5kw) wind generator plans, $10
2. Sencenbaugh — 10' diameter wind generator
3. Windworks — 25' diameter sailwing windmill plans, $25, 12' diameter wind generator plans, $15.

Helion and Sencenbaugh also sell kits and completed wind generators.

Wooden Windmill Blades
$25 to $60 from:
Thomas R. Conlon
Aero Power Research Co.
P.O. Box 2001
Burlingame, Ca. 94010
Straight, vertical-grained, kiln-dried
Douglas fir or aircraft quality Sitka spruce
blades of 5', 7'6" or 10' diameter. Supplied
with complete balancing, finishing and
mounting instructions and with complete
plans for an economical wind generator.

*The Gemini Synchronous Inverter
Papers*, $2 postpaid from Windworks
for all three:
1. "Synchronous Inversion: Concept
and Application," by Hans Meyer, 12
pp., 1976, 50¢;
2. "Synchronous Inversion for Windpower Utilization," by Alan Wilkerson,
12 pp., 1975, 50¢; and
3. "Synchronous Inversion: Technology for Utilization of Waste Energy,"
by Alan Wilkerson, 25 pp., 1976, $1.00.
A free pamphlet on the Gemini, which
allows any DC power source to put AC
power back into electrical grid and use
the existing grid rather than expensive
storage batteries, is also available. See
also the backside of the Windworks
poster on page 239.

*U.N. Rome Conference on New Sources
of Energy, Wind Power, Vol. 7*, held
August 21-31, 1961, $16 from
U.N. Publications
United Nations
New York, NY 10017
A classic wind conference, including
important items not available elsewhere,
such as Hutter's paper on windmill
blade design. In most libraries.

*1st Wind Energy Conversion Systems
Workshop Proceedings*, ed. by J.M.
Savino, NASA PB-231 341/9, 1973,
$6.50 from:
NTIS
5285 Port Royal Rd.
Springfield, VA 22161
The first major wind conference since
1961.

*2nd Wind Energy Conversion Systems
Workshop Proceedings*, ed. by Frank
Eldridge, held June 9-11, 1975, $7.40,
Stock No. 038-000-00258-9 from:
Government Printing Office
Washington, DC 20402
Over 40 papers on all aspects of wind
energy.

LARGE SYSTEMS

Wind Energy Mission Analyses by Lock-
heed and General Electric for ERDA will
be available in spring 1977. Write:
Wind Energy Conversion Branch
ERDA
Washington, DC 20545

These extremely important documents
are essentially comprehensive studies of
America's wind energy potential and
how, where and when it can be implemented. Since the large wind-electric
alternative is now less than or equal to
the costs of nuclear power, depending
upon the site windspeed and the size of
the wind-turbine, this data is very useful
to anti-nuclear intervenors. Preliminary
Lockheed findings, with such cost
charts, are found in "The High Potential
of Wind as an Energy Source" by Ugo
Coty and Michael Dubey, available from:
Wind Energy Program, Dept. 75-21-63A,
Lockheed-California, P.O. Box 551,
Burbank, CA 91520. Send a stamped,
self-addressed, business-size envelope.

Dutch Wind-Powered Sawmill

Converting wind motion into electricity
then back to mechanical energy to run
motors to pump water, saw wood, run
shop tools or other industrial processes
is expensive and roundabout. Using
windmills directly to provide mechanical power can be considerably cheaper
than wind/electricity and less than grid
electricity in some situations. Water-
pumping windmills, grainmills, and
sawmills were common in the early part
of this century, along with many wind-
powered farm shops, and their economics are appearing more favorable again
today. Used to stretch electrical supplies, or used independently with compressed air energy storage or possibly
flywheel storage in the future, wind/
mechanical systems deserve closer examination, along with their more glam-
orous sisters.

"Fresh Breeze for Denmark's Windmills" by Don Hinrichsen and Patrick
Cawood, in *New Scientist*, 10 June
1976, pp. 567-569.
Very useful to nuclear plant intervenors
as it contains a comparison by Bent
Sørensen of the relative reliability (i.e.
capacity factor) of a modern U.S. nuclear reactor and the existing Danish
Gedser windmill with and without a
24-hour storage facility. Even that small
energy storage makes the power availability of the windmill as good as that
of the nuclear plant. In addition, a description of the Tvind Colleges construction of a 2MW, 3-bladed wind-turbine
shows that the NASA-ERDA wind
program, with a smaller 1.5 MW machine scheduled for demonstration in
1979, may be beat by a Danish voca-
tional-industrial high school and college
consortium in the "big machine" sweepstakes.

"Wind Energy" by Bent Sørensen, in
Bulletin of the Atomic Scientists, Sept.
1976, pp. 38-45.
An excellent introduction to the potential for large-scale wind-electricity, covering energy storage methods, the relative costs for wind- and nuclear-power,
and their environmental impacts.

Wind-Mechanical Power

The Homemade Windmills of Nebraska,
1976, $3 from:
Farallones Institute
15290 Coleman Valley Rd.
Occidental, CA 95465
Excellent reprint of classic survey, showing mechanical windmills pumping water, running direct-driven farm shop
equipment, grinding grain, shelling corn,
sawing wood. Community shops of the
future will store energy via compressed
air tanks to power air tools during slack
wind periods.

Food from Windmills, Peter Fraenkel,
1975, $8.15 surface, $10 airmail from:
I.T. Publications Ltd.
9 King Street
London WC2E 8HN England
An excellent nuts and bolts case study
of the development of low-cost, effective water-pumping irrigation windmills
in Ethiopia. Economic, social and engineering factors evolved a Cretan sailwing windmill at a cost of $700 Ethi-
opian that out-performed imported
Dempster pumpers that cost Eth. $2,000
each. A fine account of various options
developed and suggestions for further
refinements.

An Evaluation of the Potential Environmental Effects of Wind Energy Systems Development (ERDA/NSF/97378-75/1), from:

> NTIS
> 5285 Port Royal Rd.
> Springfield, VA 22161

Excellent for the anti-nuclear intervenor presenting the now economic wind-electric alternative.

Power from the Wind, 1948, 1974, by Palmer C. Putnam. $9.95 hardbound from:

> Van Nostrand Reinhold Co.
> Litton Educational Publishing
> 450 W. 33rd St.
> New York, N.Y. 10001

In 1941 a large 175-foot diameter, two-bladed wind turbine was designed, fabricated and erected on Grandpa's Knob, a 2000' high mountain near Rutland, Vermont. Called the Smith-Putnam, it produced electricity for the Central Vermont Public Service Company's network at a cost close to that of today's nuclear/fission power plants. Putnam, an engineer and consultant to the U.S. government on renewable energy sources, describes the experiment from start to finish, in what is now the definitive and classic work on the planning and design of megawatt wind-electric systems.

Windpower Testimony, by Lee Johnson of RAIN and Ecotope Group, at Pebble Springs Nuclear Plant Hearings, ask for free reprint no. 136 from:

> Senator Mike Gravel (D-Alaska)
> U.S. Senate
> Washington, DC 20510

Sen. Gravel entered this information, designed for use by other nuclear power intervenors, in the Sept. 21, 1976, *Congressional Record*. It contains the most useful points of argument to mention when suggesting the use of large wind-electric systems, with extensive references to support them. If you're pressed for time, most large public and university libraries get the *Record*.

"Windmills Stage a Comeback" by T.S. Jayadev, in *IEEE Spectrum*, Nov. 1976, pp. 45-49.

A comprehensive primer on wind-turbine electronic options for synchronizing wind-produced power with the grid, variable-speed constant frequency (VSCF) and constant-speed constant-frequency (CSCF) systems are explained. A more technical version by the same author is "Wind-Power Electric Utility Plants," in *Journal of Engineering for Industry—ASME*, February 1976, pp. 293-296. Reading both should make wind generator options perfectly clear.

ACCESS

American Wind Energy Association (AWEA), $25/yr. membership dues, contact:

> American Wind Energy Assoc.
> 12949 Glastonbury
> Detroit, MI 48223

A non-profit organization working to further the application and use of wind energy, its objectives are 1) to stimulate public awareness, 2) provide product and service information, and 3) establish product standards for the wind energy industry. Membership includes full voting rights, a quarterly association newsletter and special rates at conferences and workshops.

Wind Power Digest, $6/yr. for 4 issues, $2/single copy, from:

> Jester Press
> 54468 CR 31
> Bristol, IN 46507

A subscription to *WPD*, membership in the AWEA and getting your name on ERDA's Wind Energy Conversion Branch mailing list should keep just about any wind energy aficionado clued in to what's happening. The Dec. '76 *WPD* is an excellent issue to start with. It contains reports from the '76 American Wind Energy Assocation conference, articles on the Zephyr Wind Dynamo, Rocky Flats Small Scale Windmill Testing, and is strewn with delightful tidbits by editor Mike Evans and associate editors Diane Burnside and Joe Carter.

Wind Energy: A Bibliography with Abstracts and Keywords, Rene Van Steyn, July 1975, $12 airmail from:

> Library Administration
> University of Technology
> Postbox 513
> Eindhoven, Netherlands

This 2-volume work is excellent in its comprehensiveness, especially on non-U.S. wind experiments in the medium- and large-scale wind-turbine range, and in the ease with which even international, foreign language reports can be accessed. The keywords, arrived at after a survey of those most useful and most often used, reflect the fact that this bibliography was produced by a working wind enthusiast for other such enthusiasts the world around.

Windworks Bibliography, 1974, $3 from Windworks (see above).

Covers all aspects but with an emphasis on small-scale systems, lists component catalogues and suppliers for the do-it-yourselfer.

1975 Wind Energy Utilization Bibliography, $10 postpaid from:

> Technology Application Center
> University of New Mexico
> Albuquerque, NM 87131

Abstracts covering both foreign and domestic sources, an author index, a corporate source index, and a permutated index of titles and keywords. Subjects include: wind power plants, wind power generators, wind machines and wind energy storage facilities, to mention a few.

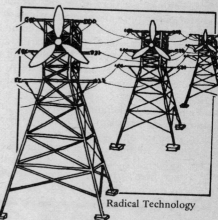

Radical Technology

Energy from the Wind: Annotated Bibliography, by Barbara Burke and Robert Meroney, Aug. 1975, available from:

> Solar Energy Applications Lab
> Colorado State University
> Foothills Campus
> Fort Collins, CO 80523

The best I have ever seen. It covers everything from laymen articles to dense theory, and covers it year-by-year. It is possible to find all the wind publications in any one year if you only know about when something was published, or you can find out how many items your favorite windpower author has written, and in what years by looking it up in an author-year index. Well done and thank you!

NSF-RANN Wind Energy Conversion Research: Recent Publications, ask for Bulletin No. 3, June 1975, from

> National Science Foundation
> Washington, DC 20550

An abstracted bibliography which some wind enthusiasts may have missed if they were not on the NSF wind mailing list. Includes Sandia Labs' vertical-axis wind turbine reports, NASA Lewis Research Center reports on the 100-KW machine, as well as NSF grantee reports. Tells you where to order what.

Federal Wind Energy Program Summary, May 1, 1975, free from:

> ERDA
> Division of Solar Energy
> Washington, DC 20545

This tells who, where is doing what work on wind for how much money.

RAIN is a group of people who have been active for a number of years in various areas discussed in this book—building windmills and solar homes, doing People's Yellow Pages, setting up and operating Community Design Centers and working on economic and energy research. We all came together out of a feeling that it seemed most useful at this point to pull together and share what we are learning so it can be accessible and useful to people working on local changes.

We've been working out of an old Victorian house in Portland, Oregon, in the land of Rain, from whence comes our name. In addition to putting out RAIN Magazine ten times a year, we publish a variety of papers and books—check the index for reviews of current publications or write for a current publications list. We've recently worked on a Skills Bank for local neighborhoods, energy conservation and renewable energy studies for Montana; Seattle, WA; the California State Architect; and helped plan the National Center for Appropriate Technology—as well as giving a lot of talks and workshops.

In an important sense, RAIN isn't us—it's a whole lot of people in nooks and crannies everywhere—thinking, feeling, building, applying, adapting, and living new ways. We're just trying to help people get out the word on good things they're doing and locate the resources for what they want to do.

This catalog is a compilation of things that have been in RAIN over the past two and a half years of its existence, plus at least as much new material collected especially for this book.

We've focused on areas we know well or have been involved ourselves in developing. There is some duplication when we felt some groups or reports were an important part of more than one section. There are also a lot of areas we wanted to cover but felt we didn't have a good enough sense of the networks and resources involved to do more than share the tips of the icebergs. The environmental and alternative learning movements, for instance, are barely outlined; the arts, consciousness and women's movement are only hinted at. But we feel we've given you some windows to look in on, a sense of the kinds of things that are happening, and ideas of where to dig further. We hope too that we've conveyed some of our optimism and joy for what is coming about.

HOW DO YOU KEEP UP WITH ALL THIS?

Read RAIN! We intend to continue expanding and updating this material through the magazine, as well as covering new areas as they develop. This means both corrections to information listed here and new material—some of which, alas, is already piling up along with our unopened mail.

Send us stuff you think should be shared with others. Tell us what you or your community have been doing. We have to rely on you all to keep the network alive. Your sharing and caring is what makes new things happen.

Subscriptions to RAIN are $10/year for 10 issues. If you're living lightly (less than $5,000/year income), you can get a year's subscription for $5. Some back issues are available for $1 each. Write for a current publications list.

INDEX

A.A. Abbingdon Ceiling Co., 142
Abbot Laboratories, 164
ABC, 111
Abelard-Schuran, Inc., 26
Abeles, Tom, 235
Abnaki Regional Land Trust, 156
Abundant Life Seed Company, 158
Academic Press, 222
Access, 59
access, 111, 112
Access (Canada), 115
Access Program, 144
Access to Television & Radio, 112
Accident Hazards of Nuclear Power, 207
Acclimatization, 84
Achley, Dana Space, 70
Acme Manufacturing, 228
ACORN, 54, 55
Acorn/Midwest Energy Alternatives Network, 5
Accountants, Public Interest, 55
Acquisition of Maps & Charts Published by the U.S. Gov., 26
Acres, USA, 159
Act of Creation, 78
Action for Children's Television, 111
Acupuncture Research Project, UCLA, 180
Adam Osborne & Assoc., 100
Adams, Joe Kennedy, 180
The Adams — Morgan Business Sector, 37
Adobe, 136-142
Adobe News, 137
Advanced & Innovative Wind Energy Concepts, 240
Advanced Solar Energy Technology Newsletter, 230
Advertising Age, 109
Aerial Photography Division, 22
AERO, See Alternative Energy Resources Organization
Acro Power Research Co., 241
Aesthetics of Silence, 82
Afshar, Farroukh, 136
Afterimage, 116
Agarwala-Rogers, Rekha, 77
Agbiz Tiller, 152
Agency for Inter. Development, 6
Aging, Admin. OR, 94, 107
Agribusiness, 150-152

Agriculture Energy Corp., 237
Agri/Energy Project Reports, 151
Agriculture in the City, 161
Agricultural Economics, Dept., 151
Agricultural Organizations & Publications, 159, 160
Agricultural Stabilization and Conservation Service, 22, 146
Agricultural Tools, 158
Agricultural & Forestry, U.S. Senate Committee, 195
Agriculture and Scale, 45, 152
Agriculture, U.S. Dept. of, 17, 25, 137, 139, 143, 146, 151, 156, 225, 226
Agri. and Economic Growth, 151
Airships: An Illustrated Hist., 126
Akwasasane Notes, 154
Alabama Environmental Quality Assn., 187, 210
Alabama Media Project, 117
Albright, David, 78
Alder and Molenaar, 158
Alexander, Bart, 105
Alexandrikov, Nicoli, 166
Alinsky, Saul D., 54
All Things Considered, 112
Allen, Indi, 116
Allen, Donna, 115, 116
Allerspach, Heinz, 52
Alley, Rewi, 61
Alliance of Infor. & Referral Ser., 107
All's Well on the Oregon Trail, 186
Alpert, John, 117
Alter, Harvey, 236
Alternate Energy Inst., 229
Alternate Media Center, 113
Alternative Agricultural Con., 70
Alternative Agriculture Resources Project, 150, 165
Alternative America, 89
Alternative Animal Waste Anaerobic Fermentation Designs, 235
Alternative Approaches to Meeting Basic Health Needs in Developing Countries, 179
Alternative Celebrations Catalog, 89
Alternative Cements in India, 137
Alternative Community Group, 86
Alternative Energy Resources Organization, 58, 203, 205
Alt. Energy & Who's Doing It, 57

Alternative Legislation Series, 54
Alternative Market News, 170
Alternative Press Index, 91
Alternative Public Policy, 54
Alternative Sources of Energy, 4, 9, 70, 90, 125, 205, 210, 214, 216
Alternative Transportation Proj., 130
Alternative Vocations & Lifestyle Center, 87
Alternative for Washington, 66
Alternatives, 134
Alternatives, 89
Alternatives to Chem. Medicines, 182
Alternatives in Print, 91
Alternatives for a Statewide Technical Skills Resource Bank for North Carolina, 68
Altman, Robert, 91
Amateur Computer Society Newsletter, 101
Amazing Life Games Co., 18, 90
American Biking Atlas and Touring Guide, 131
American Camping Assn., 84
American Doctoral Dissertations, 95
Am. Enterprise Inst. for Public Policy Research, 208
American Experience, 108
American Farmers and the Rise of Agribusiness, 152
American Film Institute, 117
American Friends Service Committee, 34, 72, 102, 213
Amer. Geographical Society, 23, 24
American Health Empire, 179
American Institute of Architects, 55, 30, 102, 143, 217, 221
Amer. Institute of Bioscience, 164
Amer. Inst. for Research, 59
American Libraries, 103
American Library Assn., 93, 95, 104, 106, 117
American Library Directory, 95
American Management Assn., 79
Am. Meteorological Soc. Bul., 239
American Public Works Assn., 196
Amer. Society of Civil Engineers, 43
American Revolution Bicentennial Commission, 108
Am. Soc. of Agri. Engineers, 236
American Society of Horticulture, 164
Am. Soc. for Info. Sciences, 104
Amer. Soc. of Planning Officials, 40
Am. Wind Energy Assn., 242
American Wood Preservers Inst., 138
American Youth Hostels, 132
Anaerobic Digestion of Dairy Cow Manure, 235

Anaerobic Digestion of Livestock Wastes, 237
Anderson, Bruce, 143, 219, 221, 229
Anderson, Chuck, 116
Anderson, L.O., 138
and/or, 118
Animator, 116
Ann Arbor People's Yellow Pages, 87
Annenberg School, 116
Annenberg, Walter, 111
Annual Agriculture Economics Bibliographies, 152
Annual Review of Entomology, 164
Another Road Side Attraction, 225
Antheneum, 111
Anthology Film Archives, 115, 117
Antioch College, 65, 83 West, 5, 161
Anybody's Bike Book, 127
Aoyagi, Akiko, 175
Appalachian Adult Educ. Center, 104
Appalshop, 118
Applesauce, 85
Appliance Manufacturer, 228
Applications of a Theory to Psychology, 106
Applied Aerodynamics of Wind Power, 240
Applied Behavioral Science, Dept. of, 150, 165
Apprentice Learning, 83
April Video, 117
Appropriate Technology, 7, 8, 9, 234
Appropriate Tech. Groups, 5,6
Appropriate Tech. Sourcebook, 4
Aquarian Research Foundation, 184
Approaches to Recycling, 186
Arbib, Michael A., 28
Arbor Day, 147
Architec. Design, 124, 125, 136, 141
Architecture for the Poor, 136, 142
Arkansas Community Organizers for Reform Now, 55
Arkansas Story, 215
Armstrong, Edwin Howard, 111
Army Corps of Engineers, 25, 29
Army Topographic Command, 25
Aronin, Jeffrey, 145
Arrakis Propane Conversion, 125
Art of Awareness, 82
Art for Our Sake, 57
Asahel Curtis Sampler, 18
Ashby, Ross W., 106
Ashdown, Paul, 109
Ashmore, Jack, 130
ASHRAE Handbook of Fund., 216
Aspen Inst. Program on Communication in Society, 112
Associated Council of the Arts, 117

Assn. for Educational Communications & Tech., 116
Association of Independent Video & Filmmakers, 117
Astrological Birth Control, 183
Astronomy, 24
Atema, H., 164
Atlas of Oregon, 26
ATS II Pictures of the Earth, 21
Attached Solar Greenhouse, 226
Attneave, Fred, 104
Auch, Charles, 118
Audiopool, 110
Audiovisual Marketplace, 95
Automobiles, 44, 123-126
Autonomous Houses, 143, 144
AV Communications Review, 116
Avalanche, 116
Avery, T. Eugene, 22
Ayer, A.J., 81
Away With All Pests, 62, 178

●

Baar, Kenneth, 45, 48
Bach, Eve, 48
Bader Company, 51
Baer, Steve, 202, 219, 223, 224
Baerg, Jim, 67
Bagdikian, Ben, 110
Bagnall, Jim, 77
Bahr, K.F., 166
Baillargeon, J.C., 212
Bainbridge, David, 129
Baisley, Barbara, 184
Bakan, Joe, 108
Baker, Kenneth F., 166
Balancing the Scales of Justice, 55
Balcomb, J. Douglas, 223, 226
Ballantine, Richard, 127
Baltimore Co. Library, 104, 105
Baltimore Sun, 105
Bamboo, 142, 146
Bandler, Richard, 82
Bank Book, 47
Bankers, 37
Banking System: Public Interest Analysis, 37
Banks of North Dakota, 47
Bar E Ranch, 143
Barden, Albie, 231
Bardwell, Elizabeth, 40
Barnes, Peter, 150, 152, 153, 154
Barnes, J.A., 72
Barnet, Richard, 32
Barnouw, Erik, 111
Bartering, 36, 65
Barefoot Doctor's Manual, 61, 181

Barth, C.L., 236
Basement Roots Library, 87, 105
Basic Construction Techniques for Houses & Small Buildings, 139
Basic Writings of Sigmund Freud, 80
Batko, William, 37, 46
Batson, Gregory, 81, 82, 106
Battelle Energy Program, 206
Batten, Barton, Durstine & Osborne, 80
Bay Area Video Coalition, 118
Baynes, Cary, 28
BBC, 3
B.C. Alternative, 86
Beadwall, 224
Beaton, David, 186
Beaty, Orren, 125
Beaubois, Henry, 126
Beck, E.J., 227
Becoming an Environmentalist, 213
Bed & Breakfasts, 49
Beer, Stafford, 99
Beginners Guide to Hydroponics, 159
Behold Man, 178
Behrens, Charles, 228
Beier, Ulli, 140
Belden, Jack, 61
Bell Springs Publishing Co., 49
The Bell System and Community Telephones, 32
Bend in the River, 67, 72
Bender, Tom, 3, 34, 140, 198, 213, 220
Beneficial Insects, 165
Benedict, R.G., 105
Bennan, Katrina, V., 51
Bennett, Hal, 85
Bennington College, 83
Bensinger, Charles, 116
Benson, Bob, 13, 25
Berg, Peter, 17, 226
Berger, Arthur Asa, 111
Bergier, Jacques, 72, 82
Bergson, Henri, 81, 82
Berkley Solid Waste Comm., 187
Berkowitz, Carl, 129
Berman, Sanford, 103
Bernays, Edward, 109
Berry, Wendell, 150, 165
Berryhill, J., 130
Bertalanffy, Ludwig von, 106
Better Light, Better Sight Bureau, 72
Best Present of All, 202
Best of Teacher Works, 84
Best of Zephyros, 84
Beverage Containers: The Vermont Experience, 186
Beyond Babel, 110
Beyond Culture, 110
Beyond Isolation, 169
Bhalla, A.S., 4, 39
Bias of Communications, 110
Bibliography of Chinese Sources on Medicine & Public Health, 181
Bibliography on Land Reform in Rural America, 154
Bicycle Activists List, 130
Bicycle Bibliography, 1976, 126
Bicycle/Pedestrian News, 129
Bicycle Repair Collective, 127
Bicycle Technology, 129
Bicycle Transportation, 127
Bicycles: All About Them, 127
Bicycling Science: Ergonomics & Mechanics, 127
Biegel, Len, 109
Big Names, Big Drains, 46
Bike ON!, 129
Bike Tripping, 139
Bikeconomics, 127
Bikeway Planning & Design, 129
Bill Day's Consumer Guide to Wood Stoves, 231
Binns, Patrick, 203
Bioconversion, 235
Bio-Dynamic Farming and Gardening Assn., 165
Bio-gas Plant, 236
Biography Index, 95
Biological Control by Natural Enemies, 164
Biological Control of Plant Pathogens, 166
Bio. Control of Water Pollution, 195
Biomass Energy Inst., 237
Biomedical Communications, 180
Bio-regions, 24
Bio-science, 164
Bio-Technology & Bio-Engineering Journal, 237
Birdless Summer, 61
Birth Book, 184
Birth Control Handbook, 184
Birth Without Violence, 184
Bit Users Assn., 100
Black Panther Party, 56
Black, Stanley W., III, 37
Blair & Ketchem's Country Journal, 92
Blazing Showers, 232
Bligh, Thomas, 138
Bliss, Raymond W., 221
Blobaum, Roger, 186, 195
Blooming Prairie Warehouse, 64
Blue and Brown Books, 82
Blue Jim, 117
Bodechtel, J., 21
Body Work for Women, 184
Boeke, Kees, 21
Boehm, B.W., 106
Boericke, Art, 140
Bois, J. Samuel, 82
Bolles, Richard, 51, 78
Bond, T.E., 225
Bonneville Power Admin. Energy Conservation Study, 212
Book of Changes, 28
Book Distribution Collective, 168
Book of Miso, 175
Book of Tofu, 175
Bookchin, Murray, 150
Bookkeeping, 49, 55
Booklegger Press, 103
Books for Organizers, 54
Books in Print, 91, 95
Boorstin, Daniel, 108, 110
Bootstraps, 49, 50
Borges, Jorge Luis, 74
Borror, D.J., 165
Bortz, Paul, 114
Bosher, Ben, 130
Boston Architectural Center, 217
Boston People's Computer Collective, 100
Boston Wind, 5
Boston Women's Health Book Collective, 88, 183
Bottle Bill, 186
Bottles & Sense, 98
Bouffier, Elezard, 147
Boulding, Kenneth, 106
Boulton, Jane, 18
Boundry Waters Canoe Area, 58
Bourne, Charles P., 94
Bowker Annual of Library & Book Trade Info., 95
Bowler, Deborah, 167
Bowling Green University, 116
Boyd, John, 158
Boyle, Geofrey, 3, 9, 144
BPA Role Environmental Impact Statement, 212
Brace Research Inst., 3, 6, 226
Bradley, Richard C., 40
Brains, Machines and Math., 27
Brainstorming, 77, 80
Brand, Stewart, 91
Brandt, Kandy, 117
Brann, Donald R., 141
Bread Box Water Heater Plans, 224
Breaking Into Broadcasting, 109
Breeding for Insect Resistance in Vegetables, 164
Brezdek, Roger, 43
Briarpatch, 68, 91
Briarpatch Review, 51
Bridges, Fields and the Omega Point, 76
Brill, A.A., 80
Bristol, Timothy, 130
Brink, Randy, 118
Brinker, John H., 237
British Columbia Access, 87
Broadcast Media Kit, 112
Broadcasting Cable Yearbook, 114
Broadcasting Magazine, 111
Broadcasting Yearbook, 111, 114
Broadside Video, 118
Brockman, John, 90, 106
Brom, Thomas, 32, 45
Brooklyn Botanical Garden, 164
Brooklyn College, 117
Brooks, C.F., 145
Browder, Sue, 131
Brown, Edward Espe, 173, 174
Brown, Evan, 235-238
Brown, Grandma Dulcie, 19, 20
Brown, G. Spencer, 28
Brown, Jovanna, 105
Bry-Air, Inc., 228
Buchler, Coral, 96
Buckingham, Edward, 47
Buddhist Economics, 3, 34
Buetow, Kurt, 49
Buffalo & Erie Co. Public Libr., 104
Build Your House of Earth, 137
Build Your House in the Old Ohana Style, 138
Building Research Advisory Brd., 145
Building Research Council, 143
Building Techniques & Materials, 136-144
Building Value: Energy Design Guidelines for State Bldgs., 220
Bulletin of the American Meteorological Society, 145
Bulletin of Atomic Scientists, 191, 221, 241
Bullock, Orin, Jr., 141
Burack, Richard, 182
Burden, Dan & Lys, 130
Bureau of Land Management, 25
Burgess, Bob, 131
Burke, Barbara, 242
Burlingame, Bo, 54
Burning Out, 78
Burns, Red, 113
Burns, Scott, 45
Burnside, Diane, 242
Burrell, Donald H., 130
Business Periodicals Index, 111
Butterflies in My Stomach, 157
Buying Back the Land: A Proposal for California, 154
By the Late John Brockman, 106
Byte Magazine, 99

●

Cable — List of Public Access Channels & Centers, 113
The Cable Book, 114
Cable Handbook, 1975-76, 114
Cable Packet, 118
Cable Television in the Cities, 114
Cable Television and the FCC, 114
Cable Television Info. Center, 114
Cable TV Service in Oregon, 109
Cablecommunications Res. Ctr., 114
Cabelines, 114
Cady, Fitch, 86
Cain, Allan, 136
Calder, Nigel, 14
California Conservation Project, 148
California Green Lacewings, Inc., 164
Calif. Office of Appropriate Tech., 17
Calif. Video Res. Proj., 116, 118
Calif. Water Resources Ctr., 193, 196
California Wood Plans, 176
Caligari, Dr., 180
Callanbach, Ernest, 15, 92, 116
Can-Pee and Other Delights, 194
Canadian Brdcstng League, 115, 118
Canadian Communications Research Information Center, 118
Canadian Hunger Foundation, 3
Can. Radio-Television Comm., 118
Canadian Whole Earth Catalog, 90
Canal Enthusiasts Handbook, 126
Canfield, Monte, 96
Canner, Glenn, 37
Cannon, James, 97
Canyon Cinema Cooperative, 118
Canyon Cinemanews, 116
Capitol Community Citizens, 40
Capturing the Sun Through Bioconversion, 235
Cardozo, Peter, 84
Career Counseling, 49-52, 78
Carlson, Rick J., 179
Carmichael, Bill, 94
Carnegie Comm. on Educ. T.V., 112
Carpenter, Carey, 171
Carpenter, Edward, 110
Carpenters and Builders Guide, 139
Carrier Current Neighborhood Radio, 122
Carrington, David, 26
Carter, Joe, 242
Casalino, Larry, 154
Cascadian Regional Library (CAREL), 67, 72, 115
Cassidy, Hopalong, 111
Castle, Alfred, 173
Catalogue of Federal Domestic Assistance, 96
Catch-44, 112
Catch the Wind:, 239
Causes of Dehumanization in Health Care, 179
Caveat Emptor, 98
Cawood, Patrick, 241
Cawood, Will, 228
CPB Reports, 112
CBS, 111
CDC News, 55
CECOCO Catalogue, 49, 158
Celebrations, 89
Cellarius, Doris, 161
Center for Advanced Computation, 43, 186, 204
Center for Advanced Television Studies, 115, 118
Center for Alternatives In/To Higher Education, 83
Center for Being, 101
Center for the Biology of Natural Systems, 151, 193
Center for Community Access Television at Amherst, 113
Center for Community College, 55
Center for Community Economic Development, 4, 18, 19, 39
Center of Concern, 101
Ctr. for Energy Policy Studies, 217
Ctr. for Governmental Respon., 203
Ctr. for Governmental Studies, 57, 66
Center for Indus. & Institutional Development, 223
Ctr. for Industrial Research & Service, 188
Center for New Art Activities, 116
Ctr. for Research & Development, 101
Center for Rural Affairs, 152, 159
Center for Rural Studies, 154
Center for Science in the Public Interest, 25, 28, 97, 101, 151, 205, 206, 209, 213
Center for Social and Environmental Concern, 203
Center for Social & Evaluation Research, 49
Ctr. for Short-lived Phenomena, 101
Center for Studies in Food Self-Sufficiency, 150
Center for Understanding Media, 116, 117, 122
Center for Urban Education, 101, 110
Ctr. for the Visual Environment, 101
Centering, 83
Central Seattle Community Council Federation, 37
Century City Educ. Arts Proj., 90
CETA, 49
Challenge for Change, 115
Chamber of Commerce, US, 44, 63, 88, 101, 104
Change, 78
Channeled Scablands, 13
Channeling Children, 111
Chapin, Suzy, 132
Charren, Peggy, 111
Chemical Engineering, 228
Cherry, Bill, 225
Chesler, Phyllis, 184
Children's Museum, 100, 187
Child's Garden of Sex, 84
China, 61-62
Education, 83
Health Care, 62, 178, 181
I Ching, 28
Language, 81, 82
Recent History, 61-62
Recycling, 186, 195
Tools, 10
China at Work, 10
China Books & Periodicals, 62
China Reader, 61
China Recycles Her Wastes By Using Them on the Land, 186, 195
China: Science Walks on Two Legs, 62, 97
China Shakes the World, 61
Chinese Written Character as a Medium for Poetry, 82
Chinook Centrex, 86
Choate, Robert, 111
Cholorination & Ozone Depletion, 192
Chomsky, Noam, 82
Chow, Brian G., 208
Christian Science Monitor, 211
Chrystal, John C., 51
Chrystallizing Public Opinion, 109
Cineaste, 116
CIRCT, 113, 118
Cities' Wealth, 45, 54
Citizen Action Press, 169
Citizen's for Better Transit, 125
Citizens for Community Cable, 113
Citizens Communications Center, 111
Citizens Energy Platform, 204
Citizen's Handbook on Solar Energy, 219
Citizen Involvement in Community Development, 55
Citizen Involvement in Crime Prevention, 66
Citizen Participation Programs, 59, 60, 75, 79
Citizen Participation, N.C. Office, 68
Citizen Participation in Urban Development, 55
Citizens Against Toxic Sprays, 63, 166
Citzens for Clean Air, Inc., 126
Citizens for Environmental Coal., 130
Citizens Groups & Broadcasting, 112
Citizens Guide to Community Development, 98
Citizens Guide to Improving TV & Radio, 112
Citizen Housing & Planning Assn., 88
City Lights Books, 82
City People's Book of Raising Food, 161
City Planning in China, 124
City Volunteer Corps, 68
Cityscape, 83
City Survival Page, 88
Civil Engineering Dept., Univ. of Minnesota, 138
Clark, Barbara, 213
Clark, Duncan, 179
Clark, James, 204
Clark, Wilson, 126, 202, 212
Clarke, Robin, 206
Clash of Culture, 44
Clean & Decent, 191
Clean Water, 195
Clear View, 97
Clement, Andrew, 100
Cleveland Public Schools, 161
CLIENT: Communication Law Info., Edited Notes By Topic, 116
Clifford, Terry, 119
Climate Under Glass, 225
Climatic Data Ref. List, 221, 225
Clivus Multrum, 161, 193
Climate and Architecture, 145
Climate Near the Ground, 145
Climate Atlas of the U.S., 26
Clopton, Boyd, 118
Cloudburst, 49, 189, 190
Cloudburst Books, 172
Coalition Against Stripmining, 210
Coast and Geodetic Survey, 25
Cocannover, J., 165
Cochran, Kye, 203
Co-Evolution Quarterly, 6, 9, 17, 26, 29, 56, 66, 86, 90, 91, 183
Coe, Nancy Bell, See: *Futures Conditional*
Coffel, Steve, See: *Spectrum*
Coles, Clarence W., 127
Colesby, John, 216
Collectors Network, 105
Collins, Jenny, 180
Collyer, Homer, 94
Colorado Express, 92
Colorado Solar Energy Assn., 230
Colorado State Treasury, 47
Colorado State University, 242
Colstad, Ken, 69
Columbia Journalism Review, 116
Columbia River as a Resource, 204
Columbia University, 116
Comindex, 100
Coming Around, 4
Coming: The Real Energy Crisis, 202
Commedia, 118
Commerce, Oregon Dept. of, 96
Committee for Nuclear Respon., 239
Committee for Open Media, 109
Committee of Small Magazine Editors & Publishers (COSMEP), 91
Common Ground(Calif.), 170
Common Ground (MN), 57
Common Sense Pest Control, 165
Common Weeds of the U.S., 165
Commoner, Barry, 91, 125, 151, 201, 202
Communication in Organization, 77
Communication Studios, Dept. of, 30
Communication Technology, 70
Communications, 89
Communications Act of 1934, 111
Communications: Challenge/Response, 108
Communications Network for Change in Higher Education, 72
Communications Press, 114
Communications Tomorrow, 116
Comm. Action Agencies, 5, 56, 203
Community Affairs, Pa. Dept. of, 214
Community Communication Technology, 59, 60, 108, 122
Comm. Design Ctr. of Minn., 173
Community Design Centers, 55, 56, 101, 138, 173
Comm. Design Centers Profile, 55

Comm. Devel. Block Grants, 55
Comm. Devel. Clearing House, 49
Community Development Dept., (Davis, CA.), 146
Community Economic Growth in Berkeley, 54
Comm. Economic Devel., 32-52
Community Environmental Council, 40, 161, 187
Community Finance, 47, 48
Community Gardens, 162
Comm. Garden Procedural Man., 162
Community Health Nursing, 88
Comm. Industry in Vermont, 49
Comm. Info. Center (B.C.), 100, 107
Community Info. Needs, 74
Community Info & Serv. Ctrs., 102
Community Information Specialists Program, 83, 94, 103
Comm. Issues Dialog Proj., 60, 75
Community Land Trust, 155
Community Media, 117
Community Media Handbook, 116
Community Meetings, 66
Community Memory, 69, 101
Community Organizing, 54-58, 63, 64
Community Ownership in New Towns and Old Cities, 48
Community Ownership Organizing Project, 32, 45, 48, 52
Community Planning Report, 57
Comm. Resource Development, 97
Comm. Radio Stations List, 121
Comm. Resource Directories, 86-90
Comm. Serv. Admin., 5, 56, 68, 226
Community Skills Bank, 68
Community Switchboard, 87
Comm. & Self-Help Transport, 125
Community Video Exchange, 117
Comnet, 70
Companion Plants and How to Use Them, 165, 166
Comparative Efficiency of Energy Use in Crop Production, 151
Comparisons of Energy Consumption between W. Germany & US, 202
Competitive Scale in Manufacturing: The Case of Consumer Goods, 167
Complaints & Disorders, 184
Compleat Backyard Fish Farmer, 5
Complete Yogurt Cookbook, 173
Composition of Foods, 176
Compost Science, 162, 186, 189, 190, 194, 195, 237
Composting, 191
Composting Privy Booklet, 193
Compu-sort Index Manuel, 72
Computer Calisthenics & Orthodontia, 99
Computer Conferencing, 79
Computer Lib/Dream Machines, 100
Computer Power & Human Reason, 99, 106
Computers, 69, 75, 76, 99-101
Conaway, Charles Wm., 104
Concept of Mind, 82
concern, 97
Concilio Campesino Del Sudoeste, 102
Concordia University, 72
Cone, J.D., 214
Conference on Alternative State and Local Public Policies, 40, 45, 54, 58
Conference Board Record, 214
Congdon, Bob, 4
Congressional Record, 31, 96, 206, 242
Congressional Quarterly Service, 96
Conlon, Thomas, 241
Connecticut Agricultural Experiment Station, 151
Conn. Res. Recovery Authority, 187
Conscious Culture of Poverty, 3
Consciousness, 27, 28
Conservation Foundation, 125
Conservation Tools & Technology, 205, 216, 239
Conservation of the Land and the Use of Waste Materials for Man's Benefits, 195
Conserver Society News, 9, 232
Conserver Society/Notes, 9, 201, 212
Conserver Society Products, 9
Construction with Surface Bonding, 137
Consumer-Farmer Foundation, 144
Consumer Federation of America, 97
Consumer Groups, 97, 98
Consumer Reports, 98, 182
Consumers' Coop. of Berkeley, 165
Consumer's Guide to Med. Care, 181
Conta, Lewis, R., 202
Contact Center, 67, 90
Continuing Education Pubs., 90
Control Data Corp., 4
Controlling Money Flows, 46
Controlling Neighborhood Devel., 57
Coomaraswamy, Ananada, 83
Cooper, Lynn, 94
Co-ops, 47, 57, 68, 167-170
Cooperative Banks, 54
Cooperative Comm. Devel., 45, 54
Coos Country TV, 66, 118
Copper Development Assn., 227
Cornell University, 209
Corporate Power, 32-40, 46, 48, 150-152
Corp. for Public Broadcasting, 112
Cosmic Economics, 198
Cosmic View, 21
Cost of Energy Slaves, 33
Costello, Carol, 174
Costs of Sprawl, 40
Costs of Tourism, 133, 134
Costs of Urban Growth, 40
Cook, James, 166
Corporate Secrecy: Agribusiness, 152
COSMEP, 91
Cottage University, 49-52
Coty, Ugo, 241
Coulson, Kinsell, 222
Council on Children, Media & Merchandising (CCMM), 111
Coun. on Economic Priorities, 34, 52
Coun. on Environmental Quality, 29
Council on Foreign Relations, 201
Council for Public Interest Law, 55
Council of State Governments, 32
Countdown to a Nuc. Moratorium, 98
Country Contacts Directory, 105
Country Inns & Back Roads, 132
Country Journal, 14, 92
Country Women, 171
Countryside, 159
Craftsman Book Co. of America, 138
Creative Computing, 100
Creative Initiative, 207
Creative Outlet, 118
Creative Thinking, 78, 80
Creativity by Committee, 77, 80
Credit Unions, 47, 64
Crickman, Robin D., 74
Crime Prevention, 66
Crippled Tree, 61
Crisis in the Health Care System, 179
Critical Mass, 43, 205
Cross Roads Resource Center, 57
Crowley, Terry, 103
Crowvitz, Herbert F., 28, 78
CTL Electronics, 116
Culkin, John, 117
Cultivator, 170
Cultural Arts Section, 109
Current & Proposed Practices in Animal Waste Management, 195
Curtis, Asahel, 18
Curve of Binding Energy, 207
Cuthbertson, Tom, 127, 131
CVRP Patch Panel, 116
Cybernetics, 106
Cyclateral Thinking, 124, 129, 130

●

Dale, Gene, 237
Danzig, Fred, 109
Davidson, Joel and Sherri, 18, 171
Dallas Public Library, 87, 105
Daly, Herman, 34, 198
Dancy, Rev. Harold K., 139
Dang, C.C., 194
Daniel, Pete, 18
Data Courier, Inc., 188
Data Survey, 106
Davis, Chuck, 30, 86
Davis, Gary A., 78, 80
Day, Bill, 231
D.C. Pirg, 37
Deadwood Ditto, 63
Dear Haven Farm, 172
Debach, P., 164
de Bono, Edward, 79
Decentralized Energy Systems Bibliography, 205
Decision-makers Guide to Solid Waste Management, 187
Decker, Craig, 5
Deering, Robert, 145
Defense Monitor, 34
Degree Programs, 83, 115, 117, 180
de Hart, Robert, 148
De Korne, James B., 226
De Laet, Christian, 72
de Latour, Louis A., 217
Delong, D., 165
Delphi Method, 79
Demand for Scientific Tech. Manpower in Selected Energy-Related Industries, 43
de Moll, Lane, 4, 220
deMoll, Lauri, 55
Demonstration of Waste Flow Reduction from Households, 196
Dennis, Landt, 239
Denver Community Video Center, 113
Denver Open Network, 72
Denver Research Inst., 114
De Prez, Gene, 110
Deppen, Dave, 202
Dervin, Brenda, 104, 106
Deryckx, Becky, 153-156, 226
Deryckx, Woody, 165-168, 226
Deschool Primers, 84
Deschooling Society, 69
Description of the Solar Energy R & D Programs in Many Nations, 220
Design Char. of Plant Materials, 145
Design With Climate, 221
Design Study for Urban Telecommunications Experiments, 114
Design With Nature, 29
Designing the Solar Tempered Home, 224
Destructive and Useful Insects: Their Habits and Control, 165
Detroit Public Library, 104
Deutsch and Poole, 158
Development of an Energy Info. Retrieval System, 205
Development & Testing of a Greenhouse for Colder Regions, 226
de Ville, Barry, 100
de Winter, F. & J.W., 220, 227
Dexter, Connie, 176
Dewey Decimal System, 107
Diagrams, 77
Diet for a Small Planet, 173, 174, 176
Digital Group, 101
Dillard, Anne, 17
Dimensions of Meaning, 110
Dindal, Daniel, 191
Directories & Catalogs, 86-90
Directory of Comm. Info. Res., 87
Directory of Community Resources in Kalamazoo Co., 87
Dir. of Current Energy Research, 205
Dir. of Environmental Scientists in Agriculture, 150
Directory of Human Services, 107
Dir. of Nuclear Activists, 208
Dir. of Pub. Telecommunications, 112
Dir. of Special Libraries, 95
Discovering Santa Barbara Without a Car, 131
Dispossessed, 155
Dissertation Abstracts Inter., 95
District Heating Development Work in Sweden, 218
Divone, Lou, 240
Djukanovic, V., 179
Doerr, Paul, 157
Doing the Media, 116
Doing It!, 57, 91
Dollar, Energy & Employment Impacts of Mass Transit, 204
Dollars and Sense, 52
Domebook II, 138
Domestic Technology Institute, 204
Donohue, Joseph C., 104, 106
Don't Go Buy Appearances, 38
Double Helix, 110, 120
Dougherty, Nina, 127
Douglas, J. Sholto, 148
Downtown Community TV Ctr., 117
Doylestown, PA., 10
Dr. Dobb's Journal, 99
Drake, Susan York, 162
Drought-Tolerant Ornamental Plants for Davis, CA., 146
Drumwall Plans, 224
Drug Abuse Council, 78
Drug Administration, Federal, 97
Dubey, Michael, 241
Dubin-Mindell-Bloome, 211
Dubos, Rene, 178
Due to Circumstances Beyond Our Control, 111
Dujack, Linda, 131, 173
Duncan, Richard, 186, 189
Dunn, P.D., 234
Dust Books, 91
Dutch Mountain Nursery Cata., 147
Dwyer Instruments, Inc., 240
Dyferman, Jan, 142
Dymaxion Research Ltd., 100
Dynamic Energy Analysis & Nuclear Power, 207
Dyna-Ships, 126

●

Eagle Bend, Self Portrait, 18
Eames, Ray and Charles, 21
EARS, See Environmental Action Reprint Service
Earth Books Lending Library, 105
Earth Chronicles, 198
Earth Geography Booklet, 11, 12
Earth for Homes, 137
Earth Journal, 92
Earth From Space, 21
Earth Covered Building Conference Proceedings, 27
Earth Station, 7, 56
Earthcyclers, 170
Earthmind, 240
Earthskills Workshop, 171
Earthwatch Oregon, 58
Earthwork, 154, 176
Easi-Bid Pattern Co., 141
East Bay Municipal Util. Dist., 146
East Coast Bicycle Congress, 130, 131
East Coast Bicycle Trail Guidebook, 131
East West Journal, 92
Easter Seal Society, 88
Eastern Montana College, 210
Eastern Queens Community Cable TV Association, 113
Eastman, G. Yale, 228
Eat Your Heart Out, 176
Eating High and Lightly, 173-176
E.B. Kaiser Co., 228
Eccli, Eugene & Sandi, 136, 139, 216, 224
Eckenfelder, W. Wesley, 237
Eco Graphix, 208
Economic Atlas of the World, 26
Economic Benefit of Preserving Old Buildings, 141
Ecological Surveys From Space, 22
Eco-tips, 97
Ecotopia, 24
Ecologist, 126, 136
Ecology Action of Mid-Peninsula, 161
Ecology of Soil Bacteria, 166
Ecology of Soil-Borne Plant Pathogens, 166
Ecology, Washington Dept. of, 188
Economic Analysis of Fuel Gas Production from Solid Waste, 235
Economic and Business State University Press, 51
Economics, 31-52
Agriculture, 150-152
Bioconversion, 235
Energy, 33-36, 39, 40, 43, 44
Energy Cons., 214, 215, 217
Growth, 32-46
Nuclear Power, 208
Rebuilding, 141, 217
Recycling, 186
Scale, 31-52
Sewers, 191
Subsidies, 31-52
Solar Energy, 220
Tourism, 133-134
Economics of Size in Farming, 151
Economics of US Subsidy Prog., 33
Economies and Diseconomies of Large-Scale Agriculture, 151
Economics as if People Mattered, 3
Ecosystem Management, 5
Ecosystem Management: A Framework for Urban Pest Control, 164
Ecotope Group, 203, 226, 235, 236-37
Ecotopia, 15
Edcentric, 85
Edmondson, Lillian & Wm., 230
Edmonton Public Library, 105
Edmund Scientific Co., 227
Education Alternatives, 69, 83-85
Education Exploration Ctr., 85
Educational Coordinating Council, 66
Educational Facilities Lab., 141
Educational & Indust. Television, 116
Effects of Landscape Development on Natural Ventilation of Bldgs., 145
Egg and Dairy Production, 150
Ehrenreich, Barbara, 184
EI & I Associates, 227
Eis, Jennifer, 83
Eisentraut, Albert, 131
Ekistics, 40, 44
El Mirasol Garden, 161
Eldridge, Frank R., 239, 241
Electric Journalist, 116
Electric Utility Expansion Plans
Electric War: Fight Over Nuclear Power, 207
Electrical Research Assn., 240
Electricity Consumption & Investment Finance in Calif., 203
Electronic Arts Intermix, 117
Elements, 91, 161
Elements Rage, 14
Elizabethtown Comm. Center, 118
Ellis, William, 6
Ellsworth, Skip, 143
Ellul, Jacques, 110
Embodiments of Mind, 28, 106
Emerging Energy Policy Prncpls, 198
Emery, F.E., 79
Emma Goldman Clinic, 64
Emory University Family Planning Program, 184
Employment, 32, 43, 44, 49-52, 204
Employment & Economic Devel., 44
Employment Impact Statement, 43
Emry, Carla, 171
Encyclopedia of Associations, 72
Encyclopedia of Social Sciences, 153
End of Medicine, 179
Energy and Agriculture, 150, 151, 226
Energy, Agri. and the Envir., 150
Energy, Agriculture and Waste Materials, 151, 235
Energy Basis for Man & Nature, 198
Energy & the Built Environment, 217
Energy Conservation Alternatives to Nuclear Power, 208
Energy Conservation through Automobile Parking Management, 124
Energy Conservation, 208, 211-218
Building, 135-146, 217, 218
Economics, 214
Home Insulation, 57
Jobs, 43, 44
Landscaping, 145-148
Recycling, 186
Transportation, 124
Energy Conservation & Economic Growth, 214
Energy Conservation: It's Nature, Hidden Benefits & Hidden Barriers, 214
Energy Conservation Legislation, 217
Energy Conservation Project, 124, 214
Energy Conservation Task Force Report to Gov. Straub, 214
Energy Conservation & Urban Transportation, 124
Energy Costs of Using Columbia River Water for Irrigation, 204
Energy Dilemma — What it Means to Jobs, 44
Energy Ecology & Econ., 29, 34, 198
Energy Efficiency in the Food Sys., 151
Energy and Employment in New York State, 43
Energy, Environment & Bldgs., 217
Energy & Equity, 124
Energy Essays, 202
Energy and Food, 151, 173
Energy Index, 206
Energy & Information, 107
Energy and Labor Demand in the Conserver Society, 44
Energy & Nutrient Conversion in Swine Waste Man, 236
Energy Office, State of Fla., 204
Energy Perspectives, 206
Energy & Power, 202, 210
Energy: The Power of the States, 203
Energy Primer, 90, 166, 202
Energy & the Regional Planner, 204
Energy Research & Development Admin. (ERDA), 206, 219, 220, 224, 225, 228, 236, 240
Energy Reporter, 206
Energy & Resources, 204 211
Energy Resources of the Earth, 210
Energy Strategies & Nucl. Power, 211
Energy Strategy: The Road Not Taken, 201
Energy for Survival, 126, 202
Energy Today, 206
Energy Use for Bicycling, 127
Energy Utilization in Ver. Agri., 150
Engineering Issues, 43
Engineering News-Record, 215
English, Deirdre, 184
Enhanced Solar Energy Collection Using Reflector-Thermal Collector Combinations, 227
Enhancing Biological Nitrogen Fixation, 151
Enoch Pratt Free Library, 104
Entrepreneurs, 49, 50, 51
Entropy Evasion League, 210
Entropy Law & the Econ. Process, 198
Environment Action Bulletin, 58, 162

Environment Canada, 4, 150
Environment, Power & Soc., 29, 198
Environment, Science & Tech., 192
Environmental Action of Colo., 208
Environmental Action Foundation, 33, 98, 110, 186, 188, 209
Environmental Action Reprint Service (EARS) 205
Environmental Communications, 118
Environmental Conservation, Vermont Dept. of, 211, 231
Environmental Defense Fund, 203
Environmental Design Primer, 140
Environmental Farm Program, 151
Environmental Groups, 58, 92, 97, 98
Environmental Information Sources Handbook, 95
Environmental Law Inst., 124, 214
Environmental Policy Center, 58
Environmental Protection, Dept. of (Maine) 187
Environmental Protection Agency, 29, 95, 127, 130, 186, 187, 192, 207, 237
Environmental Quality, Oregon Dept. of, 188
Environmental Research Lab, 226
Environmental Response, 161
Environmental Works, 56
Environmentalists for Full Employ., 52
Environmentally Approp. Tech., 94
EPA, See Environmental Protection Agency
EPA Methane Digester Report, 235
Epstein, Jay Edward, 111
Epstein, Rhoda, 118
Equal Time, 111
Era of Exploration, 12
ERDA See Energy Research & Development Admin.
ERDA Research Abstracts, 205
ERDA Solar Bibliography, 220
ERDA Speakers Bureau, 205
Erickson, Ronald P., 154
EROS Data Center, 22
ERTS, 22
Erwin, Jim, 17
Establishing an Integrated Pest Control Program for Street Trees, 164
Esteves, Roberto, 118
Eugene Community Sustaining Fund, 47, 66
Eugene Contact, 87
Europe on $5 a Day, 132
Evaluation of Methane Production from Solid Waste, 236
Evaluation of Potential Environmental Effects of Wind Energy Developments, 242
Evaluation of a Solar Heated Waterwall Greenhouse, 226
Evans, Harold, 151
Evans, Mike, 242
Evanston Chamber of Commerce, 168
Evergreen Land Trust, 156
Evergreen State College, 105
Everson Museum of Art, 117
Everyday History of Somewhere, 18
Everyday Information Needs, 106
Everything for Everybody, 68, 87
Evolution of American TV, 111
Exacting Ear, 120
Examination of Operating Characteristics of a Composting Installation for Organic Household Wastes, 193
Expanded Cinema, 110
Experiences with the Clivus Multrum & Mull-Toa Toilets in Northern Manitoba, 193
Experiences in Visual Thinking, 77
Experimental TV Center, 117
Exploitation, 32-42
Explorers Ltd. Sourcebook, 90
Exploring Energy-Efficient Futures for Canada, 201
Exporting Money, 46
Eyerly, Jack, 70, 71, 118
Ezra, Arthur, 219

●

Fabric Appliance Co., 49
Fair Witness, 78, 118
Falk, Joe, 45, 54
Family Energy Watch Calender, 213
The Family Guide to Children's TV: 112
Fanshen, 62
Farallones Compost Privy, 193
Farallones Institute, 5, 61, 83, 143, 161, 193, 194, 203, 223, 241
Farallones Scrapbook, 85
Farmer's Market Organizers' Handbook, 167
Farmer's Market Packet, 168
Farming, 150, 165
Farmworkers in Rural America, 151
Farms of Puget Sound, 67, 170
Fast Breeder Reactor: Analysis, 208
Fathy, Hassan, 136, 142
Federal Communications Commission (FCC) 111, 114
FCC Actions Alert, 112
Federal Power Commission, 206
Fear in the Countryside, 32
Federal Energy Admin., 202, 205, 206, 214, 215, 217, 227
Federal Environmental Monitoring Directory, 29
Federal Executive Boards, 96
Federal Information Centers, 88, 96
Federal Power Commission, 209
Federal Register, 96
Federal Wind Energy Programs Summary, 242
Federation of Cooperatives, 170
Feedback (Troy, NY), 66
Feedback Processes, 59, 60
Feilden, Richard, 127
Fellmeth, Robert, 152
Felsenstein, Lee, 100
Feminist Press, 184
Ferguson, Tom, 181
Fessenden Fund, 120
Festivals, 66
FHA Pole House Construction, 54
Fichter, Robert, 136
Field, R.L., 227
Film Quarterly, 116
Film & Video Makers Travel Sheet, 117
Film in the Cities, 117
Filmmakers Directory, 117
Filmmakers Newsletter, 116
Films, 21, 155, 180
Finding and Buying Your Place in the Country, 38
Finding Community, 30, 84, 97
Finding Facts Fast, 93
Finkler, Earl, 40
Fire in the Lake, 62
First Steps in Village Mechanization, 4
Fisher, Bill, 226
Fisk, Pliny and Daria, 143
Fitzgerald, F. Scott, 94
Fitzgerald, Frances, 62
Flexible Ways to Work, 52
Flexible Working Hours, 52
Floor of the Oceans, 26
Floral Clocks, 147
Floridian's Guide to Solar Energy, 219
Florida State University, 117
Flower, Robert G., 240
Folke, Ann, 118
Food and Agriculture Organ., 158
Food Co-op Handbook, 168
Food Co-op Nooz, 169, 170
Food Cooperative Directory, 169
Food Co-ops for Small Groups, 168
Food Day, 110, 173, 176
Food Dryer's Drying Booklet, 176
Food and Heat-Producing Solar Greenhouse, 226
Food for People, Not for Profit, 176
Food from Windmills, 241
For Summer Dry California, 146
Ford Foundation Enegy Proj., 96, 217
Foreign Affairs, 201
Forelaws on Board, 212
Forest Farming, 148, 159
Forest Products Research Center, 138
Forest Research Lab, 231
Forest Service, U.S., 25, 146, 147
Forester, John, 130
Forest Tree Nurseries in the US, 147
Forestation Notes, 146
Forestry, Oregon State Dept., 146
Fort Union Coal Field Symp., 210
Four Days, 40 Hours, 52
Fox, Fred, 182
Foxfire Books, 172
Foxfire Projects, 83, 97
Fragrant Garden, 147
Frank, Karen, 112
Fraenkel, Peter, 241
Frankfurt, Ellen, 184
Franz, Clifford L., 130
Free Poster Charts & Maps, 84
Free University Network, 69
Freedom to Build, 136
Freedom of Info. Clearinghouse, 96
Freedom of the Press vs. Public Access, 112
Fresh Breeze for Denmark's Windmills, 241
Freud, Sigmund, 80
Friedberg, Jerry, 125
Friend, Gil, 161
Friendly, Fred, 111
Friendly Inns of Mendocino-Sonoma Coast, 132
Friends of the Earth, 58, 125, 201, 207, 210, 212
Friends of the Earth, Ltd., 124, 211
Friends of Nature, 147
Fritsch, Albert, 151, 175, 213
Fritschien, Leo J., 222
From the Ground Up, 172
Fry, L. John, 235, 237
Ft. Vancouver Regional Library, 69
Fuel Gas Production from Solid Waste, 237
Fuies, James F., M.D., 181
Fuller, John G., 208
Fuller, R. Buckminster, 106, 110
Fulton, Len, 91
Future Associates, 45, 54
Future Strategies for Ener. Devel., 199
Futurist, 79
Futures, 79
Futures Conditional, 57, 79

●

Gadden, Elmer L., 237
Galanis, Nicholas, 194
Gale Research Company, 72, 95
Gales, Gwendolyn, 226
Galton's Walk, 28, 78
Ganglia, 103
Garbage, 49, 186-190
Garbage in America, 186
Garbage Book, 213
Garbage Guide, 188
Garden Way Publishing, 159
Gardener's Bug Book, 165
Gardening, 145-148, 159-166, 145-148
Gardening Without Poisons, 164, 166
Gardens for All, 161, 162
Gardiner, Joe, 130
Gardner, Richard, 89
Garvy, Helen, 127
Gaskin, Stephen, 184
Gay & Women's Alliance for Responsible Media, 111
Gay Yellow Pages, 89
GEE!, 30
Geiger, J., 179
Geiger, Rudolf, 145
Gemini Synchronous Inverter, 141
General Accounting Office, 96
General Semantics Bulletin, 82
General Services Admin., 217
General Systems Yearbook, 79, 106
Generation of Electricity by Wind Power, 239
Gener. of Power from the Wind, 239
Geno, Larry, 150
Gentleman, Ross, 118
Geo-Cultural Regions, 24
Geological Survey, U.S., 25
Geology Illustrated, 12
Georgescu-Roegen, Nicholas, 198, 202
Geography and Cartography, 26
Getting Clear, 184
Getting Fire, 131, 231
Getting Into Print, 109
Gobar Gas Research Station, 236
Golding, E.W., 239
Goldstein, David, 212
Gould, Peter, 28
Gierloft-Emden, H.G., 21
Gilman, Stanley F., 228
Gin, Margaret, 173
Ging Cathy, 68
Ginn, William, 187
Giono, Jean, 147
Give Way, 127
Gleaning Project, 56
Glenn's Complete Bicycle Manuel, 127
Global Reach, 32
Global Village, 109, 117
Goddard College Social Ecology Program, 83, 117, 144
Goddard Space Flight Ctr., 208
Golden Web, 111
Goldschmidt, Walter, 152
Goldstein, Jerry, 150
Gonna Rise Again, 32
Good Priorities?, 41
Good and Wild, 146, 156
Goodbye to the Flush Toilet, 191, 193
Goodfellow Catalog of Wonderful Things, 67, 89
Goodhart, Robert, 176
Goodheart-Wilcox Co., 139
Goodyear Corporation, 126
Gotaas, Harold, 191
Gothard, Inc., 164
Government Information, 88, 95, 96, 105
Government Information Div., 105
Government Organization Man., 88
Government R & D Report, 206
Governor's Commission on Food (Vermont), 150
Governor's State University, 5
Govinda, Lama Anagarika, 17
Granfalloon, 120
Graph Theory, 76
Graphics Standards, 216
Grass Roots Network, 118
Grass Roots Video, 116
Grassroots Primer, 58, 90
Gray, Stephen B., 101
Gray, T.R.G., 166
Gray, Virginia, 140
Gravel, Sen. Mike, 206, 242
Great American First, 146
Great Flood, 13
Greater Cleveland Radio & Television Council, 112
Green Gulch Greengrocer, 56
Green Revolution, 155
Greenhill, Basil, 126
Greenmarket, 168
Greenway, Robert, 85
Greenwood, David, 26
Gregg, Richard, 166
Grey Panthers Media Watch, 111
Grey Water Treatment, 194
Grillo, Virgil, 118
Grimsted, Kirsten, 90, 115
Grinder, John, 82
Grinding Wheel Inst., 72
Grogg, Sam, 115
Groundwater Newsletter, 196
Group for Environmental Educ., 30
Group Process, 78, 79
Grow it Safely: Pest Control Without Poisons, 155, 164
Growth Management, 32-46
Guerilla Television, 116
Guest Houses, 132
Guide to the Cartographic Records in the National Archives, 26
Guide to Independent Film & Radio, 115
Guide to Indust. Poll. Control, 97
Guide to Reference Books, 93
Guide to the Selection of Computer-Based Reference Services, 95
Guide to Self-Sufficiency, 172
A Guide Through the Vegetable Garden, 161

●

Habit at Teatime, 13
Habitat Forum, 6, 51, 70
Hackleman, Michael, 240
Hagens, Bethe, 5
Hagman, Folke, 143
Haldeman, Michael, 118
Halfway House Films, 180
Hall, Edward, 110
Hall, Jack, 181
Hallowell, Mary Louise, 114
Halperin, Y., 166
Hamber, Jill, 93
Hammond, Jon, 223
Handbook on Appropriate Tech., 3, 5
Handbook on Biological Control of Plant Pests, 164
Handbook for Building Homes of Earth, 137
Handbook Collective, 168
Handbook on Free Access to the Media for Pub. Serv. Adv., 109
Handbook for the Greening of Philadelphia, 146
Handbook for the New Farmer, 171
Handbook on Starting a Radio Station, 119
Handmade Houses, 140
Hand-Hewn, 138
Hands-On Building Courses, 143, 144
Hannon, Bruce, 43, 186
Haratonik, Peter, 116, 117, 122
Harding, Harold F., 78
Harmony of Interaction, 72
Harper, Peter, 3, 9, 144
Harris, Stephanie, 164, 165
Harrison, David, 224
Hartman, Chester, 32
Hartman, Ilka, 64
Harvard Journal on Legislation, 155
Have a Nice Day!
Have a Wrap Session With Your Electric Water Heater, 215
Hawaii Community Design Ctr., 138
Hawaii Council of Churches, 113
Hawaii Energy Newsletter, 206
Hawaii Health Net, 180
Hay, Harold, 221, 223, 224
Hayes, Denis, 207, 212
Hayes, John, 48
Haynes, Carl B., Jr., 137
HCL Bulletin, 103
Head Start, 56
Health, Education & Welfare, U.S. Dept. of, 62, 94, 107
Health Hazards Appraised, 181
Health & Light, 182
Health, Manpower & Medical Auxiliaries, 179
Health PAC Bulletin, 179
Heat Pipes, 228
Heathcote Center, 155
Heating with Wood, 159
Hedahl, Joan, 47
Hedstrom, James C., 223, 226
Heichel, G.H., 151
Helion, 203, 240
HELP, 69
Help (N.C.), 105
Help, for the Citizens of Wake County, 87
Help! For the Small Museum, 65
Helpfile, 105
Henderson, Bill, 91
Henderson, Hazel, 60
Hennepin County Library, 103
Henry Doubleday Research Assn., 165
Heronemus, William, 240
Herron, Chris, 174
Hess, Karl, 54, 57
HEW, 181
Hewson, E. Wendell, 239
HFIPS Press, 107
High Country News, 92
High Potential of Wind as an Energy Source, 241
High School Sexuality, 184
Hightower, Jim, 176
Hill, D.T., 236
Hill, Lawrence D., 165
Hill, Richard, 232
Hinds, Hal & Judy, 171
Hinrichsen, Don, 241
Hinton, William, 62
Hippovideo: Foundation for Mutli-Media & the Arts, 118
Hirsch, Shirley, 180
Historical Preservation of Bldgs, 141
History of Broadcasting in the US, 111
History of Technology, 10
Hitchhiking, 125
Hoag, Paxton, 118
Hochman, Sandra, 114
Hodak, Mark, 49
Hoedads Treeplanters Co-op, 50
Hoffman, George, 38
Hollander, Jan-Erik, 142
Holiday Inn, 132
Holloway, Dennis, see Ouroboros
Holman, Paul, 118
Holographs, 76
Home Business, 45, 49-52
Home, Inc., 45
Home Resource Center/Service Exchange, 67, 68
Home and Workshop Guide to Sharpening, 139
Homemade Windmills of Neb., 241
Homeowners' Federation, 37
Hommel, Rudolf P., 10
Homesteading, 19, 20, 171, 172
Urban, 141
Hopi Indian Language, 81, 82
Horizons 76, 108
Horn, J.S, 62, 178
Horowitz, Andy, 114
Horticulture-Science, 164
Houck, Oliver, 202
House, David, 240
Housing Assistance Service, 144
Housing & Building in Hot Climates, 145
Housing & Development Admin., New York City, 48
Housing and Urban Development, U.S. Dept. of, 30, 32, 137, 142, 216
Housing by People, 136
Housing Training and Info. Ctr., 37
How to Build Food Drying Equip., 176
How to Build a Low-Cost House of Stone, 137
How to Challenge Your Local Electrical Utility, 209
How to Convert Your Auto to Propane/Methane, 125

How Do You Start A Neighborhood Center?, 102
How to Get the Word Around, 110-122
How to Fix Your Bicycle, 127
How to Grow More Vegetables, 161
How to be Heard, 109
How to Make Media Work For You, 109
How to Practice Prospective Medicine, 181
How to Prepare a Candidate Survey, 97
How to Prepare a Lifeline Proposal, 97
How To Protest Your Rights in T.V. and Radio, 112
How to Rehabilitate Abandoned Buildings, 141
How to Research Your Local Bank, 37
How to Solve It, 77
How to Start Smaller Industries, 49
How to Start Your Own Small Business, 49
How To Talk Back to Your Television Set, 112
How the Weather Works, 14
Howard, J., 179
Howdy Doody, 111
Hubbard, Harlan & Anna, 171
Hubbert, M. King, 210
Huffaker, C.B., 164
Hugo's Book Service, 100
Human Use of Human Beings, 106, 110
Humane Computing, 100
Humanizing Health Care, 179
Hunger Action Ctr., 162, 167, 176, 226
Hunt, Charles B., 12
Hunter, Beatrice and Trum, 164, 166
Huntington, Dan & Sarah, See Metastasis
Hurry Tomorrow, 180
Hutchinson, Linda, 85
Hutchinson Press, 78
Hypertension Treatment Plant, 237

●

I Ching, 28
IEEE Spectrum, 242
I & R Services, 107
Idea-Research-Info. System, 88
IDEAS, 83, 97
Ideas and Methods Exchange, HUD, 142
If You Want Air Time, 109
I FOAM, 159
Illich, Ivan, 3, 60, 124, 179
Illustrated Solar Energy Guide of Flat-Plate Collectors, 227
Image, 106
Image Bank, 90
Image Empire, 111
Image: Guide to Pseudo-Events in America, 108, 110
Impact of Solar and Conservation Technologies Upon Labor Demand, 43
Impacts of Tourism on Prince Edward Island, 133
In the Bank or Up the Chimney, 216
In the Making, 49
In Wildness Is the Preservation of the World, 58
Ina May, 184
Incredible Collectors, 94
Indecks, 94
Independent Film & Video Preview Network, 117
Independent Foundation, 68
Independent Video, 116
Indian Craftsman, 83
Indian Ocean Cloud Patterns, 21
Indians, See Native Americans
Indian Tipi, 138
Indigenous Building and the Third World, 136
Industrial Common-Ownership Movement, 51
Industrial Waste Recycling, 188
INFER, 104
Inform books, 97
Informal Guide to a Lovelier Balt., 88
Information, 107
Information Centers, 101-105
Information for the Comm., 104, 106
Information Machines, 110
Information and the New Movements for Citizen Participation, 60
Information, Perception & Regional Policy, 59
Information Storage & Retrieval Systems, 94
Infra Red Scanners, 215
Inglis, David R., 239
Ingpen, Jeremy, 49
Inn Book, 132
InnFo, 118
Innis, Harold, 110
Innovative Grad. Programs Dir., 83
Input Community Video Ctr., 117
Insects, 163-166
Insect Resistance in Crop Plants, 164
Insight Exchange, 118
Institute of Arctic Environmental Engineering, 228
Inst. for Liberty and Community, 155
Institute for Local Self-Reliance, 6, 9, 37, 49, 91, 161, 171, 186, 191, 194
Institute for Policy Studies, 37, 40, 45, 54, 91, 161
Inst. for Research in Poverty, 43
Inst. of Urban and Reg. Devel., 39
Insulation, 57, 215, 216
Insulation Reporter, 215
Insulating Shutters, 216
Integral Urban House, See Farallones Inst.
Inter-Action, 118
Inter-American Housing and Planning Center, 137
Interchurch Broadcasting, 118
Interface Age, 99
Interior Dept., U.S., 59, 162
Interior and Insular Affairs, U.S. Senate Committee, 151
Intermedia, 90, 116
Intermediate Technology Development Group (ITDG), 3, 4, 6, 7, 8, 9, 137, 158, 179, 242
Intermediate Technology/USA, 5
International Assoc. for Education, Development and Distr. of Lesser known Food Plants and Trees, 146, 157
International Biomass Energy Conference, 237
International Book of Trees, 148
International Communications Institute, 118
International Directory of Little Magazines & Small Presses, 91
International Fed. of Organic Agriculture Movements (IFOAM), 159
International Fed. of Traders, 65
International Independence Inst., 155
Inter. Inst. of Communications, 116
International Labor Office, 4, 22, 39
International Non-Aristotelian Library Pub. Co., 82
International Rice Research Inst., 158
Int. Solar Energy Soc. News, 229
Int. Video Exchange Directory, 115
Int. Voluntary Services, 68
Int. Woodworkers of America, 162
Internship Programs, 83
Interpretation of Aerial Photographs, 22
Intershade Tree Conference, Inc., 164
Interstate Library Planning Group Directory, 105
Interview Techniques & Procedures, 97
Introducing the Single Camera VTR System, 116
Introduction to Cybernetics, 106
Introduction to Info. Science, 106
Introduction to Microcomputers, 100
Introduction to Reference Work, 93
Intro. to the Study of Insects, 165
Inventor's Paradox, 77
Iowa 2000, 66
Iowa Industrial Waste Information Exchange, 188
Iowa Pub. Int. Research Group, 64
Iowa State University, 150
Irish Setter, 49
Iron Oxen, 62
ISES Conference Proceedings, 220
Isothermics, Inc., 228
Ithaca Video Project, 117
I've Got a Question about Solar Energy, 219

●

Jacklin, Phil, 109
Jacobson, Michael, 98, 176
Jackson, Leah, 184
Jackson, Mildred, 182
Jahoda, Gerald, 94
Jamison, Susan, 162
Japan Consulting Inst., 49
Jaquier, Nicholas, 4
Jayadev, T.S., 242
Jaybird, 94
Jeavons, John, 161
Jensen, Mike, 226
Jennings, Ralph, 112
Jensen, Don, 118
Jerabek, Sandra, 209
Jewell, William, 151, 235, 236
Jewish Catalog, 90
Jimerson, Douglas A., 151, 173
Job Impacts of Alternatives to Corps of Engineers Projects, 25
Job Sharing, 51, 52
Job Start Corporation, 49
Jobs, See Employment
Johnny's Selected Seeds, 158
Johnson Creek, 41
Johnson, D., 198
Johnson, Frances Benjamin, 18
Johnson, Hugh, 148
Johnson, Lee (Loren L.), 203, 242
Johnson, Nicholas, 111
Johnson-Lenz, Trudy & Peter, 58-60, 69, 75, 76, 77, 78, 79, 84
Jolley, J.L., 106
Jones, Bart, 127
Jones, Ron, 30, 84, 97
Journal of Arboriculture, 164
Journal of Communication, 116
Journal of Community Communications, 60, 69, 74, 100
Journal of Creative Behavior, 78
Jour. of Engineering for Indust., 242
Jour. of the New Alchemists, 6, 9, 164, 226
Journal of Popular Culture, 116
Journey to the Beginning, 61
Joy of Birth Control, 184
Judge, Anthony, 72, 78
Jump Cut, 116
Jung, C.G., 72
Just Economics, 33

●

Kahn, Lloyd, 138, 140
Kalamazoo Info Ctr., 105
Kalamazoo Pub. Library, 87
Kamoroff, Bernard, 49
Kansas City People's Yellow Pages, 87
Kantner, Tobi, 120
Katz, Elizabeth, 103
Katz, William A., 93
Kay, Peg, 114
Kaye, Michael S., 85
Keeping Healthy in a Polluted World, 181
Keeping Warm for Half the Cost, 216
Kemper, George D., 151
Kendrick, Alexander, 111
Keown, Ian, 132
Kern County Library System, 118
Kern, Ken, 48, 136, 137, 139, 143
Kesey, Ken, 70, 174
Ketcham, Brian, 126
Key, Wilson Bryan, 108
Kilobyte, 100
King Co. Conservation District, 170
King, Robert G., 37
Kirshner, Ed, 32, 45, 48
Kispert, R.G., 235
Klein, Ted, 109
Koberg, Don, 77
Kochen, Manfred, 104, 106
Koestler, Arthur, 78
Kogan, Ted, 48, 136
Kolsbun, Ken, 131
Koplow, Richard B., 100
Korot, Beryl, 115
Koryzbski, Alfred, 81, 82
Kotelchuck, David, 179
KRAB Nebula Media Conference, 120
Kramer, Edith, 118
Krasnow, Erwin, 116
Kreitner, Philip, 168
Kubler-Ross, E., 180
Kuck, Loraine, 147
Kuhn, Thomas, 110
Kuhns, Bill, 110
Kvale, Chris, 130

●

Labor and Public Welfare, U.S. Senate Committee, 151
Laboratory for Computer Graphics & Spatial Analysis, 99
Laboratory for Maximum Potential Systems, See Max's Pot
Lacey, Louise, 183
Laitner, Skip, 43
La Mammelle, 118
Lamb, Edward, 111
Lancashire, David, 127
Land Application of Sewage Effluents, 195
Land, Bread and History, 150
Land Conservation & Development Commission, 59
Land Management, Bureau of, 25
Land-Set, 22
Land Reform, 153-156
Land Trusts, 155, 156
Land Use
Agricultural, 153-156
Bikeways, 127-129
Carrying Capacity, 29
Planning, 55
Resource Inventories, 29
Sewers, 192
Urban Growth, 39, 40, 41
Zoning, 124
Land Use in California, Nadar Study Group, 152
Landforms of the U.S., 23
Landman, Marshall, 72
Lands No One Knows, 153
Landscape Architecture, 147
Landscapes — Selected Writings of J.B. Jackson, 12
Landscaping, 145-148
Landscaping Guide to Native & Naturalized Plants of Santa Clara County, 146
Lane, Frank, 14
Langans, 166
Language, 76, 79, 81, 82
Language, Thought & Reality, 82
Lappe, Frances Moore, 173, 174
Large-Scale Sprouting as a Cottage Industry, 49
Las Truckaderos, 169
Last Whole Earth Catalogue, 77, 90, 139
Lateral Thinking in Management, 79
Lattey, Peter, 138
Laubin, Reginald & Gladys, 138
Laukes, Jim, 5
Law Enforcement Assistance Admin., 66
Law, Public Interest, 55, 58
Lawand, Tom, 226
Lawrence, William, 127
Laws of Form, 28
Laybourne, Kit, 116
LC Tracer Bullets, 205, 237
Le Duc, Don R., 114, 116
League of Women Voters, 54, 109, 186
Leap Year Papers, 67, 72
Learning, 69, 72, 83-85
Learning Resources Center, 83
Learning Resources Corp., 55
Leboyer, Frederick, 184
Lectures on Socially Appropriate Technology, 4, 234
Ledbetter, Tom, 118
Left Wing Poultry, 169
Legal Aid, 55, 58, 88
Legislative Commission on Energy Systems (NY), 43
Leich, Harold, 191
Leitch, William, 138
Len-Jay Furnace Co., 232
Lending Institutions Attitudes Toward Solar Heating, 228
Lerza, Catherine, 176
Less is More, 213
Lessing, Lawrence, 111
Let the Entire Community Become Our University, 102
Letelier, Orlando, 91
Let's Get the Railroads Moving Again, 125
Leubbers, David, 127
Levertov, Denise, 91
Lew, Wasyl M., 114
Lewallen, John, 58
Lewis, Stephen, 116
LGC Engineering, 60, 100
Libby-Owen-Ford Co., 222
Libraries in America's Future, 103
Libraries & Neighborhood Info. Centers, 104
Library of Babel, 74
Library as a Community Informaiton Referral Center, 104
Library of Congress, 95, 107, 188 205, 237
Library Hands-On Book, 105
Library Journal, 95, 103
Library Science, Univ. of Illinois, 26
Library Services and Construction Act, 103
Life in a Compost Pile, 191
Life Size Aero Design, 240
Life Support Systems Group, Ltd., 101
Lifeline Utility Regulation, 54, 209
Lifestyle Index 76, 213
Lighter than Air Society, 126
Lilly, John, 27, 106
Lime and Alternative Cements, 137
Limits to Growth, 198
Lindstone, Harold, 79
Lindstrom, Carl R., 193
Link, Ruth, 211
LION, See Living in the Ozarks
Lipkin, Efrem, 69
Lipmann, Walter, 109
Liquid Metal Fast Breeder Reactor, 96, 208
Listener-Sponsored Radio, 120
Little City Halls, 57
Little Prince, 77
Lives of a Cell, 17, 74
Living Brain, 74, 106
Living the Good Life, 171
Living/Learning Centers, 83
Living Lightly, 36, 173-176, 213-214
Living in the Ozarks, 165, 171
Living Systems, 129, 145, 218, 223
Livingston, Brian, 70, 72
Lloyd, Frank, 111
Loading Dock, 169
Lobbying, 54
Lobeck, Armin K., 26
Lock, C.B. Muriel, 26
Local Organization Directory, 114
Lockheed-California Co., 241
Lockwood, Arthur, 77
Lodge Owners Quarterly, 138
LOF Sun Angle Calculator, 222
Lond, Harley, 90
Lone Ranger, 111
Long Beach Museum of Art, 118
Long, Jim, 107
Long-Legged House, 17
Long, Nicholas, 106
Long Revolution, 61
Longview Public Library, 85
Los Alamos Scientific Lab, 221, 223, 226
Los Angeles People's Yellow Pages, 87
L.A. Sewage Treatment Plant, 237
Louisiana Society for the Arts, 117
Louisville Communications Ctr., 117
Loveless, Richard, 117
Lover's Guide to America, 132
Loving Grace Cybernetics, 69, 101
Lovins, Amory, 199-202, 211
Low-Cost, Energy Efficient Shelter, 136, 216, 224
Low-Cost Homes for Rural America, 139
Low Cost Technology, 4
Low Energy Housing, 136
Low Maintenance Gardening, 146
Lowman, Paul D., Jr., 21
Lowndes, D.H., 227
Loy, William G., 26
Lubin, Aileen, 109
Lunaception, 183

●

Ma Bell, 32
MacDonald's, 4-6, 175
Mach, E.P., 179
The Machinery of the Brain, 29
Mack, Don, 122
Machlup, Fritz, 106
Mackillop, Andrew, 136
Machine Design, 77, 80
MacMahon, Brian, 179
Macpherson, G.A., 4
Macrae, Alan, 140
Madden, Carl H., 44
Madden, J. Patrick, 151
Maddox, Brenda, 110
Madison People's Yellow Pages, 87
Madness Network News Reader, 180
Magazine of the Environment, 57
Magee, John, 176
Magers, Steve, 137
Maine Audubon Society, 5
Maine Film Alliance, 117
Maine Land Advocate, 155, 156
Maine Times, 92, 193, 231
Maine Wood Heat Co., 231
Make Where You Are A Paradise, 124, 147, 148
Making Apple Cider, 159
Making the City Observable, 30, 99
Making the Media Revolution, 116
Making the Most of Your Energy Dollars, 215
Mallow, Suni, 116
Man Adapting, 178
Man of High Fidelity, 111
Man Who Planted Hope & Grew Happiness, 147
Management in an Age of Changing Values, 44

Management & Budget, Office of, 96
Manitoba Auto Insurance Plan, 54
Mankind 2000, 78
Manpower Requirements for Nuclear & Coal Power Plants, 43
Mans, Larry, 108
Man's Role in Changing the Face of the Earth, 21
Man. of Building Construction, 139
Manual of Grey Water Treatment Practice, 194
Manual of Simple Burial, 180
Manufacturers of Pesticide Application Equipment, 158
Mao Tse-tung, 17, 61, 62
Map of Berkeley, Ca., 88
Map Collections in the US and Canada, 26
Map Reading, 26
Maple and Apple Production, 150
Maple Sugar Book, 171
Mapleville Organic Farm, 171
Mapping, 26
Mapping & Graphing Community Points of View, 59, 60, 76
Mapping the World, 25, 26
Maps of the United States, 25
Marcus, Michaela Moore, 49
Margen, Peter, 218
Margetts, William G., 206
Marier, Don & Abby, 92, See also, *Alternative Sources of Energy*
Maril, Robert Lee, 120
Marin County Transit District, 125
Marin Municiple Water District, 146
Mariner's Catalogue, 89, 126
Markets for Recyclables, 188
Marco Industries, 232
Marsh, John S., 134
Marsh, Ken & Elaine, 116, 117
Marshall, Pluria, 111
Mass Communications & American Empire, 110, 111, 114
Mass Communications Documentation Center, 115
Mass Transit, 43, 124-126
Employment Impact, 204
Mass Media Booknotes, 116
Massachusetts Inst. of Tech., 60
Matheison, Johann, 105
Max's Pot, 137, 143, 203
Mayer, Martin, 37
Mayhew, Bill, 100
Mazria, Ed, 222
Mazziotti, Donald, 205
McCall, Tom, 198
McCall, Wayne, 140
McCallum, Bruce, 4,9, 232
McCarty, Perry, 235
McCawley, James, 126
McClaughry, John, 155
McCracken, Horace, 224
McCullough, Warren S., 28, 206
McDaniels, David K., 227
McDonough, Suellen, 190
McGill University, 6, 144, 193
McGinnis, Joe, 109
McHarg, Ian L., 29
McIntyre, Joan, 28
McIsaac, Paul, 117
McKay, Grady, 222
McKim, Robert, 77
McKinney, Eleanor, 120
McLarney, Bill, 150
McLuhan, Marshall, 75, 82, 110
McMahon, David, 49
McNair, Mary, 95
McPhee Guide Publishers, 127
McPhee, John, 207
Meader, Abbott, 117
Meadow/Marsh Systems as Sewage Treatment Plants, 196
Meadows, Donella, 198
Mechanical Engineering, 202, 221
Media Access, 112
Media Access Project, 109, 111
Media Alliance, 118
Media Bus, 117
Media Exchange of Telluride, 118
Media Lab, 117
Media & Methods, 116
Media Mix, 116
Media Report to Women, 115, 116
Media Shop, 118
Media Studies, M.A, 117
Media Study, 117
Mediability: Guide for Non-Profits, 109
The Mediaworks, 118
Medical Nemesis, 179
Medical Self-Care, 181
Medicine Show, 182
Medium/Rare, 118
Mekas, Jonas, 117
Melrvine, Edward C., 107
Melton, Hollis, 115
Memory of Old Jack, 17
Mental Maps, 28
Menter, Ted, 84
Mercer, Henry, 10
Meroney, Robert, 242
Merrill, Richard, 150, 166, 202, 235
Mesirow, David, 78, 118
Messinger, P.S., 164
Metaphysics, 81, 82
Metastasis, 9, 52, 158
Metcalf, C.L., 165
Methane, 235-236
Methane Digesters for Fuel Gas and Fertilizer, 235
Methodist Hospital of Indiana, 181
Methods of Info. Handling, 94
Metrocenter, 87
Metroliner, 131
Metropolitan Ass. of Urban Designers & Environmental Planners, 129
Metropolitan Service District, (Portland, OR), 42, 190
Metro. State Hospital (L.A.), 180
Meyer, Hans, 241
Michigan University, 83
Microtek, 100
Middleton, G.F., 137
Midwest Energy Alternatives Net., 5
Midwest Exchange, 65
Midwest Video News, 116
Migratory Labor, US Senate Subcommittee, 151
Mikich, Tripp, 118
Milam, Lorenzo, 119, 120
Mills, Jan L., 203
Mills, Stephanie, 66, 184
Milne, Murray, 193, 196
Milwaukee Committee For Cooperative Cable Communication Systems, 113
Mind Managers, 110
Mind in the Waters, 28
Mineral Resources & the Environ.
Minimum Cost Housing Group, 6, 144, 193
Minnesota Geographic Society, 92
Minn. Woodworkers Supply Co., 139
Minow Newton, 111
Minuse Shower, 161
Mirth, Richard A., 228
MIT Community Dialog Proj., 60
MITRE Corp., 228, 239, 241
MITRE Air Solar Systems Rpt., 228
Mixed Media, 115-118
Model of the Brain, 28
Model Community Serv. Bureau, 100
Modern-Aire, 232
Modern Carpentry, 139
Modern Nutrition in Health & Disease, 176
Moffit, Ronni, 91
Mohawk Nation, 154
Moiliili Community Ctr., 180
Mondello, John, 110, 118
Money, Money, Who's Got The Money?, 37
Monitor, 55
Monogahela Nat. Forest, 58
Monopoly Steals FM from the People, 120
Monroe State Prison Honor Farm Methane Plant, 236
Montana Academy of Sciences, 210
Montana Alternative Agri. Conf., 67
Montford Feed Lot Methane Plant, 236
Monthly Checklist of State Pubs., 96
Montreal Health Press, 184
Montreal People's Yellow Pages, 87
Montreal Star, 212
Moodie, Patricia, 226
Moon, Moon, 17
Moonlight Gardens, 147
Moore, Donald A., 223
Moore, G.E., 81
Moore, James A., 237
Moorhead State University, 104
Moran, Robert, 30
More is Less, 40
Moreland, Frank L., 217
Morey, James, 48
Morgan, D.S., 193
Morgan, Ernest, 180
Morgan, Lawrence, 89
Morgan, Richard, 33, 209
Morgantown People's Yellow Pages, 87
Morley, David, 179
Morning of the Magicians, 70, 72, 82
Morrall, Rick, 130
Morris, David, 49, 54
Mortal Flower, 61
Mortgage Disinvestment in the District of Columbia, 37
Mortite, 216
Mosher, Craig, 64
Mother Earth News, 92
Mother Earth News Handbook of Home Bus. Ideas & Plans, 49
Mother Jones, 54, 91
Moulds, George Henry, 79
Movement for Economic Justice, 33
Movement for a New Society, 70, 72
Ms. Magazine, 51
Mud Bricks, 136, 137, 140, 142
Mud Brick Roofs, 142
Mud, Space and Spirit, 140
Mueller, Robert F., 208
Muller, Ronald, 32
Mull-Toa, 193
Multimedia Aproach to Childen's Literature, 95
Multnomah County Programs and Services, 107
Mumford, Lewis, 110
Municipal Decentralization, 57
Murray, Michael, 116
Murrow, Edward R., 111
Museum of Modern Art, 21, 117
Musica, 116
Musick, Mark, 167-170
Mussel Group, 17
Myth of the Machine, 100

●

NACLA Research Methodology Guide, 93
Nadar, Ralph, 58, 98, 101, 152, 153
Naef, Weston, 12
Nancy's Yogurt, 174
NAPSAC, 184
Narasiah, S., 194
NASA, See National Aeronautics & Space Administration
Nasr, Seyyed, 10
Nation of Energy Efficient Buildings By 1990, 217
National Academy of Sciences, 145, 157, 210
National Aeronautics & Space Administration, 22, 114, 195
Nat. Alternative Radio Conf., 120
Nat. Alternative Schools Prog., 85
Nat. Assn. of Accountants for the Public Interest, 55
Nat. Assoc. for Better Broadcasting (NABB), 111
Nat. Assoc. of Broadcasters (NAB), 111, 109
Nat. Assn. of Educ. Brodcasters, 112
Nat. Assoc. of Neighborhoods, 55
Nat. Assn. of Parents of Professionals for Safe Alternatives in Childbirth (NAPSAC), 184
Nat. Assn. of Recycling Industries, 188
Nat. Atlas of the U.S., 25
Nat. Black Media Coal. (NBMC), 111
Nat. Bldg. Research Inst., 228
Nat. Bureau of Standards, 203, 215
Nat. Buyers Guide to Recycled Paper, 188
Nat. Center for Appropriate Technology (NCAT), 5, 56
National Center for Appropriate Technology (UK), 6
Nat. Center for Atmosphere Research, 21
Nat. Cen. for Community Action, 216
Nat. Ctr. for Resource Recovery, 236
Nat. Center for Voluntary Action, 54
Nat. Citizens Committee for Broadcasting (NCCB), 111
Nat. Clearing House on Aging, 107
National Climate Center, 222
National Coalition for Land Reform (California), 154
Nat. Coalition for Land Reform (Iowa), 154
Nat. Conf. on Rural America, 154
National Conference of State Legislators, 203
National Consumers Congress, 204
National Correspondence Group, 112
National Council of Churches, 111
National Credit Union Admin., 47
National Dir. of Alter. Schools, 85
National Directory of Hotlines & Youth Crisis Centers, 89
National Educational Television, 3
National Endowment for the Arts, 117, 141
National Energy Info. Center, 205
National Environment Policy Act, 57
National Exchange, 89
National Federation of Community Broadcasters, 112, 119
National Federation of Settlements & Neighborhood Centers, 102
National Film Board, 115, 118
National Geographic, 23, 84
National Geographic Society, 23, 24
National Jogging Assn., 72
National Land for People, 154
National Latino Media Coalition, 112
National Mineral Wool Insulation Association, 215
National Ocean Survey, 22, 25
Nat. Organization for Women, 112
National Planning Assn., 44
National Public Radio, 112
National Pub. Relations Council, 109
Nat. Resource Recycling Exch., 188
National Science Foundation, 43, 59, 114, 138, 151, 157, 203, 235, 242
National Self-Help Resource Center, 55, 94, 102
National Swedish Building Research Inst., 142, 143
National Taiwan University, 236
National Technical Info. Service, 95, 166, 186, 196, 202, 203, 212, 214, 237, 239, 240, 242
Nat. Trust for Hist. Preservation, 141
National Urban Coalition, 141
National Wildlife Federation, 202
National Women's Health Net., 183
Nation's Crisis, 30
Native Americans
Land ethic, 154
Language, 82
Seven Arrows, 17
Tipis, 48, 138
Natural Air Flow Around Bldgs., 145
Natural Birth Control, 183
Natural Birth Control Book, 184
Natural Energy, 206
Natural Food Preservation Proj., 56
Natural Pest Control, 163-166
Natural Power, Inc., 240
Natural Regions of the U.S. and Canada, 12
Natural Ventilation, 136, 145, 146
Naturally Air-Conditioned Bldg., 223
Natrilite Products, Inc., 164
Nature Conservancy, 156
Naval Const. Battalion Ctr., 227
Naval Personnel, Bureau of, 139
NBC, 111
NCAT, See National Ctr. for Appropriate Tech.
Neal, Arminta, 65
Nearing, Helen & Scott, 171
Needham, Joseph, 10
Neighborhood Develop., 45, 46, 49-72
Neighborhood History, 57
Neighborhood Ideas, 57
Neighborhood Information Centers Project, 104
Neighborhood Info. System, 69
Neighborhood Power, 54
Neighborhood Trans. System, 125
Neighbors West-N.W. office, 102
Nelson, Ted, 100
Nesbitt, Patricia M., 191
Net Energy Clearinghouse, 198
Network Project, 70
Network Project Notebooks, 115
Networking, 65-72, 75, 167-170
Networks, 1977 Meeting, 72
Neuberg, Leland, 39
Neurer, Kathleen, 132
Nelms, Henny, 79
New Age Foods Study Center, 175
New Age Journal, 47, 49, 92
New Alchemy Inst., 5, 9, 164, 215
New Alchemy West, 150, 165, 235
New American Library, 108
New China, 62
New Day Films, 117
New Directions Radio, 118
New Directions for Veterans, 89
New Energy Technologies for Buildings, 217
New England Catalog, 87
New England Free Press, 93
New England Solar Energy Soc., 229, 230
New Games, 91
New Handbook on Prescription Drugs, 182
New Harbinger, 168, 218
New Life Environmental Design Network, 88
New Look at Public Power, 98
New Orleans Video Access Center, 117
New Periodicals Index, 118
New Pioneer Cooperative Society, 64
New Republic Pamphlets, 154
New School for Social Research, 117
New Schools Exchange, 85, 90
New Scientist, 241
New Ware, 120
New Ways to Work, 52
New West Trails, 87
New Western Energy Show, 203
New Women's Survival Sourcebook, 90, 115
New World Computer Services, 100
New World Press, 61
New York Geographic Society, 12
N.Y. State University College, 78
New York Times, 31
New Yorker, 125, 201
News From Nowhere, 111
Newsletter Collective, 169
Newspaper Directory, 88
Newsprint Co-op, 91
Nietzsche, Friedrich, 81
Nightwall, 224
Nikof, Krasiz, 166
Niles, Phillip, 224
Nilsson, Lennart, 178
Nin, Anais, 91
N.J. Cable Video Info. Proj., 114
No Lamb for Slaughter, 111
No More Public School, 85
No Substitute for Madness, 84
Noise, 30
Nongrowth, 32-46
Nongrowth Planning Strategies, 40
Non-Nuclear Futures, 201, 207
Norcross, Derek, 47
Noren, Don, 228
Noren Products, Inc., 228
North Am. Congress on Latin America, 93
North American Student Co-op Org. (NASCO), 168, 218
North Carolina Carologue, 87
North Country Anvil, 92
North Country Co-op, 47
North Idaho Access, 86
North State Public Video, 117
Northeast Appropriate Tech. Net., 5
Northeast Carry, 5
Northeast Micrographics, 184
No. Calif. Food Network, 176
No. Calif. Land Trust, 156
Northern Engineer, 228
Northern Plains Resource Council, 58
Northwest Alternate Communications Directory, 115
Northwest Alternative Ham Net., 118
Northwest Artists Workshop, 118
Northwest Bibliographic Center, 103
Northwest Computer Club, 101
Northwest District Association, 102
Northwest Film Study Cen., 116, 118
Northwest Media Project, 118
Northwest Regional Foun., 57, 75, 79
Northwest Trade Directory, 89, 170
Northwest Trade Network, 159
Northwest Washington Barter Fair, 65
Northwestern University, 103
Northwind, 171
Norton, John, 136
Not Man Apart, 58, 129, 192, 208, 210, 212
NOVA, 3
Novick, Sheldon, 207
NSF-RANN Wind Energy Conversion Research, 242
Nuclear Blowdown, 58, 208
Nuclear-Electric Chainsaws, 199-201
Nuclear Power Facilities in the United States, 208
Nuclear Power: The Fifth Horseman, 207
Nutrition Action, 176
Nutrition Info. Center, 176
Nutrition Scoreboard, 176
NW Cable Network, 114

●

Oak Ridge Nat. Laboratory, 127, 205
OASIS 2000, 235
Oceanic & Atmospheric Admin., 95
Oceans, 24, 25, 28, 89
Odum, Elizabeth, 198
Odum, Howard T., 29, 34, 198, 202
OECD, See Org. for Economic Cooperation & Development

OEO, 5, 56
Office of Appropriate Technology (OAT), 5, 17, 204
Office of Energy Research & Planning 29, 198, 203
Office of Neighborhood Assns., 56
Ogden, Utah Peoples Yellow Pages, 87
O'Grady, Gerald, 117
Oh What a Blow That Phantom Gave Me, 110
Ohio College Library Center, 104
Ohio State University, 120
Oilweek, 210
Old Fashioned Recipe Book, 171
Old Glory, 18, 90
Old House Journal, 141
Olgyay, Victor, 221
Olivia Record, 118
Olkowski, Bill, 161, 164
Olkowski, Helga, 150, 161, 164, 165, 194
On the Cable: The Television of Abundance, 114
On Death & Dying, 180
On Inflation, 3
On Land Speculation, 3
On Learning & Social Change, 72
On the Market, 169
On the Wall Productions, 118
Opal, 18
Open Dallas, Discover Your City, 87
Opening Networks, 70
Oppenheimer, Charles, 120
Optic Nerve, 118
Options for Energy Conservation, 43
ORE Plan, 49, 92, 149, 150, 151, 153, 154
Oregon Bottle Bill Two Years Later, 186
Ore. Environmental Council, 58, 186
Oregon Media Guide, 110
Oregon Museum of Science and Industry, 69, 75, 99, 101
Oregon State University, 109, 239
Ore. Women's Resource Guide, 90
Oregonian, 51
Organic Directory, 89, 160
Organic Farming Groups List, 160
Organic Gardening and Farming, 144, 147, 158, 159, 162, 165, 166, 194, 231
Organic Plant Protection, 165
Organization for Economic Cooperation & Development, 124
Organizer's Book Center, 54
Organizer's Manual, 109
Organizer's Notebook on Public Utilities & Energy for NY State, 209
Organizing & Conducting Community Surveys, 97
Organizing Farmers' Market, 167
Original Log House Construction, 143
Orleans, Mim, 181
Ornstein, Robert E., 78
Osborne, Alex, 80
Ostrander, Sheila, 183
Other Side of the River, 61
Other Way, 3
Ott, John N., 182
Otteraaen, Marion, 105
Our Bodies, Ourselves, 183
Our Corner of the Earth, 213
Our Man-Made Environment, 30
Our World From The Air, 21
Ouroboros Project, 143, 213
Outdoor Recreation, California Bureau of, 162
Outdoor Recreation, US Bur. of, 162
Ovulation method, 178, 184
Owens-Corning Fiberglass Co., 215
Owner-Builder and the Code, 48, 136
Owner-Building Courses, 144
Owner-Built Home, 139, 143
Owner-Built Homestead, 143
Oxford English Dictionary, 95
Oxford University, 234
Oxford World Atlas, 26
Ozarks Communicator, 171
Oz-Com, 171

●

P-Patch Program, 162
Pacific Bamboo Gardens, 146
Pacific Film Archive, 118
Pacific High School, 85
Pacific NW Forest & Range Exp. Station, 222
Pacific Northwest Research Ctr., 98
Pacific Power & Light, 215
Pacific Science Center, 101
Pacifica Radio, 120
Paid My Dues, 116
Painter, R.H., 164
Palms — Their Use in Building, 142
Palos Verdes Landfill Methane Recovery, 237
Paper, Paper, 188
Parade Magazine, 47
Parazek, Richard, 195
Paritz, Jack, 118
Park, Jack, 203, 239
Parker, Harry, 139
Parker, Jim, 203
Parker, Rev. Everett, 112
Parking Facilities for Alternate Uses, 142
Parkinson, D., 166
Parks & Recreation, L.A. County, 109
Parks & Open Space, 57
Parkway Program, 85
Parnes, Sydney J., 78
Participation Systems, Inc., 60
Parties in Interest, 112
Passive Solar Heating & Cooling Conf. Proceedings, 221
Passive Solar Water Heater, 224
Pauwels, Louis, 72, 82
Payne Hollow, 171
Peace Corps, 68
Pear Syrup, 175
Pedal Power, 234
Pediatric Priorities in a Developing World, 179
Pellman, Ronald C., 80
Penfield, Lou, 137
Pennsylvania Horticulture Society, 87, 146
Pennsylvania State Univ., 195, 196
People & Energy, 97, 206
People Index, 69
People and Land, 154, 155
People to People Indexes, 67, 86-90
People's Almanac, 89
People's Computer Club Newsletter, 101
People's Computer Company, 100
People's Guide to Home Insulation, 57
Peoples Land, 152, 153
People's Land Trust, 156
People's Yellow Pages, 86, 102
Perception & Change, 106
Perelman, Michael, 150
Performance Guidelines for Planning Community Resource Centers, 102
Performing Arts Index, 67, 90
Perennial Farming, 157
Perrin, Alwyn T., 90
Personal Computing, 100
Pest Control Without Poison, 165
Pesticides, 166
Peterson, Christina, 151
Peterson, David, 40
Peterson's Guide to Video Tape Recording, 116
Pfeiffer, E., 165
Phantom Taxes in Your Electric Bill, 33, 209
Philbrick, Helen, 166
Phila. Area Green Pages, 87, 146
Phila. Parkway Program, 85
Phillips, Bob, 118
Phillips, Michael, 42
Photo-Atlas of the U.S., 22
Photo-Graphic International, 22
Photographic Anatomy of the Human Body, 178
Physical Energy Potential of Wod, 231
Pierotti, Anne, 213
Pike, Alexander, 144
Pikes Peak Area Council of Governments, 40
Pilgrim at Tinker Creek, 17
Pioneering Communities, 19, 20
Pittsburgh Film-makers, 117
Planet Drum, 17, 24, 70
Planner's Handbook on Energy, 204
Planning Community Info. Utilities, 106
Planning for Energy Cons., 218
Planning, Portland Bur. of, 130, 205
Plant Form Studies, 145
Plant a Tree (Schumacher), 3
Plant a Tree, 145
Plants, People, & Environmental Quality, 145
Platform for Change, 99
Platt, John R., 106, 113
Platt, Rutherford, 146
Playing in the FM Band, 120
Po, Chung, 236
Point Reyes Nat'l. Seashore, 132
Poisoned Cities and Urban Gardens, 161
Pole Bldgs. in Papua New Guinea, 138
Politics of Land, 152
Polk City Directory, 88
Pollution, 97, 192
Polyai, G., 77
Pomeroy, Dave, 111
Poor, Riva, 52
Popular Economics Press, 32
Popular Science, 215
Population Distribution, Urban and Rural, in the U.S., 26
Portable Channel, 117
Porter, Eliot, 58
Portin, Sharon, 114
Portland Alliance of Neighborhoods, 56
Portland Art Museum, 116, 118
Portland Community College, 172
Portland General Electric, 215
Portland Scribe, 88
Portland State University, 189
Portola Institute, 90, 202
Portrait of Mother Earth, 26
Portrait U.S.A., 23
Port Washington Public Library, 117
Positive Media in America, 118
Possible Tape Exchange, 120
Post, Steve, 120
Post-Industrial Prophets, 110
Potential for Energy Savings Through Reductions in Hot Water Consumption, 214
Potential Natural Vegetation of Coterminous U.S., 23
Potomac Associates, 198
Pound, Ezra, 82
Poverty of Power, 201, 202
Power Line, 209
Power Over People, 209
Power from the Wind, 242
Powers of Ten, 21
Pozzo, Robert, 204, 219
Practical Building of Methane Power Plants, 237
Practical Primer for Realistic Radicals, 54
Practices in Detention of Urban Stormwater Runoff, 196
Pragtree Farm, 159, 170, 226
Pratt Inst. Center for Community & Environmental Develop., 37, 48, 57
Preliminary Assessment of Suspected Carcinogens in Drinking Water, 192
Preliminary Design & Perf. Analysis for New State Office Bldg., 223
Preliminary Study of Resistance in 20 Varieties of Cabbages to the Cabbage Worm Butterfly, 164
Preventative Medicine, 179
Prevention, 181
Price, John H., 207
Price, Monroe, 114
Prime Time, the Biography of Edward R. Murrow, 111
Prime Time School TV, (PTST), 112
Principles of Problem Formulation & Resolution, 78
Priorities, 34
Prisoners of Liberation, 62
Prisoner's Yellow Pages, 89
Private Broadcaster & the Public Interest, 111
Privacy Journal, 99
Privies, 193, 194
Problem Solving, 77, 78, 96
Producing Slide Tapes, 116, 117
Production & Distribution of Knowledge in the U.S., 106
Production and Use of Methane in Taiwan, 236
Profiles of California Community Garden Projects, 162
Prognosis Negative, 179
Programming & Metaprogramming the Human Biocomputer, 106
Project Independence, 43
Project Retro-Tech, 215
Project Survival, 207
Projecting an Energy-Efficient California, 212
Prometheus Crisis, 208
Propane Conversion, Autos, 125
Property Tax Organizing Man., 33
Proposal for a State Land Trust Act, 155
Proposals for Vermont's Agriculture and Food Future, 150
Provisional Committee for Democracy in Radio, 120
Psychiatric Drugs, 180
Psychic Phenomena, 90
Psychology of Problem-Solving, 80
Psychology of Consciousness, 78
Public Access Experience, 113
Public Advertising Council, 109
Public Broadcasting Service, 112
Public Citizen, 43, 58, 98
Visitor's Center, 101
Health Research Group, 165
Public Control of Public Money, 54
Public Information Network, 69
Public Interest Economic Foun., 52
Public Interest Economic Rev., 52
Pub. Interest Law in America, 55
Public Media Center, 109, 110
Public Interest Research Groups, 98
D.C., 37, 219
Vermont, 209
Iowa, 64
Public Interest Satelite Assn., 114
Public Opinion Quarterly, 109
Public Pension Funds as a Source of Capitol for Job Creation, 48
Public Policy Reader, 54
Public Relations Society of Am., 109
Pub. Service Satellite Consortium, 114
Public Telecommunications Rev., 112
Pub. TV: Program for Action, 112
Public White Papers, 98, 112
Publi-Cable, 114
Public Works, 48, 236
Publish it Yourself Handbook, 91
Publishing Center for Cultural Resources, 115
Publishers Weekly, 95
Puerto Rico Water Res. Auth., 214
Puget Sound Access, 18, 87
Pursuit of Loneliness, 65
Pushcart Book Press, 91
Putnam, Palmer, C., 242
Putting Together A People's Yellow Pages, 88
Pyramid Films, 21

●

Q Corporation, 179, 191
Quick City, 67
Quimary, Donald, 112

●

Rabun Gap-Nacooche H.S., 83
Radical Agriculture, 169
Radical Software, 115
Radical Technology, 3, 9, 144
Radio, 74, 88, 119-122
Railroads, 125, 141
RAIN, 9, 70, 86, 91, 198, 203, 216
Sharing Smaller Pies, 3, 34
Coming Around, 4
Employment Impact Statement, 43
Good-Bye Flush Toilet, 191, 193
Living Lightly, 213
Wood Stoves Guide, 231
Rainbow Flute, 70, 93
Raindance Corp., 115, 116
Raisz, Erwin, 23, 26
Raphael, Ray, 18
Rasberry Exercises, 85
Rasberry, Salli, 85
Rasmussen Report, 207
Rathke, Wade, See ACORN
Rathwell, Jim, 226
Raup, Philip, 151
Reaching the Public, 109
Reader's Digest Complete Do-it-Yourself Manuel, 148
Readers Guide to Periodical Lit., 95
Real Estate Research Corp., 40
Real Time, 90
Rebuilding, 141
Rechel, Ralph, 125
Recommended Country Inns of New England, 132
Recreational Comm. Gardening, 162
Recycle?, 186
Recycling: Alabama Style, 187
Recycling Information Service, 188
Recycling in Maine, 187
Recycling Switchboard, 94, 188
Recycl-it, 190
Red China Today, 61
Red Star Over China, 61
Redlining, 37, 57
Redlining: Problems and Tactics, 37
Reduce: Targets, Means & Impacts of Source Reduction, 186
Reed, J.W., 239
Reflections on Language, 82
Reference Books, 93-96
Ref. Books for Small Libraries, 95
Reforestation, 50, 146
Regional Climate Analyses, 221
Regional Cooking of China, 173, 174
Regional Electric Maps, 209
Reg. Organic Farming Groups, 160
Register of Faculty Prof. Interests, 69
Reich, Hanns, 22
Reichmuth, Howard, 226
Reid, Phoenix, 176
Reilly, John, 109, 117
Relis, Paul, 150
Renaissance House, 89
Renigades, 48
Renovation, 141
Rennie, Susan, 90, 115
Report of Cycling Britain, 127
Report of the Task Force on Women in Public Broadcasting, 112
Resch, Helmuth, 231
Research Institute of Biological Husbandry, 159
Reserve Synthetic Fuels, 237
Residential Water Cons., 193, 196
Resistance of Plants to Insects, 164
Resource Access Center, 100
Resource for the Active Comm., 115
Resource Conservation Through Citizen Involvement in Waste Management, 186
Resource Depletion/Limits, 33, 34, 91, 210
Resource File, 94
Resource Inventories, 29
Resource One, 69, 101
Resource Recovery & Cons., 235, 236
Resource Recovery & Recycling Handbook of Indust. Wastes, 187
Resources for Community Change, 32, 89, 90
Resources News Service, 57
Resources and Man, 210
Responsive Chord, 110
Restoration Manuel, 141
Resurgence, 3
Retrofitting Existing Housing for Energy Conservation, 141, 215
Return of the Gods, 140
Return of the Tall Ships, 126
Reusing Railroad Stations, 141
Reverence for Wood, 146
Revolting Librarians, 103
Rice, Bill, 219, 226
Rice, Fred, 237
Rice Media Center, 117
Richard, Pamela, 112
Richard Russel Agricultural Research Center, 137
Richard's Bicycle Book, 127
Richards, Brian, 125
Richards, M.C., 83
Richest Land, 155
Richter, H.P., 139
Rickett, Allyn & Adele, 62
Riette, Louise, 147
Riggs, Ellen R., 147
Your Rights to Express Your Views on Radio & TV, 112
Rincon-Vitova Industries, Inc., 164
Riteway, 232
Road Apple Press, 159
Robbins, Lewis, 178
Robbins, Tom, 225
Roberts, Don, 117
Roberts, Rex, 139
Robertson, James, 58
Robinette, Gary O., 145, 146
Robinson, Frank, 208
Robinson, Richard, 116
Rochester Inst. of Technology, 110
Rock, Time & Landforms, 12
Rockefeller, Abby, 193, See Clivus Multrum
Rocky Mountain Film Center, 118
Rodale Press, 58, 89, 136, 152, 153, 159, 160, 161, 165, 186, 189, 194, 195, 237
Rodale Waste Recycling Conf., 191
Rodriguez, Julio, 112
Rogers, Everett, M., 77
Roget, Peter Mark, 95
Role of the Ore. Plan in Developing a Nationwide Recycling Network, 186
Roof, Ceiling & Thermal Ponds, 224
Rosenblum, Art, 184
Rosenfeld, Arthur, 212
Rosenfield, Edward, 90
Ross, Bob & Carol, 231
Ross, David, 118
Rossman, Michael, 72
Rotzel, Grace, 85
Rouen, France, 124
Rounder Records, 117
Rowe, Nina, 130
Royal Horticultural Society, 159
Ruckelshaus, William, 97
Rudder, 126
Rules for Radicals, 54

Rural America, Inc., 154, 159
Rural Communities, 63, 64
  Pioneering, 19, 20
  Barn Raising, 136
Rural Development, AID, 6
Rural Housing Alliance, 154
Rural Industries Bureau, 142
Rural Land Use: Patterns and Proposals for Reform, 154
Rural Library, 105
Rural New Town for the West Side of the San Joaquin Valley, 45
Rural Resources & Info., 65, 70
Rural Roots, 63, 64
Rural Tribune, 56
Rush, Anne Kent, 17, 184
Russell, Bertrand, 81
Rutgers University, 104, 114
Ryle, Gilbert, 82

●

Sackman, H., 106
Sacred Places, 17, 133, 140, 153
Safe Alternatives in Childbirth, 184
Sailing Ship in the Fuel Crisis, 126
Salons and Their Keepers, 66
Sam Ely Community Land Trust, 156
Samuals, Catherine, 109
San Francisco Food Directory, 169
S.F. Info. Clearinghouse, 102
San Francisco Study Center, 152
San Francisco Zen Center, 56
San Jose State University, 109
Santa Barbara Community Cable TV Project, 113
Santa Barbara — The Impacts of Growth, 40
Santa Clara Co. Water Dist., 146
Santa Cruz People's Yellow Pages, 87
Saracevic, Tefko, 106
Satellite Communications, 114
Satellite Spies, 114
Saturday Market, 65
Saunders, Norman B., 224
Save Energy, Save Money!, 216
Sawdek, S.E., 235
Scale
  Economics, 32-52
  Agriculture, 152
Scale, Centralization & Electrification in Energy Systems, 199
Scarecrow Inc., 116
Schatz, Joel, 92, 198
Schauffler, Peter, 237
Schell, Orville, 61, 64
Schenectady Access Cable Cncl., 113
Scher, Les, 38
Schiller, Herbert, 110, 111
Schmidt, Benno, Jr., 112
Schmidt, Fred, 216
Schneider, Ira, 115
Schneider, Steve, 110
Scholastic Magazine, 239
School Gardens, 161
School Library Journal, 95
School in Rose Valley, 85
Schools, 83-85, 143, 144
Schowalter, Joyce, 105
School of Living, 155
Schrank, Jeffrey, 112, 116
Schroeder, Lynn, 183
Schulman, Harvey, 109, 111
Schumacher, F.W., 146
Schumacher, E.F., 3, 5, 39
Schurmann, Franz, 61
Schuy, David F., 204
Schwartz, Bob, 49
Schwartz, Herbert, 192
Schwartz, Tony, 110
Schwind, Dick, 240
Science, 201, 204, 211, 219
Science of the Artificial, 106
Science & Civilization in China, 10
Science & Civilization in Islam, 10
Science Council of Canada, 9, 201
Science Fiction, 15, 21, 72
Science for the People, 62, 97
Science of Sanity, 81, 82
Science Walks on Two Legs, 97
Scientific American, 74, 106, 129, 202, 210, 228, 234
Scientific & Scholarly Research, Univ. of Oregon office, 69
Scoop, 169
Scortia, Thomas N., 208
Scott Bader Company, 51
Scott, Denny R., 44
Sea-King Media Access Group, 113
Season-All Industries, 216
Seattle City Light, 98, 211
Seattle Community Information Project, 98, 112
Seattle People's Yellow Pages, 87
Seattle Trust & Savings Bank, 212
Second Alternative Public Policy Reader, 40, 54
SEDFRE, 55
Seed Catalog, 84, 90
Seeman, Dr. J., 225
Seeds, 146, 158
Seldman, Neil, 186, 191
Selected Info. Resources on Energy, 205
Selected Info Resources on Solid Wastes, 188
Selection & Characteristics of Wind-Power Sites, 240
Self-Help and Health, 179
Self-Reliance, 6, 9, 46, 57, 91, 194
Self-Management, 51
Self Regulation & Requisite Variety, 79
Self-Sufficiency, 171, 172
Seligman & Johnson, 153
Selling of the President, 109
Semantics, 81, 82
Sencenbaugh Wind Electric, 240
Septic Tank Practices, 194
Serendipity, 129
Seriatim, 92
Service for Energy Cons. in Arch., 217
Service Exchange, 65, 68
Sesame Street, 112
SEVCA Stove, 231
Seven Arrows, 17
Seven Laws of Money, 42
Sewage Treatment Technology and our Urban Communities, 191
Sewer Systems
  Economies, 192
  Jobs, 43
Sewerless Society, 191
Sex & Broadcasting, 119
Sex Stereotyping in Prime Time TV, 111
Sexual Politics of Sickness, 184
Seymour, John, 172
SD/ACORN, 55
Shadduck, Gregg, 237
Shaffer, Dale E., 84
Schamberg, Michael, 116
Shantyboat, 171
Shapiro, Andrew, 112, 231
Shapiro, Barry, 140
Sharefkin, Mark, 208
Sharing and Gathering, 65-72, 84
Sharing of Land and Resources in America, 154
Sharing Smaller Pies, 3, 34
Sharpe, William, 196
Shayon, Robt. Lewis, 112
Shearer and Webb, 40
Shelter, 138, 140
Shelter Institute, 143, 203
Shelterforce, 57
Shelton, Jay, 231
Shelton, John S., 12
Sheridan, Thomas B., 60
Shils, Maurice, 176
Shoreline School District, 151
Short Course in Cable, 114
Should Trees Have Standing, 148
Shurcliff, William, 223, 229
Shurtleff, Bill, 175
Sidel, Ruth, 62
Sierra Club, 54, 58, 161
Silent Language, 110
Silvaculture, 148
Simon Fraser University, 30
Simonds, John, 147
Simmon, Glen & Kathleen, 172
Simmons, Richard, 117
Simon, Herbert, 106
Simons, J.W., 137
Simple Building, 136-144
Simple Lifestyle Calander, 213
Simple Living, 213
Simplified Engineering for Architects and Builders, 139
Simplified Wind Power Systems for Experimenters, 240
Simpson, Norman T., 132
Simulation Analysis of Passive Solar-Heated Bldgs., 223, 226
Singer, Charles, 10
Singh, Ram Bux, 236
Sittig, Marshall, 187
Sitton, Bob, 118
Size, Efficiency and Community Enterprise, 4, 39,
Size and Growth, 39, 40
Skidmore, Owings & Merrill, 212
Skills Exchange, 65, 68
Skoog, Randy, 93
Sktabak, Darryl, 130
Skylab, 22
Skylight Energy Performance, 223
Skylights, 142, 233
Skytherm Process & Engineering, 223 224
Slater, Phillip, 65
Slide Tape Collective, 116, 117
Sloan Commission on Cable Communications, 114
Sloane, Eric, 146
Small Business, 49-52
Small Business, US Sen Comm., 151
Small Farm Project, 151
Small Homes Building Council, 143
Small is Beautiful, 3, 21, 39
Small, Maxwell, M., 196
Small Press Review, 91
Small-Time Operator, 49
Small Town, 63
Smallholder, 70, 72, 171
Smith, Charles L., 154
Smith, Douglas B., 129
Smith, J. Russel, 148
Smith, Jean, 130
Smith, Ken, 151, 203, 226, 229, 235-238
Smith, Ralph Lee, 114
Smith-Harvestore Products, 237
Smithsonian Institution, 68
Smollen, Leonard, 48
Snow, Edgar, 61
Snyder, Gary, 11, 17
Snyder, Rachel, 229
Social Ecology Program, 83, 144
Social Networks, 72
Social Services and Cable TV, 114
Societal Cost Accounting, 126
Society for General Systems Research, 79, 106
Society of Independent Artists, 65
Soc. for the Protection of New Hampshire Forests, 231
Socio-gram, 76
Soft Energy Paths: Towards a Durable Peace, 199, 201
Software Development Group, 101
Soil Bacteria, 166
Soil Cement: Its Use in Bldgs., 137
Soil Conservation Survey, 23
Soil Microorganisms and Higher Plants, 166
Solar Aquaculture Greenhouse Systems for Western Wash., 226
Solar Collector Manufacturing Activity, 227
Solar Energy, 226
Solar Energy Applications Lab., 242
Solar Energy & the Flat Plate Collector, 227
Solar Energy — Food & Fuel Workshop Proceedings, 226
Solar Energy Heat Pump Systems, 228
Solar Energy for Space Heating & Hot Water, 220
Solar Era, 221
Solar Greenhouses, 225
Solar Guide & Calculator, 222
Solar Heated Bldgs.: A Brief Survey, 223
Solar Heating of Bldgs. & Domestic Hot Water, 227
Solar Home Book, 143, 219, 221
Solar Newsletters & Dir., 229, 230
Solar Radiation Data, 222
Solar Service Corp., 219
Solar Sustenance Report, 203, 226
Solar Test Standards, 220
Solar Thermal Energy Utilization, 220
Solar Water Heating in S. Africa, 228
Solar Water Heating in So. Fla., 228
Solid Waste Information Materials Control Section, EPA, 186, 188
Solid Waste Recovery Co., 190
Solid Waste Recycling Projects, National Directory, 188
Some Performance Characteristics of the CNRS House, 224
Somerville Media Action Project (SMAP), 117
Somewhere Else, 83, 90
Sontag, Susan, 82
Sorenson, Bent, 201, 204, 211, 241
Soundscape Project, 30
Soup Time, 176
Source Catalogues, 89, 115
Sourcebook for Creative Thinking, 78
Sources of Capitol for Community Economic Development, 48
Sources of Free Teaching Mater., 84
S.E. Vermont Comm. Action, 231
S.W. Research & Info. Center, 91
S.W. Oregon Community Council, 66
Souza, Robin, 111
Spaghetti City Video Manual, 116, 117
Special Libraries Assn., 87
Spectrum, 4, 90
Spence, Robin, 137
Spetgang, Tilly, 219
Spiritual Midwifery, 184
Spiritual Places, 17, 133, 140, 153
Spock, Raymond, 18
Spokane Community Video, 118
Spring Mt. Hot Tubs, 232
Sprocket Man, 129
Squire, Elizabeth, 132
Squirrel Hill Citizens Cable TV, 113
Staff Burn Out Syndrome, 78
Stafford, William, 12
Stand Communications Center, 117
Stanford Research Inst., 202
Stapleton, Olaf, 21
Starflower, 169
Starmaker, 21
State Architect's Office (CA), 220, 223
State Bank, North Dakota, 47
State Energy Organizations Catalog
State Growth Management, 32
State & Local Environmental Libraries, 95
Steadman, Philip, 217
Steady State Economy, 34
Stebben, Gene, 120
Stein, Barry, 4, 19, 39
Stein, Jane, 217
Steps to an Ecology of Mind, 106
Stevens, Chandler Harrison, 60, 102
Stevens, Leonard A., 195
Stewart, Lee & David, 184
Stewart, Suzanne, 138
Stichting Tool, 4
Stile, Win, 146
Stoney, George, 113
Stolen Goods, 35
Stone, Christopher, 148
Stone Masonry, 137
Stone Soup Restaurant, 64
Stoner, A., 164
Stop the 5-Gallon Flush, 6, 193
Storm, Hyemeyohsts, 17
Story of the Bicycle, 127
Strange & Familiar, 77
Strassfeld, Michael, 90
Strategy for Energy Conservation, 145 223
Strauss, J., 179
Street, 57
Strip Mining, 58, 210
Strode, Nancy & Walter, 180
Structure of Magic, 82
Structure of Scientific Revolutions, 110
Studsvik AB Atomenergi, 218
Studying Your Community, 30, 98
Sturt, Georg, 83
Styles of Radical Will, 82
Subliminal Seduction, 108
Sucher, David, 18
Sun Can Heat Our Homes, 228
Sunset Magazine, 132, 146
Sunset Western Garden Book, 146
Sunspots, 202
Sunworld, 229
Super 9 Filmmaker, 116
Surface Mining in Alabama, 210
Survey of State Legislation Related to Solar Energy, 203
Survival Greenhouse, 226
Suyin, Han, 61
Svensk Byggtjanst, 215
Swan, L., 165
Swann, Bob, 155
Sweat Equity, 48, 143, 57
Swedish Building Research Reports, 142, 143
Swindon Viewpoint, 118
Sym/bios, 193
Synapse, 87, 117
Synchronicity, 72
Synchronous Inversion, 241
Syncon, 66
Synerji: Directory of Energy Alternatives, 206
Synergy Access, 70
Synetics Education Systems, 77
Syracuse Peace Council, 87
Syracuse People's Yellow Pages, 87
Systems Analysis for Skylight Energy Procedures, 223
System Energy and Recycling, 186
System of Structure, 106
Systems Science, 77, 79, 106
Systems Thinking, 79, 106

●

Taber, Sally, 94
Taft Productions, 109
Take Care of Yourself, 181
Taking Off, 83
Taking Pictures and Taking Souls, 133
Taking Charge, 98, 209
Taking Pipe, 192
Tale of Two Energies, 239
Tale of Two Towns, 152
Talent for Detail, 18
Talent Pools, 67-69
Tanzania Publishing House, 4, 123
Target List, 112
Tassajara Breadbook, 173, 174
Tassajara Cooking, 173, 174
Tate, Charles, 114
Tatum, Billy Joe, 175
Taub, Harold, 181
Tax Credits for Employment Rather Than Investment, 43
Taxes, 33, 41, 43, 49, 54
Taxing the Pavement, Not the Earth, 41
Taylor, Ronald L., 157
Taylor, David, 213
Taylor, Theodore, 207
Teacher Paper, 74
Teacher Was the Sea, 85
Teacher Works, 84
Teague, Terri, 182
Teasdale, Parry, 116
Technological Society, 110
Technological Utilization: Incentives & Solar Energy, 220
Technology Applications Center, 220, 221, 225, 242
Technology of the Cooling Effects of Trees & Shrubs, 145
Technology and Employment in Industry, 4, 39
Technology & Political Change, 3
Technology Review, 43
Technology for Utilization of Waste Energy, 242
Technotec, Inc., 4
Tekton Design Corp., 232
TeleVisions Magazine, 115
Telecommunications, US Off. of, 102
Television Bibliography, 115
Television Laboratory, 112
Television Commercial Library, 117
Televisionaries, 109
Televote, 59
Temple University, 116
Tenants Rights, 57
TerBush, Frank, 146
Tetrault, Jeanne, 171
Texas A & M Research Report, 145
Thallon, Rob, 48, 136
Thatcher's Craft, 142
The Information Place, (TIP), 104
Theater Project, 91
Theodore, Tedwilliam, 47
Theory of Open Systems in Physics & Biology, 79
Thermal Environmental Engin., 224
Thermal Eval. of a House Using Moveable Insulation, 224
Thermography Helps Save Energy, 215
Thesaurus of English Words and Phrases, 95
Thesaurus: Mass Communictns., 115
They Became What They Beheld, 110
They've All Gone to Look for Am., 54
Things Maps Don't Tell Us, 26
Think About Land, 3
Thinking Straighter, 79
Thinking With A Pencil, 79
Third Planet — Terrestrial Geology in Orbital Photographs, 21
Thomas, Anna, 173
Thomas, Anne, 171
Thomas, Bill, 120
Thomas, Lewis, 17, 74
Thomas Register of American Manufacturers, 95
Thomas, Tom, 119
Thomas, Wes, 70, 116
Thoreau, Henry David, 17, 58
Threlkeld, James L., 224
Tilly's Catch-A-Sunbeam Coloring Book, 219
Tilth, 70, 159, 170, 226
Time to Choose, 203
Time Life Multimedia, 3
Tips, 49, 138
Titanic Enthusiasts of America, 72
Tithing, 47
toast, 198
Todd, Alden, 93
Todd, John, 150, 225

Todd, Nancy Jack, 5, 226
Tofu, 49, 175
Toilets, 191-194
Toll-free Solar Info. Number, 219
Tool, 4
Tool Lending Libraries, 67
Toolshed, 105
Tools for Agriculture, 158
Tools for Arid and Tropical Regions, 158
Tools for Conviviality, 3, 179
Top Secret, 105
Topographic Maps, 25
Top Value Television, 118
Total Environmental Action, 144, 203
Tourism, 133, 134
Tourism & Development: East African Cause, 134
Toward A Steady State Economy, 34, 198, 210
Toward Tomorrow Fair, 70
Towards a Network of Community Information Exchanges, 102
Tower in Babel, 111
Towers, Graham, 124
Town Meetings, 66
Town That Fought to Save Itself, 64
Townsend, Phil, 216
Traditional Crafts of Persia, 10
Training Creative Thinking, 78
TRANET, 5, 6
Transfering from Urban Cars to Buses, 204
Transition, 29, 198, 203, 210
Transnational Institute, 91
Transportation Alternatives, 130
Transportation Policies & Energy Conservation, 125
Travel, 131-134
Tree Crops, 148

Trees
Ecotopia, 15, 16
Energy Cons., 145-146
Landscaping, 145-148
Legal Standing, 148
Silvaculture, 148
Timber Industry, 51, 57
See also Wood Energy
Trent University, 134
Tribus, Myron, 107
Trombe, Felix, 224
Trombe Wall, 137, 143, 224
Trust for Public Land, 156
Tube of Plenty, 111
Tuscon Peoples Yellow Pages, 87
Tulsa People's Resource Catalog, 87
Tulsa Public Library, 118
Turning Point in China, 62
Turning Toward the Sun, 203
Turick, Dorothy Ann, 104
Turner, John F.C., 136
Turnkey Methane Programs, 237
Turoff, M., 79
Turnover, Newsletter of the People's Food System, 169
Turtle Island, 17
TV Action Book, 112
TV Factbook, 111
TV Guide, 111
TV Guided American, 111
TV Town Hall, 66, 118
Types of Maps Published by Government Agencies, 25

●

UCAN Manual of Conservation Measures, 214
UK Video Index, 115
Undercurrents, 3, 9, 238
Underexploited Tropical Plants, 159
Underground Society and Newsletter, 138
Understanding the Ecology of Insects, 166
Understanding Media, 82, 110
Understanding the World of Work, 51
UNESCO, 115
Union of Internat'l Assoc's., 72, 78
Union for Radical Pol. Econ., 52
United Church of Christ, 112, 114
United Nations, 137
UN Rome Conference on New Sources of Energy, 241
United Stand, 136, 193, 194
United Stand Privy Booklet, 193
United Way of America, 107
Universal Traveler, 77, 78
Universe Books, 144
University/Community Video Center
University Film Study Center, 117
University of Buffalo, NY, 78
University of Calif., Berkeley, 5, 212

University of Calif., Davis, 150, 193
University of Chicago, 103
University of Cincinnati, 180
University of Colorado, 118
University of Copenhagen, 204
Univ. of Denver Research Inst., 198
University of Florida, Energy Center, 29, 34, 203
University of Illinois at Urbana-Champaign, 26, 69, 143
University of Iowa, 64, 103
University of Mass., 85, 239, 240
University of Maine, 232
University Microfilms, 95, 221
Univ. of Minn., 138, 143, 222, 237
Univ. of Nevada Library, 105
Univ. of New Hampshire, 223
Univ. of New Mexico, 220, 221
Univ. of Oregon, 69, 87, 222, 227
Univ. of Rhode Island, 202
University of Sherbrooke, 194
University of Southern Calif., 21, 107
University of Texas, 143, 217
University of Technology, 242
Univeristy of Toledo, 94, 103
Univ. of Washington, 103
University of Wisconsin, 116
Unnecessary Activities?, 38
Uplift, 55
Urban Bikeway Design Collaborative, 129, 130
Urban Gardening, 161, 162
Urban Inst., 114
Urban Growth Management Sys., 40
Urban Homesteading, 141
Urban Observation Program, 30
Urban Planning Aid, 114
Urbanarium, 110
Urban Planning Aid, 117
U.S.-China People's Friendship Association, 62
Use of Domestic Hot Water for Space Heating, 227
Use of Earth Covered Bldgs., 138
Use of Wind Energy for the Aeration of Waste Waters, 194
Using Energy Wisely, 218
Utility Regulation and Local Control, 32, 33, 48, 54, 64, 209
Utopia or Oblivion, 106, 110

●

Vaginal Infections Res. Group, 183
Vaginal Politics, 184
Vale, Robert & Brenda, 144
Vallianatos, E.G., 32
Van Den Bosch, Robert, 164
Van derRyn, Sim, See Farallones Inst.; Office of Appropriate Tech.; State Arch. Office
Van Loon, Heinrich Willhem, 12
Van Loon's Geography, 12
Van Matre, Steve, 84
Van Steyn, Rene, 242
The Vancouver Book, 30, 86, 87
Vanek, Jaroslav, 51
VD Handbook, 184
Vegetable Garden Displayed, 159
Vegetarian Epicure, 173, 174
Velasques, Elaine, 118
Velux-America, Inc., 142
Venker, Victoria, 115
Venne, Chris, 118
Verge, Nydia, 214
Veterinary Guide for Farmers, 159
Veterans, 89
Viacom Cablevision 114
Vickery, Donald M, M.D., 181
The Video Access Project, 118
Video Center, 117
Video Info., 116
Video Inn, 115, 118
Video & Kids, 116
Video Mail Service, 118
Video Primer, 116
Video Resources in N.Y. State, 115
Video Tools, 116
Videoart: An Anthology, 115
Videocassette & Cable TV Newsletter, 116
Videofreex, 116 , 117
Videography, 116
Videolani Oceanic Cablevision, 113

Videotape Book, 116
Viet, Jean, 115
Vietnam, 62, 67
Viewer's Disgust, 112
Village Technology Handbook, 4, 158, 194
Villela, Tony, 168
Viruses in Water, 192
Visher, Stephen, 26
VISTA, 54, 68
Visual Studies Center, 116
Visual Thinking, 76, 77, 79
VITA, See Volunteers in Technical Assistance
Vocations for Social Change (Cambridge), 86, 88, 102
Vocations for Social Change (Oakland), 51, 102
Voice for Eco-Agriculture, 159
Volunteers, 54, 55, 68
Volunteers in Asia, 4
Volunteers in Technical Assistance, 4, 6, 54, 68, 158, 194
Von Hoffman, Nicholas, 98
Von Schrader, Eric, 118
Voting, 59, 60

●

Wade, Alex, 213
Waggoner, Don, 186
Wagner, Willis, 139
Wahl, Diana, 186
Wake County Public Libraries, 87, 105
Wake Information Center, 105
Walden Foundation, 226
Walker & Co., 147
Walker, E. Bradford, 231
Walker Publishing Co., 111
Wall Street Journal, 31
Wallace, Bob, 93, 99-101
Wallace, Irving, 89
Wallechinsky, David, 89
Walker Art Center, 117
Walter, Charles, 159
Walter, Grey, 74, 106
Walters, Don, 236
Walton, Henry, 139
Waltzwick, Paul, 78
Ward, Don, 83
Warren, Roland L., 30, 97
Warshall, Peter, 194
Wash. Community Video Center, 115
Wash. Cntr. for Metro. Affairs, 235
Washington Center for the Study of Services, 180
Wash. Consumers' Checkbook, 180
Washington Co. Community Action Organization, 56, 107
Washington, D.C. Gazette Guide, 87
Washington Environmental Atlas, 29
Washington Information Dir., 96
Washington State Library, 103
Washington State Univ., Pullman, 166, 204
Washington Univ., 120, 151, 161, 193
Washnix, George J., 66
Wasserman, Miriam, 85
Waste Water Renovation & Conservation, 195
Wastebin, 187
Water Conservation in Calif., 196
Water Conservation Educ. Prog., 146
Water Conservation & Waste Flow Reduction in the Home, 196
Water Conserving Gardening, 146
Water Information Center, 196
Water Lifting Devices for Irrigation, 158
Water Resources, Calif. Dept. of, 146, 196
Water-Saving Planting Ideas, 146
Water Newsletter, 196
Water Quality Engineering, 237
Waterless Toilets, 193
Watkins, T.H., 153
Watson, Charles S., 153
Watson, Lewis & Sharon, 105, 137
Way of the White Clouds, 17
We Almost Lost Detroit, 208
Weakland, John, 78
Weather Machine, 14
Weatherization, 215-216
Webb, Richard E., 207
Weeds and What They Tell, 165
Weeds: Guardians of the Soil, 165
Weiner, Michael, 145
Weiner, Peter, 116
Weizenbaum, Joseph, 99, 106
Welbourne, Jim, 114
Welfare, Upside Down, 32-40
Well-Being, 182
Wells, Malcolm, 202, 219

Weltfingbild, 21
Weltraumblider, 21
Wenger, Susanne, 140
Wescott, C., 165
West, Celeste, 103
West Virginia Univ., 87, 151, 214
Western Biological Control Labs, 164
Western Electric, 32
Western High School, 83
Western Interstate Commission for Higher Education, 104
Western Regional Solar Dir., 230
Westlands, 45
WGBH Television Workshop, 112
What Color is your Parachute?, 51, 77, 78
What is Worth Doing, 34
What's Growing in Iowa?, 64
What's Happening to Our Jobs?, 32
What's Happening Where I Live, 12
Wheels of Fortune, 152
Wheelwright's Shop, 83
Where Do I Go From Here With My Life?, 78
Where It's At, 93
White, Karen Cross, 173
White, Robert F., 145
White, Rodney, 28
White, T., 127
Whitehead, Alfred North, 81
Whiteley, Opal, 18
Whitney, Rusty, 99
Whitt, Frank, 127
Who Owns the Land?, 154
Who Shops Co-ops, and Why, 168
Whole City Catalog, 87
Whole Earth Catalogue, 88, 89, 90, 139
Whole Earth Epilog, 90, 139
Whole Kids Catalog, 84, 90
Whorf, Benjamin, 81, 82
Who's Got the Power?, 205
Why Do We Spend so Much Money, 32
Why Not Just Build The House Right in the First Place?, 221
Why Not Plant for Moonlight?, 147
Wicklein, John, 114
WIDL Video,
Weiner, Norbert, 106, 110
Wigginton, Elliot, 172
Wild Foods Cookbook and Field Guide, 175
Wilden, Anthony, 106
Wilder, Louise, 148
Wilhelm, Richard, 28
Wilkerson, Alan, 241
Will the Small Family Farm Survive in America?, 151
Willamette Valley Observer, 51
Willey, W.R.Z., 203
Williams, John, 129
Wilson, David, 127
H.W. Wilson Company, 95
Wilson Library Bulletin, 103
Wilson, S.S., 234
Wilson Seed Farms, 158
Wilson, Stewart, 124
Winchell, Constance, 93
Wind Bell, 56
Wind Energy Bibliographies, 242
Wind Energy Conversion Systems Workshop Proceedings, 241
Wind Energy Mission Analyses, 241
Wind Machines, 239
Wind Power Climatology of the United States, 239
Wind Power Digest, 242
Wind-Power Electric Utility Plants, 242
Wind Power for Farms, Homes & Small Industry, 240
Wind Power Group, 240
Wind Power Testimony, 242
Wind & Solar Thermal Combinations for Space Heating, 240
Wind & Wind Spinners, 240
Windmills Stage a Comeback, 242
Windpower Calculator, 240
Windworks, 239, 241, 242
Window Book, 216
Window as an Energy Factor, 143
Winitsky, David, 222
Winneberger, John H. Timothy, 194
Winter, Florian, 133
Wired Nation, 114
Wiring Simplified, 139
Wisconsin Public Library, 117
Wise, D.L., 235
Wise Travel, 131, 132
Wittgenstein, Ludwig, 81, 82
Wolfe, Fred, 130

Women
Access, 56, 90, 105, 109
China, 62
Health, 183-184
Media, 111, 112, 115-117
Moon Cosmology, 117
Women's Action Alliance, 109
Women Behind Bars, 90
Women & Child Care in China, 62
Women & Ecology, 5
Women and Health, 183
Women & Madness, 184
Women on Words & Images, 111
Women's Educational Project, 184
Women's Health News Briefs, 183
Women's History Library, 184
Women's History Research Ctr., 105
Women's Interart Center, 117
Women's Resource Center, 183
Women's Self-Help Divorce Proj., 56
Women's Soul Publishing, 116
Wood Burning Quarterly, 231
Wood Energy, 211, 231
Wood 'n Energy, 231
Wood Tank Assn., 72
Woodburning Stoves, 231
Wooden Windmill Blades, 241
Woodford, John, 127
Wood-Frame House Construc., 138
Woodburner's Encyclopedia, 231
Woodcraft Catalog, 139
Woodcraft Supply Corp., 139
Woodstock Community Video, 117
Wooldridge, Dean E., 28
Worchester, MA Zoning for Climate, 145
Work, 43, 44, 49-52
Work/Study, 83
Workbook, 91
Working Papers for a New Society, 72
World Biological Provinces Map, 26
World Energy Strategies, 201
World From Above, 22
World Future Society, 116
World of the Japanese Garden, 147
World Meteorological Org., 225
World Soundscape Project, 30
Worldwatch Institute, 207, 212
Workbook, 86
Worker-Owned Plywood Companies: An Economic Analysis, 51
Workforce, 51
Working Papers for a New Society, 57, 154
World Atlas, 26
World Futures Society, 79
World Health Organization, 191
Worth Publishers, 148
Wright, Ilene, 205
Wright, Lawrence, 191
Wuerth, Hans, 130
Wurman, Richard Saul, 30, 99
Wulff, Hans, 10
Wyckoff, Jerome, 12

●

Yale Medical School, 181
Yanda, Bill, 203, 226
Yankee Pedal Pushers, 130
Yearbook of World Problems and Human Potential, 72, 76, 78
Yellow Pages, 86-90
Yellow Pages of Learning Resources, 30
Yepsen, Roger B., Jr., 165
Yerba Buena, 32
Yo Banfa, 61
Yogurt, 174
Yokochi, C., 178
Yosemite Planning Team, 59
Young, J.Z., 28
Young, Louise B., 209
Youngblood, Gene, 110
Your City Has Been Kidnapped, 30, 84
Your Engineered House, 139
Youth Hostels, 132
Youth Services Resource Guide, 88
Youthiac, 100
You've Got To Move, 97
Yudelson, Jerry, 17
Yukon, 232

●

Z Box, 84
Zelmer, A.C., Lynn, 116
Zen Center, 56
Zephyros, 30, 84
Zero Auto Growth, 130
Ziller, John Paul, 225
Zomeworks, 219, 223, 224
Zoom, 112
Zoning, 124
Zube, Ervin H., 12